The

Physics

of

Electricity

and

Magnetism

NEW YORK · JOHN WILEY & SONS, INC.

LONDON

The

Physics

of

Electricity

and

Magnetism

WILLIAM TAUSSIG SCOTT

Professor of Physics
Smith College

SECOND PRINTING, NOVEMBER, 1960

Library of Congress Catalog Card Number: 59-5885
Printed in the United States of America

Dedication

To the memory of David Grahame,

whose inspiration stimulated the writing of this book,

to Wayne Garrett,

who taught me what electricity is about,

and to George Uhlenbeck,

who taught me what physics is.

Preface

This text was written because, like many other teachers of physics, I was dissatisfied with available texts in the field traditionally called "Electricity and Magnetism." I felt that there was need for a text on electricity and magnetism suitable for juniors, seniors, and first-year graduate students that had the following characteristics:

1. It should present a good balance between theory and experiment, training the reader's physical intuition by use of careful physical and mathematical reasoning—i.e., it should represent the physics of the subject in the complete sense of that word.

2. It should be fairly complete as far as the topics from which most instructors would draw material for students of physics, chemistry, mathematics, and engineering. The book should have somewhat more material than can be covered in an average year course, for different instructors will wish to cut out different sections, and non-student readers will naturally have a variety of interests within the general framework. (See below for suggestions on the material to be used for various groups of readers.)

3. It should be suitable for a first course in physics involving an extensive use of the calculus and of vectors, as well as for use following courses in analytical mechanics, etc. Assuming the reader to have had a good previous grounding in the mathematics of differential and integral calculus, it should develop with some care the physical application of this branch of mathematics.

4. It should be logically accurate, with a rock-bottom minimum of "it can be shown" statements. Material not covered in detail should

be left out altogether or mentioned without deriving consequences from it. The mathematical level of the proofs should be as elementary as possible, consistent with the requirements of logic. Proofs general enough to include all exceptional cases are best avoided.

5. Certain concepts, such as the vector potential, multipoles, etc., should be introduced in a more elementary way than is usually the case, so that the reader can gain the advantages of using these concepts without having to meet them first in terms of existence proofs or boundary value calculations.

6. It should primarily stress the force rather than the energy point of view, because physical intuition is better trained starting in this way. The energy point of view must however be introduced and in a way that is integral with the rest of the subject.

7. The book should be modern in two particular respects: (a) It should be up to date as regards recent developments in the classical theory itself or in the presentation of it (cf. the material on the non-closure of lines of **D** in section 3.6 and of **B** in section 7.7, and the method of introducing the magnetic field); (b) It should make full use of modern training at the elementary college level in atomic physics, both to help the reader's imagination and to allow explanation of electrical matters that depend on atomic structure, such as chemical emfs, ferromagnetism, and semiconductors. In addition, reference at least should be given to such recent technical developments as ferrites and transistors.

This text was written in accordance with these prescriptions. Some of its special features and the reasons for them are worth reviewing here.

The concepts of field, flux, and potential, as produced by given charge distributions, are introduced in Chapter 1. Each concept is developed and examples given before the next one is taken up, a general principle which is followed throughout. Sections on div **E, curl E** and $\nabla^2 V$ are included, to be used either on first reading or postponed until later as the instructor desires. (The first two are needed in Chapter 3.) The added complication of the determination of charge distributions by conductor arrangements is taken up first in Chapter 2. Conductors are introduced with a qualitative description of the band theory of conduction and the Fermi level, to be used as an aid to the imagination for electrostatics and as a base for the material of Chapters 5 and 6. The concept of the cavity potential of a metal is introduced to provide logical exactness and pedagogical clarity in discussing the work function and contact potential difference. Electroscopes, ice pails, etc., are discussed briefly with the full use of the potential and flux concepts rather than in the traditional way at the beginning of the course.

Chapter 3 introduces dielectric behavior by starting with the dipole field and then considering how a given set of dipoles acts as a whole, using the analysis first given by Poisson for magnetism. Idealized electrets are discussed in detail, both to give a thorough understanding of the vectors **E**, **D**, and **P**, and to prepare the way for magnet calculations in Chapter 8. Ideal dielectrics are then introduced, together with the permittivity concept, and the limitations on the usual force formula for charges in a dielectric medium are clearly demonstrated.

Chapter 4 includes image calculations, an introduction to boundary-value calculations, and a discussion of energy and forces in a system of conductors. This material is arranged so that all or part of it can be omitted without influencing the study of what follows. The conjugate function method has been omitted as best reserved for readers who have had a course in complex function theory.

Chapter 5 includes standard material on direct currents and also a discussion at the beginning on the electrostatic fields in such circuits, so that the field ideas so necessary for modern high frequency work are introduced at the start. The electrical mechanism of the production of chemical emfs is established by use of the Fermi level, together with qualitative ideas concerning quantum levels in solutions. This method has proved itself capable of readily explaining phenomena that are usually dismissed with the assertion that "non-electric" forces are involved. It is hard in my viewpoint to justify training readers to deal with emfs and leaving their origin a mystery.

Chapter 6 presents material on semiconductors, thermoelectricity, and chemical effects. Thermoelectric effects are described in terms of the recently developed thermodynamics of irreversible processes; the semiconductor material is a brief introduction to the basic level structure and a description of a p-n junction for students who may otherwise miss this important topic. The treatment of electrolytic conduction and Faraday's laws emphasizes the electrical rather than the chemical aspects of the subject.

Chapter 7 introduces the magnetic field **B** in terms of the Lorentz force law, treated as a fundamental law of physics. Several consequences of the law are deduced, and then Ampère's law for the production of **B** by a system of currents is brought in, first in the directly verifiable solid-angle form and later in the Laplace rule form, the circuital form, the vector-potential form, and the Maxwell equation form (including the displacement current). Faraday's law is brought in as an extension of Ampère's law based on simple relative-motion considerations. As a consequence of this development, all of Maxwell's equations have been discussed by the end of this chapter. Their consequences for waves, however, are postponed until Chapter 10, to allow a period of assimilation. Inductance and some of the difficulties with its calculation are brought in near the end of Chapter 7. The vector potential concept is used to explain the paradox of a toroidal solenoid producing no magnetic field outside itself and yet inducing current in an exterior coil.

Chapter 8 introduces Ampère's law in the magnetic dipole form and shows how the pole fiction can be used to calculate magnetic fields. The earlier calculations on electrets and dielectrics can then be taken over directly without repetition. A clear definition of the vector **H** is given, followed by a discussion of magnetic materials. In addition to the usual treatment of hysteresis, etc., there is a discussion of the formation of permanent magnets. Galvanometers, with their differential equations, are brought into this chapter because of their connection with magnetic testing methods.

Chapter 9 gives a standard treatment of alternating-current theory based on the complex-number method. Transformers and a small amount of work on filters are included. Pulse analysis and Fourier analysis are included, with a section on Laplace transforms for those who wish to study them.

Chapter 10 introduces radiation with a discussion of signal propagation along coaxial conductors. Waves in free space, retarded potentials, the energy and momentum theorems, dipole radiation, physical optics, waves in pipes and cavities, and a section on the four-vector notation and special relativity are included.

The Appendix gives a rather complete section on vector analysis (A.2) and another on vector invariance (A.4), plus short review sections on advanced calculus concepts (e.g., Taylor's theorem in several variables), differential equations, determinants, and complex numbers, and tables of units and of physical constants.

A list of symbols and abbreviations precedes the index.

For those whose interest is primarily in the electromagnetic field, the following chapters or parts of chapters might well be omitted: Chapter 3 beyond section 3.3 (if fields in vacuo are of chief interest), sections 5.2–5.7 of Chapter 5, Chapter 6, Chapter 8 beyond section 8.2 (for fields in vacuo), and Chapter 9 (if the complex form of a-c theory is already familiar). For those who have not had adequate background in circuit theory, it would instead be advisable to consider the omission of Chapter 4, all or part of Chapter 10, and of the material just mentioned in Chapters 3, 6 and 8. Particular sections whose omission will not interfere with the study of the rest of the book include 2.4, 2.5, 2.6, 3.3, 3.9, 3.10, 4.4, 4.6, 4.7 and 4.8, 5.4 to 5.7, 6.2, 6.3, 6.4, 7.12, 8.7, 8.8 (unless the differential equations are needed for Chapter 9), 9.6, 9.7, 9.8, and 10.4 to 10.8.

A one-semester course introducing the electromagnetic field can be built on the following: Chapter 1; sections 2.1 and 2.2; sections 3.1 and 3.3; Chapter 4, omitting section 4.8 and one or more of 4.3, 4.4 and 4.5; sections 5.1 and 5.2; Chapter 7; sections 8.1 and 8.2; and Chapter 10.

The vector section A.2 is best studied before beginning the main part of the text, but it is divided into subsections so that it can be taken up in a somewhat parallel fashion. Section A.4 on invariance is primarily needed for section 10.8 on relativity. The other parts of the Appendix are intended for use as reference material.

Each chapter is quite long, and so problems are inserted at the end of appropriate sections. The fact that this points the reader to the section of the book relevant to each problem does not seem to detract from the benefit he obtains in trying to work it.

I should like to express my appreciation to certain of my colleagues and to the several classes of Smith College girls who patiently, energetically, and with considerable clarity studied the material as I prepared it, found errors in writing and in logic, and asked a large number of penetrating and helpful questions. Women who elect physics do so against a prevailing fashion; such students have on the average considerable interest and ability in physics and considerable independence and desire to learn, for all of which I am duly grateful.

In particular, I should like to thank the following for the help they have given me. The late Professor David C. Grahame of Amherst College suggested the use of the cavity-potential concept and in various ways stimulated my initial efforts at writing this book. Dr. W. J. Hamer of the National Bureau of Standards made helpful comments on an early draft of the electrochemistry sections. Mrs. Gunther K. Wertheim was particularly helpful at various stages of the work in constructively criticizing both the writing and the physics. Others who helped in these regards were Mrs. Richard H. Walters, Mrs. David Willey and the Misses Catherine H. Stevens, Blanche E. Leatherman, Louise F. Clark, Mrs. A. David May, and Judith J. Snow. The last two individuals also assisted with the preparation of the figures, along with Mr. George Gardiner, Miss Anne M. Shea, whose assistance in this aspect was particularly valuable, and Mr. W. Thompson Lawrence. Appreciation is also due Mrs. Jonathan Hoxie for her very considerable help in the typing; some valuable typing assistance was also obtained from Mrs. Vincent Erikson and Mrs. Melvin Prouser; the Misses Lindsey A. Cairns and Edith M. Christian helped in checking the manuscript, and Miss Helene Blodgett assisted in the preparation of the index.   And finally, I owe a great debt to my wife and children for their patience and encouragement, without which this book would never have been written.

WILLIAM T. SCOTT

Smith College
February 1959

Contents

xiii

Contents

Contents

1

Charge, Field, and Potential

1.1 Atomic Structure

It is the purpose of this book to present the fundamental laws of electrical and magnetic phenomena that are valid in the macroscopic, or non-atomic, realm. Although it would be perfectly logical to develop the theory without reference to the atomic nature of matter, the use of modern notions concerning atoms and their constituents is of great help in clarifying and illuminating these macroscopic principles. Hence we assume the reader to be acquainted in a general way with the modern concept of the structure of matter. We give here a brief summary of the relevant material.

Matter is composed of atoms roughly 10^{-8} cm in diameter, each containing a nucleus of dimensions of the order of 10^{-12} cm. Electrons move about the nucleus of each atom, and it is their electrical influence on the electrons of other atoms that effectively defines the atomic dimensions. Electrons are negatively charged and are all alike, regardless of where they are found.

Most of the mass of an atom is contained in its nucleus.   Each nucleus bears a positive charge, numerically equal in electronic units to the atomic number of the atom in question, that is, to its ordinal number in the periodic table of the elements.

Thus there are two kinds of electrical charge in matter, positive and negative.   Like charges repel; unlike attract.   Because of the attraction of unlike charges each atom or molecule in its normal state has as many electrons as it has units of positive charge in its nucleus or nuclei, and thus is electrically neutral.

Nearly all the large-scale effects of electricity arise from the fact that electrons may become separated from their atoms under appropriate circumstances, thus leading to a separation of positive and negative charges by distances appreciably greater than atomic dimensions.   As far as is known, the entire universe contains equal amounts of positive and negative electricity, with the result that an excess of one sign at any place implies the location elsewhere of an equal and opposite charge.   Furthermore, net amounts of electric charge can neither be created nor destroyed (law of conservation of charge).

Isolated positive and negative charges will attract one another, and this attraction will result in a flow of charge if a conducting path is available. The flow of charge may consist of the motion of electrons (as in metals), the motion of ions—atoms that have gained or lost electrons—(as in solutions), or the motion of bare atomic nuclei (as in cyclotrons, etc.). The motion of positive charge in one direction has the same effect on the increase or decrease of excess (unneutralized) charge anywhere as has the motion of negative charge in exactly the opposite direction.   We shall see later that the magnetic effects of moving charges are also symmetric in this way.   Certain effects of combined electric and magnetic fields are not symmetric (cf. section 7.3), but for most of our results the fact that it is only the electrons that move in metallic conductors has no bearing, other than being a help to the imagination.

1.2   Coulomb's Law and Electric Field Strength

Our subject begins with electrostatics, which is the study of charges at rest (in the macroscopic sense).   All of electrostatics is derived from the experimentally verifiable Coulomb law of electrostatic force,[1] and from certain specific properties of matter.   We shall write Coulomb's law as follows:

$$\mathbf{F} = \frac{q_1 q_2}{4\pi\epsilon_0 r^2}\, \mathbf{1}_r \tag{1.2--1}$$

[1] Coulomb's own experiments were actually rather rough.   An accurate but indirect experimental proof of Coulomb's law will be taken up in section 2.6.

where **F** is the force between point charges of magnitude q_1 and q_2 situated a distance r apart (a point charge is one which occupies a region of space small compared with the error in the measurement of distances).   The force is a vector or directed quantity and will be represented by bold-face type, like other vectors in this book.[2]   The magnitude of the force, denoted by F, is the scalar $q_1 q_2/4\pi\epsilon_0 r^2$, and its direction is that of the unit vector $\mathbf{1}_r$, a vector of unit length drawn from the charge considered to be the agent toward the charge upon which the force is calculated, i.e., in the r direction (see Fig. 1.2a).   The force represented by eq. 1.2–1 is completely unaffected by the presence of other charges or other materials.

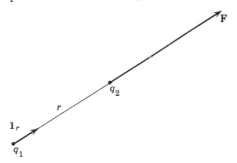

Fig. 1.2a.   The force of q_1 on q_2 lies in the direction of $\mathbf{1}_r$.

The quantity ϵ_0 is a constant whose value depends on the units used for q; it is generally called the "permittivity of free space."   In this book we shall use primarily the meter-kilogram-second (MKS) system of units,[3] with force in newtons (1 newton = 1 kg-m/sec^2 = 10^5 dynes), and shall measure q in coulombs,[4] to be defined later in terms of forces between currents (see section 7.5).   For this system, $\epsilon_0 = (8.85417 \pm 0.00003) \times 10^{-12}$ coulomb^2/newton-m^2 (1958 value), or approximately 8.85×10^{-12} coulomb^2/newton-m^2.   We shall see later that $\epsilon_0 = 10^7/4\pi c^2$, where c is the velocity of light, $(2.997928 \pm 0.000004) \times 10^8$ m/sec.   For many calculational purposes involving Coulomb's law, the value $1/4\pi\epsilon_0 = 9 \times 10^9$, good to 0.14%, is convenient.   The 4π which appears to complicate matters here will be seen to disappear in certain practical formulas to be derived later.

The electrostatic system of units, of which we shall make secondary use as part of the Gaussian system, is based on the centimeter-gram-second system of mechanical units.   In this system, $4\pi\epsilon_0 = 1$.   Equation 1.2–1

[2] Appendix A.2 gives a summary of vector analysis.

[3] Cf. Appendix A.7 for a summary of units.

[4] For many purposes, the microcoulomb, which is equal to 10^{-6} coulomb, is more useful.

then is not only the elementary law of force but also the equation that defines the unit of charge, called the esu of charge or the statcoulomb. One statcoulomb is equal to 3.33563×10^{-10} coulomb, or one coulomb $= 2.99793 \times 10^9$ statcoulomb $\simeq 3 \times 10^9$ statcoulomb.

The best (1958) value of the electronic unit of charge, which we denote by the symbol e, is $(1.60209 \pm 0.00003) \times 10^{-19}$ coulomb, or $(4.80294 \pm 0.00008) \times 10^{-10}$ statcoulomb. One coulomb $= 0.624184 \times 10^{19}$ electron charges; and 1 esu $= 2.08206 \times 10^9$ electron charges. An electron thus has a charge of $-e$ and a proton of $+e$.

Equation 1.2–1 is the fundamental elementary law of force. It gives the only force acting on two point charges remote from all other charges, i.e., lying in an evacuated region and far from the walls of this region. The power of r in the denominator has been shown to be accurately 2 within one part in 10^8, by an experimental method to be discussed in section 2.6.

Coulomb's law for two point charges, however, is not sufficient to deal with the general case in which many charges exert mutual forces on each other. We must generalize it by adding another law called the *principle of superposition*: When many charges are present, the force on any one is the vector sum of the separate forces exerted on that charge by all other charges taken independently. The mechanical law by which the forces on several charges can be added when the charges can be treated as a group, is sometimes included in this principle.

Superposition may be treated as an implicit part of Coulomb's law, or as an independent physical principle. In either case, it is fundamental to our theory and may be said to be justified directly by the same experiments that established eq. 1.2–1 and indirectly through the verification of many of the results deduced from the parts of our theory that include it.[5]

The superposition principle allows us to define the electric field strength or intensity **E**, frequently called electric field for short, although the word "field" by itself usually connotes a *region*. In fact, the force on a charge q at a point $\mathscr{P}$ may be written

$$\mathbf{F} = q\mathbf{E} \qquad (1.2\text{--}2)$$

where **E** is a vector given by

$$\mathbf{E} = \frac{1}{4\pi\epsilon_0} \sum_n \frac{q_n}{r_n{}^2} \mathbf{1}_n = \sum_n \mathbf{E}_n \qquad (1.2\text{--}3)$$

In eq. 1.2–3, the summation is over all charges q_n near enough q to have an appreciable force on the latter; r_n is the distance from q_n to the point $\mathscr{P}$, and $\mathbf{1}_n$ is a unit vector in the direction defined by a line from q_n to $\mathscr{P}$. $\mathbf{E}_n$ is the field strength at $\mathscr{P}$ due to q_n alone. (See Fig. 1.2b.) The sum

---

[5] For a detailed discussion of the logical meaning of Coulomb's law, see the article by the Coulomb's Law Committee, *Am. Journ. Phys.*, **18**, 1 (1950), especially pp. 5 and 6.

is a vector sum in the usual geometrical sense.   The respective vectors of lengths $q_n/4\pi\epsilon_0 r_n^2$ may be added successively tail-to-head; alternatively each of the three rectangular components of **E** may be found as the algebraic sum of the corresponding components of $\mathbf{E}_n$.   Vector addition is commutative and associative—it does not matter in which order the several vectors are added.   For instance, we may apply superposition "in the large" by finding separately the fields due to two or more separate collections of charge and then combining these separate charge distributions and adding their fields.   An example might be one in which some of the charge present is distributed on a straight wire and the rest uniformly on a nearby plane.

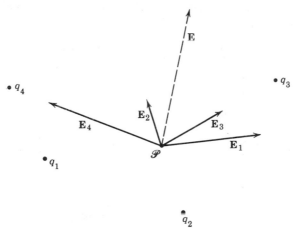

Fig. 1.2b.   The vector **E** is the sum of the fields produced at $\mathscr{P}$ by the charges shown.

In the MKS system, E is measured in newtons/coulomb or joules/meter-coulomb, which we will identify later with volts/meter.   The electrostatic unit is the dyne/statcoulomb, or statvolt/cm.

We are considering here forces exerted by charges at rest.   In eq. 1.2–2 we assume **E** to remain constant when the magnitude of q is changed, or when q is removed.   Actually, in most cases a change in the magnitude or position of q would cause a shift or motion in the other charges q_n.   To be precise, we shall define the field strength **E** at any point in space as the force per unit charge that *would* be exerted on a test charge put there, *if* this charge did not affect the neighboring charges.

We shall normally assume that we can introduce an appropriately small test charge, which is possible in principle in the macroscopic realm.   The situation is very different in the atomic realm where the smallest test charge, that of an electron, may be large enough to have serious disturbing effects.   Some of these effects are discussed in Chapter 2, but we are not concerned at present with the atomic realm.   Furthermore, an adequate macroscopic theory must be developed before the construction of modern atomic (quantum) theories can be understood.

Note that we have divided the problem of forces between charges into two problems—that of the sources of electric field, given by eq. 1.2–3, and that of the effect of the field on a local charge q, given by eq. 1.2–2.   Both of these equations will be generalized in Chapter 7.   We shall say nothing, here or later, about whether **E** exists as an actual independent entity. The reader may think of it as real or as a convenient device for calculation. We shall make such sufficient use of the field-strength concept that we will undoubtedly imagine it as real and will find it thereby a great help to our intuition, but no philosopical discussion of it will be necessary in this book.

Problem 1.2a.   Use Coulomb's law to find the force between an electron and a proton separated by a distance of 0.529×10^{-10} m.   Compare this with the gravitational force of attraction $F = Gm_1m_2/r^2$ where $G = 6.67 \times 10^{-11}$ newton-m^2/kg^2, the electron mass is 9.11×10^{-31} kg, and the proton mass is 1837 times greater.

Problem 1.2b.   Find the relation between q and θ when two pith balls hung from a common point on light strings of length l stand apart from each other at an angle θ.   Each has a mass m and a charge q and is small enough to be treated as a point.

1.3   Calculation of Field Strengths

The simplest cases are those in which only a few source charges are present and the vector sums can be found directly.   The reader may be familiar with such problems, but if not, he is urged to try one or more of problems 1.3a, b, c, and d.

Cases of more complexity, met more often in practice, consist of continuous distributions of charge on linear elements, on surfaces, and in volumes.   We shall define, for instance, the surface charge density σ as the charge per unit area at a point $\mathscr{P}$ on a surface.   The field at a point $\mathscr{P}$ whose coordinates are (x, y, z) produced by a surface charge distribution (which may or may not contain the point $\mathscr{P}$) may then be written as

$$\mathbf{E}_{\mathscr{P}} = \frac{1}{4\pi\epsilon_0} \int_S \frac{\mathbf{1}_r \sigma \, dS'}{r^2} \qquad (1.3\text{–}1)$$

where the integral is a surface integral over the surface S (Fig. 1.3a), r is the distance to $\mathscr{P}$ from a point $\mathscr{P}'$ whose coordinates are (x', y', z') in the surface element dS', and both σ and $\mathbf{1}_r$ are in general functions of the variable point (x', y', z').[6]

---

[6] We shall generally use primed letters for the coordinates of points of integration, and unprimed letters for points at which a desired quantity, like **E**, is evaluated.

Of course, no distribution of atomic charges can be continuous.   We can, however, treat certain distributions as if they were continuous, provided that we deal only with macroscopic phenomena.   To be more specific, we can use the notion of continuity when negligible errors are made in the integrals used for calculation.   An integral is the limit of a sum.   We suppose that instead of taking the actual limit we can stop short with a large but finite number of small but not infinitesimal elements or intervals, in such a way as to make the resulting error less than a preassigned value related to the experimental errors involved in applications.   If the intervals (areas, volumes, etc.) that we stop with are still large enough to contain each a great many electrons and/or protons, our assumption of continuity will be justified.   These particles are so small that there is almost never any trouble in using the assumption of continuity and, in fact, the subject would be enormously complicated by any attempt to avoid it.   We shall therefore use it throughout the book.

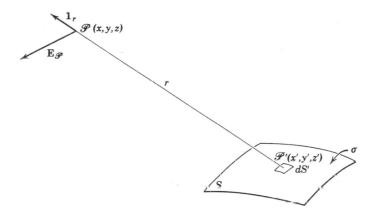

Fig. 1.3a.   The field at $\mathscr{P}$ is a vector integral over the surface S.

A rigorous definition of σ is that it is the limit of $\Delta q / \Delta S'$ at a point $\mathscr{P}'$ on the surface as the surface element $\Delta S'$ containing a charge Δq goes to zero.   The integral in eq. 1.3–1 is the limit as $N \to \infty$ of the sum $\displaystyle\sum_{n=1}^{N} \mathbf{1}_{rn}\sigma_n \, \Delta S'_n / r_n^2$, where the surface is divided into N elementary areas $\Delta S'_n$, and where $\mathbf{1}_{rn}$, σ_n, and r_n are all calculated for some point within $\Delta S'_n$.   (See Appendix A.2.)   Actual calculations involving such integrals will be made only in the simplest and most symmetrical of cases.

The case of volume distributions can be treated in a similar way.   We shall denote by ρ the volume charge density, i.e., the charge per unit volume at a point $\mathscr{P}'$.   Then if ρ is known as a function of the coordinates of $\mathscr{P}'$, we can find $\mathbf{E}$ at $\mathscr{P}$ from

$$\mathbf{E}_{\mathscr{P}} = \frac{1}{4\pi\epsilon_0} \int_{\tau} \frac{\mathbf{1}_r \rho \, d\tau'}{r^2} \tag{1.3–2}$$

where $d\tau'$ is an element of volume at $\mathscr{P}'$ (Fig. 1.3b), τ is the entire volume containing the charge, and 1_r, ρ, and r are taken at the point $\mathscr{P}'$ at which $d\tau'$ is taken. (The Greek τ, tau, is used for volume since V will generally be used for potential, and v for velocity.)

The total charge on a surface S or in a volume τ is given by

$$Q = \int_S \sigma \, dS' \tag{1.3--3a}$$

or

$$Q = \int_\tau \rho \, d\tau' \tag{1.3--3b}$$

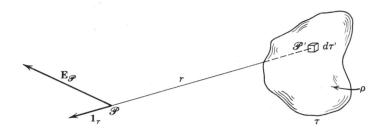

Fig. 1.3b. The field at $\mathscr{P}$ is an integral over the volume τ.

It is also possible to have a line distribution of charge, λ coulombs per unit length, for which

$$Q = \int_l \lambda \, dl' \tag{1.3--3c}$$

Let us as a first example find the field at a distance R from a straight, infinite, uniformly charged, thin wire with a constant charge density λ (Fig. 1.3c).

We have in general

$$\mathbf{E}_{\mathscr{P}} = \frac{1}{4\pi\epsilon_0} \int_l \frac{1_r \lambda \, dl'}{r^2} \tag{1.3--4}$$

for a line l (curvilinear or straight). To evaluate the integral in this case, we can use the distance x' of $\mathscr{P}'$ from the foot of the perpendicular from $\mathscr{P}$ as the independent variable. Then we have $dl' = dx'$ and $r^2 = R^2 + x'^2$.

The unit vector 1_r is variable in direction, so we shall write it as a linear combination of two constant unit vectors. As shown by the small diagram in the figure, we have

$$1_r = -1_x \sin\theta + 1_R \cos\theta$$

As x' varies from $-\infty$ to $+\infty$, $\sin\theta$ takes on first negative values and then positive values. It is easy to show by consideration of symmetry that the integral $\int \sin \theta \, dx'/r^2$ vanishes. Physically this is equivalent to saying that the components of field strength parallel to the wire produced by elements at x' and at $-x'$ will just cancel.

We have then only the term $\mathbf{1}_R \cos \theta$ to consider. Since $\cos \theta = R/(x'^2 + R^2)^{\frac{1}{2}}$, we have

$$\mathbf{E} = \frac{\lambda \mathbf{1}_R}{4\pi\epsilon_0} \int_{-\infty}^{\infty} \frac{R \, dx'}{(x'^2 + R^2)^{\frac{3}{2}}} = \frac{\lambda \mathbf{1}_R}{2\pi\epsilon_0 R} \tag{1.3-5}$$

The integral in eq. 1.3–5 may be most easily carried out if one uses the angle θ as a new variable, writing $x' = R \tan \theta$.   Such a trigonometric

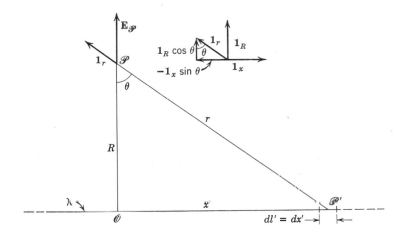

Fig. 1.3c.   Illustrating the evaluation of eq. 1.3–4 for a long straight wire.

substitution suggested directly by the geometry of the problem is often useful in evaluating integrals of this sort.

To illustrate eq. 1.3–5, suppose we have 3.0×10^{-6} coulomb/m on a long straight thin wire. The field strength at a distance of 0.1 m from the wire is $E = 18 \times 10^9 \times 3.0 \times 10^{-6}/0.1 = 5.4 \times 10^5$ newtons/coulomb (or volts/meter).   The force on an electron at this point would be $5.4 \times 10^5 \times 1.60 \times 10^{-19} = 8.64 \times 10^{-14}$ newton, and its acceleration $8.64 \times 10^{-14}/9.11 \times 10^{-31} = 9.48 \times 10^{16}$ m/sec^2, since the mass of an electron is 9.11×10^{-31} kg.

Now let us find the field at a point $\mathscr{P}$ a height z above an infinite plane distribution of uniform density (Fig. 1.3d).   For the element dS' in eq. 1.3–1 we shall use $dx' \, dy'$, where x' and y' are the Cartesian coordinates of a point $\mathscr{P}'$ in the plane, with the origin $\mathscr{O}$ at the foot of the perpendicular from $\mathscr{P}$. We see that $r^2 = x'^2 + y'^2 + z^2$ and that the vertical component of $\mathbf{1}_r$ is z/r. Hence we may write

$$E_z = \frac{\sigma}{4\pi\epsilon_0} \int_{-\infty}^{\infty} dy' \int_{-\infty}^{\infty} \frac{z \, dx'}{(x'^2 + y'^2 + z^2)^{\frac{3}{2}}}$$

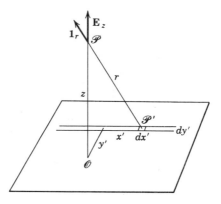

Fig. 1.3d. Calculation of the field outside an infinite charged plane.

The x'-integration is the same as in the last problem (if we set $R^2 = y'^2 + z^2$) and we find

$$E_z = \frac{\sigma}{4\pi\epsilon_0} \int_{-\infty}^{\infty} dy' \frac{2z}{y'^2 + z^2} = \frac{\sigma}{2\epsilon_0} \tag{1.3--6}$$

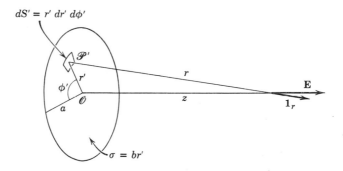

Fig. 1.3e. Calculation of the field produced by a charged disk.

The x and y components of $\mathbf{E}$ vanish, by symmetry. We note that the field strength $E_z(=E)$ at a point $\mathscr{P}$ outside an infinite plane distribution of charge is independent of the distance z of $\mathscr{P}$ from the plane. However, the field is in the opposite direction on the other side of the plane, and hence suffers a discontinuity at the plane.

As a third example, let us find the field strength on the axis of a disk of radius a, at a distance z from the center $\mathcal{O}$ (Fig. 1.3e) when the surface density σ on the disk at a distance r' from $\mathcal{O}$ is given by $\sigma = br'$ coulomb/m², with b a constant.

For reasons of symmetry, we calculate only the axial component, E_z. We shall let $dS' = r'\, dr'\, d\phi'$ and must take the variation of σ into account. We have

$$E = E_z = \frac{1}{4\pi\epsilon_0} \int_0^a \frac{br' \cdot r'\, dr' \cdot z}{(r'^2 + z^2)^{\frac{3}{2}}} \int_0^{2\pi} d\phi'$$

$$= \frac{bz}{2\epsilon_0} \int_0^a \frac{r'^2\, dr'}{(r'^2 + z^2)^{\frac{3}{2}}}$$

$$= \frac{bz}{2\epsilon_0} \left(\ln \frac{a + (a^2 + z^2)^{\frac{1}{2}}}{z} - \frac{a}{(a^2 + z^2)^{\frac{1}{2}}} \right) \qquad (1.3\text{-}7)$$

The total charge on the disk is

$$Q = \int_0^a br' \cdot 2\pi r'\, dr' = \tfrac{2}{3}\pi ba^3.$$

A more difficult example is the field at an arbitrary point outside a uniformly charged spherical shell. Although the calculation is straightforward, and the interested reader may work it for himself, we shall postpone this example until we have developed two simpler methods. It is interesting to note in passing that this problem is essentially the same as calculating the gravitational field outside a spherical body such as the earth or moon. It is reported that Newton had his gravitational theory ready to publish except for proving that a spherical body acts like a point mass located at its center. It took him twenty years to develop the calculus to the point where he could prove this fact by integration, and only then did he publish his now famous theory.[7]

Problem 1.3a. Point charges of $+3.0$ and $+7.0$ microcoulombs, respectively, are located at the origin and at the point $(0.50 \text{ m}, 0)$ in an x–y plane. Find the direction and magnitude of **E** at the points $(0.50 \text{ m}, 0.90 \text{ m})$, $(1.0 \text{ m}, 0)$, and $(1.0 \text{ m}, -0.3 \text{ m})$. Calculate the result for the last point both by components and by trigonometry.

Problem 1.3b. Find where $\mathbf{E} = 0$ in the situation of problem 1.3a. Also find where $\mathbf{E} = 0$ if the $+7.0$ microcoulomb charge is changed to -7.0 microcoulombs.

[7] See, for instance, Sir William C. Dampier, *A History of Science*, 4th ed., Cambridge 1949, pp. 150–154.

Problem 1.3c. Point charges of $+3.0$, $+4.0$, and -7.0 microcoulombs, respectively, are located in an x–y plane at points $(0, 0)$, $(0.20 \text{ m}, 0.30 \text{ m})$, and $(0.50 \text{ m}, 0)$. Find the direction and magnitude of $\mathbf{E}$ at $(0.50 \text{ m}, 0.50 \text{ m})$.

Problem 1.3d. Find the direction and magnitude of $\mathbf{E}$ at the origin in an x–y–z space, if point charges are located as follows: -3.0 microcoulomb at $(0.15 \text{ m}, 0, 0)$; -4.0 microcoulomb at $(0, 0.40 \text{ m}, 0)$; and $+2.0$ microcoulomb at $(0.20 \text{ m}, 0.20 \text{ m}, 0.35 \text{ m})$.

Problem 1.3e. Find E just outside a plane distribution of charge of effectively infinite extent that carries 1 electronic charge per square Ångstrom unit ($1 \text{ Å} = 10^{-8}$ cm). What acceleration would an electron experience in this field (mass of electron $= 9.11 \times 10^{-31}$ kg)? How long would it take the electron to acquire a velocity of 3×10^8 m/sec under this acceleration (neglect any relativity effects)?

The reader who has studied the Bohr theory of the hydrogen atom will find it instructive to compare this acceleration with the centripetal acceleration of an electron in the lowest state of a Bohr hydrogen atom.

✓ **Problem 1.3f.** Find a formula for the field at a point on the axis of a uniformly charged circular disk of radius a. Show that as $a \to \infty$ the infinite plane result is obtained. Find E if $\sigma = 1.6 \times 10^{-8}$ coulomb/m², $a = 5$ cm, and z (distance of point from center) $= 8$ cm.

✓ **Problem 1.3g.** Show that when z is very large, the formula of problem 1.3f is approximately the same as the result for a point charge (Coulomb's law).

✓ **Problem 1.3h.** Suppose that the disk of Fig. 1.3e has a radius of 20 cm and carries a total charge of 3×10^{-9} coulomb. Find the field strength on the axis at a point 75 cm from the center of the disk.

Problem 1.3i. Repeat problem 1.3g for eq. 1.3–7.

Problem 1.3j. Find the field at a point on the axis of a disk of radius a, if $\sigma = br'^{-1} \cos^2 \phi$.

Problem 1.3k. Consider a general surface distribution σ, continuously variable on a continuously curved surface. Because of continuity, about any point $\mathscr{P}$ on the surface a circle of radius a can be drawn such that (1) σ varies by less than $\frac{1}{3}\%$ within the circle and (2) the maximum distance of points on the surface within the circle from a tangent plane constructed at $\mathscr{P}$ is less than $\frac{1}{3}\%$ of a. Hence the field at a height h above the surface produced by the charge within the circle differs from the uniform disk result by less than $\frac{2}{3}\%$ (actually considerably less, in general).

Find h so that the difference between the uniform disk result and the infinite plane result is less than $\frac{1}{3}\%$, so that the actual field is within 1% of eq. 1.3–5.

Problem 1.3l. Prove explicitly that the horizontal components vanish in the calculation of eq. 1.3–5 in the text.

Problem 1.3m. Discuss the convergence of the integrals 1.3–1, 1.3–2, and 1.3–4 when the point (x, y, z) lies in the region of integration. *Hint:* Use suitable polar coordinates (for the first two cases) and consider only the portion of an integral arising from a region of integration very near (x, y, z).

Problem 1.3n. A cylindrical volume of height h and radius a contains charge whose volume density ρ is given by the formula $\rho(r, z) = br^2z^2$, where r is the distance of a point from the axis of the cylinder and z is the distance of a point from the center of the cylinder, measured in a direction parallel to the axis. Find E on the axis of the cylinder a distance $z_1 > h/2$ above the center.

1.4   Flux and the Gauss Flux Law

The first new method for calculating fields involves the concept of flux. With this concept we shall prove a general law, credited to Gauss, which is of great use in calculating symmetrical fields and also is a powerful tool for establishing some of the properties of conducting media.

The electric flux Φ_E through an elementary area S is defined as the product of the area and the component of field strength normal to that area. One direction through the surface must be specified as the positive

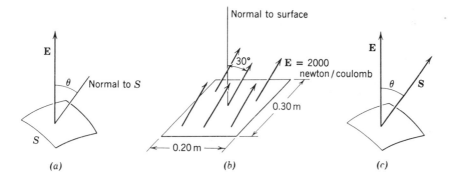

Fig. 1.4a–c.   Illustrating electric flux Φ_E.

normal (Fig. 1.4a).   That is, $\Phi_E = ES \cos \theta$, where S is the area in square meters and θ is the angle between the direction of E and the positive normal to S.   The MKS unit of flux is the newton-m²/coulomb;   the electrostatic unit is the dyne-cm²/statcoulomb.

For instance, a rectangular surface of 0.20 m × 0.30 m (Fig. 1.4b) placed with its normal at an angle of 30° in a uniform field of 2000 newton/coulomb would have passing through it a flux of 0.06 × 2000 × cos 30° = $60\sqrt{3}$ = 104 newton-m²/coulomb.

It is customary and convenient to attribute the positive normal direction to the quantity S itself, and to write S as a vector $\mathbf{S}$ (Fig. 1.4c).   Then θ is the angle between two vectors, and the flux can be written as a scalar product of the two vectors[8]

$$\Phi_E = \mathbf{E} \cdot \mathbf{S}$$

[8] Cf. Appendix A.2, eqs. A.2–5 to A.2–11.

If S is large or **E** varies considerably over it, we must break S into elementary areas ΔS, calculate for each one the flux $\Delta\Phi_E = \mathbf{E} \cdot \mathbf{\Delta S}$, and sum over all the $\mathbf{\Delta S}$. As a result, we define the flux through a general surface, plane or curved, by the integral

$$\Phi_E = \int_S \mathbf{E} \cdot \mathbf{dS} \qquad (1.4\text{--}1)$$

For closed surfaces the outward direction is taken as positive. A rule for open surfaces is given in section 7.4 and in the paragraphs on Stokes' theorem in section A.2. It can be evaluated when necessary in a similar way to the integrals which give values of **E**.

The real justification of any definition is its use in later work, and the usefulness of the concept of flux will shortly appear. However, we might say here that

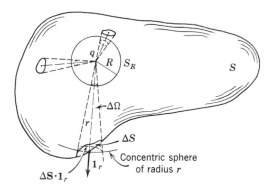

Fig. 1.4d. Calculation of the flux of q through S.

the name "flux" and the notion of adding elements of it together to get a total, as in eq. 1.4–1, are derived by analogy with the flow of a liquid or gas. If we substitute for the vector **E** a vector **v** representing the velocity of the particles of fluid at the point in question, the expression $\Delta\Phi_v = \mathbf{v} \cdot \mathbf{\Delta S}$ is equal to the product of the displacement per second perpendicular to the area ΔS, and the area. We see that $\Delta\Phi_v$ is the volume flowing per unit time through ΔS and that Φ_v is the volume flowing through S.

"Flux" is the Latin word for "flow" and describes here an accurate mathematical analogy. There is, of course, no actual motion associated with **E**.

Let us consider a single point charge q. The field at a distance R from it is $\mathbf{E} = q\mathbf{1}_R/4\pi\epsilon_0 R^2$. On any sphere S_R, drawn with q as center (Fig. 1.4d), **E** is normal to the surface, and E is constant all over the sphere. Hence the total flux Φ_E through the sphere in the outward direction is $(q/4\pi\epsilon_0 R^2)(4\pi R^2) = q/\epsilon_0$, a result independent of R. One would expect the same answer for an arbitrary surface S surrounding q.

To show that this expectation is correct, divide all the space surrounding q into elementary conical volumes or elements of solid angle,[9] one of which is $\Delta\Omega$ in Fig. 1.4d.   Let ΔS in Fig. 1.4d be the area cut out by $\Delta\Omega$ on the arbitrary surface S.   Now ΔS is not in general oriented with its normal along the axis of the cone.   The projection of $\mathbf{\Delta S}$ along the axis, ΔS_r, is $\Delta S_r = \Delta S \cos\theta = \mathbf{\Delta S \cdot 1}_r$ and is equal to the area cut by $\Delta\Omega$ on a concentric sphere of radius r.   Thus $\Delta\Omega = \mathbf{\Delta S \cdot 1}_r/r^2$.

On the other hand, the flux through ΔS is

$$\Delta\Phi_E = \mathbf{\Delta S \cdot E} = \mathbf{\Delta S \cdot 1}_r q/4\pi\epsilon_0 r^2 = q\Delta\Omega/4\pi\epsilon_0.$$

The entire flux through S is thus obtained by addition of all the elements of solid angle:

$$\Phi_E = \int d\Phi_E = q(4\pi)/4\pi\epsilon_0 = q/\epsilon_0$$

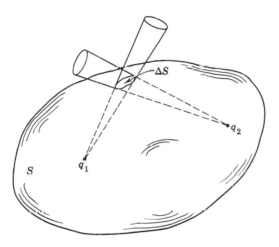

Fig. 1.4e.   Flux produced by two charges inside S.

If q is negative, Φ_E is negative and inwardly directed.

By the distributive law of the scalar product and the principle of superposition, we can add the fluxes through any dS due to several distinct charges $q_1, q_2, \cdots$ (Fig. 1.4e):

$$\mathbf{E}_1 \cdot \mathbf{\Delta S} + \mathbf{E}_2 \cdot \mathbf{\Delta S} + \cdots = (\mathbf{E}_1 + \mathbf{E}_2 + \cdots) \cdot \mathbf{\Delta S} = \mathbf{E} \cdot \mathbf{\Delta S}$$

[9] A solid angle Ω (Greek capital "Omega") is measured by the area it cuts out on a concentric sphere of unit radius.   Since the area cut out on any sphere will be proportional to the square of the radius, we can alternatively say that $\Omega = S/R^2$, where S is the area cut out by the cone on an arbitrary sphere whose radius we denote by R. The entire solid angle around a point is one that includes an entire sphere, $\Omega = 4\pi R^2/R^2 = 4\pi$.

Hence we have the Gauss flux law, namely that the total flux through any closed surface due to any number of charges inside is

$$\Phi_E = \int_{\text{closed } S} \mathbf{E} \cdot d\mathbf{S} = \frac{1}{\epsilon_0} \sum_n q_n \qquad (1.4\text{-}2)$$

$\sum_n q_n$ is to be replaced by appropriate integrals $\int \rho \, d\tau$, $\int \sigma \, dS$, or $\int \lambda \, dl$ (eqs. 1.3–3) for the various types of continuous distributions or by a combination of sums and integrals in complex cases. Note that flux may be thought of as originating or "starting" on positive charges ("sources") and ending on negative charges ("sinks"), even though no motion is involved.

If a particular solid angle cuts a surface three or more times, as $\Delta \Omega'$

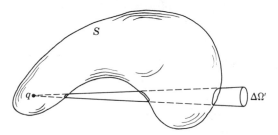

Fig. 1.4f.   Flux counted only once when $\Delta \Omega'$ intersects the surface more than once.

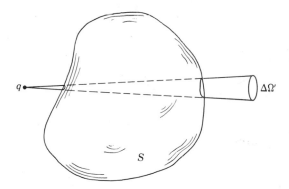

Fig. 1.4g.   No net flux from q external to S.

in Fig. 1.4f, the calculation will involve a cancellation of inwardly and outwardly directed parts in pairs. Charges outside the surface contribute nothing to Φ_E (Fig. 1.4g). The surfaces ("Gaussian surfaces") to which eq. 1.4–2 applies are imaginary surfaces to be placed at convenience of the investigator, and usually do not coincide with any real material surfaces.

Equation 1.4–2 can be used in cases of high symmetry to make simple and elegant calculations of fields.   For instance, an isolated sphere of radius r_0 bearing a symmetrically distributed surface or volume charge of total amount Q must have a spherically symmetric field (Fig. 1.4h). Here E is a function of $\mathbf{r}$ only, and we have for a Gaussian sphere of radius $r > r_0$, $\Phi_E = E(4\pi r^2) = Q/\epsilon_0$ leading to $E = Q/4\pi\epsilon_0 r^2$.   The vector equation reads

$$\mathbf{E} = Q\mathbf{1}_r/4\pi\epsilon_0 r^2 \tag{1.4-3}$$

The field outside such a sphere is the same as that of a point charge equal

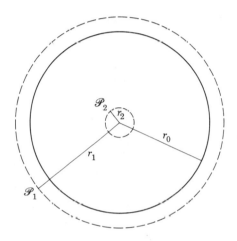

Fig. 1.4h.   Gaussian surfaces for a sphere, of radii r_1 and r_2 for points $\mathscr{P}_1$ and $\mathscr{P}_2$.

in magnitude to the total charge on the sphere and located at its center. This is the theorem Newton waited so long to prove.

By Newton's third law of motion ("action and reaction") one can also show that the force on a symmetrical spherical distribution of charge in any external field is the same as the force on the same total charge located at the center of the sphere (cf. problem 1.4a).

Equation 1.4–3 applies of course to a point charge as a special case, and thus we have derived Coulomb's law from Gauss'.   The two laws are logically equivalent.   Note that the proof of Gauss' law combines the inverse square law for field strengths and the r^2 variation of the area included in a solid angle.

On the other hand, the field at a point inside the sphere is not the same as that for a point charge Q.   For the field at a distance $r < r_0$ from the center, consider a new Gaussian surface of radius r. The same calculation as before now leads to

$$E = Q_r \mathbf{1}_r / 4\pi\epsilon_0 r^2 \qquad (1.4\text{--}4)$$

where Q_r is the total amount of charge within the Gaussian surface. That is to say, the charge lying between the spheres of radii r and r_0 produces no field within the radius r. In particular, a uniformly charged spherical surface has no field anywhere in its interior. On the other hand, if the charge density ρ is constant within the sphere, $Q_r = \frac{4}{3}\pi r^3 \rho$ and

$$E = \rho r \mathbf{1}_r / 3\epsilon_0 \qquad (1.4\text{--}5)$$

The interior field strength is proportional to the radius in this case.

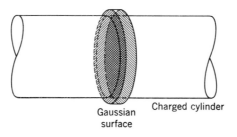

Fig. 1.4*i*.   Gaussian surface for a cylinder.

For an infinite symmetrically charged cylinder, a Gaussian surface as in Fig. 1.4*i* may be used, and the field shown to be

$$E = \lambda \mathbf{1}_r / 2\pi\epsilon_0 r \qquad (1.4\text{--}6)$$

where λ is the total charge per unit length carried by the cylinder, and we have therefore the same result as in eq. 1.3–5 (problem 1.4*b*).

The result of eq. 1.3–6 for a uniform, infinite plane distribution of charge ($\sigma =$ constant) may also be obtained, and in a simpler way, by using as a Gaussian surface a cylindrical surface perpendicular to the plane in question that cuts it in some area S and is capped by two planes each of the same area, parallel to the distribution of charge and equidistant from it on opposite sides (Fig. 1.4*j*). The charge inside the Gaussian cylinder is σS; by symmetry an equal amount of flux passes out through each end and none through the sides. Thus $\Phi_E = 2ES = \sigma S/\epsilon_0$ and $E = \sigma/2\epsilon_0$ directed outward from the surface.

If we have two infinite planes, parallel and separated by a distance h, one of charge density σ and one of $-\sigma$, we can readily add the fields produced by each plane.   In between the planes the magnitudes add and

$$E = \sigma/\epsilon_0. \qquad (1.4\text{--}7)$$

Outside either plane the fields are in opposite directions and the resultant

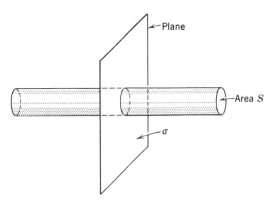

Fig. 1.4*j*.   Gaussian surface for an infinite plane.

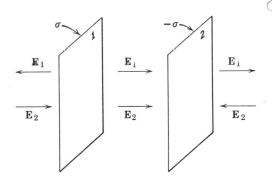

Fig. 1.4*k*.   Combination of fields produced by two infinite planes.

is zero (see Fig. 1.4*k*).   This is the result for the field far from the edges in an ordinary plane-parallel condenser, to be treated in more detail later.

   Problem 1.4a.   By considering first the force of a symmetrically charged sphere on a single external point charge, develop a rigorous argument for the statement that the force of *any* external field *on* such a sphere is the same as if all the charge in the sphere were at the center.

   Problem 1.4b.   Prove eq. 1.4–6 for the field outside a cylindrically symmetric charge distribution.

Problem 1.4c. Find the field strength at a distance r from the axis of a cylindrically symmetric charge distribution when (a) ρ is constant out to a radius $r_0 > r$ and (b) ρ is proportional to the radius, out to a radius $r_0 > r$.

Problem 1.4d. Give an argument to demonstrate the assertion in the text that the field outside a spherically symmetric charge distribution is directed along the radius and depends in magnitude only on R.

Problem 1.4e. Describe the symmetries of a sphere, a right circular cylinder, and a plane by giving the changes of coordinates (rotations, translations, reflections) that can be made without changing the signs and magnitudes of any physical quantities.

Problem 1.4f. Noting the result that a uniform spherical shell of charge has no field within it, use the Gauss flux law to derive directly a relation between the surface charge density and the field just outside the surface.

Problem 1.4g. Find the flux through a circle of radius a produced by a charge q on the axis of the circle and at a distance z from its center, by integration over the circle.

Problem 1.4h. Solve problem 1.4g, but take the integration over the portion of a spherical surface whose center is at q, bounded by the edge of the circle.

Problem 1.4i. Find the flux through the curved side of a right circular cylinder of length $2z$ and radius a, produced by a single charge q at its center.

Problem 1.4j. Find E at an arbitrary point inside a sphere of radius r_0 if $\rho(r) = br^2$, where b is a constant.

1.5 Differential-Equation Form of the Flux Law[10]

For the case of volume distributions of charge, including the case $\rho = 0$ (vacuum), we can apply Gauss' flux law to an infinitesimal volume of space and obtain a relationship between the partial derivatives of the components of E with respect to the coordinates of a point in that volume and the charge density ρ at that same point. It is clear that each component of E can vary with all three coordinates. For instance, E_x for eq. 1.4–3 is $Qx/4\pi\epsilon_0 r^3$ (components of $\mathbf{1}_r$ are given by eq. A.2–4).

As shown in the appendix, the flux out per unit volume at a point is given by the divergence of a vector, eq. A.2–21. Hence Gauss' law becomes

$$\text{div } \mathbf{E} = \nabla \cdot \mathbf{E} = \left(\frac{\partial E_x}{\partial x} + \frac{\partial E_y}{\partial y} + \frac{\partial E_z}{\partial z} \right) = \frac{\rho}{\epsilon_0} \qquad (1.5\text{--}1)$$

In empty space, of course,

$$\nabla \cdot \mathbf{E} = 0 \qquad (1.5\text{--}2)$$

The differential equation 1.5–1 will find uses in later sections in connection with the motion of charge in vacuum tubes and semiconductors, in which volume distributions of electrons give rise to variations of electric field.

[10] The material for this section is not used until section 3.5 and may be postponed until the latter section is taken up.

It is, of course, an expression of Coulomb's law and is the first of Maxwell's famous equations for electromagnetic radiation.

At present, we wish to show that eq. 1.5–2 holds in two cases we have considered. In the first place, a uniform plane distribution of charge produces a uniform field so that E_x, E_y, E_z are constants, with respect to variations in x, y, and z. Hence all their derivatives vanish, and div $\mathbf{E} = 0$. An exception to this rule occurs at the charged plane, where the field abruptly changes from $\sigma/2\epsilon_0$ in one direction to the same value in the opposite direction. If the normal to the plane is in the z-direction, we then have the result that $\partial E_z/\partial z$ is infinite at the plane, assuming the charge to be in a layer infinitesimally thin. However, the volume density of charge will also be infinite, and eq. 1.5–1 is not violated. The case of a layer of finite thickness is considered in problem 1.5a.

A second example is the field near a point charge or a symmetrically charged sphere, eq. 1.4–3. The three components are $E_x = Qx/4\pi\epsilon_0 r^3$; $E_y = Qy/4\pi\epsilon_0 r^3$, $E_z = Qz/4\pi\epsilon_0 r^3$. To calculate div $\mathbf{E}$, note that

$$\partial r/\partial x = \frac{\partial}{\partial x}(x^2 + y^2 + z^2)^{\frac{1}{2}} = x/(x^2 + y^2 + z^2)^{\frac{1}{2}} = x/r$$

with corresponding relations for y and z. Hence

$$\frac{\partial E_x}{\partial x} + \frac{\partial E_y}{\partial y} + \frac{\partial E_z}{\partial z} = \frac{Q}{4\pi\epsilon_0}\left[\left(\frac{1}{r^3} - \frac{3x}{r^4}\cdot\frac{x}{r}\right) + \left(\frac{1}{r^3} - \frac{3y}{r^4}\cdot\frac{y}{r}\right)\right.$$

$$\left. + \left(\frac{1}{r^3} - \frac{3z}{r^4}\cdot\frac{z}{r}\right)\right]$$

$$= \frac{Q}{4\pi\epsilon_0}\left[\frac{3}{r^3} - \frac{3}{r^5}(x^2 + y^2 + z^2)\right] \equiv 0$$

It is interesting to reconstruct Gauss' law eq. 1.4–2 from eq. 1.5–1. Using the divergence theorem, e.g., (A.2–22), we have on the one hand

$$\int_\tau (\nabla\cdot\mathbf{E})\,d\tau = \int_S \mathbf{E}\cdot d\mathbf{S} = \Phi_E$$

and on the other, using eq. 1.5–1,

$$\int_\tau (\nabla\cdot\mathbf{E})\,d\tau = \int_\tau \frac{\rho}{\epsilon_0}\,d\tau = \frac{Q}{\epsilon_0}$$

where Q is the total charge enclosed in the volume τ bounded by the surface S.

Problem 1.5a. A pair of parallel infinite planes, which are separated by a distance $2z_0$, contain between them a uniform distribution of charge of density ρ. Using the Gauss law, find $\mathbf{E}$ at points inside and outside the pair of planes. Test the relation div $\mathbf{E} = \rho/\epsilon_0$ for your solution. Graph the magnitude of $\mathbf{E}$.

Problem 1.5b. Prove that the fields of eqs. 1.4–5 and 1.4–6 obey eq. 1.5–1.

Problem 1.5c. Find the charge density at a point (x, y, z) for the fields given by (a) $\mathbf{E} = b_1(x\mathbf{1}_x + y\mathbf{1}_y + z\mathbf{1}_z)/(x^2 + y^2 + z^2)^{\frac{3}{2}}$ and (b) $\mathbf{E} = b_2(x\mathbf{1}_x + y\mathbf{1}_y + z\mathbf{1}_z)(x^2 + y^2 + z^2)$ where b_1 and b_2 are constants.

Problem 1.5d. Solve problem 1.5c for the field $\mathbf{E}$

$$\mathbf{E} = b_3(\mathbf{1}_x\cos\theta + \mathbf{1}_y\sin\theta)(x\cos\theta + y\sin\theta)^{\frac{1}{2}}$$

where b_3 and θ are constants.

Problem 1.5e. Prove that the solid angle subtended by a circle at a point $\mathscr{P}$ on the axis of the circle is $2\pi(1 - \cos\theta)$, where θ is the angle between the axis and a line from $\mathscr{P}$ to any point on the circle. Find the flux through the circle produced by a charge q at $\mathscr{P}$.

Problem 1.5f. Prove that $\nabla \cdot \mathbf{1}_r = 2/r$ and that $\nabla \cdot \mathbf{r} = 3$.

1.6   Lines and Tubes of Force

A graphic representation of the electric field strength in a given region may be obtained by use of the concept of lines of force. Through any point in a field we may draw a short segment of a line having the direction of the field vector. If we imagine space to be filled with such segments, they will fit together to form continuous lines that are tangent to the field vectors $\mathbf{E}$. Alternatively, a single such line may be started at any point and continued until a discontinuity in the field is reached, which by eq. 1.2–3 can only occur at the locations of charges. These lines are called lines of force (lines of field would be better but the historical terminology is generally adhered to).

A concept that is sometimes useful is that of a tube of force, which is a region bounded by a cylinder-like surface whose walls are composed of lines of force. A tube of force may have a regular or an irregular cross section (Fig. 1.6a).

The special significance of such a tube derives from the flux theorem. In a region free of charge ($\rho = 0$), the net flux through the sides and two ends of a section of such a tube is zero. The sides being lines of force and tangent to $\mathbf{E}$, there is no flux through them. Thus the flux in through one end of the tube is equal to the flux out through the other. Flux bears an analogy to the volume or mass flow of liquid through a pipe—it is "conserved" along a tube in charge-free regions of space. We can thus get a quantitative and graphic description of a field by considering all space to be occupied by such tubes, each carrying one unit of flux (or some convenient multiple, such as 10^{-4}, 10^{-8}, etc.). Each charge q thus is the "source" or starting point of q/ϵ_0 tubes, and each $-q'$ is the "sink" or end-point of q'/ϵ_0 tubes.   Since the flux is a constant we can write, if each tube is sufficiently thin, $\Phi_E = ES = 10^{-8}$ say, where S is the cross-sectional area of a tube, so that $E = 10^{-8}/S$, or the field strength is inversely proportional to S.   In fact, E can be measured by the number of tubes of flux per square meter.

Fig. 1.6a.   A tube of force.

Another method of representation is to draw a line of force down the center of each tube and count the lines per unit area.   (The tubes are not needed at all in this case.)   This method has the advantage that in certain cases one can actually draw diagrams with lines of force spaced quantitatively.   The disadvantage of the use of lines is the difficulty of thinking of a fractional line, in contrast to the ease of imagining a tube of fractional flux content   However, the concepts of lines and tubes of force are chiefly of use as aids to the imagination, and the choice between them may be left to the reader.[11]   It is important to note that in combining two fields by the principle of superposition, there is no simple geometric relation between the lines of force in the two separate fields and those of the combined fields

Tubes of flux can be more readily combined than can lines of force, since flux is a scalar.   However, the graphical superposition of fields is best carried out by methods to be described in section 1.11.

In concluding this section, it is well to note that if Coulomb's law were not true, flux would not be conserved along a tube, and the concepts of

---

[11] The line-of-force concept runs into further difficulties when used for fields that have a circulatory or non-source character, such as the electric field of magnetic origin (section 7.9), the magnetic induction **B** (section 7.7), the displacement field **D** (section 3.6), the magnetic field **H** (section 8.4), and the vector potential **A** (section 7.6).

flux, of lines, and of tubes although definable would lose much of their usefulness.   Note also that a line of force gives the direction of the force and hence of the *acceleration* that would be experienced by a small charge if free to move at the point in question but that the motion of the particle

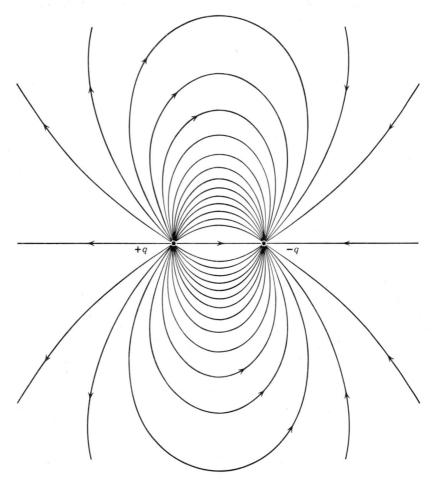

Fig. 1.6b.   Lines of force for $+q$ and $-q$.

is in general along a quite different path, owing to inertia.   This distinction is made in a simple case in problem 1.6a.   Note finally that a line of force can never intersect itself or any other line, for the direction of a line (the direction of the field) is uniquely defined at every point.

Figures 1.6b–f show lines of force for the fields of a few simple cases involving point charges.   Figures 1.6g and h show lines of force from a uniformly charged sphere and a uniformly charged cylinder, and Fig. 1.6*i* shows those for a single infinite plane and a pair of infinite planes.

Tubes of force of equal flux content can be drawn readily in the most symmetrical cases.   Each of the diagrams in Figs. 1.6*g* and 1.6*h* shows a

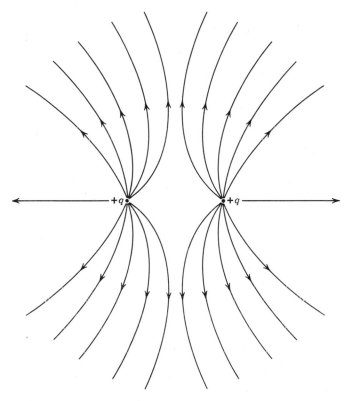

Fig. 1.6c.   Lines of force for +*q* and +*q*.

tube bounded by dashed lines.   The spherical case shows how to construct tubes of force whose intersections on the sphere are all of equal area, sides of these intersections being formed by planes through a common diameter of the sphere, equally spaced in angle, and by planes perpendicular to this diameter, equally spaced along it.

Problem 1.6a.   A beam of electrons moving with a speed of 20×10^5 m/sec passes between a horizontal pair of plates that carry charge densities, plus and minus, of 6.0×10^{-10} coulomb/m^2 respectively.   Assume that the field is the same as for an infinite set of plates, that the beam moves originally parallel to the plates, and that the beam leaves the field after passing a horizontal distance of 1 cm in it.   Find the resulting deflection of the electrons.

Problem 1.6b.   Prove that the tubes of flux in the sphere referred to above contain equal amounts of flux.

Problem 1.6c.   Three charges q_1, q_2, and q_3 lie on the x-axis at $x = x_1$, x_2, and x_3 respectively.   Find the flux produced by all three charges through a circle of radius r, normal to the x-axis, with its center at the point $(x, 0, 0)$. Then find the equation of a tube of flux and hence of a line of force.

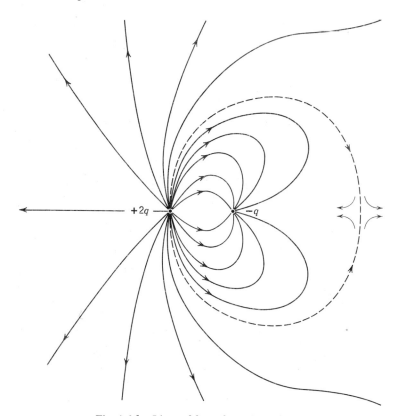

Fig. 1.6d.   Lines of force for $+2q$ and $-q$.

1.7   Potential

We turn now to a concept that has proved to be of the greatest value in the field of electrical phenomena: the concept of potential.[12]   With this concept we are able to make use of the far-reaching principle of the conservation of energy and will for this reason achieve a great simplification for a number of otherwise complicated calculations.   The potential is also of value in that it is a scalar quantity and is frequently easier to compute than the vector electric field strength, although it must be

[12] This concept was given its name by the mathematician George Green in 1828.

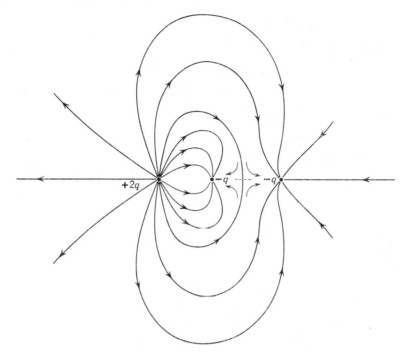

Fig. 1.6e. Lines of force for $+2q$, $-q$, and $-q$ on a straight line.

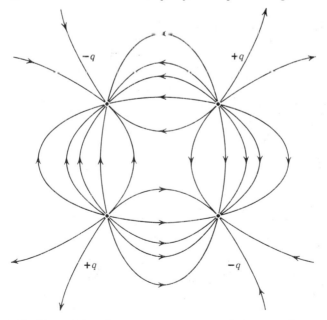

Fig. 1.6f. Lines of force for $+q$, $-q$, $+q$, $-q$ on the corners of a square.

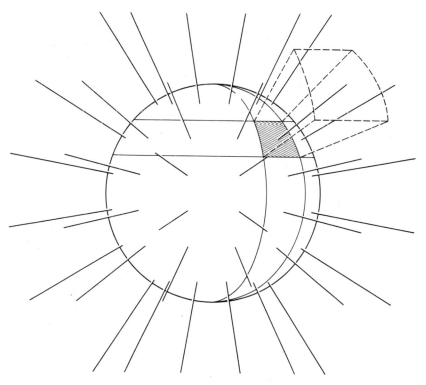

Fig. 1.6g. Lines of force and tube construction for a uniformly charged sphere.

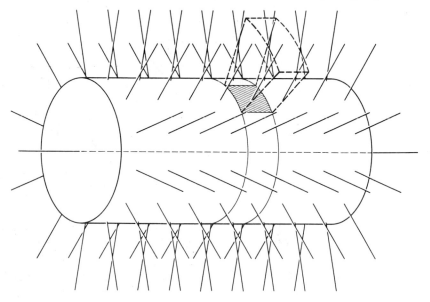

Fig. 1.6h. Lines of force and tube construction for a uniformly charged infinite cylinder.

emphasized that calculations with the latter quantity can yield the same information that is contained in a knowledge of the former, since the two are not independent. We have described the space around a distribution of charge where other charges can experience forces, in terms of the field vector **E**. We now introduce a scalar V to describe the same region. The potential V at any point $\mathscr{P}$ is defined as the *work per unit charge*

Fig. 1.6i. Lines of force for one plane and for two oppositely charged planes.

necessary to bring a small test charge from an arbitrary reference or zero point to $\mathscr{P}$. It is, in fact, the added *potential energy per unit charge* that would be present in the system if a test charge were placed at $\mathscr{P}$. (The test charge should be small enough that the charges whose effects at $\mathscr{P}$ are being calculated would not be disturbed by its presence. The remarks on pp. 5–6 concerning **E** apply here too.)

Our definition of potential makes no mention of the path by which the test charge is brought from the reference point to $\mathscr{P}$. The fact that the work is independent of the path is equivalent to the fact that the law of conservation of energy applies here, and this will be proved in the next paragraphs.

The reader will recall that work is defined as force times distance, provided the force is in the direction of the displacement. That is, if a force **F** acts on a body while the body suffers a displacement **dl**, the work dW is $(F \cos \theta)\, dl$; θ is the angle between **F** and **dl** so that $F \cos \theta$ is the component of **F** responsible for the work done. Note that we may also say that dW is F times the component of **dl** in the direction of **F**. We thus have another important physical application of the scalar product: $dW = \mathbf{F} \cdot \mathbf{dl}$, or for a path of finite length,

$$W = \int_l \mathbf{F} \cdot \mathbf{dl}$$

where the integral is a line integral taken along the path over which the body is moved.

For the electric case, the work per unit charge is to be calculated from the force per unit charge. Furthermore, in calculating potential energy we must remember that the work is done by a mechanical force that opposes the electric force. (In order to avoid consideration of any kinetic energy that might be acquired by a moving charge, we shall assume that the mechanical and electrical forces just balance each other.) Thus we must replace $\mathbf{F}$ by $-\mathbf{E}$, and write

$$V_{\mathscr{P}} = -\int_{\mathscr{P}_0}^{\mathscr{P}} \mathbf{E} \cdot \mathbf{dl} \tag{1.7-1}$$

$\mathscr{P}_0$ is the reference point, and $\mathscr{P}$ is the point at which the potential is desired. It will be noted that it is really potential difference (PD) that is defined and measured. The potential at a point involves an arbitrariness due to the freedom of choice of the reference point $\mathscr{P}_0$, but potential difference has no such arbitrariness. The minus sign in eq. 1.7–1 can most easily be kept in mind if we remember the analogous case of gravity: potential energy increases as we go up, in a direction opposite to the force.

The unit of potential in the MKS system is the joule/coulomb, which is called a volt. A thousandth of a volt is called a millivolt (10^{-3} v = 1 mv) and a millionth of a volt is called a microvolt (10^{-6} v = 1 μv). The electrostatic and Gaussian unit of potential is the erg/statcoulomb, or statvolt. One statvolt is readily seen to be equal to nearly 300 v—more exactly, 299.793 v.

In most considerations dealing with the atomic aspect of matter, it is convenient to measure charge in units of e and potential in volts. This leads to the introduction of a new energy unit, the electron-volt (abbreviated ev), which is the work done in taking a charge e through a PD of one volt. Clearly 1 ev = 1.602×10^{-19} joule = 1.602×10^{-12} erg.

Let us calculate the potential at a point $\mathscr{P}$ near an isolated point charge q, using for $\mathscr{P}_0$ an arbitrary point. (See Fig. 1.7a.)

We may write $\mathbf{E} \cdot \mathbf{dl}$ as $E(dl \cos \theta) = E \, dr'$ where dr' is the change in the distance from q of the test charge δq. Thus

$$V = -\int_{\mathscr{P}_0}^{\mathscr{P}} \mathbf{E} \cdot \mathbf{dl} = -\int_{r_0}^{r} E \, dr' = -\int_{r_0}^{r} \frac{q \, dr'}{4\pi\epsilon_0 r'^2}$$

$$= \frac{-q}{4\pi\epsilon_0} \left(-\frac{1}{r'}\right)\Big|_{r_0}^{r} = \frac{q}{4\pi\epsilon_0} \left(\frac{1}{r} - \frac{1}{r_0}\right)$$

The potential is thus seen to be independent of the path. The result takes on a particularly simple value if the point $\mathscr{P}_0$ is taken at infinity, so that $1/r_0$ is zero:

$$V = \frac{q}{4\pi\epsilon_0 r} \tag{1.7-2}$$

This convention for $\mathscr{P}_0$ will be generally used whenever feasible. In practice, it means that in dealing with a system of charges, infinity is taken to be any point situated at a distance sufficiently large compared to the dimensions of the system (which must include all points at which values of V and E are desired) that resulting errors are less than the desired limits of experimental accuracy.

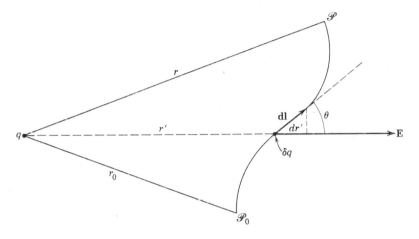

Fig. 1.7a.   Calculation of potential difference in a region near a point charge.

The potential at a point $\mathscr{P}$ in a system of charges is the scalar sum of the potentials produced by each charge separately, as we can easily prove:

$$V = -\int_{\infty}^{\mathscr{P}} \mathbf{E} \cdot \mathbf{dl} = -\int_{\infty}^{\mathscr{P}} \left(\sum_n \frac{q_n \mathbf{1}_{rn}}{4\pi\epsilon_0 r_n'^2} \right) \cdot \mathbf{dl} = \frac{-1}{4\pi\epsilon_0} \int_{\infty}^{\mathscr{P}} \left(\sum_n \frac{q_n \, dr_n'}{r_n'^2} \right)$$

so that

$$V = \frac{1}{4\pi\epsilon_0} \sum_n \frac{q_n}{r_n} \qquad (1.7\text{–}3)$$

In these expressions, r_n' is the variable distance of the test charge δq from the nth charge q_n of the given system, and r_n is the distance of point $\mathscr{P}$, the final position of δq, from q_n. This result shows that V is in general independent of the path used to calculate it and thus proves the validity of the energy conservation law for all distributions of charges at rest.

If we consider two different arbitrary paths from $\mathscr{P}_0$ to $\mathscr{P}$, we can calculate a closed-loop line integral of $\mathbf{E} \cdot \mathbf{dl}$ by reversing the sign for one of the two chosen paths. The result is a more direct expression of the law of conservation of energy for this case:

$$\oint \mathbf{E} \cdot \mathbf{dl} = 0 \qquad (1.7\text{–}4)$$

where the $\oint$ sign refers to a closed-loop line integral and applies here to an *arbitrary* loop. In general, the integral $\oint \mathbf{A} \cdot \mathbf{dl}$ for any arbitrary vector $\mathbf{A}$ is called the circulation of $\mathbf{A}$ around the path in question. The circulation of $\mathbf{E}$ is always zero, which means that any charged particle that executes motion in a closed loop under the action of electrostatic forces will suffer no net change in energy.

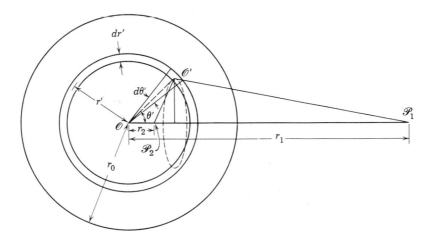

Fig. 1.7*b*.   Calculation of the potential for a spherical distribution of charge.

Equation 1.7–3 can be written in forms suitable for continuous distributions of charge, exactly as in the case of eqs. 1.3–1, 1.3–2, and 1.3–3 for the field strength. For line, surface, and volume charge densities λ, σ, and ρ, we have

$$V = \frac{1}{4\pi\epsilon_0} \int_{\text{line } l} \frac{\lambda \, dl'}{r'} \qquad (1.7\text{–}5)$$

$$V = \frac{1}{4\pi\epsilon_0} \int_{\text{surface } S} \frac{\sigma \, dS'}{r'} \qquad (1.7\text{–}6)$$

$$V = \frac{1}{4\pi\epsilon_0} \int_{\text{volume } \tau} \frac{\rho \, d\tau'}{r'} \qquad (1.7\text{–}7)$$

We shall illustrate the formulas in eqs. 1.7–5, 1.7–6, and 1.7–7 by finding the potential due to a spherically symmetrical distribution of charge, without using the known value for $\mathbf{E}$ in this case, eq. 1.4–3.

Consider a sphere of radius r_0, filled with charge of density $\rho(r')$, a function of r' only. We calculate the potential at a point $\mathscr{P}_1$ (Fig. 1.7*b*) at a distance $r_1 > r_0$ from the center, and at $\mathscr{P}_2$ a distance $r_2 < r_0$ from the center. Let us first divide the sphere into spherical shells and calculate the potential produced by one of them of radius[13] r' and thickness dr'. The charge per unit area of this shell is $\rho(r') \, dr'$, so if we write $\rho \, dr' = \sigma$, we have a surface distribution problem with σ uniform over the sphere and could use eq. 1.7–6.

We can specialize still further and divide the shell into rings, coaxial with the line $\mathcal{O}\mathcal{P}_2\mathcal{P}_1$ of cross section $r' \, d\theta' \, dr'$ and radius $r' \sin \theta'$ (see Fig. 1.7b). For such a ring, the linear density $\lambda = \sigma r' \, d\theta' = \rho r' \, dr' \, d\theta'$; for this case, we can use eq. 1.7–5. Furthermore, in eq. 1.7–5 we replace r' by the value of $\mathcal{O}'\mathcal{P}_2$ or $\mathcal{O}'\mathcal{P}_1$ which, by the law of cosines, is $(r'^2 + r_2^2 - 2r'r_2 \cos \theta')^{\frac{1}{2}}$ or $(r'^2 + r_1^2 - 2r'r_1 \cos \theta')^{\frac{1}{2}}$ for $\mathcal{P}_2$ and $\mathcal{P}_1$ respectively. Since these values are constant along a ring, the integral to be calculated is just $\int dl$, the circumference of the circle, so the potential of the ring at $\mathcal{P}_1$ is

$$V_{\text{ring},1} = \frac{\lambda(2\pi r' \sin \theta')}{4\pi\epsilon_0(r'^2 + r_1^2 - 2r'r_1 \cos \theta')^{\frac{1}{2}}}$$

$$= \frac{\rho r'^2 \sin \theta' \, d\theta' \, dr'}{2\epsilon_0(r'^2 + r_1^2 - 2r'r_1 \cos \theta')^{\frac{1}{2}}} \tag{1.7–8}$$

with r_2 instead of r_1 for $V_{\text{ring},2}$.

To get the potential produced by the whole shell, we must integrate this result over θ' from 0 to π, which will result in covering the entire sphere just once by ring elements. We have

$$V_{\text{shell},1} = \frac{\rho r'^2 \, dr'}{2\epsilon_0} \int_0^\pi \frac{\sin \theta' \, d\theta'}{(r'^2 + r_1^2 - 2r'r_1 \cos \theta')^{\frac{1}{2}}}$$

$$= \frac{\rho r'^2 \, dr'}{2\epsilon_0} \left[\frac{(r'^2 + r_1^2 - 2r'r_1 \cos \theta')^{\frac{1}{2}}}{r'r_1} \right]_0^\pi \tag{1.7–9}$$

wherein r_1 is to be replaced by r_2 to get $V_{\text{shell},2}$. When we evaluate the indefinite integral in brackets at the indicated limits, we have the problem of which sign of square root to take. We must remember that the r' in eqs. 1.7–5, 1.7–6, and 1.7–7 is always a positive number, so that the radicals in eq. 1.7–9 must be positive. When $\theta' = \pi$, the expression is $(r'^2 + r_1^2 + 2r'r_1)^{\frac{1}{2}}$, clearly equal to $r' + r_1$. When $\theta' = 0$, we have $(r'^2 + r_1^2 - 2r'r_1)^{\frac{1}{2}}$, which is either $r' - r_1$ or $r_1 - r'$. To get a positive result for $\mathcal{P}_1$ we use $r_1 - r'$, whereas for $\mathcal{P}_2$ we use $r' - r_2$. Thus

$$V_{\text{shell},1} = \frac{\rho r'^2 \, dr'}{2\epsilon_0} \left[\frac{(r_1 + r') - (r_1 - r')}{r'r_1} \right] = \frac{\rho r'^2 \, dr'}{\epsilon_0 r_1} = \frac{q}{4\pi\epsilon_0 r_1} \tag{1.7–10a}$$

---

[13] For clarity in what follows, we shall temporarily assume $\mathcal{P}_2$ to be inside the shell ($r' > r_2$). The reader can readily handle the case $r' < r_2$ which we shall shortly need, by using the treatment for $\mathcal{P}_1$.

and

$$V_{\text{shell},2} = \frac{\rho r'^2 \, dr'}{2\epsilon_0} \left[\frac{(r_2 + r') - (r' - r_2)}{r' r_2} \right] = \frac{\rho r' \, dr'}{\epsilon_0} = \frac{q}{4\pi\epsilon_0 r'} \qquad (1.7\text{–}10b)$$

using $q = \int \sigma \, dS = 4\pi r'^2 \rho \, dr'$ for the total charge on the shell. We see that outside a shell the potential is the same as that of a single point charge at $\mathcal{O}$, whereas inside the potential is *constant*, i.e., independent of r_2. It is everywhere equal to the value it has at the surface of the shell where $r_2 = r'$. This result agrees with that of p. 18 for such a shell—if **E** is zero inside, no work would be done on moving a small test charge about. Such a region of constant potential is called an *equipotential volume*. A surface of constant potential, such as, in this case, any spherical surface with center at $\mathcal{O}$, is similarly called an *equipotential surface*.

The extension of the calculation to the entire sphere of Fig. 1.7b is now easy. For a point $\mathcal{P}_1$, we can add all the shells into which the sphere can be divided and find

$$V_1 = \frac{Q}{4\pi\epsilon_0 r_1} \qquad (1\cdot7\text{–}11)$$

where Q is all the charge in the sphere. For $\mathcal{P}_2$, we have two parts for V:

$$V_2 = \frac{Q_2}{4\pi\epsilon_0 r_2} + \frac{1}{\epsilon_0} \int_{r_2}^{r_0} \rho(r') r' \, dr'; \qquad r_2 \leqslant r_0 \qquad (1.7\text{–}12)$$

where the first term includes all the charge Q_2 situated within a radius r_2 and the second is an integral over eq. 1.7–10b for $r' \geqslant r_2$. The details of the calculation are not particularly instructive, and specific examples are left to problems 1.7c and d.

We have shown in this example the power of the integral calculus to provide in a straightforward way an answer to a physical problem in which a discontinuity appears—E is discontinuous at the surface of the shell, and the derivative of V with respect to r is discontinuous. More advanced work in electromagnetic theory involves many such integrals. Figure 1.7c shows a plot of E and V against r for a uniformly charged spherical shell.

There are some occasions when it is desired to find V directly from its definition eq. 1.7–1 instead of from the charge distributions as in eqs. 1.7–5, 1.7–6, and 1.7–7. The case of the point charge, eq. 1.7–2, is of course the simplest example. Sometimes the field **E** is already known; sometimes it is easier to calculate than V. As examples we shall take the infinite plane and infinite line distributions dealt with in eqs. 1.3–6 and 1.3–5 respectively. If for the plane we choose as origin a point $\mathcal{P}_0$ at a distance z_0 from the plane, we find that at a point $\mathscr{P}$, whose distance is z on the same side of the plane,

$$V = -\int_{z_0}^{z} E_z \, dz = -\frac{\sigma}{2\epsilon_0}(z - z_0) \tag{1.7-13}$$

As z_0 approaches infinity, this result becomes infinite, a difficulty that reflects merely the impossibility of having a truly infinite plane distribution

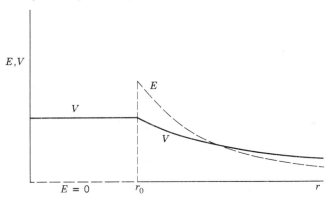

Fig. 1.7c.   E and V plotted against r for a spherical shell.

of charge!   However, as illustrated in problem 1.3h a finite plane has, to any desired approximation, the same field as an infinite plane for points sufficiently close to the plane compared to their distance from its edges. Equation 1.7-13 is thus valid if z and z_0 are both small enough.

If z is on the other side of the plane, we have to calculate the integral in two parts, because of the discontinuity at the plane.   It is left to the reader to get an expression for this case (problem 1.7f).

For the case of an infinite line of charge, a similar difficulty arises about the potential at infinity.   For finite points at distances r_0 and r from the line, it is easy to prove from eq. 1.3-5 that

$$V = -\int_{r_0}^{r} \mathbf{E} \cdot d\mathbf{l} = \frac{\lambda}{2\pi\epsilon_0} \ln \frac{r_0}{r} \tag{1.7-14}$$

Suppose we have two long parallel wires with charge densities $+\lambda$ and $-\lambda$.   By symmetry, the plane that is the locus of points equidistant from the two wires is an equipotential.   This plane extends to infinity and hence may properly be taken as the zero equipotential.   Using eq. 1.7-14 for the two wires, with r_0 equal to one-half the distance between them, we find that the potential at a point $\mathscr{P}$ (Fig. 1.7d) is given by:

$$V = \frac{\lambda}{2\pi\epsilon_0} \ln \frac{r_2}{r_1} \tag{1.7-15}$$

The calculation of the equipotentials and lines of force for this case is of considerable importance and will be taken up in Chapter 4 in connection with calculations involving charged conducting surfaces.

Let us note in conclusion of this section that the existence of the potential does *not* depend on the inverse square law but does depend on the principle of superposition and on the existence of a force law giving a radial force

Fig. 1.7d.   Calculation of the potential for a pair of infinite cylinders.

that depends only on the distance r between point charges. Potentials can be defined for instance for inverse cube fields or any other power. They can also be defined for certain fields in which the force is not radial and depends on angles made by the radius vector with specified directions in space (see section 3.1). We shall later find two examples of fields which do not possess uniquely defined scalar potentials (the magnetic field, section 7.6, and the electric field of magnetic origin, section 7.9).

The fact in addition to the existence of the potential that makes the law of conservation of energy hold in electrostatics is that one charge can move about without necessarily having work done on the other charges— they only need to be sufficiently fixed in position. When uniquely defined scalar potentials do not exist, it also happens that one system (charge or current) cannot move without work necessarily being done on other systems (see section 7.12).

Problem 1.7a.   Find the potential at the points in problem 1.3a at which **E** was to be calculated.

Problem 1.7b.   Find the value of V at the point at which **E** = 0 when point charges of +3.0 and +7.0 microcoulombs are located at (0, 0) and (0.50m, 0) in the x–y plane, as in problem 1.3b. Find also the value of V at the four points which are 0.02 m away from the point where **E** = 0, in the positive and negative

x and y directions. Describe the variation of V in the neighborhood of this point.

Problem 1.7c. Find the potential at an arbitrary point inside a uniformly charged sphere, by evaluating eq. 1.7–12.

Problem 1.7d. Find the potential at an arbitrary point inside a symmetrically charged sphere when (a) $\rho(r') = b_1 r'$, $r' \leqslant r_0$; (b) $\rho(r') = b_2/r'$, $r' \leqslant r_0$; and (c) $\rho(r') = b_3 r' e^{-b_4 r'}$, $r' \leqslant r_0$ [$\rho(r')$ is to be taken as zero for $r' \geqslant r_0$].

Problem 1.7e. Calculate the potential on the axis of a uniformly charged disk (cf. problem 1.3f).

Problem 1.7f. Complete the calculation referred to in the text for the PD between two points on opposite sides of an infinite uniformly charged plane. For an arbitrary z_0, sketch a plot of V against z as z varies from $-2z_0$ to $+2z_0$. Also plot E_z for this case.

Problem 1.7g. Find the potential as a function of z for the thick infinite slab of charge described in problem 1.5a, taking $V = 0$ at the center of the slab. Sketch a graph of $V(z)$.

Problem 1.7h. Two parallel infinite wires carry equal and opposite uniform line distributions of charge. The wires are 10 cm apart. If the PD is 6 v between two points whose distances to the two wires are respectively 6 cm and 8 cm, and 8 cm and 6 cm, find the value of λ.

Problem 1.7i. A "double layer" at an electrode-solution interface in a certain chemical cell consists of plane layers of positive and negative charge, each of surface density 1.0 electronic unit per 100 square Ångstroms (1 Å $= 10^{-8}$ cm) separated by a distance of 1.5 Ångstroms. Find the PD between the two layers.

Problem 1.7j. A sphere of radius 2.0 m is uniformly filled out to half its radius with negative charge of density 8.4×10^{-6} coulombs/m³. The remainder is filled uniformly with positive charge of density 1.2×10^{-6} coulomb/m³ Find the potential as a function of r, inside and outside the sphere. Find the work done in taking an electron from the center of the sphere to its edge.

Problem 1.7k. Suppose E is given by $\mathbf{E} = (300x + 500y)\mathbf{1}_x + (500x - 400)\mathbf{1}_y - 300z\mathbf{1}_z$. Find the PD between the origin and the point $(0.80m, -0.48m, 0)$ using two different paths of integration.

Problem 1.7l. Find the potential at a point $(x, y, 0)$ outside a line of charge of constant density λ, extending along the x axis from $x = 0$ to $x = a$.

Problem 1.7m. Find the work done in taking an electron from the point $(2a, 0, 0)$ to the point $(0.5a, 2a, 0)$ in the example of problem 1.7l, if $\lambda = 7.0 \times 10^{-12}$ coulombs/m and $a = 50$ cm.

Problem 1.7n. What fraction of the work done in taking an electron to infinity from the surface of a spherical distribution of total charge Q and radius a is performed in taking the electron to a radius na where $n > 1$?

Problem 1.7o. Discuss the convergence of the integrals 1.7–5, 1.7–6, and 1.7–7, for the same circumstance as in problem 1.3m.

1.8   The Curl of E[14]

We have considered in section 1.5 the differential-equation expression for the flux law. We turn now to a similar expression for the conservative

---

[14] This material can be postponed until just before section 3.2 is taken up.

property expressed in eq. 1.7–4, namely the vanishing of the circulation $\oint \mathbf{E} \cdot \mathbf{dl}$.

In Appendix A.2 it is shown that for any vector $\mathbf{A}$ that varies from point to point, another vector called **curl A** can be constructed whose component in any direction is the circulation of the vector $\mathbf{A}$ per unit area around a small area whose normal is in that direction. If $\oint \mathbf{E} \cdot \mathbf{dl} = 0$ for any closed path, **curl E** must vanish. Using eq. A.2–38a for the Cartesian components, we can write

$$\left.\begin{aligned}
(\text{curl } E)_x &= \frac{\partial E_z}{\partial y} - \frac{\partial E_y}{\partial z} = 0 \\[2ex]
(\text{curl } E)_y &= \frac{\partial E_x}{\partial z} - \frac{\partial E_z}{\partial x} = 0 \\[2ex]
(\text{curl } E)_z &= \frac{\partial E_y}{\partial x} - \frac{\partial E_x}{\partial y} = 0
\end{aligned}\right\} \tag{1.8–1}$$

In terms of the vector operator ∇, we write, simply,

$$\mathbf{curl\ E} = \nabla \times \mathbf{E} = 0 \tag{1.8–2}$$

Using Stokes' theorem, (A.2–39), we can reverse the argument and show that, if **curl E** $= 0$, then $\oint \mathbf{E} \cdot \mathbf{dl} = 0$ around any closed path. In fact, we have

$$\oint_l \mathbf{E} \cdot \mathbf{dl} = \int_S \nabla \times \mathbf{E} \cdot \mathbf{dS} = 0 \tag{1.8–3}$$

We can thus replace the earlier statement that the field depends only on the vector distances from the point charges that are its sources, with eqs. 1.8–1 or 1.8–2 as the condition that a potential exists, i.e., that the line integral $\int_{\mathscr{P}_1}^{\mathscr{P}_2} \mathbf{E} \cdot \mathbf{dl}$ between two points $\mathscr{P}_1$ and $\mathscr{P}_2$ is independent of the path.

As a simple example, let us assume that $\mathbf{E}$ lies entirely in the x direction in a certain region. Then from eq. 1.8–1 we find, setting $E_y = E_z = 0$,

$$\frac{\partial E_x}{\partial z} = \frac{\partial E_x}{\partial y} = 0$$

so that E_x cannot vary in the y and z directions. If ρ is also zero in this region, then from $\nabla \cdot \mathbf{E} = 0$ we have

$$\frac{\partial E_x}{\partial x} = 0$$

so that E_x does not vary with x either—it has a constant value throughout the region.

It is not hard to verify eq. 1.8–1 for the various fields we have already calculated (cf. problems 1.8a, b, c).

Problem 1.8a.   Using Cartesian coordinates, verify eq. 1.8–1 for the field of a uniform spherical distribution of charge, both inside and outside the radius r_0 of the sphere.

Problem 1.8b.   Solve problem 1.8a for a long uniformly charged cylinder.

Problem 1.8c.   Repeat problems 1.8a and 1.8b using, respectively, spherical and cylindrical coordinates.

Problem 1.8d.   Test for vanishing of **curl E**, the fields given by (a) **E** = $b_1\{3x^2yz\mathbf{1}_x + [x^3z + yz^2(yz)^{\frac{1}{2}}]\mathbf{1}_y + [x^3y + y^2z(yz)^{\frac{1}{2}}]\mathbf{1}_z\}$, (b) **E** = $b_2(y\mathbf{1}_x - x\mathbf{1}_y)$, and (c) **E** = $b_3[y\mathbf{1}_x/(x^2 + y^2) - x\mathbf{1}_y/(x^2 + y^2)]$. ($b_1$, b_2, and b_3 are constants.) Evaluate **curl E** in the cases in which it does not vanish.

Problem 1.8e.   Find the charge density ρ at a point (x, y, z) for each of the fields given in problem 1.8d.

Problem 1.8f.   Calculate $\int$ **E** · **dl** from the origin to a point x_0, y_0 in the x–y plane for the field **E** = $b_2(y\mathbf{1}_x - x\mathbf{1}_y)$ along three different rectilinear paths: (a) from $(0, 0)$ to $(0, y_0)$ to (x_0, y_0); (b) from $(0, 0)$ to $(x_0, 0)$ to (x_0, y_0); (c) from $(0, 0)$ along a radius directly to (x_0, y_0).

Problem 1.8g.   Solve problem 1.8f, but use cylindrical coordinates and choose two different paths composed of radii and arcs of circles.

1.9   Potential Gradient

We have seen how to find the potential V if the field **E** is known (eq. 1.7–1) and how to find V if the charge distribution is known (eqs. 1.7–5, 1.7–6, and 1.7–7). We have also shown how to find **E** from the charge distribution (eqs. 1.3–1, 1.3–2, and 1.3–4). Let us show how to find **E** if V is known.

The field **E** is a vector, whereas V is a scalar.   We should hence be able to calculate *components* of **E** from a knowledge of V.   In fact, if we wish to know the force per unit charge in a given direction at a given point, we may imagine a small test charge δq to move a distance dl in the given direction.   Then, using our knowledge of V as a function of position, we calculate the change dV in the potential energy per unit charge.   If the field component is E_l, we have $dV = -E_l\, dl$ (potential *decreases* in the direction of the field).   Hence, $E_l = -dV/dl$, or as it is usually written to indicate that only one specific direction is involved,

$$E_l = -\partial V/\partial l \qquad (1.9\text{–}1)$$

We see that the component of field strength in a given direction is the negative of the directional derivative of the potential in that direction, evaluated at the point in question.   Equation 1.9–1 is the inverse of eq. 1.7–1.

In particular we can find the Cartesian components of **E**:

$$E_x = -\partial V/\partial x, \qquad E_y = -\partial V/\partial y, \qquad E_z = -\partial V/\partial z \qquad (1.9\text{–}2)$$

and hence may construct the vector **E**:

$$\mathbf{E} = -\left(\mathbf{1}_x \frac{\partial V}{\partial x} + \mathbf{1}_y \frac{\partial V}{\partial y} + \mathbf{1}_z \frac{\partial V}{\partial z}\right) \qquad (1.9\text{–}3a)$$

$$= -\left(\mathbf{1}_x \frac{\partial}{\partial x} + \mathbf{1}_y \frac{\partial}{\partial y} + \mathbf{1}_z \frac{\partial}{\partial z}\right) V \qquad (1.9\text{–}3b)$$

$$= -\nabla V \equiv -\mathbf{grad}\, V \qquad (1.9\text{–}3c)$$

in accordance with eqs. A.2–15. The name "gradient" is derived from the analogy of gravitational potential, as expressed in our use of the gradient for the slope of a hillside. It is clear from eqs. 1.9–3, as well as from the definition of the volt, that the units in which E is measured may be called volts/meter, which is in fact the most common designation.

In terms of the gradient, we can write for any component E_l,

$$E_l = -\frac{\partial V}{\partial l} = -\nabla V \cdot \mathbf{1}_l \qquad (1.9\text{–}4)$$

(see eq. A.2–18) and conversely for a differential or increment of V, corresponding to a vector displacement **dl**

$$dV = \nabla V \cdot \mathbf{dl} = -\mathbf{E} \cdot \mathbf{dl} = -E_l\, dl \qquad (1.9\text{–}5)$$

(see eq. A.2–19).

An important proposition, generally referred to as Earnshaw's theorem,[15] states that an isolated charge cannot remain in stable equilibrium under the action of electrostatic forces only. In other words, there can be no maximum or minimum of the potential function $V(x, y, z)$, in free space. For suppose there were a minimum at a point $\mathscr{P}$, where no charge resides. Then just outside $\mathscr{P}$ the gradient of V would everywhere be directed away from $\mathscr{P}$, and the electric field would be directed toward $\mathscr{P}$. Application of the flux theorem shows that a negative charge must exist at $\mathscr{P}$, contrary to the assertion that $\mathscr{P}$ was in free space. It is possible for the gradient to be zero at $\mathscr{P}$ (field zero), but we cannot have V increase in all directions away from $\mathscr{P}$. Any such zero-field point is therefore one of unstable

[15] S. Earnshaw, *Trans. Cambridge Phil. Soc.*, **7**, 97–112 (1842), showed that particles in an elastic medium cannot be held in equilibrium by inverse-square forces. J. C. Maxwell, *Treatise on Electricity and Magnetism* 2nd or 3rd ed., Clarendon Press, Oxford, 1881 and 1904, article 116, applied the theorem to electrostatics, including application to forces on charged conductors.

equilibrium.   A graph of $V(x, y)$ for a two-dimensional case would show a "saddle point" at $\mathscr{P}$ (Fig. 1.9a) and the three-dimensional case is similar but harder to picture.

In a region of continuous charge distribution ρ, a maximum or minimum could exist, but a continuous distribution is an idealization.   We have to consider each electron or proton as an isolated charge, and pure electrostatic equilibrium is impossible.

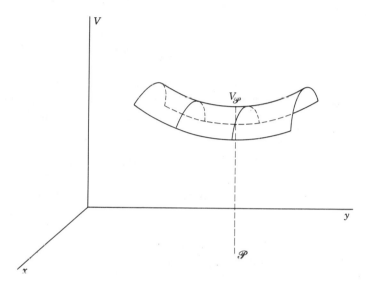

Fig. 1.9a.   Graph of $V(x, y)$ in neighborhood of a point $\mathscr{P}$ of unstable equilibrium.

Problem 1.9a.   Use eq. 1.9–1 to find the field outside a symmetrically charged sphere if the potential is given by eq. 1.7–11.

Problem 1.9b.   Find the potential at a point (x, y) produced by the charges in problem 1.3a, and from the expression find the x and y components of the field.   Use the result to check the answers for problem 1.3a.

Problem 1.9c.   Find the field strength at an arbitrary point inside each sphere in problem 1.7d.

Problem 1.9d.   Find the field strength in the sphere of problem 1.7j at a point 1.50 m from its center.

Problem 1.9e.   In fair weather, an upward potential gradient of about 100 v/m is observed at the earth's surface.   Assuming the earth to carry a uniform distribution of charge on its surface and none in its interior, find the value of σ. If an equal and opposite charge exists in a thin layer at an altitude of 18 km (1 km $= 10^3$ m), what is the potential at the surface of the earth, considering it to be an isolated sphere?

Problem 1.9f.   Prove that the potential found in problem 1.7c has an extreme value at the center of the sphere.

Problem 1.9g. Show that $\nabla r = \mathbf{1}_r$ and $\nabla(1/r) = -\mathbf{1}_r/r^2$, where r is the distance of a point (x, y, z) from a fixed point (x_0, y_0, z_0).

1.10   The Laplace and Poisson Equations[16]

We can now combine the results of sections 1.5 and 1.9. Equations 1.5–1 and 1.9–3c together yield $-\nabla \cdot \nabla V = \rho/\epsilon_0$, which we abbreviate to

$$\nabla^2 V = -\rho/\epsilon_0 \qquad (1.10\text{–}1a)$$

or

$$\frac{\partial^2 V}{\partial x^2} + \frac{\partial^2 V}{\partial y^2} + \frac{\partial^2 V}{\partial z^2} = -\rho/\epsilon_0 \qquad (1.10\text{–}1b)$$

The operator $\nabla \cdot \nabla = \nabla^2$ is frequently written as Δ and is called the Laplace operator, or Laplacian.   Equation 1.10–1 is a partial differential equation for the scalar potential function $V(x, y, z)$ in terms of the "source" ρ of this potential and is called Poisson's equation.   From section 1.7, it is clear that knowledge of the function $\rho(x, y, z)$ and the special cases of surface and line densities and isolated point charges, is sufficient to determine V uniquely.   It has been proved by Dirichlet and others that the corresponding purely mathematical problem is similarly determined. That is, if ρ is given everywhere, there is one and only one V that satisfies eq. 1.10–1.   In fact, the solution is just eq. 1.7–7.   In most cases of interest, however, conductors are involved (Chapter 2) and surface distributions of charge prevail (although σ is not usually given in advance).   The solution becomes eq. 1.7–6, and in the space outside the conductors, the equation becomes the Laplace equation:

$$\nabla^2 V = 0 \qquad (1.10\text{–}2)$$

Every potential function derived from any electrostatic distribution whatsoever must obey this equation in free space.   The values of σ at the boundaries of the empty portion of space thus become what we call the *boundary conditions* for solutions of Laplace's equation.   These conditions and others involving the potentials of conducting surfaces, will be taken up in Chapter 4.

One direct application of eq. 1.10–2 is to make a new proof of Earnshaw's theorem.   A maximum or minimum of $V(x, y, z)$ requires that the three second derivatives

$$\frac{\partial^2 V}{\partial x^2}, \qquad \frac{\partial^2 V}{\partial y^2}, \qquad \frac{\partial^2 V}{\partial z^2}$$

---

[16] To be postponed if the material in section 1.5 has not yet been studied.   The results of this section are not needed until Chapter 4 is taken up.

be all of one sign (or zero).   This is patently impossible from eq. 1.10–2, unless all are simultaneously zero, a condition not met with in practice unless V is constant, when of course there is no *stable* equilibrium at any point.   A higher-order minimum or maximum involving the simultaneous vanishing of these three derivatives is in fact impossible, but the proof will not be considered here.[17]

Plane Diode with Space Charge.   An interesting application of Poisson's equation occurs in the steady flow of electrons between a plane cathode and a plane anode in a diode vacuum tube.   The potential and charge density in this case will be functions only of x, where x is the coordinate perpendicular to the planes.   We will see in section 5.8 that in such a case, the charge density ρ will be inversely proportional to the electron speed v.   The sum of the kinetic and potential energies of each electron will be constant,

$$\tfrac{1}{2}mv^2 - eV = \text{constant}$$

and the constant will be zero if V is measured from a point where v is zero.   Such a point will be shown to exist at a minimum of $V(x)$, so that we have for $x = x_1$,

$$v(x_1) = 0; \qquad V(x_1) = 0; \qquad \left(\frac{dV}{dx}\right)_{x=x_1} = 0 \qquad (1.10\text{–}3)$$

Consequently we can write Poisson's equation as (ordinary derivatives are used because only one independent variable enters)

$$\frac{d^2V}{dx^2} = \frac{a}{[V(x)]^{\frac{1}{2}}} \qquad (1.10\text{–}4)$$

where a is a positive constant (since ρ is negative).

This equation can be integrated if we multiply each side by $2(dV/dx)$, since

$$\frac{d}{dx}\left(\frac{dV}{dx}\right)^2 = 2\frac{dV}{dx}\frac{d^2V}{dx^2}$$

and

$$4a\frac{d}{dx}(V^{\frac{1}{2}}) = 2aV^{-\frac{1}{2}}\frac{dV}{dx}$$

We therefore find on integrating that

$$\left(\frac{dV}{dx}\right)^2 = 4a[V(x)]^{\frac{1}{2}} + \text{constant}$$

[17] See, for instance, Sir James Jeans, *Electricity and Magnetism*, Cambridge University Press, Cambridge, 1946, Art. 50, p. 42; also W. R. Smythe, *Static and Dynamic Electricity*, McGraw-Hill, New York, 1939, p. 13.

The constant of integration must be zero if eq. 1.10–3 is to be valid for $x = x_1$. For points $x > x_1$, beyond the minimum, $dV/dx > 0$, and we can take the positive square root of each side:

$$\frac{dV}{dx} = 2a^{\frac{1}{2}}[V(x)]^{\frac{1}{4}} \tag{1.10–5}$$

or, separating the variables,

$$\frac{dV}{V^{\frac{1}{4}}} = 2a^{\frac{1}{2}} \, dx$$

and

$$\tfrac{4}{3}[V(x)]^{\frac{3}{4}} = 2a^{\frac{1}{2}}(x - x_1) \tag{1.10–6}$$

where the second constant of integration has also been set by reference to eq. 1.10–3.   From this result, it is possible to find the way in which E, ρ, and v all vary with x (problem 1.10g).   Volume-charge distributions that appear in connection with currents in vacuum tubes or semiconductors are frequently called space-charge distributions.

Problem 1.10a. Show that $V = q/4\pi\epsilon_0(x^2 + y^2 + z^2)^{\frac{1}{2}}$ satisfies the Laplace equation.

Problem 1.10b.   Show that $V = (\lambda/2\pi\epsilon_0) \ln [r_0/(x^2 + y^2)^{\frac{1}{2}}]$ satisfies the Laplace equation.

Problem 1.10c. Show that the potential of problem 1.7c satisfies the Poisson equation.

Problem 1.10d. Show that the potentials of problem 1.7d satisfy the Poisson equation.

Problem 1.10e. Show that the potential of problem 1.7g satisfies the Poisson equation.

Problem 1.10f. Show that the solid angle subtended by an arbitrary curve at a point $\mathscr{P}(x, y, z)$, namely $\Omega = \int d\mathbf{S} \cdot \mathbf{1}_r/r^2$, satisfies Laplace's equation.

✓ **Problem 1.10g.**   Find how E, ρ, and v vary with x in the electron-flow example of the text.

✓ **Problem 1.10h.**   The so-called rectifying barrier layer at the surface of certain semiconductors consists of a negative surface distribution of charge of density $\sigma = -\sigma_1$ and a positive volume distribution of density $\rho = \rho_1$ below the surface to a depth $x = b$ (the problem can be treated as one dimensional).   Beyond the point $x = b$, we have $\mathbf{E} = 0$ and $V = V_0$.   Find an expression for the potential as a function of depth below the surface, and the PD between the interior of the semiconductor and a point just outside its surface, treating these idealized charge distributions as the only sources of electric field.

1.11   Equipotential Surfaces

Just as lines of force provide a graphic description of the variations of field in a given portion of space, so can equipotential surfaces describe the variations of potential.   An equipotential region is the locus of points all at the same potential.   We have met in the case of the uniformly charged spherical shell an equipotential *surface*, which is the shell itself, and an equipotential *volume*, which is its interior.   The volumes are special cases, however (although important ones!), and for the most part we are concerned with surfaces.   An equipotential surface can be drawn through any point in an electric field.   Since the field strength is the negative of the potential gradient and has the direction of the greatest space rate of change of the potential, it must everywhere be perpendicular to the equipotential surfaces, which contain the directions of zero change of potential.   Another way of showing the same fact is to remark that by definition it takes no work to move a small test charge around on an equipotential surface, so that there must be no component of force on the charge parallel to the surface, leaving the force and field to be necessarily normal to the surface.

   If lines of force have been drawn, equipotentials can be drawn perpendicular to them.   In simple cases, the equations of equipotentials can be obtained, and the surfaces described analytically.   For instance, for a point charge or a sphere, by eqs. 1.7–2 and 1.7–11, we have $r = q/4\pi\epsilon_0 V$; if we keep V constant, we obtain the polar-coordinate equation of a sphere whose radius depends on the value of V.   For a line of charge, eq. 1.7–14, we have cylinders whose radius for a given V is $r = r_0 e^{-2\pi\epsilon_0 V/\lambda}$. For a plane, the equipotentials are parallel planes, with $z = z_0 - 2\epsilon_0 V/\sigma$. Figures 1.11a and 1.11b show lines of force and equipotentials for the latter two cases, drawn for equal intervals of potential.

   It is of course possible to draw equipotential surfaces for any values of V whatsoever and in fact to fill all space with them.   But the most graphic description occurs when equal intervals of potentials are used as in these figures.   In fact, if the equipotentials are close together, we may write

$$E = -\left(\frac{\partial V}{\partial l}\right)_{\text{normal}} \simeq -\frac{\Delta V}{\Delta l}$$

where ΔV is the potential interval between adjacent surfaces, and Δl is the distance, measured along a normal.   If ΔV is the same for a whole family of surfaces, we see that Δl is inversely proportional to the field strength.

   We have also seen that the number of lines of force per unit area is proportional to E.   In the so-called "two-dimensional cases," or cases of cylindrical symmetry, where all lines of force lie in planes parallel to one given plane and form the identical pattern in each of these planes, we can take tubes of force bounded by a pair of such planes (Fig. 1.11c).   A picture of the lines in one of the parallel planes thus will have the linear separation of the lines of force (that is, the width of the tubes) inversely proportional to E. Hence the equipotential lines in the diagram will have spacings proportional to those of the lines of force.   By proper choice

Fig. 1.11a.   Equipotentials about a line of charge.

Fig. 1.11b.   Equipotentials about a plane of charge.

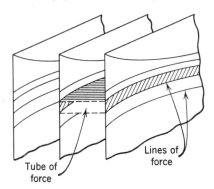

Fig. 1.11c.   Illustrating "two-dimensional" field patterns.

of ΔV, the spacings can be set equal, forming the so-called curvilinear squares, illustrated in Fig. 1.11d which gives part of the field surrounding two parallel wires of equal and opposite linear charge density (see section 4.5).   This property is of material assistance in sketching the figures.

The scalar property of the potential makes the construction of the equipotentials for a complex case somewhat easier than the construction of lines of force.   Equipotentials for each separate charge are drawn for a considerable number of equal intervals of V.   Then several points of intersection can be joined for which the sums of the separate values are

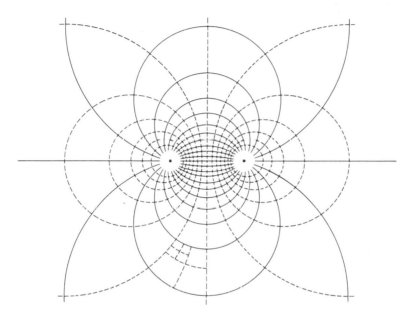

Fig. 1.11d.   Equipotentials (dashed) and lines of force (solid) about two parallel wires. (Taken from *Electricity and Magnetism*, Milan Wayne Garrett; Ypsilanti, Michigan: University Litho-printers p. 51, Fig. 4,12.).

some one given value.   Lines of force are sketched in when the equipotentials are thus completed.[18]   Problems 1.11a, b, and c will give the reader some practice in such construction and more familiarity with such field maps.   Figure 1.11e shows the field of charges $+4q$ and $-q$.

There are several important properties of equipotentials and lines of force which we shall now consider.   Some of these properties are important because, as we shall see in Chapter 2, when conductors are present the equipotential surfaces are determined by the construction of the conductors.   Hence it becomes natural to consider the accompanying charge distributions as derivable from the equipotentials, in contrast to the treatment we have given so far in which we consider the locations of

[18] Lines of force and equipotentials can be located experimentally using electrostatic voltmeters and small probes, or using straws or bits of hair to give the field direction. Cf. E. Weber *Electromagnetic Fields*, John Wiley, New York, 1950, Vol. I, Chapter 5.

the charges to be known and the potential distributions to be derived from this knowledge.

In the first place, the potential V varies continuously as a function of x, y, and z, with discontinuities appearing only at charged points and lines (where V becomes infinite).[19] As we have seen, we arrive at the same

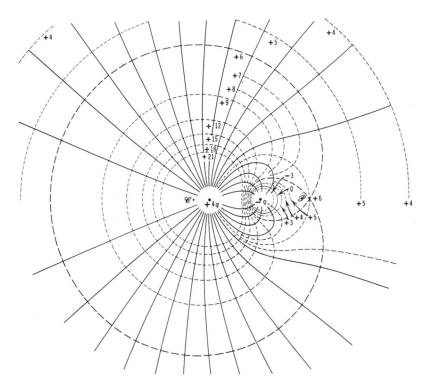

Fig. 1.11e.   Equipotentials and lines of force for $+4q$ and $-q$. The dotted line through $\mathscr{P}$ separates flux that passes from $+4q$ to $-q$, from flux that passes from $+4q$ to infinity. (From Garrett, *op. cit.*, p. 48, Fig. 4,7.)

values of V at (x, y, z) when we start from a zero reference point and consider the variation of V from the reference point to (x, y, z) over any path whatsoever; i.e., V is single valued.   Therefore no two equipotentials can intersect each other, since then a single point would have two values of V.

[19] A true electric "double layer," where two equal and opposite, infinitely strong, surface distributions of charge are located an infinitesimal distance apart, would be the location of a finite discontinuity in V. However, such double layers are idealizations that will not be dealt with in this book.

Furthermore, within any region where the field strength is not zero there must be equipotentials just inside and just outside any given equipotential that differ only infinitesimally from the given one.   One of these must correspond to a higher value of V, and one to a lower value (see Fig. 1.11f).   Lines of force pass through a surface in the direction of lower potential values.   As we let our consideration travel from one equipotential surface to the next, we can imagine a rubber sheet or balloon that is gradually and continuously being deformed passing from coincidence

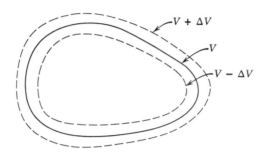

Fig. 1.11f.   Three adjacent equipotentials.

with one equipotential to coincidence with another.   This process can be continued until a discontinuity or a surface bounding an equipotential volume (field-free region) is reached; if neither occurs, we can go to "infinity."

In any given field, there can be at the most just one equipotential surface that extends from nearby points to infinity, namely, a surface whose potential is equal to the value assigned to infinity (usually zero).   The zero surfaces in Figs. 1.7d and 1.11d are examples.   Problems 1.11a and 1.11f will give further examples.

The equipotentials at a great distance from a collection of charges whose total sum is not zero are approximately spheres.   This follows from eq. 1.7–3, since the r_n's for all the charges will be nearly the same and may be taken as approximately equal to the distance r_0 measured from some average or representative point $\mathscr{P}_0$ near the center of the collection (see Fig. 1.11g).

The value of the potential will of course be approximately that of a single point charge equal to the sum of the original collection.   (More accurate approximations to the field far from a collection of charges will be discussed in sections 3.1 and 3.3.)

From our remarks in section 1.1 concerning the neutrality of the universe and from the statement in section 1.6 that lines of force start on positive charges and end on negative, we conclude that whenever we have a finite distribution that does not add up to zero, there is "at infinity" a charge equal and opposite to the net excess in the given distribution. This charge may be thought of as distributed uniformly on the inside of an infinitely large sphere. In actual laboratory problems, too, the charges on the walls have frequently to be taken into account. Any charge at infinity that relates to other distributions that are disregarded as being far from the one under consideration may clearly be disregarded itself.

From the foregoing, it is clear that there only can be an equipotential

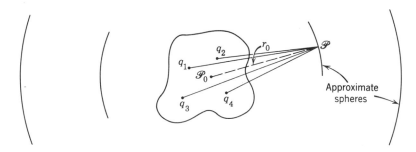

Fig. 1.11g.   Equipotentials for a collection of charges.

surface that extends from finite points to infinity if the total charge present adds up to zero.

If an equipotential surface is isolated—i.e., if it does not form part of an equipotential volume—and is closed, it must contain a net excess of charge, either on or inside itself. This is seen to be true from the flux theorem because there must be a potential gradient just outside the surface of a constant sign with respect to the outward normal, and hence a net positive or negative flux through the surface. The converse theorem, that any closed equipotential surface that is known to contain no net charge inside itself (e.g., that contains a vacuum or completely neutral atoms) must enclose an equipotential volume, is also easy to prove (problem 1.11d).

Any region that is known to be an equipotential volume must contain no net charge at any place within it, for, if it contained any type of distribution whatever, there could be found small regions containing charge of one sign, which will have net flux out through their boundaries and hence non-vanishing potential gradients. (Remember that we shall consider only regions which are large compared to atomic dimensions.)

Furthermore, if it is known that a certain surface is the boundary of an equipotential volume, it must be true that some charge resides on the surface, for there is clearly no field inside the surface although there must be a variation of potential outside or the surface would not be the boundary.   Thus flux must end *at* the surface, on charges residing there.

Finally for the reader who has not omitted section 1.10, we can show that at a point $\mathscr{P}$ where **E** vanishes, the equipotential surface intersects itself, and vice versa.[20]   As we have seen on p. 43, at least one of the second derivatives $\partial^2 V/\partial x^2$, $\partial^2 V/\partial y^2$, and $\partial^2 V/\partial z^2$, must be positive, and one must be negative.   If we consider the variation of V along lines through $\mathscr{P}$ in these two directions (say the x and y directions) then V will

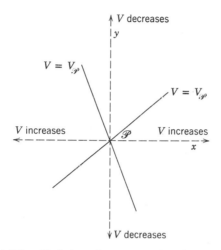

Fig. 1.11*h*.   Variation of V near a point of equilibrium.

be a minimum at $\mathscr{P}$ along one line and a maximum at $\mathscr{P}$ for the other, as in Figure 1.11*h*.   In a plane containing these directions there are four regions in between these lines, *each* of which must contain a line of constant V equal to $V_{\mathscr{P}}$.   Thus the equipotential surface through $\mathscr{P}$ intersects itself, either in a line or a point.   Whether the surface consists of two parts as in problem 1.11*f*, or only one as in Fig. 1.11*e*, is another matter. Note the lines of force in Fig. 1.11*i* and their asymptotes, which are the lines of greatest rate of increase and decrease, respectively, of V.   The asymptotes are perpendicular to each other; without proving this we shall make it evident by noting that, if the second derivatives do not vanish, V in the neighborhood of $\mathscr{P}$ is approximately a quadratic function of x, y, and z, and intersections of the equipotentials in the plane of Fig. 1.11*i* will be conic sections—in fact, hyperbolas—whose axes are the lines in question and are mutually perpendicular.

[20] We consider points where the first derivatives of V vanish but not the second derivatives.   The argument in the text can be modified without much difficulty so as to handle the exceptional cases.   See problem 1.11*g* for such a case.

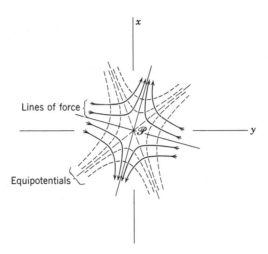

Fig. 1.11*i*.   Lines of force and equipotentials near a point of equilibrium.

Problem 1.11a.   Make a careful drawing of the lines of force and equipotentials for two equal and opposite charges.

Problem 1.11b.   Draw equipotential curves for charges of 3×10^{-8} coulomb and -1×10^{-8} coulomb separated by 0.10 m.

Problem 1.11c.   Draw equipotential curves for charges of 3×10^{-8} coulomb and 1×10^{-8} coulomb separated by 0.10 m.

Problem 1.11d.   Prove that a closed equipotential surface known not to contain any net charge anywhere within itself must enclose an equipotential volume.

Problem 1.11e.   Under what conditions can there be adjacent to an isolated equipotential of value V one of value $V + \Delta V$ on each side of $V (\Delta V > 0)$?

Problem 1.11f.   Sketch equipotentials for four equal charges, two plus and two minus, placed alternately around the corners of a rectangle 4 cm $\times$ 6 cm in dimension.

Problem 1.11g.   Four charges, of magnitudes $-8q, q, q,$ and $-8q$, are placed on the x-axis at values of x equal respectively to $-2x_1$, $-x_1$, x_1, and $2x_1$. Write a formula for V at a point (x, y) in the x–y plane, and expand this result in powers of x and y up to fourth-degree terms.   Discuss the behavior of V near the origin.

Metallic
Conductors

2.1 Electric Conduction

In Chapter 1 we were concerned with fields and potentials produced by various given charge distributions. We are now ready to consider the properties of matter that help to determine the charge distributions and that are involved in measurement of fields and potentials. The most relevant property of matter is conduction, the ability to transfer charge, which we explain by the mobility of charged particles within a material substance. Materials vary in this property all the way from the good conductors, the metals, to the very poor conductors, the insulators. Metallic conductors are by far the most important class of materials, and we shall deal mostly with them, giving only brief attention to electrolytes and semi-conductors, and leaving the discussion of conduction in gases to more specialized textbooks.

Since metallic conduction involves the motion of electrons, we give here an elementary summary of the modern theory of metallic conduction.[1]

Metals are elements whose isolated atoms in the ground state have (generally) one, two, or three electrons outside the last completely occupied "shell." These electrons, often called "valence electrons," can be lost easily, leaving the atoms ionized. In fact, they give rise to most of the chemical properties of metals. Atoms of non-metals have outer shells that are more nearly filled and have a tendency to gain rather than lose electrons.

When many atoms of a metallic element are packed together, all the valence electrons move about all the atoms (in a completely "communal" way) and provide a sort of over-all negative "glue" which holds together the positive ions or "cores" (nuclei plus the filled electron shells). It is these freely moving electrons which account for the conductivity of metals.

There are a great many different ways that electrons with their wavelike properties can move about in a large collection of positively charged cores. These different ways might be described as standing waves of different wave lengths and directions of propagation or as back-and-forth motions, involving reflection at boundaries and scattering by impurity atoms or imperfections that disturb the perfectly repeating nature of the crystal structure. Electrons can also be scattered by the thermal vibrations of the atoms themselves.

By the Pauli exclusion principle, no two electrons can have the same motion, whether they are in one atom or in one piece of metal. The wide variety of motions they will take up in a metal involves a range of energies, so that the electrons, instead of having the one, two, or three different energy values they would have if all the atoms were isolated from each other (as in a gas), will have many, many different energies—so many in any ordinary-sized piece of metal that we can assume the existence of a continuous band of possible energies.

A consideration of the numbers of possible electron motions in a metal shows that, if there are N atoms, then to each shell of say eight possible orbits in the isolated atoms there will be a band of $8N$ possible motions in the solid. If only one or two of these original orbits were filled before the atoms were brought together to form a solid, the corresponding band will be only partially filled. The electrons will fill, of course, the lowest N or $2N$ levels, at least at absolute zero. We can picture the energies on an

---

[1] Our presentation is necessarily simplified and is given here for the reader who has not studied solid-state physics. A more extensive introduction can be found in F. Seitz, *The Physics of Metals*, McGraw-Hill, New York, 1942; C. Kittel, *Introduction to Solid State Physics*, 2nd ed. John Wiley, New York, 1956; J. C. Slater, *The Quantum Theory of Matter*, McGraw-Hill, New York, 1953. A thorough treatment is given in W. Shockley, *Electrons and Holes in Semiconductors*, D. Van Nostrand, Princeton, 1950.

energy level diagram, as in Fig. 2.1a, wherein the conduction band is the whole set of energy levels corresponding to the valence energy shell in the atom, and the filled portion contains all the valence electrons actually present.   Electrons can be transferred to empty levels above the filled portion but cannot enter other already occupied levels.   Note that above the conduction band there is an energy gap containing no possible levels and then another band, corresponding in general to an entirely empty shell in isolated atoms.

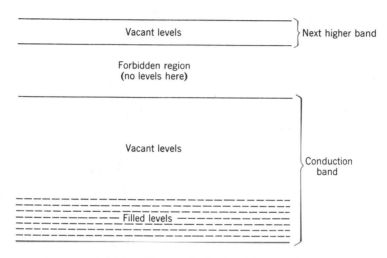

Fig. 2.1a.   The conduction band in a metal

At ordinary temperatures, some of the electrons near the top of the filled group of levels can get enough energy to jump to available empty levels, and there will be a certain distribution of electrons in these nearby levels, but the lower-lying electrons cannot change their motions in this way.

A careful study of electron distributions by the methods of statistical mechanics[2] shows that the way in which the available energy levels are filled is described by a certain universal function which depends on the energy of the level under consideration, on the temperature, and on a single parameter that could be described roughly as the "average" top of the distribution.   More specifically, this parameter is the half-way point— the energy U_F such that a level of this energy is occupied on the average just one half the time.

This universal function gives the probability that any level of energy U is occupied, and, although we do not need to derive it nor to use it explicitly

[2] Cf. W. Shockley, *op, cit.*, Chapter 16.   W. P. Allis and M. A. Herlin, *Thermodynamics and Statistical Mechanics*, McGraw-Hill, New York, 1952, section 63.

in this book, we need its qualitative nature, and so we shall write it down for clarity.   It is called the "Fermi distribution function" $F(U)$:

$$F(U) = \frac{1}{1 + e^{(U - U_F)/kT}} \qquad (2.1\text{-}1)$$

Figure 2.1b shows $F(U)$ for two values of T.

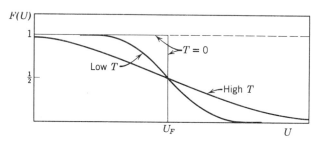

Fig. 2.1b.   The Fermi distribution function $F(U)$.

The symbol k represents the Boltzmann constant (gas constant per molecule, 1.38×10^{-16} erg/°K), and the parameter U_F is called the Fermi energy.   The electron energy level that has this energy is called the Fermi level.   The value of U_F is nearly independent of temperature for a metal but may vary with temperature and in other ways in solutions (section 6.4) and in semiconductors (see below).   We will shortly deal with the most important variation of U_F, namely its variation with the electrostatic potential of the piece of metal under consideration.

It will be noted that, when U is larger than U_F and $U - U_F$ is large compared to kT, $F(U)$ is very small—levels considerably above the Fermi level remain empty at normal temperatures.   If U is less than U_F and $U_F - U$ is large compared to kT, $F(U)$ is nearly 1—the lower levels remain filled.   Only for $|(U - U_F)|$ approximately equal to kT is there a definite variation of F with U.

The energy difference between the bottom and top of the filled part of a band is generally one or more electron-volts. (Cf. the definition of the electron-volt on p. 30.)   In contrast to 1 or 2 ev for the entire filled group of levels, the room-temperature value kT of the range over which $F(U)$ has most of its variation is approximately (1.38×10^{-16}) erg/°K $\times$ (300 °K) $\times$ $(10^{12}/1.6)$ ev/erg = 0.0259 ev, and so the falling off from filled levels to empty levels occurs over a relatively small fraction of the available levels.

The most important property of the Fermi level for our purposes is the statistical and thermodynamic fact that the *average* energy possessed by a group of electrons after they are introduced into the metal under conditions of constant temperature and pressure is just U_F, although some electrons may enter higher levels and some lower. We thus can avoid consideration of the details of the thermal effects by assuming that all electrons go to the Fermi level when they enter the metal and leave from this level when they are removed.

The symbols U and U_F used above represent energies that can be referred to any arbitrary zero. When we choose the zero of energy as the usual infinity in a vacuum of electrostatics, we can replace U_F by the symbol commonly used in physical chemistry, namely $\bar{\mu}$, which is called the "electrochemical potential of the electrons" although it represents the potential *energy* of an electron or the work needed to bring it from infinity to the interior of the metal. We measure it here in joules or electron-volts per electron; in chemistry it is usually measured in terms of energy per mole, i.e., Avogadro's number (6.023×10^{23}) of electrons.

In the absence of an external electric field, the motions of the electrons in the filled levels will be equally distributed over all directions in space, and no large-scale motion will be detectable. When a field $\mathbf{E}$ is applied, electrons moving in the direction of $-\mathbf{E}$ (say the positive x-direction) will be accelerated, i.e., on the diagram their energy levels will be shifted upward. Those moving in the opposite direction will be slowed down, and the corresponding energy values reduced. Except near the top of the filled group of levels, this shift of levels will simply replace electrons at any given level with other electrons in the over-all distribution and no net change will occur. But near the top, higher levels will be occupied that correspond to a positive v_x (x-component of velocity) than that correspond to a negative one.

The result of this would be a steadily *increasing* average v_x if it were not that electrons in the higher levels with positive v_x will jump down into lower levels corresponding to negative v_x, as a result of the various kinds of scattering referred to above. After $\mathbf{E}$ has been present a short time, the average v_x will become steady, with the gains due to acceleration balancing the losses due to scattering. In fact, the average value of $\mathbf{v}$ in general is proportional to $-\mathbf{E}$, and we have a steady electron flow called a current. Each electron gets accelerated on the average for a certain time t_m, called the "mean free time." Typical values of t_m are about 10^{-14} sec.

The proportionality of $\mathbf{v}$ and $-\mathbf{E}$ is the basis for Ohm's Law, which we shall take up in some detail in Chapter 5. The demonstration from solid-state theory that this proportionality should hold over a wide range of values of $\mathbf{v}$ is more complicated than we can give in this book,[3] but it is not hard to show this fact experimentally.

We have not given a reference or zero value for the energy scale of

[3] An excellent and relatively elementary presentation of the theory of the electrical conductivity of metals is given by V. F. Weisskopf, *Am. Journ. Phys.*, **11**, 1–12, (1943).

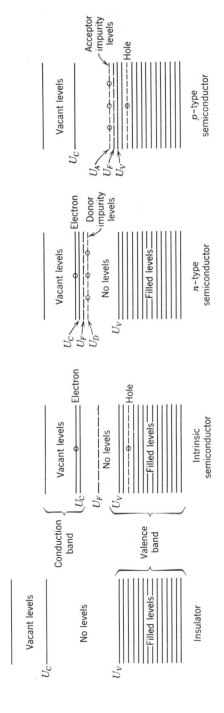

Fig. 2.1c. Energy level diagrams for four types of non-metals, showing the highest level in the valence band U_V, the lowest level in the conduction band U_C, the Fermi level U_F, and the donor and acceptor levels U_D and U_A.

Fig. 2.1*a*. A suitable value might be the energy of an electron when it has been taken to some point just outside the metal. It always takes work to remove an electron, so that this zero level is always above the bands of the figure. Further consideration of the zero of energy will be given later. Aside from this zero reference question, it is quite appropriate to think of the conduction electrons in a metal as free to move at the Fermi level U_F.

Insulators and Semiconductors. Insulators differ from conductors in that the electrons in the atoms or molecules of the former are all in closed shells, largely because they share their outer electrons by chemical combination in covalent bonds just so as to achieve this state. Consequently the lowest energy bands that develop when the units are closely packed are also filled; a relatively large amount of energy is needed for any electron before it can jump into the next higher band. In a diagram like that of Fig. 2.1*a*, an insulator would have the conduction band all filled, in which case it is called a valence band, as in Fig. 2.1*c*.

When an electric field is applied to a filled band, one might expect that the levels would again be distorted so as to produce a net current. But the electrons at the top of the band have short wave lengths and like X rays are easily deflected. These electrons are reflected in particular at the boundaries in such a way that acceleration in one direction becomes almost immediately acceleration in the opposite direction. A filled band in fact shows no net conduction. It is perhaps simplest just to think of a filled band as allowing no place for the electrons to "go" to provide a net current.

An intrinsic semiconductor is a substance whose conduction band is filled but which has an energy gap small enough so that thermal excitation causes electrons to jump into the next higher band, called in this case the conduction band. Figure 2.1*c* shows level diagrams for an insulator, with a large gap $U_C - U_V$ (the subscripts stand for "conduction band" and "valence band") and an intrinsic semiconductor with a small gap. For instance, diamond has an energy gap of 6 or 7 ev and is an insulator, whereas the chemically similar crystalline elements silicon and germanium have gaps of 1.10 and 0.72 ev respectively and are semiconductors.

The number of electrons that are available in the conduction band is determined by the temperature through the Fermi distribution function. The Fermi level U_F will vary in accordance with the number of electrons that make the jump. For not too high temperatures, it will lie about half-way between the two levels U_V and U_C; this means that, when a few electrons are added to a semiconductor, about half of them will enter the conduction band and half will enter the levels near the top of the valence band that are left empty.

These latter empty levels are of considerable importance.   Because a filled band shows no conduction in an electric field, a filled band minus one electron will show conduction in that the "hole" from which the electron has been removed travels in the opposite direction to the electrons. A detailed study of wave mechanics shows that such a hole indeed acts like a positive charge—in fact, like a charge whose mass is somewhere near that of an electron.   Thus an intrinsic semiconductor has an equal number of holes and electrons that can move under the influence of a field.

This type of semiconductor is called intrinsic to contrast it with impurity semiconductors.   The latter class of semiconductors contains foreign atoms or impurities that can be of two types.   One type has extra electrons that do not take part in chemical binding and are readily made free to move about.   Such atoms are called "donors."   Their extra electrons occupy what are called "donor impurity levels"; as shown in Fig. 2.1c, these levels, denoted by U_D, are just below the conduction band.   Consequently, electrons from the donor levels are easily excited into the conduction band, leaving behind ionized donor atoms that are fixed in position.   Such materials conduct almost entirely by electrons (negative charges) and are called "n-type" semiconductors.

The other type of impurities are atoms that each lack an electron for complete chemical binding and so have vacant levels into which they can accept electrons.   They are called "acceptors" and their levels, denoted in Fig. 2.1c by U_A, are just above the top of the valence band.   Electrons from the valence band are excited by thermal energy into these levels, where they become trapped or localized so that they cannot move.   The holes that remain behind can move, so that conduction is by positive charges, and the material is labeled "p-type."

2.2   Conductors with Charges at Rest

The electric field that produces an average drift of electrons in one direction (or of holes in the other) is an average field, produced by large-scale excesses or deficiencies of electrons in or on the conductor or elsewhere.   The fluctuations from point to point of the local atomic fields disappear in the average.   It is of fundamental importance to note that any motion of charge is always in the direction that automatically leads to a reduction of the field that produces the motion.   As electrons move in a certain direction in an isolated conductor, one side of the conductor must become negatively charged and the other side positively charged, thus giving rise to a contribution to the field that would by itself produce the opposite motion.

If a conductor is placed in an electric field $\mathbf{E}_0$, its electrons will continue to move until they produce a field $\mathbf{E}_1$ that just cancels the original at all points within the conductor, so that $\mathbf{E}_1 + \mathbf{E}_0 = 0$. No matter how complicated the shape of the conductor, the field within it will be zero everywhere when all charges have come to rest. For most metals, the time for equilibrium to be established is extremely small, of the order of 10^{-19} sec. (Section 5.8.) This process of the separation of positive and negative charges is called *induction*.

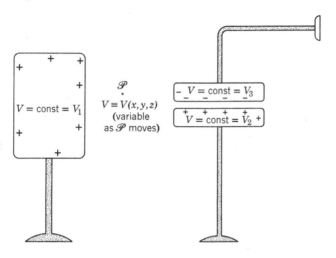

Fig. 2.2a. The potential is variable in the space surrounding the conductors but is constant within each one.

Another way of stating this fundamental property of conductors is: when charges are at rest on a conductor, the entire space occupied by conducting material is an equipotential volume. As proved in section 1.11, there can be no net (macroscopic) charge density within the volume. All the charge, if any, must reside on the surface. The potential $V(x, y, z)$ calculated from $\int \sigma \, dS / 4\pi\epsilon_0 r$ for a collection of statically charged conductors (see Fig. 2.2a for an example) will be a variable function for points (x, y, z) in the field-occupied space outside the conductors but will be constant throughout the volume of each conductor. The gradient of V will therefore be normal to the conducting surfaces at each point on them, and there will be no field tangent to any surface, tending to move the surface charges about. It is evident that σ must in general have a very complex variation over the surfaces of the conductors and may even have opposite signs at different points on the same conductor. In fact, it is possible to calculate its value only in cases of sufficient symmetry.

The various properties of equipotential surfaces and volumes discussed in section 1.11 are immediately applicable to conductors, but before proceeding in the next section to consider such application, we must say two things about the atomic nature of electricity.   In the first place, the actual amounts of excess of or deficiency of electrons that occur in practice are never enough for the discrete nature of the electron to make itself felt in chemical action or in discontinuities in the charge distribution. Problems 2.3d and 2.3f involve a calculation which justifies this statement.

On the other hand, if the potential in a conductor is to be measured with electrons, the effects of atomic structure enter in an unavoidable way, which is connected with the problem of how to choose a zero energy level for Fig. 2.1a.   When an electron approaches a metal, work will be done on it by whatever electric fields are present.   However, when it gets to the surface, it will enter the metal, jumping down into one of the unoccupied levels at the top of the band of conduction electrons already present (on the average, it jumps down to the Fermi level).   The potential energy per unit charge thus involved is in addition to any that would be calculated by the methods of Chapter 1 and may be said to arise from the fact that we cannot use an infinitesimal test charge, we cannot get the electron into the surface without disturbing the charge distribution on the surface, and we cannot prevent the electron from changing its kinetic and potential energies in accordance with the energy level to which it goes. The amount of energy given up when an electron enters a metal, or that has to be supplied to remove one from the metal, is called the work function and will be considered in section 2.4.   We shall temporarily avoid the problem of defining the potential in a conductor in this way and instead assign it a value obtained by calculation from the charge distributions assumed present.   Then at the end of the next section we shall show how to make a logical definition that avoids the difficulty.

2.3   Properties of Conductors as Equipotential Volumes

If a conductor lies in an external field, its surface will be the boundary of an equipotential volume and so must contain charge.   Let us use the flux theorem to calculate the charge density in terms of the field just outside the surface.   We construct a Gaussian surface in the form of a small pill box with sides of infinitesimal height and with the bottom of the box just inside the surface of the conductor and parallel to it, the top being in the field just outside. (Fig. 2.3a.)   Then the flux per unit area leaving the surface all passes through the top of the box and is equal to the charge per unit area, giving the result

$$E = \frac{\sigma}{\epsilon_0} \qquad (2.3\text{--}1)$$

where E refers to the limiting value of the field strength as the point of observation approaches the surface from the outside. The direction of **E** is, of course, normal to the surface.

We referred above to the complicated way in which charge distributes itself on an arbitrary set of conductors. Let us show in an elementary way that, if the n conductors of a given set are each given prescribed net charges Q_1, $Q_2 \cdots Q_n$, there is only *one* way in which these charges can distribute themselves over the conductors and reduce the field to zero in

Fig. 2.3a. A Gaussian surface at a conductor boundary.

each one. If this theorem were not true, it might be possible, for instance, to get different results by charging the objects one after another in different orders.

The proof uses the superposition principle. Consider two differently obtained equilibrium distributions of the same charges $Q_1 \cdots Q_n$, and suppose temporarily that the charges are spread out differently on some of the conductors, in the two cases. Each makes all the conductors equipotential volumes.

Now let us imagine calculating for each point on each conductor the difference between the two values σ' and σ'' for the two arrangements. With the values $\sigma' - \sigma''$ we can next imagine making a third arrangement in which we place at each point on each conductor a charge density $\sigma''' = \sigma' - \sigma''$. Since the first two charge arrangements each produced a potential distribution which is constant inside each conductor, so also will the third one, and thus it will be an equilibrium arrangement (there will be no forces that can vary σ'''). Once in place, the charge density σ''' will remain.

If σ''' is not zero everywhere, there will be flux leaving various points on the conductors. However, since the *total* charge on each conductor was the same for σ' and σ'', it will be zero for σ'''. Any conductor that has σ''' different from zero anywhere must have both positive and negative values of σ''' and must have flux both entering and leaving. Since a line of force begins and ends at different potentials, each line that enters or leaves a conductor must have its other end on another conductor. Thus each conductor that bears a non-vanishing σ''' is intermediate in potential between two other conductors.

Even if we include "infinity" as a conductor (which is not necessary if all the Q's are zero, for then no flux passes to infinity) it is impossible for *all* the conductors to be intermediate in potential. Any "highest" one would only have flux leaving it which is also impossible. So the set of conductors with zero net charge must have zero surface charge density at every point, and no field anywhere. Therefore the two original distributions of σ must have been identical, and the theorem is proved.

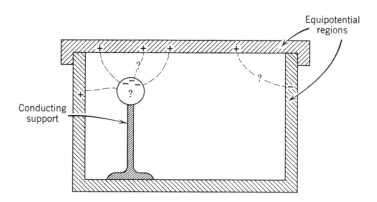

Fig. 2.3b. A conductor with a cavity containing no isolated charges can have no inner charge or flux.

Let us now consider a conductor with a cavity in it. A completely closed metal box is a good example. (Fig. 2.3b.) The inner surface of such a cavity is of course an equipotential surface. If the box is empty (strictly, if it contains no non-conductors and no disconnected or insulated conductors), we have the case of a closed equipotential surface known to have no charge within itself, and therefore the enclosed space is an equipotential volume. There must also be no charge *on* the inside surface, for if so there would be flux within the enclosure. Another way of seeing this result is to note that since no flux can pass into the metal itself, any flux present must begin and end on the surface. But the two ends of a line of flux cannot be at the same potential, and so the existence of flux would lead to a contradiction.

Any conductors placed in the box that make electrical contact with it must of course be included as parts of the same conducting volume.[4] But consider an object in the box on an insulating support. (Fig. 2.3c.) This object can be charged, and all the flux on it must end on the inside surface of the box. A Gaussian surface drawn within the metal of the box can be used to prove that the sum of all cavity charges within and on the cavity surface is zero.

[4] Provided they are made of the same material. See section 2.4.

We have here a case of electrostatic shielding. Let us consider the matter in more detail. Suppose a charge Q is brought up to the outside of the box. By Coulomb's law, the field of this charge extends everywhere, even into the inside of the box. However, the net effect on the contents of the box will always be exactly zero. Let us suppose that the conducting objects inside the box remain fixed in position. Then consider

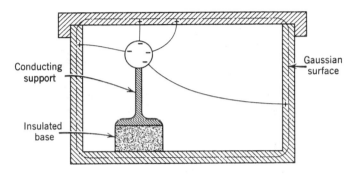

Fig. 2.3c. An insulated object in a cavity can have a charge.

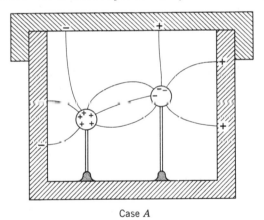

Case A

Fig. 2.3d. Shielding, case A. Charge inside, none outside.

the two circumstances: (A) in which the external charge Q is absent (Fig. 2.3d) and (B) in which it is present (Fig. 2.3e). Consider a third charge distribution (Fig. 2.3f) obtained by subtracting at each point the charges or charge densities that were present in cases A and B respectively. The potential at any given point will then be the difference $V_B - V_A$ between the values for (A) and (B). The inside of the box will then have no net charge on any isolated object. Thus it will be an equipotential volume. (The reader should be able to show (problem 2.3h) that an insulated conducting object in the cavity could not have a positive charge on one part of its surface and an equal negative charge on the other.) Therefore there can be no charge density anywhere in the cavity, and the two original distributions of cases A and B must have been identical. The inside of the box is thus said to be "shielded" or "screened" from

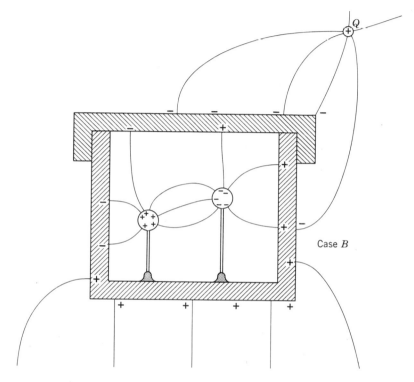

Fig. 2.3e.   Shielding, case B.   Charge inside and outside.

outside influences.   The result of bringing up the external charge Q is merely to induce on the outside of the box a charge distribution that exactly cancels the field that Q itself produces inside the box.

In a similar way it can be shown that motion of charges inside a cavity or changes in their magnitudes can have no external effect, provided that the total charge on the outside of the hollow conductor does not change. (Problems 2.3a and 2.5a.)   It may be assumed in either of these cases that electrical communication with the interior is made possible through an arbitrarily thin, insulated wire that passes through a hole of negligible size in the side of the box.

We can now give a definition of the potential in a conductor that avoids the work-function difficulty.   Consider a small, evacuated cavity of any shape completely surrounded by the conductor.   With no charge inside, there will be no field, and therefore the potential in the cavity will be the same as that which we have assigned to the conductor.   We can measure the potential in the cavity, however, without having to have a test electron

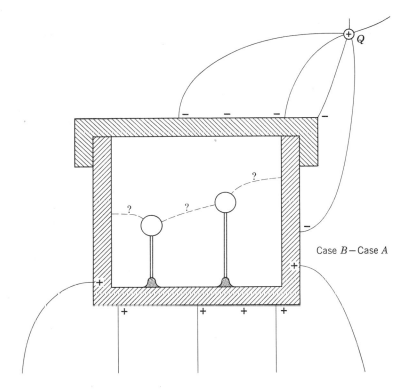

Fig. 2.3f.   Shielding, case *C*.   Subtraction of surface densities for cases *A* and *B*.

taken inside the metallic material.   The effects of the finite charge of an electron can be made negligible by making the cavity spherical with radius *r* large enough that the potential $e/4\pi\epsilon_0 r$ produced at the surface by an electron in the center is small compared to the errors of measurement. Thus we *define* the potential *V* of a piece of metal as the potential in a suitable cavity in it.[5]   When it is necessary to emphasize this point, we

---

[5] A point "just outside" the conductor can be used if distances of atomic size are not considered, and many authors define the potential in such terms.   The use of a cavity avoids all difficulties involved in imagining a limiting process that stops outside the surface "somewhere" beyond distances of atomic size.   The author is indebted to Prof. D. C. Grahame of Amherst College for suggesting the use of a cavity in this way.

refer to V as the cavity potential. It makes the most appropriate zero for energy diagrams such as Figs. 2.1a and 2.1c.

Communication with the outside may be made in principle by imagining a very slender cylindrical channel connecting the cavity with the outside, narrow enough that the unavoidable field distortions at its two openings have negligible effect. One can also imagine taking an electron into the metal through the outer surface and out through the inner, canceling the work-function effect.

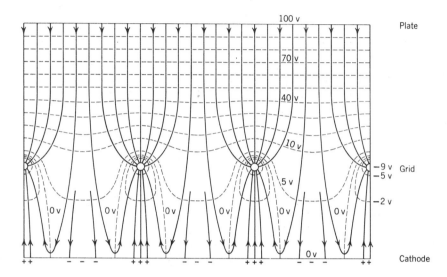

Fig. 2.3g. Lines of force and equipotentials in a plane triode, shown in cross section (moderately negative grid).

An interesting example of field and potential distributions around a system of conductors is given in Fig. 2.3g. (See also problem 2.3e.)

Forces on Conductors. In order to explain various phenomena of electrostatics, we must complete our picture of the action of conductors in fields by a discussion of the forces exerted on conductors. Electric fields act on charges. In conductors, the charges are prevented from leaving by atomic forces, and thus any forces exerted on the electrons and protons are transmitted to the solid as a whole by means of these atomic forces. We need only to calculate the forces on the charges, and evidently we need to consider only surface distributions of charge. We give here a simple calculation originally suggested to Poisson by Laplace.[6]

[6] See Sir E. T. Whittaker, *A History of the Theories of Aether and Electricity*, Thomas Nelson, London, 1951, Vol. I, p. 62.

Any small area on the surface of a conductor may be treated as approximately a plane.   As in problem 1.3k, at points sufficiently near the surface the field produced by the charge on this area will be $\sigma/2\epsilon_0$ away from the surface on *each* side.   Within the metal, however, $\mathbf{E} = 0$.   Therefore all the rest of the charges, whether on the remainder of the conductor or on other bodies, must produce a field (the "distant field") that exactly cancels the "local field" $\sigma/2\epsilon_0$ inside the metal (Fig. 2.3h).   The local field has a discontinuity at the surface, but the distant field must be continuous.

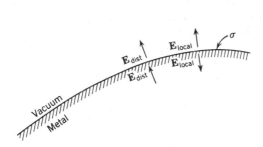

Fig. 2.3h.   Distant and local fields at the surface of a conductor.

Therefore the two fields just outside the metal surface are each $\sigma/2\epsilon_0$ in the same direction.   In adding them we have found another proof for eq. 2.3–1.   We have also divided the field into a local part that can exert no force on the charge producing it[7] and a distant field that can act on the local charges.   Since $F = qE$, the force per unit area is σE_{dist} or

$$f_S = \sigma^2/2\epsilon_0 \tag{2.3–2}$$

We use a small f for the stress or force density, with a subscript to indicate that it is calculated per unit area.   (A force per unit volume would be written f_r.)   Then f_S is always outward, since, if σ is positive E_{dist} is directed outwardly and if σ is negative, the field is inward but the force outward.

In terms of field strength just outside the surface, eq. 2.3–1, we have

$$f_S = \tfrac{1}{2}\epsilon_0 E^2 \tag{2.3–3}$$

This result is chiefly used to find the total force on a given conductor by integration:

$$\mathbf{F} = \int f_S \, d\mathbf{S} \tag{2.3–4}$$

[7] The electrons or protons in the surface layer exert forces on each other parallel to this layer, in equal and opposite pairs that add up to zero.

It may also be used for deformable conductors along with the mechanical properties of such bodies to determine the equilibrium shape they take in the given electrical circumstances.

Problem 2.3a. Prove the theorem stated in the text to the effect that changing or moving charges inside a cavity in a hollow conductor can lead to no external effect if the net charge on the outside of the conductor is unchanged.

Problem 2.3b. Prove that in a set of charged, isolated conductors there must be at least one whose surface charge density has everywhere the same sign.

Problem 2.3c. Write the field and potential just outside the surface of an isolated charged conducting sphere in terms of the charge density on the sphere. Do the same for the field and potential at a distant point.

Problem 2.3d. The field strength at which normal air becomes conducting is approximately 3×10^6 v/m. What charge density on the surface of a conductor will produce this field? How many excess electrons per square Ångstrom will there then be?

Problem 2.3e. Sketch lines of force and equipotentials for the triode structure of Fig. 2.3g, in the cases (a) when the grid is sufficiently negative that no flux passes from plate directly to cathode and (b) when the grid is at zero potential. In each case, the plate is to remain highly positive in potential.

Problem 2.3f. A certain kind of brass has a tensile strength of 5×10^4 lbs/in^2 or 3.5×10^8 newtons/m^2. What charge density on this material will be enough to break it by electrostatic forces? How many excess electrons per square Ångstrom will there then be? How many coulombs on a brass sphere of diameter 10 cm? What is the value of E just outside the surface?

Problem 2.3g. What is the electrostatic stress on a conductor charged just to the point that the air outside becomes conducting? (Cf. problem 2.3d.)

Problem 2.3h. Show that an insulated conductor situated within an enclosed cavity in another conductor cannot have some positive charge on one part of its surface and an equal amount of negative charge on another part.

2.4   The Work Function and Contact Potentials

We saw in the last section that the work necessary to remove an electron from a metal can be defined without considering electrostatic fields outside the metal if we imagine taking the electron into a cavity. Since $-\bar{\mu}$ is the work needed to take the electron from the Fermi level to infinity, and $-eV$ is the work needed to bring it back to the cavity, the net work, that is the work function ϕ, is the sum of these:

$$\phi = -\bar{\mu} - eV \qquad (2.4\text{--}1)$$

If ϕ and $\bar{\mu}$ are measured in electron-volts, we need only to set $e = 1$ to use V in volts in eq. 2.4–1.[8] Values of ϕ for most metals range from 2 to 6 ev.

[8] Some authors treat ϕ as a potential difference, in volts, rather than as a potential *energy* difference.

It is perhaps more instructive to write eq 2.4–1 as follows:

$$\bar{\mu} = -\phi - eV \tag{2.4–2}$$

which states that the electrochemical potential is the sum of the work-function potential energy, which is a property of the metal itself, and the macroscopic electrostatic potential energy, which depends on the charge and capacitance of the piece of metal and its electrical environment. It is

Fig. 2.4a. Energy levels in and outside of a piece of metal. The quantities $\bar{\mu}$, V, and ϕ are positive as shown.

particularly to be noted that when the net charge on a piece of metal is changed, $-eV$ and $\bar{\mu}$ change together, leaving ϕ constant. A shift ΔV in V produces a shift of all the energy levels together of amount $-e\Delta V$.

In most cases of external fields, the variation of potential outside the metal is gradual enough that there is a considerable region beyond the range of the atomic fields where the potential is closely equal to the cavity value V. Hence eq. 2.4–2 applies to taking an electron to any point in this region, without appreciable error. (Cf. problem 2.4a.)

Figure 2.4a gives a simple energy-level diagram that is adequate for our purposes.

The work function ϕ is of importance in the photoelectric effect, as it represents the difference between the amount of energy given to an electron by a photon which may fall on a metal surface and the maximum kinetic energy with which the electron can emerge. The study of the photo-electric effect was one of the crucial steps in the establishment of the quantum theory, and is described in any text on modern atomic physics.[9]

Another phenomenon related to the work function is thermionic emission. When the temperature of a metal is raised sufficiently, electrons may not only jump up into any of the conduction levels, but also they may get enough energy to leave the metal completely. This is the principle of operation of the various electron-emitting surfaces used in vacuum tubes.[10]

It is also possible to apply a strong enough field to a piece of metal to produce emission at lower temperatures than would otherwise be needed. Fields at a surface of the order of 3×10^9 v/m can produce copious emission at room temperature. This effect is called "field emission". Problem 4.3o involves a simplified calculation dealing with this effect.

It might be thought that a potential corresponding to the potential energy $\bar{\mu}$ would be a useful quantity to introduce. However, we wish to use the concept of potential to apply only to cases in which the potential can be written as an integral of the form $\int dq/(4\pi\epsilon_0 r)$ over macroscopic charge distributions.

It is possible to define a potential for the interior of a piece of metal as the average over all the space in and around the atoms. This potential is sometimes misnamed the Galvani potential V_G, galvanic effects having to do with currents being fundamentally dependent on $\bar{\mu}$ rather than on V_G. In contrast, the cavity potential V is sometimes called the Volta potential. Since the interior of the metal is neutral in the macroscopic sense, V_G like V is to be calculated from the macroscopic charge distribution on the metal surface and in all the surrounding space. It differs from V because a piece of metal has in general a surface double layer (cf. problem 1.7i) with a potential difference, generally called the χ-potential (χ is a small Greek "chi"). The reason for this is that the electrons at the edge of the metal are not forced by neighboring atoms into the same restricted paths as they would follow in the interior and consequently spend enough time just outside the edge to constitute a layer of negative charge out beyond a corresponding layer of positive charge (i.e., of "electron holes"). We therefore write $V_G = V - \chi$.

Unfortunately, it is extremely difficult to make accurate calculations of the magnitude of χ and almost impossible to measure it, so that we can make no practical use of either χ or V_G.

Contact Potential Difference. Now let us consider two different pieces of metal at the same temperature and ask what happens when they are placed in electrical contact. We can suppose that they have initially the same cavity potential V; its value makes no difference. But the work

[9] See also C. Herring and M. H. Nichols, *Revs. Mod. Phys.*, **21,** 185 (1949), especially pp. 220–223, for a discussion of the details and difficulties of the measurement of ϕ from the photoelectric effect.

[10] T. S. Gray, *Applied Electronics*, 2nd ed., The Technology Press, M.I.T., and John Wiley, New York, 1954, pp. 75–95; J. Millman and S. Seely, *Electronics*, McGraw-Hill, New York, 1941, Chapter VI; Herring and Nichols, *op. cit.*, section I.3. K. R. Spangenberg, *Fundamentals of Electron Devices*, McGraw-Hill, New York, 1957, Chapter 8.

functions ϕ_1 and ϕ_2 of two different substances are generally different, so that the level diagrams would be as shown in Fig. 2.4b. If the metals are in contact so that electrons can pass from one to the other, some electrons of higher electrochemical potential in metal 1 will pass over to metal 2.[11] The passage of a few electrons to metal 2 will make V_2 more negative and leave V_1 more positive. Thus the energies of all the electrons in metal 2 will be raised, and those in the other metal lowered. The process will continue until the electrochemical potentials or Fermi levels of the two

Fig. 2.4b. Energy levels for adjacent metals at the same V, not in contact.

metals are equal, when equilibrium will set in (Fig. 2.4c). The condition for no current between two adjacent metals in contact is clearly

$$\bar{\mu}_1 = \bar{\mu}_2 \tag{2.4-3}$$

It will be seen both from Fig 2.4c and eq. 2.4–2 that the resulting difference of potential between the two metals is equal to the difference in work functions measured in electron-volts, since the use of ev and volts implies setting $e = 1$. In general,

$$e(V_1 - V_2) = \phi_2 - \phi_1 \tag{2.4-4}$$

The difference of potential $V_1 - V_2$ is called the *contact potential difference* of the two metals. Its sign can be remembered from the fact that the metal with the largest work function gives up electrons the least readily and becomes the more negative.

As will become evident in Chapter 5, voltmeters and potentiometers

[11] It might appear that an electron must acquire energy ϕ_1, to get out of metal 1 before it can enter metal 2, that is, to go over a "barrier." This is not a strict requirement, however, for the wave properties of electrons allow them to pass narrow barriers without having enough energy to go over them.

measure differences of $\bar{\mu}$ rather than V.   Measurements of contact potential difference are relatively difficult, and are generally performed by a method outlined in section 2.7.

Triboelectricity is an effect produced by contact potential differences between insulating materials and can result in rather large residual charges. The lack of conductivity means that each small section of one insulator (e.g., a piece of fur) that comes into contact with the other (e.g., hard rubber) will acquire its own local charge and potential.   In order to have

Fig. 2.4c.   Energy levels for adjacent metals in contact when equilibrium has been established (Fermi levels coincident).

any considerable amount of charge transferred, there must be a large area of contact, which normally requires rubbing the two substances together. This is the origin of the common but fallacious notion that friction is necessary to produce a separation of electric charge.   (The word triboelectricity comes from the Greek "tribein," to rub.)

A detailed study of this oldest-known manifestation of electricity[12] would involve complexities beyond the concern of this book, but we can list here in Table 2.4A the so-called "triboelectric series," a list such that, if any two materials on it are rubbed together, the first mentioned will become positive.   The reader will recognize that the list is therefore in order of decreasing work function.   Numerical values of work functions are difficult to obtain because of variability in surface conditions.   Values for certain clean metal surfaces are given in Table 2.4B.

A useful and also traditional method of obtaining a negative charge for electrostatic experiments is to wipe a rod of resinous material or hard

[12] Amber, in Greek "elektron," was the earliest substance used for triboelectricity— probably by rubbing on cloth—and has provided us with names for our subject matter and our negative elementary charge.

Table 2.4A

The Triboelectric Series

Each substance on this list will become more positive than one below it, on contact under average conditions.   (*Smithsonian Tables*, 9th ed.)

Asbestos	Woods, Iron
Rabbit's fur	Tinned Iron
Glass	Cork, Ebony
Mica	Amber
Wool	Slate
Quartz	Resins
Calcite	Cu, Ni, Co, Ag, Sn, As, Bi, Sb, Pd, C,
Cat's fur	Brass
Ca, Mg, Pb	Para rubber
Silk	Sulfur
Al, Zn, Cd, felt, human skin	Pt, Au
Cotton	Celluloid
Rock salt	India rubber

Table 2.4B

Work Functions for Clean Metal Surfaces

(Most probable values,* measured in electron-volts)

Potassium	2.25
Sodium	2.28
Lithium	2.46
Barium	2.52
Calcium	3.20
Silicon	3.59
Magnesium	3.70
Lead	4.04
Aluminum	4.20
Zinc	4.27
Carbon	4.36
Tin	4.39
Copper	4.48
Mercury	4.53
Wolfram (tungsten)	4.53
Iron	4.63
Silver	4.70
Nickel	4.91
Platinum	5.36

* From Landolt-Börnstein, *Zahlenwerte u. Funktionen*, 6th ed., Springer-Verlag, Berlin, 1955, Vol. I, Part 4, pp. 759–761.

rubber with fur or wool.   The rod becomes negative and the fur positive. Positive charges are readily obtained on a piece of glass by contact with silk.   It was Benjamin Franklin[13] who gave the negative and positive signs respectively to what had been called "resinous" and "vitreous" electricity and whom the reader can blame for the confusion attendant on the attachment of the minus sign to the common type of charge carrier.

Problem 2.4a.   If the work function ϕ of a piece of tungsten is 4.5 ev and a field of 10^6 newtons/coulomb is applied to its surface, within how many Ångstrom units from the metal is the variation of potential less than 0.1 % of (ϕ/e)?

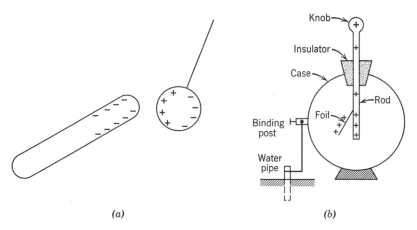

(a)   (b)

Fig. 2.5a, b.   (a) Why a pith ball is attracted to a charged rod.   (b) Schematic diagram of an electroscope.

2.5   Experimental Electrostatics

We are now in a position to describe and explain some of the experimental aspects of electrostatics that are usually used as introductions to the subject, as well as for experimental proofs of our basic assumptions (Coulomb's law, superposition, and the free mobility of charges in conductors).

If a negatively charged rod is brought near a light ball of pith, rendered conducting by a coating of aluminum, the ball will be attracted to the rod. This is because of inductive separation of the charges on the surface of the pith ball, required to reduce the field inside the ball to zero.   There will be positive charge near the rod and an equal amount of negative on

---

[13] I. B. Cohen, ed., *Benjamin Franklin's Experiments*, Harvard University Press, Cambridge, Mass., 1941, p. 175.   Franklin assumed a one-fluid theory of electric charge, intending "positive" to refer to an excess and "negative" to a deficiency of the hypothetical fluid.

the far side (Fig. 2.5a). The attraction of the negative rod for the positive induced charge is larger than the repulsion on the negative because of the different distances, so that the conductor as a whole is attracted. We may refer to the ball as having been "polarized," a term of which we shall make much use in Chapter 3.

A positive rod will also attract the pith ball, for the same reason but with the signs of all charges reversed. If the pith ball touches the rod in either case, it may acquire enough of the charge on the rod that the repulsion of like charges overcomes the attraction due to polarization and the ball flies away. The ball may be discharged by contact with a large, uncharged conductor—e.g., a human body—and the attraction by polarization repeated.

Electroscopes are primitive forms of charge- and potential-measuring devices. A typical electroscope is shown in Fig. 2.5b. If a charged conducting body is connected to the knob, charge will flow into rod and foil, and the foil will stand out from the rod at such an angle that the gravitational and electrical forces on it just balance. The electrical forces are partly those of mutual repulsion of the charge on the rod and that on the foil, but other forces act as well, as can be seen by the following considerations. The flux that leaves (or enters) the charges on rod and foil must end elsewhere. Thus there must be, somewhere in the neighborhood (or even at infinity), some charge of the opposite sign that may *attract* the foil away from the rod.

If the electroscope case is of glass or other insulating material, the flux may end on charges that have accumulated by chance on the glass or go off to some laboratory "infinity."

Reliable behavior is obtained by having part of the case made of metal, and by connecting this case to the earth, for instance by connecting it to a water pipe as in Fig. 2.5b. The earth is such a large conductor that it can absorb or give up unlimited amounts of charge without changing its potential. It is referred to in this connection as *ground* and the connection of any conductor to it is called *grounding*. The symbol $\doteqdot$ is used in schematic diagrams to indicate a ground connection. The potential of ground is conveniently taken to be zero.[14]

Thus the case of the electroscope is at ground potential. When the rod and foil are positively charged, the region surrounding them rises in potential. The case can only remain at ground potential if a counteracting negative charge appears on its inside. That is, the field in the grounding wire produced by the plus charge on the rod will move electrons

---

[14] In actual practice, there is usually no conflict between this zero for potential and the "infinity" discussed on pp. 30-31, since experiments with isolated conductors must be performed with all extraneous objects including walls at a considerable distance.

up to the case until their minus charge cancels this field. There will still be some flux from the rod and foil to more distant grounded points, since the metal case does not usually surround the rod if visual observation is to be allowed, but, if no other conductors are near the case, the amount of this flux ("stray field") will be very small.

A given deflection of the foil corresponds to a given amount of charge on it and hence to a given strength and distribution of the field between

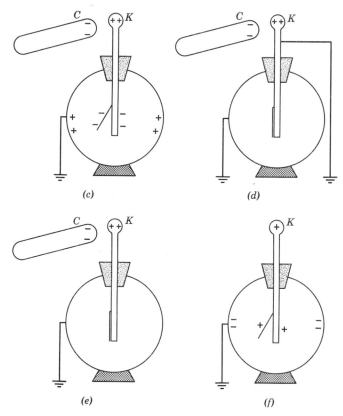

Fig. 2.5c-f.   Charging an electroscope by induction.

rod and case. Or, more simply, a given deflection involves a corresponding *potential* of rod, foil, and knob. The electroscope is essentially a potential-difference-measuring device, as generally used (see problem 2.7*i*).

Another method of charging the electroscope (or for that matter, any conductor) is to use the process of induction. Suppose the knob and rod to be uncharged and hence at ground potential. Bring, say, a negatively charged conductor C (Fig. 2.5c) to the neighborhood of the knob, but do *not* make contact.   The negative conductor will be at a negative potential since some of the lines of force that end on it must start on grounded objects.[15]   The knob will have positive charge induced on it, and there will be an equal negative charge distributed on rod and foil.   Considerations of the field inside the case shows the knob and rod also to be at negative potential.   Consideration of the knob K and the conductor C shows that C is the more negative.   Now the knob is grounded (Fig. 2.5d) *without* removing C; K goes to zero potential, the foil drops, and there is no field inside the case.   The potential difference between K and C must increase, since K is at zero.

The field between C and K being larger, more flux passes from C to K than before (increasing the positive charge on K) and less flux therefore passes from C to ground.   This means that C is less negative than it was, although it cannot fall in potential as much as did the knob K.

Now the ground wire is removed from K (Fig. 2.5e), making no change if the wire is thin enough to bear no appreciable charge on its own surface. Note that we now have an isolated conductor at zero potential with a net positive charge.   Finally C is removed (Fig. 2.5f) and the positive charge on K will spread out into rod and foil.   More precisely, the negative charge on C, which acting with the plus charge on K produced zero potential on the latter, has been removed so that the potential of K rises to a positive value.   The foil deflects in accordance with this potential, and the electroscope has been positively charged, by a method far more convenient and reliable in practice than the method of direct contact. It should be remarked that C need not be a conductor but could be an insulator—e.g., a charged rubber rod.   All the foregoing argument will apply except that the rod will not be an equipotential volume and reference will have to be made to some average value of its potential.

We turn now to the experiments that Faraday performed with an ice pail and that are still referred to as "ice-pail experiments."   Our "ice pail" will be a hollow conductor with a small opening which allows objects to be put in and removed without touching the sides.   For practical purposes, the opening need only to be small compared to the dimensions of the conductor, but for use of the experiments for precise verification of theory (e.g., of the conclusions of section 2.3), the opening should have a cover, which can have insulating strings hanging from its under side to support the objects to be inserted.

Let us connect the pail to the knob of an uncharged electroscope, as in Fig. 2.5g.   Let us take a small positively charged metal ball or disk B

[15] The reader will observe the deductive nature of this and the following statements.

mounted on an insulating handle—a so-called proof plane—and insert it into P without touching the latter. The electroscope leaf diverges, and it is clear that there will be a negative charge on the inside of P and a positive charge divided between its outside and KR, each of the same magnitude as that on B. Motion of B inside the hollow will produce no effect on the electroscope. The potential of P remains constant during such motion. That of B is higher and variable as its position is changed.

Now let B touch the inside of P. While in contact it becomes part of the equipotential volume made by the material of P. According to the discussion of section 2.3, B will be completely discharged, neutralizing

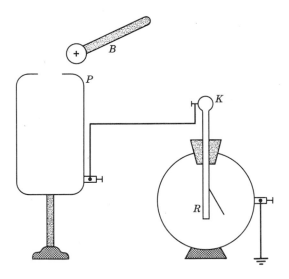

Fig. 2.5g. Apparatus for Faraday "ice-pail" experiments.

the negative charge inside P and making no change on the outside of P or on KR. If B is now removed, no change takes place in the electroscope. We have clearly charged the pail and the electroscope combination with a charge equal to that originally on B.

The fact that B has no charge when removed after touching P is an *experimental proof* that the space inside P is an equipotential volume. If it were not, electrons would move on or off B to make the latter an equipotential volume. (It is logically possible that for certain special positions of B the state of equilibrium could be established by a polarization that did not involve any net charge; but this could not happen for all points of contact and various shapes of P and B, as is experimentally observed.)

Problem 2.5a.   Explain why grounding a hollow metal box makes it into a satisfactory electrostatic shield with respect to the influence of internal charges on the external field.

Problem 2.5b.   Prove that, if an insulated, uncharged conductor is placed near a charged conductor and no other conductors are present, the uncharged body must be intermediate in potential between that of the charged body and that of infinity.

Problem 2.5c.   Make a sketch of a circumstance in which a positively charged body is certainly at a negative potential with respect to ground.

Problem 2.5d.   Prove that, if a single isolated charged conductor is near a grounded one, the two conductors have opposite charges and the distribution on each is of one sign only.

Problem 2.5e.   Show how to get a charge on a pail-electroscope combination that is *opposite* to that on a proof plane, but equal in magnitude.

Problem 2.5f.   How can the Faraday ice pail be used to show that no net charge is created in triboelectricity?

Problem 2.5g.   Show how to use a small pail that fits inside a large one and an insulated ball with a charge Q on it to get a charge on the large pail equal to nQ where n is any positive or negative integer.

Problem 2.5h.   Discuss the evidence from experiments discussed in section 2.5 and in the above problems for the validity of the principle of superposition.

Problem 2.5i.   Discuss in terms of potential what happens when (a) a positively charged object and (b) a negatively charged object is brought near the knob of a positively charged electroscope.

2.6   Indirect Proofs of Coulomb's Law

Coulomb[16] in 1785 established the law that bears his name by means of difficult but direct measurements of the force between two small charged spheres.   He used a torsion balance and was not able to get very great accuracy.   Actually, Priestley[16] (1766) and Cavendish[16] (1771) each had established the same law before this date by consideration of the field inside a hollow conductor.   The discussions in sections 1.11 and 2.3 concerning the absence of charge in an equipotential volume, etc., all depend on the flux law which is equivalent to Coulomb's inverse square law.   A proof of the inverse square law, or the flux law, can be made if (a) we establish experimentally that hollow charged conductors have no charges inside their cavities and (b) we can show that *only* the inverse square law can lead to this result.

The ice-pail experiments in the previous section (and indeed any electrostatic-screening experiments) show that there is no charge on the inner surface of a hollow conductor when the cavity itself is empty.   They also show that in this case the cavity itself is an equipotential volume.   That the interior of the metal is equipotential follows solely from the free mobility of charge.

[16] Whittaker, *op. cit.*, pp. 53–59.

From the fact that the above-mentioned experiments work for ice pails and proof planes of any shape and size, we can deduce that the interior of the metal must also have no charge, unless within a distance from the outer surface less than the least thickness of any material yet used in any screening experiment, for otherwise a suitably shaped proof plane would surely be able to remove some charge—e.g., make the proof plane in the form of a flexible foil and temporarily line the cavity with it.

These tests, however, are not particularly sensitive. Plimpton and Lawton[17] have made an extremely accurate test for the non-existence of a charge within a completely enclosed conductor. They used a five-foot diameter spherical conductor, for mathematical reasons to be mentioned below, and mounted a galvanometer with a sensitive battery-operated amplifier permanently inside the sphere, so as to avoid any errors due to work-function difficulties. This detector measured the flow of charge to or from a 4-foot hemisphere concentric with the 5-foot sphere. Observation of the galvanometer was made through a window consisting of a glass cup set into the sphere and filled with conducting liquid (salt water) so as to make a closed conducting surface. The outside of the sphere was slowly and regularly charged and discharged to a maximum of 3000 v. The galvanometer was shown in another experiment to be capable of detecting charge corresponding to a potential on the hemisphere of 10^{-6} v. If the inverse-square law were not true, the inner hemisphere would have to bear a charge if it were at the same potential as the outer sphere, and conversely, if it did not bear a charge, it would have *not* been at the same potential, as follows from the proof we are about to give.

No detectable motion of the galvanometer could be seen through the window. The method was sensitive enough that blowing some of the salt water from the cup introduced a noticeable effect and was used to test the operation of the apparatus!

The theory of these results is considerably more difficult than that used in Chapter 1, where the inverse-square law was assumed to be true. There are two simple cases that can be handled, the sphere and the plane. Laplace proved, using differential equations, that, if the field is everywhere zero inside a uniformly charged spherical shell, the law of force must be the inverse square.[18]

[17] S. J. Plimpton and W. E. Lawton, *Physical Review*, **50**, 1066–71 (1936).

[18] Laplace's proof can be found in J. C. Maxwell, *Electricity and Magnetism*, 2nd or 3rd ed., Clarendon Press, Oxford, 1881 and 1904, article 74e; in A. G. Webster, *Theory of Electricity and Magnetism*, Macmillan, New York, 1897, Part II, article 129; in J. H. Jeans, *Mathematical Theory of Electricity and Magnetism*, Cambridge, 1908, article 47; and in R. M. Whitmer, *Electromagnetics*, Prentice-Hall, Englewood Cliffs, 1952, pp. 37–41.

A simpler proof, due to Poynting,[19] is as follows. Figure 2.6*a* shows the cross section of a uniformly charged spherical shell, of charge density σ. The field at any point $\mathscr{P}$ is calculated by dividing up the space around $\mathscr{P}$ into double-ended cones, each of solid angle $d\Omega$, cutting the sphere at $\mathscr{M}$ and $\mathscr{N}$. Since the chord $\mathscr{M}\mathscr{P}\mathscr{N}$ cuts the sphere in equal angles at $\mathscr{M}$ and $\mathscr{N}$, the charges intercepted by the cone are equal respectively to $\overline{\mathscr{M}\mathscr{P}}^{2}\sigma\,d\Omega\sec\theta$ and $\overline{\mathscr{N}\mathscr{P}}^{2}\sigma\,d\Omega\sec\theta$. If the inverse-square law is true, the fields at $\mathscr{P}$ due to these two charge elements will cancel, as the reader

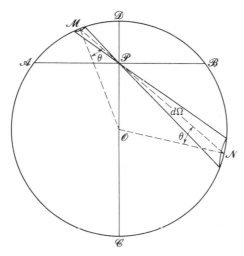

Fig. 2.6*a*.   Illustrating Poynting's proof for the inverse-square law.

can readily prove. If the law is not true, suppose first that the more distant charge always gives the greater (or the lesser) field.   Then all the resultant fields produced as $\mathscr{N}$ swings over the entire part of the sphere below $\mathscr{A}\mathscr{B}$ will be upward (or downward) and cannot add to zero, which is contrary to experiment. Suppose then that the more distant charges give a larger result for certain distances and smaller for others in such a way that the resultant field is zero.   There must then be some particular position of $\mathscr{N}$ *between* $\mathscr{B}$ and $\mathscr{C}$ for which the two contributions cancel. For this particular $\mathscr{N}$, the ratio of fields produced per unit of charge on the surface is inversely as the square of the distance, and so we have proved that there must be at least *one* ratio $\overline{\mathscr{M}\mathscr{P}}/\overline{\mathscr{N}\mathscr{P}}$ for which the inverse-square law is true.

But $\mathscr{P}$ can be at any position, for we understand as experimentally proved that there can be no field *anywhere* inside the sphere.   For

[19] J. H. Poynting, *Collected Scientific Papers*, Cambridge, 1920, pp. 165–7.

each value of $\mathscr{P}$ there will clearly be a *different* particular ratio $\overline{\mathscr{MP}}/\overline{\mathscr{NP}}$ for which the inverse-square law must surely hold. For instance, if $\mathscr{P}$ is near $\mathscr{D}$, $\overline{\mathscr{MP}}$ will have to be small and $\overline{\mathscr{NP}}$ large. If $\mathscr{P}$ is near $\mathscr{O}$, the two distances will be nearly equal. Thus the inverse-square law holds for all experimentally accessible ratios. Finally, the experimental result holds for spheres of any size, and so the inverse-square law holds for all actual distances as well as all ratios. Q.E.D.

The other simple case is that of a uniform plane distribution of charge. If we let the potential $V(r)$ at a distance r from an isolated charge q be $q/4\pi\epsilon_0$ times an unknown function $f(r)$, it is easy to show that the field outside a uniform plane distribution of density σ is

$$E_z = \frac{\sigma}{2\epsilon_0}\, zf(z) \qquad (2.6\text{--}1)$$

where z is the perpendicular distance from the plane to the point at which the field is calculated. (See problem 2.6a.)

Now if we take as established the fact that the charge resides on the surface of a conductor and divide the field just inside the surface into local and distant fields, as in section 2.3, we must as before have the distant field constant over a sufficiently small region and the total field zero inside the surface. Thus the local field, eq. 2.6–1, must be constant for small z, which can only be true if $zf(z)$ is a constant, or $f(r) = \text{constant}/r$, which proves Coulomb's law (the mathematical properties of f are independent of the symbol used for the independent variable). To make this proof more rigorous would require a consideration of possible undetected volume distributions of charge in the interior of conducting materials and of the deviation of the surfaces used from planarity. (The larger the radius of curvature of the surface, the larger the values of z over which $zf(z)$ is constant.)

Although any deviation from the inverse-square law should probably not be considered as simply a change from one power of r to another,[20] one can express the result of Plimpton and Lawton's work in such terms. If the exponent in the force law is $2 \pm \alpha$, the correction α was shown by them to be less than 2×10^{-9}. No experiments of this sort, of course, can detect any variation within atomic distances. However, Rutherford's famous alpha-particle scattering experiment with which the atomic nucleus was discovered amounts also to a sensitive test of Coulomb's law

---

[20] If it is taken as established that similar figures have similar electrical properties when only the scale of dimensions is changed (for instance, that lines-of-force patterns remain similar), then the law of force must be a power law. See Maxwell, *loc. cit.*, and problem 4.7i.

down to distances of the order of 10^{-11} cm or better; modern experiments in the scattering of electrons of a few hundred million electron-volts carry the range of validity down to about 10^{-13} cm.

Problem 2.6a. Find the field of a uniform plane distribution of charge at a point $\mathscr{P}$, at a distance z from the plane, if the formula for the potential of a charge q is $(q/4\pi\epsilon_0)f(r)$.

Hints: Find the resultant field directly, without calculating the potential. Use polar coordinates, and use as the variable in the integration the distance from $\mathscr{P}$ to the charge element. It must be assumed that $f(\infty) = 0$.

Problem 2.6b. Discuss the logical distinction between the assertions (a) that there is no charge within the material of a conductor and (b) that there is no field there.

Problem 2.6c. Does the experiment of Plimpton and Lawton prove the inverse-square law only for repulsions between charges of like sign, or does it also include the attractive forces?

2.7 Capacitance

The quantitative study of electrostatic phenomena is greatly facilitated by the fact that the relation between the charges on a set of conductors and the resulting potentials depends only on the geometric arrangement of the conductors. This result is a consequence of the fact that given charges can distribute themselves in only one way on a given set of conductors, as proved in section 2.3.

Let us first consider a single, isolated conductor of any shape. If we place a charge Q on it, the charge will distribute itself in some particular equilibrium pattern on the surface of the conductor. The distribution obtained from this one by multiplying σ everywhere by a fixed constant m would also be an equilibrium arrangement, since the potential would then be m times greater (m would factor out of the equation $V = \int m\sigma\, dS/4\pi\epsilon_0 r$). This therefore must be the unique way in which a charge mQ would distribute itself if placed on the conductor. Thus the potential of the conductor would be multiplied by m, and we see that V is proportional to Q. We write

$$Q = CV$$

and call the constant of proportionality C the capacitance[21] of the conductor. Now C is measured in coulombs/volt, which are called *farads*. The electrostatic unit is called the statfarad; it is of course a statcoulomb/ statvolt (cf. problem 2.7a).

[21] The term "capacity" is also used, but of course no reference to how much charge a conductor can "hold" is intended.

In particular, if the conductor is a sphere of radius R_0 we have $V = Q/4\pi\epsilon_0 R_0$ from eq. 1.7–11, so that

$$C = 4\pi\epsilon_0 R_0 \qquad (2.7\text{–}1)$$

With R_0 measured in meters and $\epsilon_0 = 8.85 \times 10^{-12}$ farads/m, most capacitances of isolated conductors are numerically very small (the values for non-spherical objects will be of the same order of magnitude as those for spheres of comparable size), so that the microfarad (μf) $= 10^{-6}$ farad

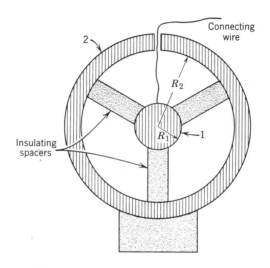

Fig. 2.7a.   Spherical condenser.

and the micromicrofarad ($\mu\mu$f) $= 10^{-12}$ farad are the units in common use.

The flux that leaves the isolated body goes to infinity. If the amount Q is changed, the flux pattern will change its density but not its shape. Consider now a pair of conductors so arranged that all the flux from one conductor, say conductor 1, passes to the other one. Such a pair of conductors is called a condenser or capacitor. Changing the charge on conductor 1 involves an equal and opposite change on conductor 2 and results in a change of potential difference without a change in the relative way the charge is distributed or, except for scale, in the flux pattern. We again have the charge and potential difference proportional to each other and write

$$Q = C(V_1 - V_2) \qquad (2.7\text{–}2)$$

C is again called the capacitance. Q represents the amount of charge on one of the conductors, usually the one taken arbitrarily as positive. Note

that an isolated body together with "infinity" may be considered as a
special case of a condenser with $V_2 = 0$.

A simple way to ensure that all the flux from conductor 1 passes to
conductor 2 is to enclose conductor 1 in a cavity in conductor 2. The
spherical condenser is the most symmetrical example. A spherical metal
ball is enclosed in a hollow spherical shell and kept in its central position
by suitably spaced insulating spacers. (Fig. 2.7a.) Ignoring the influence
of these spacers (cf. Chapter 3), we can readily find the capacitance of this

Fig. 2.7b.   Parallel-plate condenser, showing "stray" flux.

condenser. The field inside the space between the ball and the shell is
$\mathbf{E} = Q\mathbf{1}_R/4\pi\epsilon_0 R^2$ (this is a special case of eq. 1.4–4) and hence

$$V_1 - V_2 = -\int_{R_2}^{R_1} \frac{Q}{4\pi\epsilon_0 R^2}\, dR = \frac{Q}{4\pi\epsilon_0} \int_{R_1}^{R_2} \frac{dR}{R^2} = \frac{Q}{4\pi\epsilon_0}\left(\frac{1}{R_1} - \frac{1}{R_2}\right)$$

Hence

$$C = \frac{Q}{V_1 - V_2} = 4\pi\epsilon_0 \frac{R_1 R_2}{R_2 - R_1} \qquad (2.7\text{–}3)$$

Note that although all the flux from conductor 1 passes to conductor 2,
the reverse is not true. A proper way of using such a condenser to
measure either Q or $V_1 - V_2$ when the other is known would be to
ground the outer shell and measure the charge and potential on the
central ball by means of the thin wire passed through the shell.

For most uses, it is not necessary to have *all* of the flux from one
conductor pass to the other. The parallel-plate condenser is a good
approximation to a perfect capacitor. Two parallel metal plates of the
same shape (usually rectangular) are placed in close proximity. Suppose
as in Fig. 2.7b, that conductor 2 is connected to ground and conductor 1
is given a charge. For the pair of plates to act as a condenser, plate 1
and its wire must be remote from the ground. Then if this plate is given

a positive charge, it will be at a positive potential V.   Since the distance from plate 1 to plate 2 is small, there must be a relatively strong field between the plates, since $V = -\int \mathbf{E} \cdot \mathbf{dl}$ over this short distance.   On the other hand, there must be a much weaker field between plate 1 with its wire and the ground itself, because $\int \mathbf{E} \cdot \mathbf{dl}$ over the long path must also equal V.   Therefore nearly all the flux passes from plate 1 to plate 2. That part of the flux that passes directly to ground may be attributed to another capacitance, generally called the "stray capacitance" of the edges and back of plate 1 and its connecting wire.

Ignoring the stray capacitance for a moment, let us calculate C for a parallel-plate condenser, of area S and plate separation d.   We have also to ignore the fact that flux near the edges is not perpendicular to the plates (the so-called fringing field), although the field near the center is the same as that for two infinite planes and is in the perpendicular direction. The field in the center is thus given by eq 1.4–7, $E = \sigma/\epsilon_0$.   Therefore $V_1 - V_2 = Ed = \sigma d/\epsilon_0$.   Insofar as we can neglect the effects of the fringing field, we can assume that σ is constant over the area S, and write $Q = \sigma S$.   Dividing these last two equations, we find for the capacitance of a parallel-plate condenser (in vacuo)

$$C = \frac{\epsilon_0 S}{d} \qquad (2.7\text{--}4)$$

A simple physical interpretation of ϵ_0 can be derived from these results, namely that ϵ_0 is the capacitance per square meter of a plane-parallel condenser of 1 m separation.

Consideration of the details of condenser construction is left to other texts; the behavior of the dielectric materials with which they are usually filled is considered in Chapter 3.   Let us consider here only certain forms of standard capacitors, operated generally in air or in a vacuum. The spherical condenser is one form of standard; two other forms depend for accuracy on an ingenious method of avoiding the effects of fringing fields.

The method is that of the "guard ring."   Consider a parallel-plate condenser made with a circular bottom plate and a top plate consisting of two parts—one a ring whose outside diameter matches that of the bottom plate, and the other a disk, smaller than the lower plate, that just fits inside the ring leaving a small ring-shaped slot for insulation. Figure 2.7c shows a cross section of such a condenser.   The ring and disk are always charged to the same potential but are discharged separately so that the charge Q on the disk itself may be measured (for instance, by a ballistic galvanometer, discussed in section 8.8).   The fringing field is now at the outside edge of the ring.   Thus, as indicated in the figure, E and hence σ are uniform over the area of the disk.   The finite width of the slot is corrected for by using the geometric mean of the inner and outer radii of the slot for calculating the area S.[22] Such capacitors are made with values ranging from 5 $\mu\mu$f down to 0.1 $\mu\mu$f, and are described in detail by Harris in the reference given in the footnote.

A similar arrangement can be made in the cylindrical condenser, shown in Fig. 2.7d. Two coaxial cylinders constitute a condenser, with a center

Fig. 2.7c. Guard-ring condenser, cross-sectional view.

section of the inner cylinder cut apart from its two guard-ring ends. It is left to the reader (problem 2.7b) to show that the capacitance of the central portion is

$$C = \frac{2\pi\epsilon_0 l}{\ln \dfrac{R_2}{R_1}} \tag{2.7-5}$$

where R_1 is the radius of the central cylinder and R_2 is the inner radius of the outer cylinder. The same formula, of course, gives approximately the capacitance of an ordinary coaxial condenser without guard rings.

If a group of condensers are connected together and two connections made to the combination, the latter may be treated as a single condenser

Fig. 2.7d. Cylindrical guard-ring condenser.

whose capacitance is equal to the ratio of the charge Q added to one terminal (and removed from the other) to the resulting potential difference.

[22] For accuracy, the width of the ring should be at least 4 or 5 times the spacing d. A more accurate correction can be made by using a formula given by F. K. Harris, *Electrical Measurements*, John Wiley, New York, 1952, p. 683.

The two simple methods of connection are the *series* and *parallel* arrangements.

The parallel arrangement is shown schematically in Fig. 2.7e.   When a potential difference is applied to the two terminals $\mathscr{A}$ and $\mathscr{B}$, all the condensers acquire the same potential difference, and the charge put into

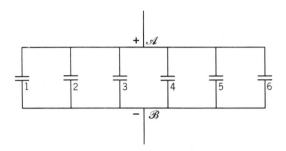

Fig. 2.7e.   Capacitors in parallel.

the combination at $\mathscr{A}$ is the sum of the charges on each condenser.   That is and

$$Q = Q_1 + Q_2 + \cdots = C_1 V + C_2 V + C_3 V + \cdots$$

and

$$C = \frac{Q}{V} = C_1 + C_2 + C_3 + \cdots \tag{2.7-6}$$

If the condensers are connected as in Fig. 2.7f, we have a series connection.   If all the condensers are initially uncharged, and then charges $+Q$ and $-Q$ are applied to $\mathscr{A}$ and $\mathscr{B}$, a charge of the same amount Q will appear on the opposite plate of C_1, leaving a charge of $+Q$ on the first plate of C_2, and so forth.   Every condenser will have the same charge Q. By virtue of the series connection, however, the potential difference V will be the sum of the separate PD's.   Thus

$$V = V_1 + V_2 + V_3 + \cdots = \frac{Q}{C_1} + \frac{Q}{C_2} + \frac{Q}{C_3} + \cdots = Q\left(\frac{1}{C_1} + \frac{1}{C_2} + \cdots\right)$$

so that

$$C = \frac{Q}{V} = \frac{1}{\dfrac{1}{C_1} + \dfrac{1}{C_2} + \cdots}$$

or

$$\frac{1}{C} = \frac{1}{C_1} + \frac{1}{C_2} + \frac{1}{C_3} + \cdots \tag{2.7-7}$$

The stray capacitance of connecting wires, outsides of plates, etc., referred to above can also be considered, approximately, as separate condensers with very small capacitance connected between various parts of the circuit and ground. They will thus frequently be in parallel with the principal capacitance, adding only a small amount to its value. We shall see later (Chapter 10) that when the charges and currents vary with great rapidity, it is no longer possible to think of the stray capacitance in this fashion as "lumped," but a more careful analysis of its "distributed" nature is required.

Fig. 2.7f. Capacitors in series.

The parallel-plate guard-ring condenser can be used to measure a potential difference in terms of force and length. In this case we do not try to measure the charge Q on the disk, but rather the force. The disk is movable and connected to a balance of some type so that the force of attraction exerted by the field on its lower side can be balanced by a known weight. By eq. 2.3–3 we can write

$$F = \epsilon_0 E^2 S/2$$

Furthermore $V = Ed$, so we have

$$F = \epsilon_0 V^2 S/2d^2$$

or, finally,

$$V = d\left(\frac{2F}{\epsilon_0 S}\right)^{\frac{1}{2}} \tag{2.7-8}$$

A precise measure of the difference of two potentials can be made by maintaining F constant and changing d by means of a micrometer screw that moves the lower plate. Such an instrument is called an "attracted-disk" or "absolute" voltmeter, the word absolute referring to the measurement of an electrical quantity in mechanical terms.

There are several other forms of electrostatic voltmeter. They all have the advantage of drawing no steady current in operation and the disadvantage of requiring especially good insulators, careful suspensions, etc. The forces involved are not as easy to calculate as in the absolute instrument just described, but, since the field at a particular point in a system of conductors is proportional to the PD applied, F will still be proportional to V^2. (This proportion is only approximate for instruments in which the moving element is subjected to different fields and presents a different area or length along which the force acts when it is in different positions.) These various instruments all require calibration against a standard.[23]

Absolute voltmeters and other electrostatic devices are affected by contact potential differences if not made of homogeneous materials with clean surfaces.   Consider the condenser plates in Fig. 2.7g made of, say, copper and zinc.   Each has a wire attached to it of the same material, with a junction at $\mathcal{O}$.   Temporarily suppose that all the surfaces are clean. Zinc gives up electrons more readily than does copper, so that zinc has

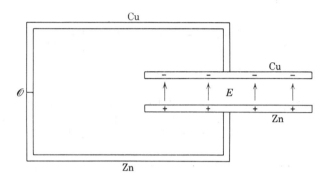

Fig. 2.7g.   Contact potential difference between copper and zinc.

the lower ϕ and is positive with respect to the copper.   Therefore, there must be an electric field as shown between the plates and of course a force of attraction.   The amount of charge on the plates will be determined by the capacitance C and the contact potential difference:

$$Q = C(V_{Zn} - V_{Cu}) = C(\phi_{Cu} - \phi_{Zn})/e \qquad (2.7\text{–}9)$$

The electrochemical potential $\bar{\mu}$ of the electrons is constant throughout the system.

If a copper or a zinc wire is connected to the plates and placed in the space between them, *no current will flow* (except that involved in the change of C produced by the introduction of the wire).   Then $\bar{\mu}$ in the wire will become equal to $\bar{\mu}$ for the rest of the system, regardless of the material of which the wire is made.   In fact any number of conductors of other materials can be connected between the plates, or inserted in series at the point $\mathcal{O}$, without changing $V_{Zn} - V_{Cu}$.

Although extraneous materials that are electrically connected between two metals do not affect their contact potential difference, dirt or other materials on the surfaces of condenser plates can affect the fields between them.   Figure 2.7h shows a case with two similar materials, one bearing

[23] For details on electrostatic voltmeters, see Harris, *op. cit.*, pp. 443–454.

an exaggerated lump of "dirt," which could also be a region of the same composition as the copper plate but different crystal structure.   We have taken as example a lump more negative than the copper.   This figure shows why electrometers must have very carefully cleaned and homogeneous surfaces.

If by means of a potentiometer (section 5.7), a measurable difference $\Delta\bar{\mu}$ is introduced between two condenser plates whose work-function difference is $\Delta\phi$, the charge on the capacitor will be $Q = (\Delta\phi + \Delta\bar{\mu})C/e$.

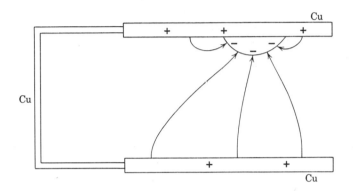

Fig. 2.7h.   Two similar metal plates with contamination, showing lines of force.

If now, furthermore, the capacitance is made to vary in time, by mechanical vibration of one condenser plate, a current

$$i = dQ/dt = e^{-1}(\Delta\phi + \Delta\bar{\mu})(dC/dt)$$

will flow in and out of the condenser.   The quantity $\Delta\phi$ can be measured if, using a suitable current detector, $\Delta\bar{\mu}$ is adjusted until $i = 0$, for then $\Delta\phi = -\Delta\bar{\mu}$.

Problem 2.7a.   Prove that the electrostatic unit of capacitance has the dimensions of centimeters.   Show also that the dimensions of ϵ_0 in the MKS system are farads/meter as stated in the text.

Problem 2.7b.   Prove eq. 2.7–5.

Problem 2.7c.   Consider that an ideal condenser is charged up by taking small increments ΔQ of positive charge from one plate to the other.   Show that the total work done is $Q^2/2C$ and express this work in terms of Q and V and in terms of V and C, where Q and V are the final values of charge and potential. Make an argument to show that this work can be interpreted as potential energy.

Problem 2.7d.   Two small metal spheres, of radii a and b, are separated by a distance c between their centers.   Find the capacitance of the condenser formed by the two, when c is large enough that the charge on each can be assumed to be distributed symmetrically and that the potential of each sphere produced by the charge on the other can be taken as the value produced at the center of the former.   *Ans. $C = 4\pi\epsilon_0/(1/a + 1/b - 2/c)$.*

Problem 2.7e.   Two coaxial cylindrical air capacitors are made with pieces of the same brass stock of 0.380 cm wall thickness.   The inner cylinder has an inside diameter (i.d.) of 7.471 cm;   the outer cylinder has an i.d. of 8.563 cm. The two cylinders of one capacitor each have a length of 13.70 cm;   the other cylinders are 29.20 cm long.   Find the difference between the capacitances of the two condensers.

Problem 2.7f.   Find the capacitance between the pair of spheres used by Plimpton and Lawton, assuming the dimensions to refer to the outside diameter for the inner sphere and the inside diameter for the outer sphere.

Problem 2.7g.   A cathode-ray tube has a pair of deflection plates in the form of rectangles 1.50 cm × 3.00 cm, separated by 4.00 mm in vacuo.   Find their capacitance approximately.

Problem 2.7h.   Find the shape of the plates of a variable air condenser (e.g., find r as a function of θ, using polar coordinates) if the capacitance is to vary with angle of turning θ according to

$$C = \frac{a}{(b + \theta)^2}$$

Problem 2.7i.   Using the concept of capacitance, describe the difference between the circumstance in which an electroscope is primarily a potential-measuring device and one in which it is primarily a charge-measuring device.

Problem 2.7j.   Find the capacitance of the earth, in farads.

Problem 2.7k.   A metal electrophorous disk is placed on a somewhat rough sulfur plate which has been charged negatively.   The disk is grounded;   the ground is removed;   the disk is then touched to an insulated sphere;   finally it is returned to the sulfur disk.   Describe the changes of potential and capacitance that occur during each stage of the charging process.   What limits the charge that can be placed on the sphere?   What other shape of insulated collecting object would not have this limitation?

Problem 2.7l.   Find how the capacitance of an arbitrary condenser will vary if all its dimensions are increased by the same factor k, and the law of force between two charges contains r to the power $-(2 + \alpha)$.

Dielectric
Materials

3.1 The Dipole Field

An insulator is a substance whose electrons or ions cannot move about under the influence of an applied electric field. Such substances in general consist of neutral polyatomic molecules, except for the rare gases (helium, neon, argon, xenon, and radon) which are monatomic in nature and some crystals whose energy gaps are so large that their semiconducting properties are negligible. There are no *perfect* insulators, as all substances have some measurable conductivity, but we shall deal here with those materials whose conductivity is extremely small and shall omit for the time being the consideration of any effects resulting from their conductivity.

Insulators also have the property of *molecular polarizability*. That is, the presence of an electric field may shift the positive and negative charges within a molecule away from their average positions, so that an inductive redistribution of charge occurs that is quite similar to the inductive effect on the small pith ball discussed in section 2.5. Insulators are called "dielectrics"[1] when their polarizability is under consideration.   Strictly speaking, all substances are polarizable, but the effects of polarizability are readily observed only in the absence of appreciable conductivity.

Now the redistribution of charges on the pith ball or on any conductor involves the transfer of a very small amount of charge in terms of electronic units per atom (see problems 2.3d and 2.3f), over macroscopic distances. Molecular polarization, on the other hand, involves the motion of one or more electrons per atom over subatomic distances.   This chapter is devoted to a study of the macroscopic effects of such transfers.   We shall first calculate the magnitude of the effects involved for single atoms or molecules, and then consider matter in bulk.

Let us think of a molecule as consisting of a collection of positive and negative point charges all located within distances of the order of 10^{-10} m of each other.   We are interested in the field at large distances from the molecule—say 10^{-4} m or more.   To a first approximation, we may neglect altogether the intramolecular distances and following the discussion on p. 49 write the potential as

$$V = \frac{1}{4\pi\epsilon_0} \sum_i \frac{q_i}{r_i} \simeq \frac{1}{4\pi\epsilon_0 r_0} \sum q_i \qquad (3.1\text{--}1)$$

where r_i is the distance to a point of observation from the ith charge, and r_0 is the distance from some central point in the molecule.

This formula is the one we will normally use for the molecules that have a net charge, because these molecules usually appear separated by distances large compared to their dimensions.   On the other hand $\Sigma q_i = 0$ for neutral molecules; to get a value of V different from zero, we will need a closer approximation than that made above.

To make such an approximation, let us pair off each electron with a nuclear proton and consider the field produced by each of these pairs. We shall show that a calculation made in this way, with neglect of the spatial separation of the various pairs in a molecule, constitutes a completely adequate approximation for dealing with dielectrics.

The rest of this section will be devoted to obtaining an appropriate expression for the field produced by a single such pair.   Consider a positive and a negative charge, each of value q, separated by a small distance δl, as in Fig. 3.1a.   Such a pair will be called an "electric dipole."

The potential at $\mathcal{O}$ is given by

$$V_{\mathcal{O}} = \frac{1}{4\pi\epsilon_0} \left(\frac{q}{r} - \frac{q}{r'} \right) = V_{+q,\mathcal{O}} + V_{-q,\mathcal{O}}$$

[1] The word "dielectric" was coined by M. Faraday, *Experimental Researches in Electricity*, Bernard Quaritch, London, 1839, vol. I, §1168.

which is the same as the *difference* between the potential $V_{+q,\mathcal{O}}$ that $+q$ produces at $\mathcal{O}$ and $V_{+q,\mathcal{O}'}$ that $+q$ produces at $\mathcal{O}'$; from the figure we can see that V produced by $-q$ at $\mathcal{O}$ (i.e., $V_{-q,\mathcal{O}}$) equals $-V_{+q,\mathcal{O}'}$. We assume that the separation δl between the two charges is so small in comparison to r that we may treat it as a differential (actually it is smaller than the practical limit discussed on p. 7). Now, the length δl has some specific direction, so we shall call it a vector $\mathbf{\delta l}$ and by convention let its positive direction be toward $+q$. (The symbol δ is used to indicate a quantity

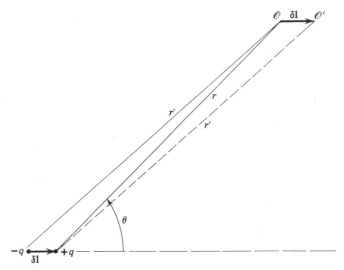

Fig. 3.1a. Illustrating the calculation of the dipole potential.

small enough to be a differential, but one that we need not let go to zero.) We can now calculate the difference $V_{\mathcal{O}} = V_{+q,\mathcal{O}} - V_{+q,\mathcal{O}'} = \delta V$ by use of the gradient (eq. A.2–19). The negative sign must be used because $\mathbf{\delta l}$ is directed toward $\mathcal{O}'$. We have

$$V_{\mathcal{O}} = \delta V = -(\mathbf{\nabla} V_{+q}) \cdot \mathbf{\delta l} = \frac{-q}{4\pi\epsilon_0} \left(\mathbf{\nabla} \frac{1}{r}\right) \cdot \mathbf{\delta l}$$

so that the potential at point $\mathcal{O}$ produced by the pair is given by

$$V_{\mathcal{O}} = \frac{-q\,\mathbf{\delta l} \cdot \mathbf{\nabla}\left(\dfrac{1}{r}\right)}{4\pi\epsilon_0}$$

The quantity $q\,\mathbf{\delta l}$ is the vector that determines the strength of the dipole pair. It is called the *electric dipole moment* and will be given the symbol **p**.

Its magnitude $q\, \delta l$ will thus be the scalar p.   Thus we can write, dropping the subscript,[2]

$$V = -\frac{1}{4\pi\epsilon_0}\mathbf{p}\cdot\nabla\left(\frac{1}{r}\right) \qquad (3.1\text{-}2)$$

It is easy to show (problem 1.9g) that

$$\nabla\left(\frac{1}{r}\right) = -\frac{\mathbf{r}}{r^3} = -\frac{\mathbf{1}_r}{r^2} \qquad (3.1\text{-}3)$$

Another expression for the dipole potential is therefore

$$V = \frac{\mathbf{p}\cdot\mathbf{1}_r}{4\pi\epsilon_0 r^2} \qquad (3.1\text{-}4)$$

and if we write $\mathbf{p}\cdot\mathbf{1}_r = p\cos\theta$ we have an expression without vectors:

$$V = \frac{p\cos\theta}{4\pi\epsilon_0 r^2} \qquad (3.1\text{-}5)$$

V is inversely proportional to the square of the distance along any radius drawn from the center of the dipole.

The equipotential surfaces are clearly surfaces of revolution about an axis through the dipole.   Their intersections in a plane containing the axis are curves whose polar coordinate equation can be written

$$\cos\theta = Kr^2 \qquad (3.1\text{-}6)$$

with $K = 4\pi\epsilon_0(V/p)$.   We see that $\theta = \pm 90°$ when $r = 0$, so that all curves pass through the dipole at right angles to its axis.   The zero equipotential is that for which $\cos\theta = 0$ for all r, i.e., the entire plane through the origin normal to $\mathbf{p}$.   The largest values of r occur for $\cos\theta = +1$ when K is positive ($\theta = 0°$) and for $\cos\theta = -1$ when K is negative ($\theta = 180°$).   Figure 3.1b shows some of the equipotential curves given by eq. 3.1-6, along with lines of force.

The field of a dipole at a point $\mathcal{O}$ is found by taking the negative gradient of V.   It is most convenient here to use polar coordinates and eq. 3.1-5.   The radial component of $\mathbf{E}$ is given by a directional derivative with $dl = dr$.   The component normal to the radius, in the direction of increasing θ, is that for which $dl = r\, d\theta$.   There is of course no component of $\mathbf{E}$ normal to the plane containing $\mathcal{O}$ and $\mathbf{p}$.

[2] A true mathematical dipole occupies a point and is the limit of $q\, \delta l$ as $\delta l \to 0$ and $q \to \infty$ in such a way that the quantity $\mathbf{p}$ remains constant.   The potential of eq. 3.1-2 which approximates that of an actual charge pair is exact for a true dipole.   As far as is known, no true electric dipoles exist, and we do not need to consider them.

Thus, we have at $\mathcal{O}(r, \theta)$

$$E_r = -\frac{\partial V}{\partial r} = \frac{2p \cos \theta}{4\pi\epsilon_0 r^3} \qquad (3.1\text{-}7a)$$

$$E_\theta = -\frac{1}{r}\frac{\partial V}{\partial \theta} = \frac{p \sin \theta}{4\pi\epsilon_0 r^3} \qquad (3.1\text{-}7b)$$

so that the field strength E is

$$E = \sqrt{E_r^2 + E_\theta^2} = \frac{p}{4\pi\epsilon_0 r^3}\sqrt{\sin^2\theta + 4\cos^2\theta}$$

$$= \frac{p}{4\pi\epsilon_0 r^3}\sqrt{1 + 3\cos^2\theta} \qquad (3.1\text{-}8)$$

It is evident that E falls off as r^{-3} along any radius vector. The lines of force all pass from the positive end of the dipole around to the negative

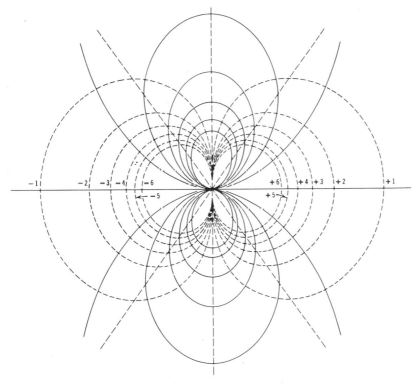

Fig. 3.1b. Lines of force (solid) and equipotentials (dashed) of a horizontal dipole. The numbers represent potential values (in arbitrary units). The dashed straight lines are loci of points where the field direction is vertical. (Taken from *Electricity and Magnetism*, Milan Wayne Garrett, University Lithoprinters, Ypsilanti, Michigan, p. 29, Fig. 3,4.)

end, as is easily seen by comparing Fig. 3.1b with Fig. 1.6b. Note that the field is directed along the radius for $\theta = 0°$ and $\theta = 180°$ and perpendicular to it for $\theta = \pm90°$.

The potential produced by a molecule with several electron-proton pairs can be found by adding the potentials due to each pair. The same degree of approximation will be involved in neglecting the distances between the centers of the various dipoles as was involved in treating the length of a single dipole as an infinitesimal. From the vector expression eq. 3.1–2 or eq. 3.1–4 we see that the sum of the potentials is given by replacing $\mathbf{p}$ by the sum $\sum_i \mathbf{p}_i$ of the moments for all the pairs so that

$$ V = - \frac{1}{4\pi\epsilon_0} \left(\sum_i \mathbf{p}_i\right) \cdot \nabla \frac{1}{r} = \frac{\mathbf{1}_r \cdot \left(\sum_i \mathbf{p}_i\right)}{4\pi\epsilon_0 r^2} \qquad (3.1\text{–}9) $$

Thus any molecule or other small collection of charges is equivalent to a simple dipole whose vector is the sum of the separate dipole vectors for all the charge pairs in the system. The net dipole strength of each atom can in fact be represented by a dipole consisting of the positive nucleus and an equal negative charge at the center of the electronic charge cloud. If the center of this cloud coincides with the nucleus, as in the case of symmetric atoms, the dipole strength will of course be zero. The fact that the electrons are continually in motion is taken into account by making a time average for the charge cloud.

Problem 3.1a. Write eq. 3.1–6 in Cartesian coordinates, and show that the equipotentials are not spheres.

Problem 3.1b. Write eq. 3.1–5 in Cartesian coordinates, and show that the potential satisfies Laplace's equation.

Problem 3.1c. Find the Cartesian components of $\mathbf{E}$ from $-\nabla V$ and also from eq. 3.1–7. Find the locus of points for which the lines of force are perpendicular to the direction of $\mathbf{p}$.

Problem 3.1d. Show that all the lines of force from a dipole meet any given radius at the same angle, and similarly for the equipotentials. Find the direction of that radius for which the intersecting lines of force make an angle of 45° with $\mathbf{p}$.

Problem 3.1e. Calculate the flux from a dipole that passes through a spherical cap whose axis is collinear with $\mathbf{p}$ and whose edge is made by the circle generated when $\mathcal{O}(r, \theta)$ is rotated about the axis. How must θ vary with r to keep this flux constant? Obtain in this way the equation of a line of force, and check by comparing its direction with that given in eq. 3.1–7. Show that each line of force is closed.

Problem 3.1f. Using polar coordinates, prove that **curl E** $= 0$ for the dipole field.

3.2   Forces and Torques on Dipoles[3]

Before we proceed to consider polarized molecules in bulk, let us find expressions for the torque $\mathscr{L}$ and the force **F** on a dipole in an arbitrary external electric field.   The expression for the torque is simpler, and so we shall consider it first.   Consider a dipole of length δl with charges $+q$ and $-q$, in an electric field **E** that makes an angle θ with $\boldsymbol{\delta l}$.   Referring to Fig. 3.2a, we readily find the torque about the center of the dipole to be $2 \cdot qE \cdot \frac{1}{2}\delta l \sin \theta = q\, \delta l E \sin \theta$, so that

$$\mathscr{L} = pE \sin \theta \qquad\qquad (3.2\text{--}1a)$$

which in accordance with eq. A.2–37 we can write as a vector:

$$\mathscr{L} = \mathbf{p} \times \mathbf{E} \qquad\qquad (3.2\text{-}1b)$$

The reader can readily show that the torque $\mathscr{L}$ is the same if any other point is chosen as the center.   If **E** is not uniform in the neighborhood of

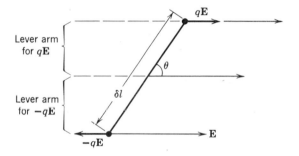

Fig. 3.2a.   Torque on a dipole.

the dipole, so that its value at $-q$ is different from that at $+q$, an average value taken at the center will be a good approximation.   (The torque on a true dipole of zero length would be given by eq. 3.2–1 independently of any variation in **E**.)

The net force on a dipole is zero if the field is the same at the two ends, for then we have two equal and opposite forces.   Thus the force must depend on the variation of the field.   More specifically, the net force in the x-direction F_x depends on the difference of the x-components of the field, the y-force F_y on the difference of the E_y's and the same for F_z and E_z.   For instance, $F_x = qE_{x,+q} - qE_{x,-q}$.   The difference for any component of **E** can be calculated by the differential formula involving the

[3] Some results from section 1.8 are used in this section.

gradient, since each component is a scalar function of position. Thus the components of the force on the dipole are given by

$$F_x = q\,\delta l \cdot \nabla E_x = \mathbf{p} \cdot \nabla E_x = p_x \frac{\partial E_x}{\partial x} + p_y \frac{\partial E_x}{\partial y} + p_z \frac{\partial E_x}{\partial z}$$

$$F_y = \mathbf{p} \cdot \nabla E_y$$

$$F_z = \mathbf{p} \cdot \nabla E_z \tag{3.2-2}$$

These three equations can be combined into a single vector formula if we treat $(\mathbf{p} \cdot \nabla)$ as a special scalar differential operator, and write

$$\mathbf{F} = (\mathbf{p} \cdot \nabla)\mathbf{E} \tag{3.2-3}$$

This formula is convenient for calculation, but a form more convenient for later development can be obtained by transforming this expression, using the conservative field property expressed by eqs. 1.8–1 or 1.8–2. The derivatives $\partial E_x/\partial y$ and $\partial E_x/\partial z$ in the expression above for F_x can be replaced by their equals, $\partial E_y/\partial x$ and $\partial E_z/\partial x$, giving

$$F_x = p_x \frac{\partial E_x}{\partial x} + p_y \frac{\partial E_y}{\partial x} + p_z \frac{\partial E_z}{\partial x} = \frac{\partial}{\partial x}(\mathbf{p} \cdot \mathbf{E})$$

since $\mathbf{p}$ and its components are constants. Therefore, F_x is the x-component of a gradient, and we can write for $\mathbf{F}$ the expression[4]

$$\mathbf{F} = \nabla(\mathbf{p} \cdot \mathbf{E}) \tag{3.2-4}$$

Just as the electric force per unit charge is the negative gradient of the potential energy per unit charge, so also is any conservative force the negative gradient of a potential energy. We see that the potential energy U of the dipole can be written

$$U = -\mathbf{p} \cdot \mathbf{E} \tag{3.2-5}$$

Let us corroborate this by calculating the potential energy by means of the torque formula. Imagine bringing the dipole from infinity to the point where its energy is to be evaluated, in such a way that $+q$ and $-q$ are at all times on the same equipotential ($\mathbf{p}$ is always perpendicular to $\mathbf{E}$). The work done on $+q$ will therefore exactly cancel that on $-q$. Now rotate the dipole from $\theta = 90°$ to the chosen θ. (See Fig. 3.2a.) The work done by the electric field, which lowers the potential energy, is given for an angular displacement $d\theta$ by $\mathscr{L}\,d\theta = pE \sin\theta\,d\theta$. Hence the total work done is $-\int_{\pi/2}^{\theta} pE \sin\theta\,d\theta = pE \cos\theta = \mathbf{p} \cdot \mathbf{E}$, where the minus

---

[4] This result can be calculated in vector terms by expanding $\mathbf{p} \times (\nabla \times \mathbf{E}) = 0$. Cf. problem A.2$l$.

sign is used because the direction of the torque is that of decreasing θ. This is the entire work done by the field in moving the dipole from ∞ to the position in question, so the potential energy must be its negative, as given by eq. 3.2–5.

Problem 3.2a. ·A dipole of strength 4.8×10^{-18} statcoulomb-cm is situated 5×10^{-8} cm from a nucleus of charge equal to $+3$ electronic units. Find the force and torque on the dipole (a) when it is oriented along a radius from the nucleus, positive end further away; (b) when it is at right angles to a radius; (c) when it makes an angle of $45°$ with the radius, positive end towards the nucleus.

Problem 3.2b. Two dipoles of strengths respectively 3×10^{-13} coulomb-m and 5×10^{-13} coulomb-m are located 2 cm apart. Find the force between them (a) when both dipole vectors point in the same direction along the line joining them; (b) when one dipole points towards the other, and the second points at right angles to the line of centers; (c) when both point at right angles to the line of centers, and in the same direction; (d) same as (c) but pointing oppositely. Verify in each case that Newton's law of action and reaction holds.

Problem 3.2c. Find the torques of each dipole of problem 3.2b on the other. Can you resolve the apparent difficulty entailed in the failure of these torques to obey the law of action and reaction in some of the cases given?

Problem 3.2d. Find the force and torque on a dipole located at a radius r outside a uniformly charged cylinder of density λ coulomb/m when $\mathbf{p}$ is oriented at an angle θ with $\mathbf{r}$, in the plane containing r and the axis of the cylinder.

3.3 Closer Approximations to Molecular Fields

Although the dipole field calculated in section 3.1 will turn out to give a completely adequate account of dielectric phenomena, it is of interest to see how higher approximations can be calculated, partly in order to be able to estimate the error involved in using the dipole field and partly because the same calculations are important in dealing with radiation from antennas, from molecular systems, and from nuclei, as well as in considering forces that act on atoms, molecules, and nuclei.

We shall begin with a step beyond the calculation of section 3.1. Suppose that the dipole moments of a given molecule add to zero. A next approximation would start with a pair of equal and opposite dipoles, separated by a displacement $\boldsymbol{\delta l}'$. Just as the potential was previously found by use of the gradient formula for a differential, $V = -\boldsymbol{\delta l} \cdot \nabla(V_{+q})$, we have now $V = -\boldsymbol{\delta l}' \cdot \nabla(V_{+p})$, so that using eq. 3.1–2,

$$V = -\boldsymbol{\delta l}' \cdot \nabla \left(\frac{-\mathbf{p} \cdot \nabla \frac{1}{r}}{4\pi\epsilon_0} \right) \tag{3.3–1}$$

We shall not go through the details of the expansion of this expression (another method of calculation is given in detail below) but shall discuss the results qualitatively.   The two dipoles may be situated with respect to each other in various ways, as shown in Fig. 3.3a.

Any of these configurations is called an "electric quadrupole."   Symmetry considerations often allow only the form in which the two dipoles are collinear.   Since the dipole potential varies inversely as the square of the distance from the molecule and the quadrupole potential involves

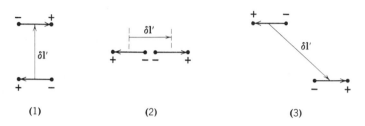

Fig. 3.3a.   Three quadrupole types.

another differentiation, the latter will evidently vary as $1/r^3$, with the quadrupole field varying as $1/r^4$.

Similarly, we might have a cancellation of the quadrupole field and be led to make another differentiation, obtaining the *octupole field*, with $V \propto 1/r^4$ and $E \propto 1/r^5$.   Higher multipole fields are generally called 16-pole, 32-pole, etc.

Now let us consider the error made by use of the true dipole formula for a dipole of finite length.   One can write r and r' in Fig. 3.1a in exact form using the law of cosines and the distance r_0 from $\mathcal{O}$ to the center of the dipole.   Then if an expansion is made in powers of $\delta l/r_0$ by means of the binomial theorem, one gets a series with terms that vary as $1/r^2$, $1/r^4$, etc., giving the actual potential as a sum of dipole, octupole, 32-pole terms (problem 3.3a).   Another way to see that this must be so is to replace the dipole by a group of dipoles including fictitious positive and negative charges whose combined effect is zero.   One such combination that is equivalent to $+q$ and $-q$ separated by δl is shown in Fig. 3.3b.

If the dipole of length $\frac{1}{2}\delta l$ and charge $2q$ be superimposed on the two quadrupoles, all the fictitious charges cancel, and we are left with the original dipole.   The shorter dipole has the same moment, and the two quadrupoles together form an octupole, so that an actual dipole of a given length is equivalent to one of the same strength but half the length plus an octupole, whose displacements are $\frac{1}{2}$ and $\frac{1}{4}$ the original length. If the process were to be continued, we would continue to add octupole moments until we reached the limiting value that is obtained in the series referred to above.

Similarly, higher actual multipoles can be reduced to a series of ideal multipoles. We may also consider more complex combinations of charges as the sum of a "monopole" field, a dipole field, a quadrupole field, etc. Problem 3.3c deals with a case of three point charges.

A continuous distribution of charge $\rho(x, y, z)$ located near an origin $\mathcal{O}$, at a distance small compared to the coordinates (x_0, y_0, z_0) of a point of

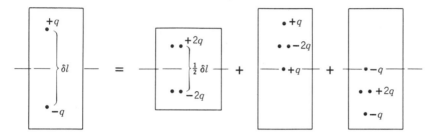

Fig. 3.3b. One dipole and two quadrupoles that are equivalent to a single dipole. If the three figures on the right are slid together along the dashed line and superimposed, they will give the figure on the left.

observation, gives rise to a potential which can be expressed in multipole orders by use of the binomial expansion. We have, integrating over the charged region,

$$
\begin{aligned}
V &= \frac{1}{4\pi\epsilon_0} \int \frac{\rho \, d\tau}{[(x_0 - x)^2 + (y_0 - y)^2 + (z_0 - z)^2]^{\frac{1}{2}}} \\
&= \frac{1}{4\pi\epsilon_0} \int \frac{\rho \, d\tau}{[(\mathbf{r}_0 - \mathbf{r}) \cdot (\mathbf{r}_0 - \mathbf{r})]^{\frac{1}{2}}} \\
&= \frac{1}{4\pi\epsilon_0} \int \frac{\rho \, d\tau}{[\mathbf{r}_0 \cdot \mathbf{r}_0 - 2\mathbf{r}_0 \cdot \mathbf{r} + \mathbf{r} \cdot \mathbf{r}]^{\frac{1}{2}}} \\
&= \frac{1}{4\pi\epsilon_0} \int \frac{\rho \, d\tau}{r_0 \left[1 - \dfrac{2\mathbf{r}_0 \cdot \mathbf{r}}{r_0^2} + \dfrac{r^2}{r_0^2} \right]^{\frac{1}{2}}}
\end{aligned}
\tag{3.3-2}
$$

which by the use of the binomial expansion becomes, letting $\mathbf{r}_0/r_0 = \mathbf{1}_{r0}$ and carrying the expansion only to quadratic terms in r,

$$
V = \frac{1}{4\pi\epsilon_0} \int \frac{\rho \, d\tau}{r_0} + \frac{1}{4\pi\epsilon_0} \int \frac{\rho \mathbf{r} \cdot \mathbf{1}_{r0}}{r_0^2} \, d\tau + \frac{1}{4\pi\epsilon_0} \int \rho \, \frac{3(\mathbf{r} \cdot \mathbf{1}_{r0})^2 - r^2}{2r_0^3} \, d\tau + \cdots
\tag{3.3-3}
$$

The first term is clearly the potential that would be produced by the total charge if it were placed at the origin.   If we place an equal negative charge at the origin and combine it with the second term, we see that to each $\rho \, d\tau$ at a displacement $\mathbf{r}$ from the origin we can associate $-\rho \, d\tau$ at the origin and consequently an elementary dipole potential.

The total or net dipole moment is thus seen to be given by the integral

$$\mathbf{p} = \int \rho \mathbf{r} \, d\tau \tag{3.3–4}$$

and so the second term of eq. 3.3–3 represents the dipole potential of the distribution.   The third term represents the quadrupole potential, as is apparent from dimensional arguments.   An explicit demonstration of this assertion requires the definition of the quadrupole moment as a two-subscript affair (i.e., a tensor):

$$Q_{xx} = \int \rho x^2 \, d\tau; \qquad Q_{xy} = \int \rho xy \, d\tau; \qquad \text{etc.} \tag{3.3–5}$$

and the evaluation of the field produced by each of the nine combinations by use of eq. 3.3–1.   For each element of charge $\rho \, d\tau$ which has a dipole moment $\rho \mathbf{r} \, d\tau$ there is assumed to be an opposite dipole at the origin. The details are left to the reader.   (Problem 3.3b.)

Now we can explain why quadrupole and higher moments are not important for a discussion of dielectric materials.   Dipole moments are important because, although the dipole fields are much weaker than monopole fields, there are many more dipoles than free monopoles in any ordinary piece of material.   Quadrupole fields however must be compared to dipole fields as produced by the *same* number of molecules, and hence the macroscopic effects of atomic quadrupoles are expected to be small—roughly in the ratio of atomic dimensions to distances of experimental observation.

Forces on multipoles clearly involve higher derivatives of the electric field—second derivatives for quadrupoles, third for octupoles, in general Nth derivatives for 2^N poles.   An important example is that of many non-spherical atomic nuclei.   The protons in these nuclei are apparently arranged in such a way that in addition to the monopole field there is a substantial symmetrical quadrupole contribution.   There are thus forces on nuclei that depend on the second derivative of the average molecular field; experiments involving the absorption of high-frequency radiation "tuned" to the quadrupole moment thus give a measure of this second derivative at the position of the nucleus.

Problem 3.3a.   Write r and r' for the dipole of Fig. 3.1a in terms of the distance r_0 from the center of the dipole to the point of observation and the angle θ between $\mathbf{r}_0$ and $\mathbf{p}$.   Use the binomial theorem to calculate the dipole and octupole potentials for this physical dipole.

Problem 3.3b. Complete the demonstration mentioned in the text that the last term of eq. 3.3–3 is indeed the quadrupole potential.

Problem 3.3c. Two charges of value $+q$ each are located at two corners of an equilateral triangle, and one charge of value $-q$ is located at the other vertex. Show how the resulting field can be calculated as the sum of a single charge field, a dipole field, and two quadrupole fields.

3.4 The Field Produced by Polarized Dielectric Material

In general, nearly every molecule of a dielectric is polarized and contributes through its dipole moment to the total field. Some molecules are permanently polarized for chemical reasons, and are called "polar molecules." Materials composed of them are called "polar substances." The molecular agitation due to heat usually distributes these dipoles in a random way, so that their net effect is zero, but the presence of an external electric field will tend to line them up in some given direction. The resulting equilibrium between the thermal agitation and the external force means that each molecule contributes to the total field during some small fraction of the time. In a few polar substances, called "ferroelectrics," there is a strong tendency for the dipoles to keep each other lined up in spite of the random heat motion.

There are also a few substances in which the polar molecules can be lined up while in the liquid state and then solidified, so that a permanent over-all polarization is frozen in. These substances are called "electrets" and, although their actual behavior is complex and they are not much used in practice, their theoretical resemblance to bar magnets makes them of considerable importance for this book. We shall discuss them in section 3.6.

Finally, a great many molecules are normally unpolarized and become polarized under the influence of an external field. Polar molecules will also have their dipole strengths changed by an external field. In both these cases, the electrons are shifted more or less as a group toward one side of the molecule or atom, so that the center of the electron cloud is displaced relative to the nucleus.

Before considering further the physical properties of molecules, we wish to calculate the external field produced by an arbitrary piece of polarized material. We shall do this first in a general and straightforward way originally introduced by Poisson, and shall repeat the process in a somewhat idealized but simple fashion that helps to provide a more concrete explanation of the results.

The potential outside a body of dielectric is obtained in Poisson's method by applying eq. 3.1–9 to a small volume $d\tau'$ containing many molecules and then making a volume integral. If $d\tau'$ is small enough, we can add the dipole moments of all the molecules within and use for r in eq 3.1–9 a radius drawn from (x', y', z'), a point in $d\tau'$, to the point of observation. The sum of the moments will be proportional to the number of molecules (as long as there are enough to be a representative sample for the purpose of averaging) and hence to the volume $d\tau'$. Let us call it $\mathbf{P}\,d\tau'$, so that

$$\sum_i \mathbf{p}_i = \mathbf{P}\,d\tau' \qquad (3.4\text{–}1)$$

where $\sum_i$ refers to a summation over all individual dipoles in the volume $d\tau'$. The vector $\mathbf{P}$ is called the *electric polarization*; more explicitly it is the electric dipole moment per unit volume. It is generally a function that varies in both direction and magnitude from point to point.

The potential produced at (x, y, z) by the dipoles in $d\tau'$ may now be written by eqs. 3.1–9 and 3.4–1 as

$$dV = -\frac{1}{4\pi\epsilon_0}\,\mathbf{P}\cdot\mathbf{\nabla}\left(\frac{1}{r}\right)d\tau'$$

The potential produced by the entire piece of dielectric is therefore the integral

$$V = -\frac{1}{4\pi\epsilon_0}\int_\tau \mathbf{P}\cdot\mathbf{\nabla}\left(\frac{1}{r}\right)d\tau' = +\frac{1}{4\pi\epsilon_0}\int_\tau \mathbf{P}\cdot\mathbf{\nabla}'\left(\frac{1}{r}\right)d\tau' \quad (3.4\text{–}2)$$

The $\mathbf{\nabla}$ in this expression contains derivatives with respect to x, y, and z, the coordinates of the point of observation, whereas $\mathbf{\nabla}'$ contains derivatives of x', y', and z'. Derivatives of $r = [(x - x')^2 + (y - y')^2 + (z - z')^2]^{\frac{1}{2}}$ with respect to the primed coordinates have an opposite effect to those taken with respect to unprimed coordinates,[5] so that $\mathbf{\nabla} = -\mathbf{\nabla}' = -[\mathbf{1}_x\,(\partial/\partial x') + \mathbf{1}_y\,(\partial/\partial y') + \mathbf{1}_z\,(\partial/\partial z')]$.

We shall now perform a type of integration by parts. A generalization of the formula $u\,dv = d(uv) - v\,du$ that applies to our case is the following vector identity (see Appendix, Table A.2B, item 4):

$$\mathbf{P}\cdot\mathbf{\nabla}\left(\frac{1}{r}\right) = \mathbf{\nabla}\cdot\left(\frac{\mathbf{P}}{r}\right) - \frac{1}{r}\mathbf{\nabla}\cdot\mathbf{P}$$

which can be proven easily by writing out components. After integration, the "integrated part" uv will correspond here to the volume integral of div $(\mathbf{P}/r)$, which can be transformed into a surface integral by the divergence theorem, eq. A.2–22. Thus we have

$$V = \frac{1}{4\pi\epsilon_0}\int_\tau \mathbf{P}\cdot\mathbf{\nabla}'\left(\frac{1}{r}\right)d\tau' = \frac{1}{4\pi\epsilon_0}\int_\tau \mathbf{\nabla}'\cdot\left(\frac{\mathbf{P}}{r}\right)d\tau' - \frac{1}{4\pi\epsilon_0}\int\frac{\mathbf{\nabla}'\cdot\mathbf{P}}{r}\,d\tau'$$

[5] If r increases for a certain displacement of the point (x, y, z), it will be decreased if the same displacement is applied to (x', y', z').

and, transforming the first integral of the last expression and continuing to use the operation indicated by ∇' but dropping the prime, we get

$$V = \int_S \frac{\mathbf{P} \cdot \mathbf{dS}}{4\pi\epsilon_0 r} - \int \frac{\nabla \cdot \mathbf{P}}{4\pi\epsilon_0 r}\, d\tau \tag{3.4-3}$$

This expression is exactly the same as the formula for the potential due to a combined surface and volume distribution, provided we take (a) $\sigma\, dS = \mathbf{P} \cdot \mathbf{dS}$ or

$$\sigma = \mathbf{P} \cdot \mathbf{1}_S = P_n \tag{3.4-4a}$$

where $\mathbf{1}_S$ is normal to the surface, and P_n denotes the normal component of $\mathbf{P}$, and (b)

$$\rho = -\nabla \cdot \mathbf{P} \tag{3.4-4b}$$

Thus we have proved that a polarized piece of dielectric produces electric field as if it had a charge density on its surface equal in magnitude to the normal component of the polarization at the surface and a volume distribution throughout its interior equal at every point to the negative divergence of the polarization at that point.

These charge densities are sometimes called "fictitious," which in a sense they are. However more common and less misleading names are "bound charge" or "polarization charge." When their nature needs to be explicitly indicated we shall use the symbols σ_P and ρ_P. Charge acquired by a dielectric as a result of triboelectricity or by any contact with an already charged object is called "free charge," a name used generally for any charge other than polarization charge.

We have implicitly assumed here that the dielectric material ends abruptly at its surface. By P_n we mean the limiting value as we approach the surface from an interior point. For some purposes it is convenient to avoid the resulting discontinuity between P_n inside the surface and that just outside by imagining the surface of the dielectric to be slightly diffuse—that is, we think of P_n as changing from its interior value to zero in a very thin but finite layer at the surface. In this case we will have a concentrated volume distribution of charge in the thin layer and a large value of div $\mathbf{P}$, but no surface charge σ and no limiting P_n. This amounts to shifting all the contribution of the first term of eq. 3.4–3 into the second. However, for most physical interpretations, the infinitesimal surface layer is the most useful concept.

Let us now make the alternative calculation referred to above. For this purpose we shall idealize the dielectric by assuming that all molecules in a given region are polarized identically, each by the motion of a charge $+q$ through a displacement $\delta\mathbf{l}$ ($+q$ is for instance the charge on a nucleus or group of nuclei). Let the number of molecules per unit volume be N. Then we have $\mathbf{P} = Nq\, \delta\mathbf{l}$. We shall furthermore consider all the positive and negative charges separately and replace the discrete distributions of the two signs by continuous charge clouds. Thus we assume there to be a positive charge density $\rho_+ = Nq$, and a negative one $\rho_- = -Nq$. When the dielectric is unpolarized, these distributions are everywhere equal and opposite. Polarization involves the displacement of the entire positive charge distribution with respect to the negative one. We may allow ρ_+, ρ_-, and δl to vary from place to place.

Now at the surface, the edges of the negative and positive clouds

Fig. 3.4a.   Surface polarization charge.

coincide before polarization occurs. If the positive cloud moves out by a displacement δl, there will be a positive excess of charge at the surface. (If δl is inward, a negative excess is left behind.) The amount of excess in an area dS is given by ρ_+ times the volume of a cylinder of base dS and slant height δl (Fig. 3.4a). Let the height of this cylinder, which is the component of δl normal to the surface, be called δl_n. Then the volume is $\delta l_n \, dS$ and the charge $\sigma_P \, dS = \rho_+ \delta l_n \, dS = Nq \, \delta l_n \, dS = P_n \, dS = \mathbf{P} \cdot \mathbf{dS}$, so that $\sigma_P = P_n$, eq. 3.4–4a. The surface charge is seen to result from a lack of cancellation of ρ_+ and ρ_- at the boundary.

To calculate the volume charge, we note by the calculation just given that $\mathbf{P} \cdot \mathbf{dS}$ represents the amount of charge that passes through a surface element $\mathbf{dS}$ when polarization occurs. The net amount of charge that leaves a small volume $d\tau$ may thus be called the flux of $\mathbf{P}$ out of the surface. Now, the flux per unit volume of any vector, leaving an infinitesimal volume at a given point, is the divergence of this vector evaluated at the point in question. Thus the charge decrease per unit volume resulting from polarization is $\nabla \cdot \mathbf{P}$, and its negative $-\nabla \cdot \mathbf{P}$ is the charge added, or ρ_P.

The expression 3.4–3 is valid for the potential at points outside the dielectric medium. It also must hold for any interior point insofar as it is legitimate to use the assumption of continuity and the averaging process implied in the definition of $\mathbf{P}$. As a result, eq. 3.4–3 gives the *average* potential at a point inside the dielectric material.

Let us verify this by a more explicit calculation. As we consider a point $\mathcal{O}$ in the medium, we can divide the material into two parts, the one a small sphere of radius a drawn about $\mathcal{O}$ and the other the remainder (Fig. 3.4b). The sphere is to be large enough to contain a good average representation of the molecules in their various states of polarization. The potential and field produced at $\mathcal{O}$ by the dipoles outside the sphere is given by eq. 3.4–3, including the field produced by the fictitious surface charge P_n on the inside of the sphere (the magnitude of this field is calculated in section 3.9). Taking $\mathbf{1}_r$ as outward on the spherical surface (i.e., into the material) we can write P_n as $-\mathbf{P} \cdot \mathbf{1}_r$.

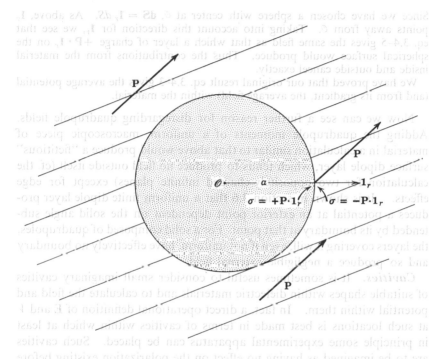

Fig. 3.4b.   Illustrating the calculation of the average field at a point $\mathcal{O}$ in a dielectric medium.

Let us calculate the field at $\mathcal{O}$ produced by the material in the sphere by a volume integral of the field $d\mathbf{E}$ produced by the $N\,d\tau$ molecules in each volume element $d\tau$ of the sphere. This field depends only on the relative coordinates of the point $\mathcal{O}$ and the center of the group of $N\,d\tau$ molecules. The integral $\int d\mathbf{E} = N\int \mathbf{E}_P\, d\tau$ where $\mathbf{E}_P$ is the field of a single dipole, is $N\tau$ times the integral one would get by placing one molecule at the center of the sphere—τ being the total volume—and calculating the *average* field produced by it in the sphere, which is $(1/\tau)\int \mathbf{E}_P\, d\tau$ (each infinitesimal contribution to this integral has the same value corresponding to the same relative coordinates as the corresponding contribution to the integral we started to calculate).

Now, since for a single molecule, $\mathbf{E}_P = -\nabla V_P$ where V_P is the dipole field, we can use the theorem given by eq. A.2–24 and write

$$\int_\tau \mathbf{E}_P \, d\tau = -\int_\tau \nabla V_P \, d\tau = -\int_S V_P \, d\mathbf{S}$$

and

$$N\int_\tau \mathbf{E}_P \, d\tau = -N\int_S V_P \, d\mathbf{S} = -\int_S \frac{N\mathbf{p} \cdot \mathbf{1}_r}{4\pi\epsilon_0 r^2} \, d\mathbf{S} = -\int_S \frac{\mathbf{P} \cdot \mathbf{1}_r}{4\pi\epsilon_0 r^2} \, d\mathbf{S} \quad (3.4\text{–}5)$$

Since we have chosen a sphere with center at $\mathcal{O}$, $d\mathbf{S} = \mathbf{1}_r \, dS$. As above, $\mathbf{1}_r$ points away from $\mathcal{O}$. Taking into account this direction for $\mathbf{1}_r$, we see that eq. 3.4–5 gives the same field as that which a layer of charge $+\mathbf{P} \cdot \mathbf{1}_r$ on the spherical surface would produce. Thus the contributions from the material inside and outside cancel exactly.

We have proved that our original result eq. 3.4–3 gives the average potential (and from its gradient, the average field) within the material.

Now we can see a further reason for disregarding quadrupole fields. Adding the quadrupole moments of a uniform, macroscopic piece of material in a calculation similar to that above would produce a "fictitious" surface dipole layer, which tends to produce no field outside itself (cf. the calculation for two oppositely-charged infinite planes) except for edge effects. It is shown in section 3.6 that a uniform finite dipole layer produces a potential at an exterior point dependent on the solid angle subtended by its boundary at that point. For a solid composed of quadrupoles, the layers covering it will, even if not uniform, have effectively no boundary and so produce a negligible external field.

Cavities. It is sometimes useful to consider small imaginary cavities of suitable shapes within dielectric materials and to calculate the field and potential within them. In fact, a direct operational definition of $\mathbf{E}$ and V at such locations is best made in terms of cavities within which at least in principle some experimental apparatus can be placed. Such cavities are to be imagined as having no effect on the polarization existing before they were made.

Now, a cavity will in general have components of $\mathbf{P}$ normal to its surfaces and thus carry a charge σ_P. But if its dimensions are small, the potential gradients produced by this extra surface charge will have only a small effect on V. Thus we shall assume that eq. 3.4–3 also applies to the potential in any small cavity.

We must be careful, however, in calculating the field from the gradient of eq. 3.4–3 since the cavity surface charges can produce an appreciable field even when their dimensions are infinitesimal. There is one shape and orientation of cavity, however, for which the cavity charges are negligible. Consider a very thin cylindrical needlelike cavity or drill hole, parallel to **P** (see $\mathscr{A}\mathscr{B}$ in Fig. 3.4c).   Now P_n will be zero along the sides of this cavity. If the cylinder is sufficiently thin compared to its length, the field produced at its center by the polarization charges on its ends will be negligible (problem 3.4e).   Thus the field inside the cavity at its center will be given by the gradient of a potential calculated from eq. 3.4–3 and from any extended charges present.   Therefore the field in a needlelike cavity parallel to **P** is equal to the field in the medium itself.

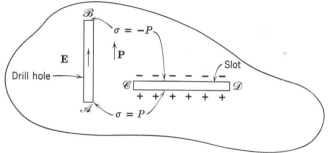

Fig. 3.4c.   Cavities in a dielectric.

If the drill hole is not parallel to **P**, there will be a contribution to the field from the surface polarization, but near the center of the cavity these contributions will be perpendicular to its length, so that the parallel component of **E** in such a cavity is equal to the component in the same direction in the medium.   Therefore, we can imagine calculating $\int \mathbf{E} \cdot \mathbf{dl}$ along the paths through the dielectric by locating the paths in needle-like tunnels.

Let us consider another simple cavity shape. $\mathscr{C}\mathscr{D}$ in Fig. 3.4c is a cross section of a flat coin-shaped cavity or slot with top and bottom perpendicular to **P** and lateral dimensions large compared to its thickness. Such a cavity will have a plane distribution of charge on top and bottom, and a field inside produced by this charge, of magnitude $E_P = \sigma_P/\epsilon_0$ in the same direction as **P** itself.   Thus the total field strength in the slot (far from the edges) is

$$\mathbf{E}_{\text{cavity}} = \mathbf{E} + \sigma_P \mathbf{1}_P/\epsilon_0 = \mathbf{E} + \mathbf{P}/\epsilon_0 \qquad (3.4\text{–}6)$$

where $\mathbf{1}_P$ is a unit vector in the direction of **P**, and **E** denotes as before the field inside the dielectric (whose sources are the external charges and all the polarization volume and surface charges, except those on the walls of the cavity).

Problem 3.4a.   What surface density of charge will appear on a slab of dielectric which is polarized normal to the surface in an amount corresponding to a shift of one electron per molecule through a distance of 6×10^{-10} cm? Assume 3×10^{22} molecules/cm³ in the material.

Problem 3.4b.   Suppose that in a certain medium, P is entirely in the x-direction and is variable.   Suppose that the resulting volume charge density corresponds to one extra electron per million molecules.   Find $\partial P_x / \partial x$.   If $P_x = 0$ when $x = 0$, find P when $x = 1$ cm.   Find the corresponding displacement of charge in this region, if one electron in each molecule actually shifts. Assume 4×10^{22} molecules/cm³.

Problem 3.4c.   Calculate the total dipole moment of a piece of dielectric, $\int P \, d\tau$, from ρ_P and σ_P by use of eq. 3.3–4 and the equivalent surface integral. (*Hint*: use eq. A.2–25.)

Problem 3.4d.   If one electron per cubic Ångstrom moves when a certain piece of dielectric is polarized, how far does it move when σ_P on a surface normal to P is equal to the value found in problem 2.3d?

Problem 3.4e.   A drill hole parallel to P in uniformly polarized material is a circular cylinder of radius r and length l.   Find a formula for E at its center, taking the fields produced by the bound charges on the two ends as (*a*) uniform disk fields and (*b*) point charge fields.   Show from (*a*) how to get both the result for a coin-shaped cavity of infinitesimal height and that for a drill hole of infinitesimal radius.

3.5   Application of the Flux Law to a Dielectric Medium

A particular form of the flux law that is useful when dealing with dielectrics can be obtained by dividing the total charge inside an arbitrary Gaussian surface into free and bound parts.   If the Gaussian surface lies entirely outside a piece of dielectric, the total bound charge inside is zero, and we have nothing new (except of course that the piece of dielectric may be so shaped as to destroy symmetry otherwise present and prevent any practical use of Gauss' law).

Consider a Gaussian surface that lies partly or wholly in a dielectric medium.   In accordance with the calculations made in the last section, we can find the polarization charge that has been transferred *into* the surface by calculating the integral $q_P = -\int P_n \, dS = -\int \mathbf{P} \cdot \mathbf{dS}$ over the surface.   (There is no contribution from any part of the surface not lying in the dielectric since P will be zero on these parts.)   Let us write eq. 1.4–2 again, denoting the *free* charges inside the surface by $\sum_n q_{n,\text{free}}$ and the total polarization charge by q_P,

$$\epsilon_0 \Phi_E = \epsilon_0 \int_{\text{closed } S} \mathbf{E} \cdot \mathbf{dS} = \sum_n q_{n,\text{free}} + q_P = \sum_n q_{n,\text{free}} - \int \mathbf{P} \cdot \mathbf{dS}$$

or, transposing and combining terms,

$$\int_S (\epsilon_0 \mathbf{E} + \mathbf{P}) \cdot \mathbf{dS} = \sum_n q_{n,\text{free}}$$

We can now write a flux law that *does not contain the polarization charge explicitly* if we define a new field vector and a new flux. We write the new vector, in the MKS system,[6]

$$\mathbf{D} = \epsilon_0 \mathbf{E} + \mathbf{P} \qquad\qquad \text{MKS} \quad (3.5\text{-}1a)$$

and in the Gaussian and electrostatic systems:

$$\mathbf{D} = \mathbf{E} + 4\pi\mathbf{P} \qquad\qquad \text{Gaussian} \quad (3.5\text{-}1b)$$

We shall call $\mathbf{D}$ the "electric displacement" (a name introduced by Maxwell) and its flux,

$$\Phi_D = \int_{\text{any } S} \mathbf{D} \cdot d\mathbf{S} \qquad\qquad (3.5\text{-}2)$$

will be called the flux of displacement. In empty space, it is equal to $\epsilon_0 \Phi_E$ (in MKS units). Now we can write the flux law for dielectrics:

$$\Phi_D = \int_{\text{closed } S} \mathbf{D} \cdot d\mathbf{S} = \sum_n q_{n,\text{free}} \qquad\qquad \text{MKS} \quad (3.5\text{-}3a)$$

$$\Phi_D = \int_{\text{closed } S} \mathbf{D} \cdot d\mathbf{S} = 4\pi \sum_n q_{n,\text{free}} \qquad\qquad \text{Gaussian} \quad (3.5\text{-}3b)$$

The differential form of this law, corresponding to eq. 1.5-1, is

$$\nabla \cdot \mathbf{D} = \rho_{\text{free}} \qquad\qquad \text{MKS} \quad (3.5\text{-}4a)$$

$$\nabla \cdot \mathbf{D} = 4\pi\rho_{\text{free}} \qquad\qquad \text{Gaussian} \quad (3.5\text{-}4b)$$

In free space, $\mathbf{D}$ is equal to $\epsilon_0 \mathbf{E}$ (MKS), and we can draw lines or tubes of displacement that coincide with lines or tubes of force. In dielectrics for which $\mathbf{P}$ is parallel to $\mathbf{E}$ (see section 3.7 below), $\mathbf{D}$ is also, although the density of lines of displacement will differ from that of the lines of force in a way that depends on the relation of $\mathbf{P}$ to $\mathbf{E}$. In general, however, $\mathbf{P}$ may have a direction different from that of $\mathbf{E}$, and $\mathbf{D}$ will point in still a third direction.

Maxwell interpreted $\mathbf{D}$ in terms of his theory of "ether strains" but for our purposes it is best to think of it as a convenient, auxiliary vector that is useful when we do not want to take the locations and magnitudes of the polarization charges into explicit account. We can define $\mathbf{D}$ in an operational way by making it equal to ϵ_0 times the field in a disk-shaped cavity normal to $\mathbf{P}$, in accordance with eq. 3.4-6.

---

[6] Whenever important formulas are written differently in the MKS and Gaussian systems, we give them in both systems (unless the difference lies only in the value of ϵ_0).

In the electrostatic system of units, $\epsilon_0 = 1/4\pi$ and the field in a disk-shaped cavity is $\mathbf{E} + 4\pi\mathbf{P}$. For this system, $\mathbf{D} = \mathbf{E}$ and $\Phi_D = \Phi_E$ in free space.

A simple application of eq. 3.5–3, of quite a general nature, is to derive a condition on the values of $\mathbf{D}$ on the two sides of a boundary of a dielectric medium or an interface between two different media. Let us construct a Gaussian pillbox of infinitesimal height, just as we did for the surface of a conductor (see section 2.3), with its top on one side of the interface and its bottom on the other. Assuming there to be *no free charge* at the boundary, we deduce that the displacement flux into the bottom of the box is equal to that out through the top or that the normal component of $\mathbf{D}$ is the same on the two sides.

$$D_{n1} = D_{n2} \text{ (at a dielectric boundary with no free charge)} \quad (3.5\text{–}5)$$

The flux law gives us no information about the components of $\mathbf{D}$ parallel to the boundary. However, we can easily get a relation between the tangential components of $\mathbf{E}$ from other considerations. It is clear from the discussion in section 2.3 of local and distant fields at the surface of a conductor that the only difference in $\mathbf{E}$ that can occur between two points on opposite sides of a charged surface must be a difference in the normal components, since a layer of charge (polarization charge in this case) does not produce a local field parallel to itself. Thus the tangential component of $\mathbf{E}$ is the same on the two sides,

$$E_{t1} = E_{t2} \text{ (at a dielectric boundary with no free charge)} \quad (3.5\text{–}6)$$

Another way of seeing the same result is to note that V will be continuous across any boundary, and therefore its derivative *along* the boundary will be the same on each side. The result, although not this second argument, is still valid for electric fields in non-static cases.

It is evident that the lines of force and of displacement will have changes in direction at dielectric boundaries (see problem 3.8*a*).

Problem 3.5a. Find boundary conditions that hold at an interface between two dielectrics for the *tangential* component of $\mathbf{D}$ and the *normal* component of $\mathbf{E}$.

3.6   Ideal Electrets

As we remarked in section 3.4, there are a few substances which can be put into a state of permanent polarization. The complicated physical characteristics of actual electrets will be discussed briefly in section 3.10 in connection with other properties of dielectrics. The calculation of field and displacement for an ideal, uniformly polarized electret is on the other hand straightforward and relatively simple. It will serve as a good first application of the theory of sections 3.4 and 3.5, and the calculations we make here will be easily transferable to the corresponding magnetic cases in section 8.3.

Let us consider first a long slender cylindrical bar of dielectric that is uniformly and permanently polarized with the constant vector **P** parallel to the axis, as shown in Fig. 3.6a. According to our theory, the field **E** at any point inside or outside the bar can be calculated from the surface densities $\sigma_P = P$ and $-\sigma_P = -P$ at the ends of the bar. The value of **E**

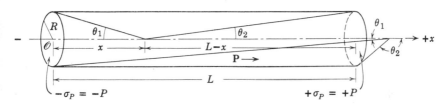

Fig. 3.6a. Calculation of **E** on the axis of a uniform bar electret, at points inside and outside the bar.

on the axis can be found from the answer to problem 1.3f, namely, that the field on the axis of a uniformly charged disk of radius R, at a point a distance x from the center, is

$$E = (\sigma/2\epsilon_0)[1 - x/(x^2 + R^2)^{\frac{1}{2}}]$$

Thus at a point x meters from the origin $\mathcal{O}$ at the negative end of the bar, the field is

$$E_{\text{axis}} = \frac{-P}{2\epsilon_0}\left(1 - \frac{x}{(x^2 + R^2)^{\frac{1}{2}}}\right) - \frac{P}{2\epsilon_0}\left(1 - \frac{L - x}{[(L - x)^2 + R^2]^{\frac{1}{2}}}\right) \quad (3.6\text{–}1)$$

This formula can be written in terms of θ_1 and θ_2 as shown in Fig. 3.6a

$$E_{\text{axis}} = \frac{-P}{\epsilon_0} + \frac{P}{2\epsilon_0}(\cos \theta_1 + \cos \theta_2) \quad (3.6\text{–}2)$$

When $x > L$, the contribution from the right-hand end must have its sign changed, yielding

$$E_{\text{axis}} = \frac{-P}{2\epsilon_0}\left(1 - \frac{x}{(x^2 + R^2)^{\frac{1}{2}}}\right) + \frac{P}{2\epsilon_0}\left(1 - \frac{x - L}{[(x - L)^2 + R^2]^{\frac{1}{2}}}\right)$$

$$= \frac{P}{2\epsilon_0}(\cos \theta_1 + \cos \theta_2) \quad (3.6\text{–}3)$$

since $\cos \theta_2$ is negative in this case.

Just inside the negative end of the bar, the field is

$$E_{x=0+} = \frac{-P}{2\epsilon_0} - \frac{P}{2\epsilon_0}\left(1 - \frac{L}{(L^2 + R^2)^{\frac{1}{2}}}\right)$$

If R is much smaller than L, the parenthesis can be simplified by the use of the binomial theorem

$$1 - \frac{L}{(L^2 + R^2)^{\frac{1}{2}}} = 1 - \left(1 + \frac{R^2}{L^2}\right)^{-\frac{1}{2}}$$

$$= 1 - \left(1 - \frac{R^2}{2L^2} + \frac{3R^4}{8L^4} + \cdots\right)$$

$$= \frac{R^2}{2L^2} - \frac{3R^4}{8L^4} + \cdots$$

$$\simeq \frac{R^2}{2L^2} \qquad (3.6\text{-}4)$$

The error resulting from neglect of the fourth-power term is about 2.5% if the diameter of the bar is equal to its length, and $\frac{1}{16}$ of this for half this diameter. $R^2/2L^2$ itself is less than 1% if R is less than about $L/7$. Thus for any reasonably long thin bar the field on the axis near the negative end is just $-P/2\epsilon_0$, namely, the value for an infinite plane distribution $-\sigma_P$, and similarly it can be readily seen that the field near the positive end is also $-P/2\epsilon_0$. The fields just *outside* the two ends are each obviously $+P/2\epsilon_0$. At the center, on the other hand, $x = L/2$ and

$$E = \frac{-P}{\epsilon_0}\left(1 - \frac{L/2}{[(L/2)^2 + R^2]^{\frac{1}{2}}}\right) \simeq \frac{-P}{\epsilon_0}\cdot\frac{R^2}{2(L/2)^2} = \frac{-2PR^2}{\epsilon_0 L^2}$$

a value very much smaller than at either end.

Lines of force and equipotentials are shown in Fig. 3.6b. They are continuous across the sides of the bar because there is no surface charge there ($P_n = 0$).

Let us now consider the electric displacement $\mathbf{D} = \epsilon_0\mathbf{E} + \mathbf{P}$. We see immediately that $\mathbf{E}$ and $\mathbf{P}$ are in exactly opposite directions on the axis and approximately so elsewhere in the bar. Just inside each end, on the axis, $D = \epsilon_0(-P/2\epsilon_0) + P = P/2$, using the approximation that $E \simeq -P/2\epsilon_0$. The same value clearly holds just outside each end. At the center, D is approximately P, since E is so small. Thus $\mathbf{D}$ is in the same direction as $\mathbf{P}$ along the axis, and in contrast to $\mathbf{E}$, it has its greatest value at the center. Furthermore, since no *free* charge is present, there can be no beginning or ending of the flux of $\mathbf{D}$, so the lines of $\mathbf{D}$ must be *closed* curves in cases of ideal symmetry like this one. (The reader should be able to show that, except for those along the axis, lines of **D** could not go out to infinity in opposite directions.)   Outside the bar, $\mathbf{D} = \epsilon_0\mathbf{E}$ and the lines of force and of displacement coincide except for density or

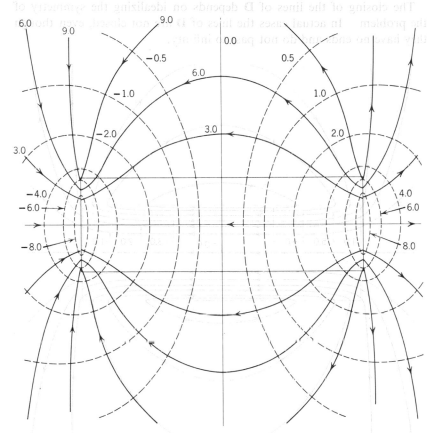

Fig. 3.6b.   Lines of **E** and equipotentials for a uniform bar electret.   The numbers represent flux Φ_E contained in surfaces of revolution and potential values (arbitrary scales).

scale factor.   Lines of **D** are shown in Fig. 3.6c.   Note that these lines show sharp breaks at the edge of the electret, in contrast to those for **E**. Note also that the flux of **D** at the center of the bar is approximately $\pi R^2 P$, whereas at the ends it is approximately $\frac{1}{2}\pi R^2 P$; half the flux of **D** leaves the bar through its sides and half through its ends.

At distances from the bar large compared to R but not to L, one can approximate the field **E** by replacing the distribution on each end by a point charge

$$Q = \pm\sigma_P(\pi R^2) = \pm\pi R^2 P$$

and one has a field like that of the two opposite point charges in Fig. 1.6b.

At great distances from the bar (large compared to L), **E** is approximately the field of a dipole of strength $\pi R^2 \sigma_p L = \pi R^2 P L$, which is the product of P and the volume of the bar.

The closing of the lines of **D** depends on idealizing the symmetry of the problem. In actual cases the lines of **D** are not closed, even though they have no ends and do not pass to infinity.

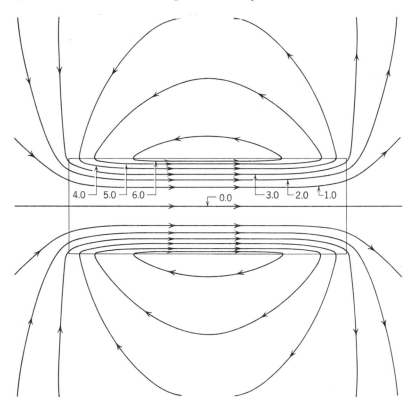

Fig. 3.6c. Lines of **D** for a uniform bar electret. The numbers represent flux Φ_D contained in surfaces of revolution (arbitrary scale).

Consider for instance a uniform bar electret which has been given a slight bend or twist. Then a line of **D** will not leave one end at exactly the same radius and azimuthal angle at which it entered at the other end. When it passes around outside the bar, it will undergo very little "twist," tending to remain in one plane, and so will not come back on itself when it reenters the bar. (Fig. 3.6d.)

In this way, a line of **D** clearly will circulate a number of times. In fact, it can only close on itself if after some number of circulations it exactly comes back to the starting point. Although in exceptional cases it might come very close after a few circulations, the inevitable limits of precision in any physical situation prevent its ever being truly closed. One line, in fact, can be drawn with enough circulations to fill out any given surface through which it passes as densely as we please.

The number of lines of **D** per unit area can thus be made to measure **D** only if each one is restricted by arbitrarily ending it in some way so as to

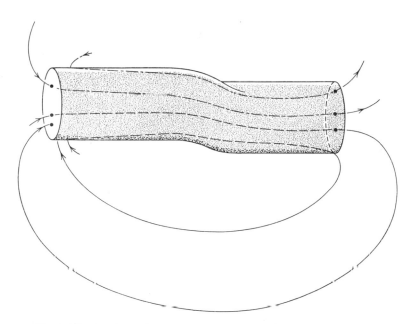

Fig. 3.6d.   Unclosed lines of **D** for a distorted bar electret (schematic).

have not more than one circulation. Such a restriction can be called a "topological restriction"; one can assume whenever necessary that topological restrictions have been introduced.[7]

Consider next a sphere of dielectric of radius a with a constant polarization throughout. (Fig. 3.6e.) One can make the calculation most readily by considering separately the fields produced by the positive and the negative charges on the dipoles. Since **P** is constant in direction and magnitude, the charge separation δl must also be constant. Thus we are led to finding the fields of a positive and a negative sphere of uniform volume density $\pm \rho = \pm Nq$ (see section 3.4, p. 110). We calculated the

[7] See article by Joseph Slepian, "Lines of Force in Electric and Magnetic Fields," *Am. Journ. Phys.*, **19,** 87 (1951).

field at an internal point of one such sphere in section 1.4; by eq. 1.4–5, it is

$$\mathbf{E}_+ = \frac{\rho_+ r \mathbf{1}_r}{3\epsilon_0} = \frac{\rho_+ \mathbf{r}}{3\epsilon_0}$$

In Fig. 3.6f, we have indicated the vectors $\mathbf{r}$ and $\mathbf{r}'$ that determine $\mathbf{E}$ for the two spheres, whose centers are respectively at $\mathcal{O}_+$ and $\mathcal{O}_-$. The resultant field at the point $\mathcal{P}$ is

$$\mathbf{E} = \frac{\rho_+ \mathbf{r}}{3\epsilon_0} + \frac{\rho_- \mathbf{r}'}{3\epsilon_0} = \frac{Nq}{3\epsilon_0}(\mathbf{r} - \mathbf{r}')$$

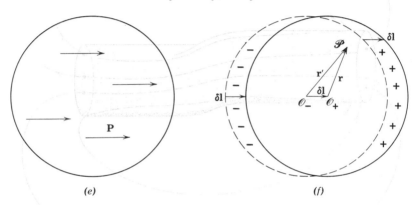

(e)　　　　　　　　　　　　　　　　　(f)

Fig. 3.6e-f.　A spherical electret.

From the figure, $\mathbf{r} - \mathbf{r}'$ is equal to the displacement from $\mathcal{O}_+$ to $\mathcal{O}_-$ which is $-\boldsymbol{\delta}\mathbf{l}$. Therefore the field at $\mathcal{P}$ is

$$\mathbf{E} = -\frac{Nq\,\boldsymbol{\delta}\mathbf{l}}{3\epsilon_0} = -\frac{\mathbf{P}}{3\epsilon_0} \qquad \text{MKS} \quad (3.6\text{–}5a)$$

For Gaussian units, we can set $4\pi\epsilon_0 = 1$, yielding:

$$\mathbf{E} = -\tfrac{4}{3}\pi\mathbf{P} \qquad \text{Gaussian} \quad (3.6\text{–}5b)$$

It is a remarkable fact that the field inside a uniformly polarized sphere is constant throughout its interior. In the region outside the sphere, we may treat the field produced by the positive and negative spheres as if all the charge were at the center and obtain the field of a dipole of strength

$$\mathbf{p} = \tfrac{4}{3}\pi a^3 \rho_+ \,\boldsymbol{\delta}\mathbf{l} = \tfrac{4}{3}\pi a^3 \mathbf{P} \qquad (3.6\text{–}6)$$

Similarly, the force and torque on such a sphere in an external field may be calculated by the use of this equivalent dipole, in accordance with Newton's third law of motion (cf. p. 17 and problem 1.4a).

Third, let us consider a thin disk of dielectric with a uniform polarization perpendicular to its surface (Fig. 3.6g).

To find the field at a point $\mathcal{O}$, let us consider a small area dS of the disk. Let t be the thickness of the disk. Then the total dipole moment in the volume of area dS and thickness t is $Pt\, dS$. The potential at $\mathcal{O}$ produced by this dipole is, by eq. 3.1–4,

$$dV = t\, dS\, \frac{\mathbf{P}\cdot\mathbf{1}_r}{4\pi\epsilon_0 r^2} = tP\, \frac{d\mathbf{S}\cdot\mathbf{1}_r}{4\pi\epsilon_0 r^2} = P_S\, \frac{d\mathbf{S}\cdot\mathbf{1}_r}{4\pi\epsilon_0 r^2} \qquad (3.6\text{–}7)$$

since the vectors $d\mathbf{S}$ and $\mathbf{P}$ have the same direction. The quantity $tP = P_S$

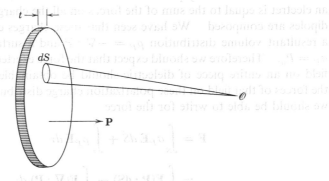

Fig. 3.6g. A disk electret.

is the dipole moment per unit area of the disk. But $d\mathbf{S}\cdot\mathbf{1}_r/r^2 = d\Omega$, the solid angle subtended by dS at $\mathcal{O}$. Thus, we have $dV = tP\, d\Omega/4\pi\epsilon_0$, or integrating, $V = tP\Omega/4\pi\epsilon_0$ where Ω is the solid angle subtended by the boundary of the disk at $\mathcal{O}$, a result which applies to any shape of boundary and even to "disks" that are not plane. We have, finally,

$$V = P_S\Omega/4\pi\epsilon_0; \qquad P_S = Pt \qquad (3.6\text{–}8)$$

Thus the calculation of $\mathbf{E}$ outside the disk can be reduced to calculating a solid angle and taking its gradient. Note that as the point $\mathcal{O}$ moves around from the positive to the negative side of the disk, Ω reduces to zero and then must take on negative values if eq. 3.6–8 is to be of general validity. It is a remarkable fact that V depends *only* on the boundary and on P_S but not on the shape of the surface.

Inside the disk, we have the field of two plane charge distributions. Discounting the fringing effects near the edges, we have approximately $E = -\sigma_P/\epsilon_0 = -P/\epsilon_0$ and $D = \epsilon_0 E + P = 0$. The surprising result occurs that the displacement is nearly zero inside the dielectric.

This result can, however, be readily found from the fact that E and consequently D must be approximately zero just outside the disk (except near the edges) and from the condition 3.5–5 that D is the same on both sides of the boundary.

An accurate value for a point on the axis of the disk can be found from eq. 3.6–3. It is left to the reader (problem 3.6b) to show that on the axis just outside a disk of "length" $L = t$ and radius a, D is approximately given by

$$D = P_S/2a \qquad (3.6\text{–}9)$$

Now let us consider in general the action of an external field on an electret or in fact on any piece of dielectric material. The total force on an electret is equal to the sum of the forces on all the charges of which the dipoles are composed. We have seen that these charges combine to give a resultant volume distribution $\rho_P = -\nabla \cdot \mathbf{P}$ and a surface distribution $\sigma_P = P_n$. Therefore we should expect that the force exerted by an external field on an entire piece of dielectric should be obtainable by calculating the forces of that field on these polarization charge distributions. That is, we should be able to write for the force

$$\mathbf{F} = \int_S \sigma_P \mathbf{E}\, dS + \int_\tau \rho_P \mathbf{E}\, d\tau$$

$$= \int_S \mathbf{E}(\mathbf{P} \cdot d\mathbf{S}) - \int_\tau \mathbf{E}(\nabla \cdot \mathbf{P})\, d\tau \qquad (3.6\text{–}10)$$

where the integrals are taken respectively over the entire surface and entire volume of the electret in question. Note that we have not tried to calculate the forces on part of an electret or a portion of an extended dielectric. Such calculations are complicated and involve, in the first place, making a careful definition of such a force (i.e., by defining what sorts of possible motions under the action of the force are contemplated), and second, the problem of mechanical pressures and other stresses in the medium. We shall not consider such calculations in this book.[8]

A proof of eq. 3.6–10 could be constructed by Newton's third law, as in problem 1.4a. However, a direct formal proof of this equation may be obtained by adding up the forces on each dipole. By eq. 3.2–3, the force on any one of the dipoles is given by $\mathbf{F} = (\mathbf{P} \cdot \nabla)\mathbf{E}$. The total force on an electret is to be obtained by adding up for each dipole only that part of $\mathbf{F}$

[8] Some calculations of this sort are made in G. P. Harnwell, *Principles of Electricity and Electromagnetism*, 2nd ed., McGraw-Hill, New York, 1949, pp. 69–73; W. R. Smythe, *Static and Dynamic Electricity*, 2nd ed., McGraw-Hill, New York, 1950, sections 1.14 and 1.17; W. K. H. Panofsky and M. Phillips, *Classical Electricity and Magnetism*, Addison-Wesley, Cambridge, Mass., 1953, Chapter 6.

resulting from the external field.   (The internal forces will cancel out in equal and opposite pairs in this addition.)

For a small volume $d\tau$, we can write

$$\mathbf{dF} = \sum_i (\mathbf{p}_i \cdot \nabla)\mathbf{E} = \left[\left(\sum_i \mathbf{p}_i\right) \cdot \nabla\right]\mathbf{E}$$
$$= (\mathbf{P} \cdot \nabla)\mathbf{E}\, d\tau$$

since $\mathbf{P}\, d\tau = \sum_i \mathbf{p}_i$ taken over all the dipoles in $d\tau$.   Now, the transformation that was made from eq. 3.2–3 to eq. 3.2–4 assumed that $\mathbf{p}$ was a constant.   On the other hand, $\mathbf{P}$ may vary from point to point.   Let us make a transformation of $(\mathbf{P} \cdot \nabla)\mathbf{E}$, utilizing the fact that ∇ may operate on both $\mathbf{P}$ and $\mathbf{E}$.   Let us, in fact, use the convention adopted in the appendix that the quantities to the right of ∇ upon which it is to operate are indicated by a superior bar, where necessary to avoid ambiguity. Then the product rule for derivatives becomes (cf. Appendix Table A.2B, item 8)

$$\overline{(\nabla \cdot \mathbf{P})\mathbf{E}} = (\mathbf{P} \cdot \nabla)\mathbf{E} + \mathbf{E}(\nabla \cdot \mathbf{P}) \tag{3.6–11}$$

so that $\mathbf{dF}$ becomes

$$\mathbf{dF} = \overline{(\nabla \cdot \mathbf{P})\mathbf{E}}\, d\tau - \mathbf{E}(\nabla \cdot \mathbf{P})\, d\tau \tag{3.6–12}$$

The second term of this expression yields the second term of eq. 3.6–10 on integration.   To calculate the integral of the first term, we can use the vector theorem A.2–27 in the form

$$\int_\tau \overline{(\nabla \cdot \mathbf{P})\mathbf{E}}\, d\tau = \int_S \mathbf{E}(\mathbf{P} \cdot \mathbf{dS}) \tag{3.6–13}$$

a result which shows that the first term of eq. 3.6–12 integrates to the first term of eq. 3.6–10.

The calculation of the torque of an external field upon an electret can be carried out in a similar way, but we shall not perform the calculation here, postponing it to the corresponding magnetic case in section 8.3.

Problem 3.6a.   Discuss the field of a disk electret at a distance from it which is large compared to its lateral dimensions.   Sketch lines of $\mathbf{E}$ and $\mathbf{D}$ for small and large distances.

Problem 3.6b.   Prove eq. 3.6–9 by an appropriate expansion from eq. 3.6–3. When is eq. 3.6–9 exact?

Problem 3.6c.   Find $\mathbf{D}$ inside the uniform spherical electret, and sketch lines of $\mathbf{D}$ and $\mathbf{E}$ for this case.

Problem 3.6d.   Prove eqs. 3.6–11 and 3.6–13 by using Cartesian components instead of vector notation.

Problem 3.6e. Find the total dipole moment of a bar electret for which **P** is parallel to the axis of the bar, of magnitude $P = a + bx$ where x is the distance from one end.

Problem 3.6f. A sphere of radius a contains dielectric material in which **P** $= k\mathbf{r}$, where **r** is a vector from the center of the sphere. Find ρ_P, D, and E as functions of r.

Problem 3.6g. Find **E** just outside a spherical electret at a point (a) on a diameter parallel to **P** and (b) on a diameter perpendicular to **P**.

3.7 Parallel-Plate Condenser with Dielectric; Dielectric Constants

Polarization generally occurs only with applied fields. As a simple case involving an outside source of field, let us consider an ideal parallel-plate condenser with charge Q, area S and separation d, in which the space is partly filled with a dielectric of uniform polarization everywhere

Fig. 3.7a. A plane slab of dielectric between two metal plates.

normal to the planes of the plates, with **P** pointing toward the negative plate (Fig. 3.7a). The direction of **E** will also be toward the negative plate, so that **E**, **P**, and **D** are all parallel. A Gaussian surface such as G_1 with one end in the metal plate and the other in the evacuated space x–x can be used to show that E in this space is the familiar value $E = \sigma/\epsilon_0 = Q/S\epsilon_0$. Since $P = 0$ here, we have $D = \sigma$.

A surface like G_2 can be used with the flux Φ_D to show that D in the dielectric is also equal to σ. Since $D = \epsilon_0 E + P$, E in the dielectric is $(\sigma - P)/\epsilon_0$. We can also see this by noting that the upper surface of the dielectric appears to bear a charge density $\sigma_P = -P$, and the lower surface a charge $\sigma_P = +P$. The field of these two surface densities has a value P/ϵ_0 upward inside the dielectric and zero elsewhere. The E inside the dielectric is thus the resultant of the fields produced by two pairs of plane-parallel surface densities.

We can draw lines of force and displacement to illustrate this discussion (Fig. 3.7b). The displacement is continuous across the surface of the dielectric, so the lines run from one plate to the other and are exactly the same as if no dielectric were present.   Lines of E leave the positive plate, some running to the negative charge on the dielectric, and some running through the dielectric to the other plate.[9]   Of course, lines also leave $+\sigma_P$ on the lower side and pass to $-\sigma$.   The reduction of E inside the dielectric is clearly shown in the resulting diagram.

Let us calculate the potential difference between the plates.   Denoting by x and y the two distances between plates and dielectric and by d' the thickness of the dielectric slab, we have

$$V = V_1 - V_2 = \int E \cdot dl = (\sigma/\epsilon_0)x + (\sigma - P) \, d'/\epsilon_0 + (\sigma/\epsilon_0)y$$

$$= [\sigma(x + y) + (\sigma - P) \, d']/\epsilon_0$$

In terms of the charge $Q = \sigma S$, we have, using $d = x + y + d'$,

$$V = \frac{Qd}{\epsilon_0 S} - \frac{Pd'}{\epsilon_0} \qquad (3.7\text{-}1)$$

Lines of E   Lines of D

Fig. 3.7b.   Lines of E and D for Fig. 3.7a.

The arguments presented above are also valid if P is uniform throughout the material but is not perpendicular to the plane of the plates.   We only need to use P_n, the component of P in the perpendicular direction, in the various formulas above.

Now suppose we do not know the value of P but put a homogeneous[10] slab of dielectric in the position indicated, place charges Q and $-Q$ on the two plates, and ask what value of P results.   Because of the homogeneity and symmetry of the material we can deduce that D and E must also be homogeneous in the condenser (except near the edge) and must be directed normally to the plate. P will also be the same throughout.   If the material

[9] We assume here that $\sigma_P < \sigma$.

[10] Homogeneous means having the same properties at each point.

is also isotropic[11] one can conclude from symmetry considerations that the other components of **P** must vanish.   Its value can be found from eq. 3.7–1 by measuring Q and V.

As a matter of fact, for nearly all substances that can be placed in such a condenser, it is found that Q and V are strictly proportional over a wide range of V.   That is, the condenser containing the dielectric has a meaningful capacitance $C = Q/V$.   By eq. 3.7–1, if V is proportional to Q, P is also proportional to Q and the three quantities D, E, and P are all proportional to one another.   For non-electrets, **P** is always in the same direction as **E**, never in the opposite direction.   For isotropic media, to which we shall largely restrict ourselves, we may then say that the vectors **D**, **E**, and **P** vary in strict proportion to one another.

The most fundamental expression of this relation would be to relate **P** to the field that acts on the molecules and polarizes them.   This field, however, is not the average field **E** in the medium, since this average includes the field produced by the molecule on which we might calculate the external force.   The correct expression for the average field acting *on* a molecule will be calculated in section 3.9.

It is, however, still useful to consider how **P** is related to **E**.   When they are proportional, we write

$$\mathbf{P} = \chi\epsilon_0\mathbf{E} \qquad\qquad \text{MKS} \quad (3.7\text{--}2a)$$

$$\mathbf{P} = \chi\mathbf{E} \qquad\qquad \text{Gaussian} \quad (3.7\text{--}2b)$$

where the constant χ (Greek "chi") is called the "electric susceptibility" and characterizes the material in question.   It is always positive, is generally a function of temperature, and may be a function of position.

From this relation we can find one between **D** and **E**.   We have in MKS units $\mathbf{D} = \epsilon_0\mathbf{E} + \mathbf{P} = \epsilon_0(1 + \chi)\mathbf{E}$, and in Gaussian units $\mathbf{D} = \mathbf{E} + 4\pi\mathbf{P} = (1 + 4\pi\chi)\mathbf{E}$ which we write for the two systems in the forms

$$\mathbf{D} = \epsilon\mathbf{E} \qquad\qquad \text{MKS} \quad (3.7\text{--}3a)$$

$$\mathbf{D} = \kappa\mathbf{E} \qquad\qquad \text{Gaussian} \quad (3.7\text{--}3b)$$

where ϵ is another constant called the "permittivity" of the medium and is always greater than ϵ_0.   Like the latter, ϵ is measured in farads/m.   The constant κ (Greek "kappa") is a dimensionless number greater than one and is generally called the "dielectric constant."   In the MKS system,

---

[11] Isotropic means that at any point in the material, the properties are the same in all directions.

we also use κ as the dielectric constant or relative permittivity,[12] defined by

$$\kappa = \epsilon/\epsilon_0 \qquad\qquad \text{MKS} \qquad (3.7\text{-}4)$$

The relation between susceptibility and dielectric constant is clearly

$$1 + \chi = \kappa \qquad\qquad \text{MKS} \qquad (3.7\text{-}5a)$$

$$1 + 4\pi\chi = \kappa \qquad\qquad \text{Gaussian} \qquad (3.7\text{-}5b)$$

Any medium for which a dielectric constant exists so that **D**, **E**, and **P** are proportional may be referred to as linear. The theorem of superposition can be applied in such cases for all three vectors (provided bound as well as free charge is taken into account). All gases and liquids are linear and isotropic. All gases and most liquids are homogeneous. Solids are generally linear but frequently are not isotropic—in fact, only amorphous solids and cubic crystals are reasonably isotropic. They are often non-homogeneous—by virtue of non-uniform mechanical strains set up in the process of crystallization or of machining, if not by virtue of being chemically inhomogeneous. Thus, dielectric constants have a precise meaning for gases and liquids but usually only an approximate one for solids. For single crystals, the relation 3.7–3 can be replaced by a more complicated relation connecting all the various components of **D** with all those of **E**, taken with respect to preferred directions in the crystal. We shall not consider such relations here.

Another type of limitation on dielectric constants comes when extremely large fields are applied. It is to be expected that materials will become non-linear under these circumstances because there should be some limit to the degree to which molecules can be polarized. This effect has indeed been observed, but only to an extent of a few parts per million at the very highest fields available.[13] Still another consideration has to do with the rate at which the fields **E** and **D** are made to change and is discussed in section 3.10. Table 3.7A lists the values of κ for several substances, measured for static fields.

Let us note further that for a homogeneous linear medium, there can be no volume polarization charges. We have $\mathbf{P} = \mathbf{D}(1 - 1/\kappa)$ and $\nabla \cdot \mathbf{P} = \nabla \cdot [\mathbf{D}(1 - 1/\kappa)]$. If κ is a constant, so that its x, y, and z derivatives vanish, then $\rho_P = -\nabla \cdot \mathbf{P} = -(1 - 1/\kappa)\nabla \cdot \mathbf{D} = -(1 - 1/\kappa)\rho_{\text{free}}$. Since

---

[12] Also called "specific permittivity" or "specific inductive capacitance." Because it is not a constant with respect to temperature, some authors call it the "dielectric coefficient." The name dielectric constant appears to be firmly established by long tradition and common usage.

[13] See for instance, J. H. Van Vleck, *Electric and Magnetic Susceptibilities*, Clarendon Press, Oxford, 1932, p. 87.

Table 3.7A
Dielectric Constants

Gases at 760 mm. pressure

	Temp. °C	Dielectric Constant κ		Temp. °C	Dielectric Constant κ
Air	0	1.000590	Hydrogen	0	1.000264
Ammonia	0	1.0072	Oxygen	0	1.000523
Carbon dioxide	0	1.000985	Water (steam)	100	1.0126
Helium	0	1.0000684	Water (steam)	140	1.00785

Liquids

	T. °C	κ		T. °C	κ
Ammonia	20.5	15.5	Cottonseed oil	14	3.10
Benzene	20	2.283	Transformer oil	20	2.24
Ethyl acetate	20	6.4	Water	0	88
Glycerol	20	43	Water	20	80
Hydrogen	−253	1.22	Water	100	48

Solids at Room Temperature

	κ		κ
Corning Glass 0010	6.32	Pyrex 7070	4.00
Corning Glass 0080	6.75	Vycor 7911	3.8
Pyrex 7050	4.77	Quartz (fused)	3.75–4.1
Barium nitrate	5.9	Alkyd resin (plastic)	5.0
Beryl, ⊥ optic axis	7.02	Mica	2.5–7.0
Beryl, ‖ optic axis	6.08	Neoprene	4.1
Diamond	5.5	Rubber	2–3.5
Lead nitrate	37.7	Vinyl butyral resin	3.92
Naphthalene	2.52	Amber	2.65
Ruby, ⊥ optic axis	13.27	Beeswax, yellow	2.9
Ruby, ‖ optic axis	11.28	Paraffin wax	2.1–2.5
Silver chloride	11.2		

dielectric materials do not usually have free charge distributed anywhere within them, ρ_P is also zero.

Finally, observe that although **P** produced by **E** is parallel to **E** in an ideal medium, the field $\mathbf{E}_{pol}$ produced by **P** is in general not parallel to **P**, as shown by the calculations in section 3.6.

3.8 Ideal Dielectrics

Dielectric materials that are homogeneous, isotropic, and linear have a number of simple and useful properties, and we shall hereafter refer to such material as "ideal dielectrics." As indicated above, any actual material that approximates an ideal dielectric will almost certainly be a liquid or gas. We shall deal in this section with a number of applications of interest.

Consider first the capacitance of the condenser discussed in the last section. We have $P = (\kappa - 1)\epsilon_0 E$, where $E = D/\kappa\epsilon_0 = Q/S\kappa\epsilon_0$ is the field inside the dielectric. Thus eq. 3.7–1 becomes

$$V = Q\left(d - \frac{\kappa - 1}{\kappa} d'\right)\bigg/\epsilon_0 S$$

so that the capacitance Q/V is

$$C = \frac{\kappa\epsilon_0 S}{\kappa d - (\kappa - 1)\, d'} \tag{3.8–1}$$

Now, if $x = y = 0$ so that the entire space is filled with dielectric, $d = d'$ and we have

$$C = \kappa\epsilon_0 S/d \tag{3.8–2}$$

We note that the effect of the dielectric is to multiply the capacitance of the completely filled condenser by κ over the value it has when the space is evacuated.

This property is quite a general one, as we shall now show. Consider the plane case a bit further. Just below the layer of charge σ on the top plate is a layer of polarization charge $-\sigma_p = -P$ on the adjacent dielectric. Since $P = (\kappa - 1)D/\kappa$, $\sigma_p = (\kappa - 1)\sigma/\kappa$, and the *sum* of the two adjacent distributions is $\sigma_{net} = \sigma - \sigma_p = \sigma/\kappa$. Therefore the field everywhere between the condenser plates is that produced by an effective charge of $1/\kappa$ times the charge actually on the plates, so that the PD between the plates is likewise multiplied by a factor $1/\kappa$, thus accounting for the larger capacitance. (The presence of the dielectric does not of course change the amount of free charge on an insulated conductor.)

Now consider a condenser of arbitrary shape. If it is filled completely with a dielectric medium with dielectric constant κ, then at every point on the surface of either conductor, a charge density σ will produce fields **E** and **D** just outside it of the same values as those which hold throughout in the plane-parallel case, so that the same charge density $-\sigma_p$ will be induced on the adjacent dielectric. If σ varies from point to point, so will σ_p. Thus the net charge at the surface is σ/κ, whatever the value of σ. Now, the charge will distribute itself so as to make all conducting surfaces into equipotentials. This will occur with the same relative distribution as in the case of the empty condenser, for if and only if this is so will the field and potential be everywhere equal to those produced by a charge density $1/\kappa$ times that of the one actually on the conductors. All equipotentials will thus have the same shape and have the values of their potentials divided by κ.

If a condenser has a fringing field, as in the parallel-plate example, the proportionality of C to κ will only hold exactly if the dielectric material extends beyond the edges to allow all the fringing flux to pass through it, since otherwise there will be polarization charges at the extraneous boundaries that destroy the exact geometric similarity of the field patterns with and without the dielectric. Furthermore, if there is any stray flux passing to distant conductors and this flux passes out of the dielectric material, a similar result will hold. In most practical cases, however, this effect is small.

Let us consider a spherical condenser filled with an ideal dielectric. At the inner surface of radius R_1 there will be a charge density $\sigma = Q/4\pi R_1{}^2$ on the conductor and a net charge density $\sigma_{\text{net}} = Q/4\pi\kappa R_1{}^2$. The displacement D in the space between the conductors obeys the formula $D = Q/4\pi r^2$; the field is $E = Q/4\pi\kappa\epsilon_0 r^2$ where r is the radial coordinate of any point between the two conductors. Consequently P is also variable and is given by $P = (\kappa - 1)Q/4\pi\kappa r^2$. The charge densities on the outer dielectric surface and the inner surface of the outer conductor (radius R_2) are thus smaller in magnitude than at the inner surface, with $\sigma = -Q/4\pi R_2{}^2$ and $\sigma_{\text{net}} = -Q/4\pi\kappa R_2{}^2$. The capacitance is κ times that of eq. 2.7–3:

$$C = \frac{4\pi\kappa\epsilon_0 R_1 R_2}{R_2 - R_1} \tag{3.8–3}$$

If R_2 is allowed to go to infinity, we have the case of a sphere embedded in an infinite ideal dielectric. As a special case of this, consider a free point charge q surrounded by a dielectric in the presence of other free charges. We may suppose the point to be inside a small spherical cavity. If the radius of the cavity is small enough, the field at its inside surface produced by the point charge q is very much greater than that produced by distant charges, so that the polarization just outside the cavity surface is effectively that of a single isolated sphere embedded in the dielectric. That is, the field at a distant point produced by q and by the polarization charge on its cavity is the same as that produced by a charge q/κ at the same place with no dielectric present, i.e., $\mathbf{E} = q\mathbf{1}_r/4\pi\kappa\epsilon_0 r^2$.

By the principle of superposition, we can calculate $\mathbf{E}$ for a collection of free charges immersed in an infinite ideal medium according to the rule

$$\mathbf{E} = \sum_n{}' \frac{q_n \mathbf{1}_r}{4\pi\kappa\epsilon_0 r^2} \tag{3.8–4}$$

The appearance of κ in this rule may be described as a device to allow the polarization charges to enter the formula implicitly by means of κ whereas the free charges q_n appear explicitly in the usual way.

We must be careful, however, in dealing with the force exerted by such a field on another macroscopic charge q' embedded in the same medium. The force on q' depends on the field in the cavity in which it is put.   Consider two charges q and q'.   Only if q' is in a long needlelike cavity parallel to the radius drawn from q will the force be given by the formula (sometimes called "Coulomb's law for a dielectric medium"):

$$\mathbf{F} = \frac{qq'\mathbf{1}_r}{4\pi\kappa\epsilon_0 r^2} \tag{3.8-5}$$

Since the field in a coin-shaped cavity normal to $\mathbf{D}$ is equal to $\mathbf{D}/\epsilon_0$ or κ times $\mathbf{E}$ in the medium, $F = qq'/4\pi\epsilon_0 r^2$ if q' lies in such a cavity.   The case of a spherical cavity will be considered in section 3.9.

A different situation results if we define "force on a charge in a dielectric" to mean the sum of the electric forces on q' itself and on the surrounding polarization charges, plus the mechanical forces in the fluid near q' that are called into play as a reaction to the electric forces in the body of the dielectric.   This sum of forces is that which must be balanced if an external agent (e.g., gravity acting on an oil drop in a gaseous dielectric) is to move the charged body through the medium at essentially zero speed (no energy going into friction).   That this force must be equal to $q'\mathbf{E}$, with $\mathbf{E}$ the field calculated as above, can be seen if we assume conservation of energy to apply to the motion of q' around an arbitrary closed path, part in the medium and part out. (Any factor multiplying $q'\mathbf{E}$ would lead to a violation of the conservation law, since we know that $\oint \mathbf{E}\cdot\mathbf{dl} = 0$ for *any* path.)   Thus eq. 3.8-5 holds when the force on the medium is included.[14]

Another important restriction on the validity of this modified "Coulomb law" has to do with the presence of boundaries.   Our discussion so far has had to do with infinite media so that no extraneous surface polarization charges can add to the fields we have calculated.   A specific example to illustrate the effect of a boundary is that of a charge q embedded in a semi-infinite piece of ideal dielectric whose boundary is a plane.   The surface distribution and resulting field pattern are calculated in Chapter 4, section 4.3.   It is shown there that, if q is at a point $\mathcal{O}$ at a distance h from the plane boundary (Fig. 3.8a), the field $\mathbf{E}$ at points in the dielectric is the same as if there were no medium present but as if a charge q/κ resided at P and a charge $q_I = q(\kappa - 1)/\kappa(\kappa + 1)$ resided at $\mathcal{O}_I$, which is the mirror image of $\mathcal{O}$ on the other side of the plane.   The charge q_I thus produces the same field as is actually made by σ_P on the plane surface

---

[14] See the Report of the Coulomb's Law Committee, *Am. Journ. Phys.*, **18**, 6–11 and 83–84 (1950), for a more detailed discussion.

of the dielectric. For example, the field at a point $\mathcal{O}'$ nearer the plane whose distance is h' from $\mathcal{O}$ on the perpendicular to the plane is given by

$$E' = q/4\pi\kappa\epsilon_0 h'^2 - q(\kappa - 1)/4\pi\kappa(\kappa + 1)\epsilon_0(2h - h')^2$$

$$= \frac{q}{4\pi\kappa\epsilon_0 h'^2}\left[1 - \frac{\kappa - 1}{\kappa + 1}\frac{h'^2}{(2h - h')^2}\right] \tag{3.8-6}$$

For a dielectric of $\kappa = 3$, the correction to the infinite-medium result is 25% when $h' = 0.828h$ and 10% when $h' = 0.618h$.

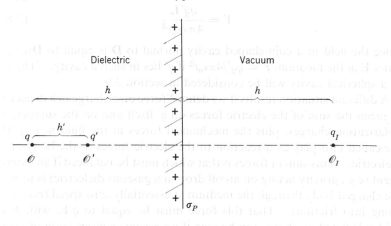

Fig. 3.8a. A charge q embedded in a dielectric near a boundary, acting on a charge q'. Charge q_I at point $\mathcal{O}_I$ is an "image charge" in terms of which the force can be calculated.

We conclude this section with the calculation of the force on a small dielectric object, such as a pith ball, in an external field. We shall consider the object to have a low susceptibility, so that the external field is not appreciably modified by the polarization of the object. Then eq. 3.7–2 can be written

$$\mathbf{P} = \chi\epsilon_0\mathbf{E}_{\text{ext}}$$

and the dipole moment of the small object is

$$\mathbf{p} = \mathbf{P}\tau$$

if its volume is τ.

The force on it by eq. 3.2–3 is

$$\mathbf{F} = (\mathbf{p} \cdot \mathbf{\nabla})\mathbf{E}_{\text{ext}} = \tau\chi\epsilon_0(\mathbf{E}_{\text{ext}} \cdot \mathbf{\nabla})\mathbf{E}_{\text{ext}}$$

The operator in parentheses calls for a derivative in the direction of $\mathbf{E}_{\text{ext}}$; let us call this direction the x-direction. Then we have

$$\mathbf{F} = \mathbf{1}_x\tau\chi\epsilon_0 E_{\text{ext}}\frac{\partial}{\partial x}E_{\text{ext}} = \tfrac{1}{2}\mathbf{1}_x\tau\chi\epsilon_0\,\partial(E_{\text{ext}}^2)/\partial x \tag{3.8-7}$$

showing that the force is parallel to the direction of the field and acts in the direction toward which the magnitude of the field increases. That is, a pith ball or similar object is always pulled into a region of stronger field, regardless of the sign of the field or the charge producing it.

Inclusion of the local field produced by the polarization, so that the restriction of low susceptibility can be removed, can be done by methods to be given in Chapter 4.

Problem 3.8a. Use the conditions 3.5–5 and 3.5–6 along with the relation 3.7–3 between **D** and **E** in ideal dielectrics to obtain a "law of refraction" for lines of **D** and **E** at a plane boundary between two dielectrics.

Problem 3.8b. Explain why the "law of refraction" referred to in the previous problem cannot be used with suitably shaped surfaces to "focus" electric fields and so strengthen them.

Problem 3.8c. Consider a long thin rod of ideal dielectric placed in an originally uniform electric field E_{dist} at an arbitrary angle with the field. Indicate on a sketch (a) the location of the surface polarization charges; (b) the direction of the field E_{local} produced in the rod by this surface charge (neglect end effects); (c) the direction of the resultant field $E_{local} + E_{dist}$; (d) the direction of **P** in the rod; and (e) the direction of the torque if any of E_{dist} on **P**. What does the rod tend to do?

Problem 3.8d. Consider by the method of the previous problem the torque on a thin plane sheet of ideal dielectric, free to rotate about an axis contained in its plane and perpendicular to the external field, and show that this torque is proportional to χ^2 when χ is small.

Problem 3.8e. A layer of neoprene 0.5 cm thick is placed in contact with two plates, each of area 30 cm². Find the capacitance of the combination, neglecting edge effects. If a PD of 100 v is placed on the capacitor, find D, E, and P in the neoprene. (See Table 3.7A.)

Problem 3.8f. If a diamond were polarized so that $P = 7.0 \times 10^{-6}$ coulomb/m², by what distance would the center of the cloud of 6 electrons on each carbon atom be shifted from the nucleus, assuming that all the carbon atoms were polarized alike? The density of diamond is 3.51 g/cm³ and 12 g of carbon contain $N_0 = 6.02 \times 10^{23}$ atoms.

Problem 3.8g. A spherical capacitor has an inner sphere of radius 12 cm and an outer sphere of inner radius 17 cm. The inner sphere is covered with 2 cm of dielectric of $\kappa = 2.0$, and the rest of the space is filled with dielectric of $\kappa = 4.0$. If 5×10^{-9} coulomb are placed on the inner sphere, find E, D, and P, as functions of r. Find also the polarization charge densities and the total polarization charge at the three boundaries. Calculate the PD between the metal spheres by integration, and find the capacitance.

Problem 3.8h. Find the capacitance of the condenser in Fig. 3.7a, if $S = 12$ cm², $d = 1.00$ mm, $d' = 0.75$ mm, and $\kappa = 2.2$.

Problem 3.8i. What would be the difference in capacitance between the two cylinders of problem 2.7e if they were both filled with benzene at 20°C?

Problem 3.8j. If the force exerted on a charge q' in a long drill hole oriented in the direction of another distant charge q imbedded in a spherical cavity in an ideal dielectric of permittivity ϵ is $qq'/4\pi\epsilon r^2$, does it follow that the force exerted on q is also of this amount? What other charges take part in each force?

Problem 3.8k. A coaxial cable has an inner conductor of o.d. (outer diameter) 0.250 in., and outer conductor of i.d. 0.600 in., and is filled with dielectric of $\kappa = 2.7$. Find its capacitance per meter.

Problem 3.8l. Find the field strength, potential, displacement, and polarization as a function of distance for a dielectric sphere of radius a and permittivity ϵ which bears a uniform volume distribution of free charge ρ. Find also the distribution of polarization charge.

Problem 3.8m. Derive a formula for the force on a small pith ball in the field of a uniformly charged sphere.

Problem 3.8n. Derive a formula for the force on a small pith ball located at a distance r from a dipole of strength p, on the axis of the dipole.

3.9   Spherical Cavities and Effective Polarizing Fields

Let us now calculate the actual or effective field E_{eff} that acts on any chosen spherical piece of material in a uniform polarized dielectric medium. As in section 3.4 we divide the material up into a small sphere and the remainder. The remainder produces a field within the sphere equal to E in the medium plus the contribution of the surface charge density P_n on the inside surface of the spherical "cavity" which contains the small sphere.

Now, this surface density is just the opposite of that on a spherical electret of the same dimensions and polarization, for the direction of the outward normals are opposite in the two cases. In fact, the material within the sphere constitutes just such an electret, the internal field of which is just $E_{sph} = -P/3\epsilon_0$, by eq. 3.6–5a.

Thus the field produced by the remainder is

$$E_{eff} = E + P/3\epsilon_0 \qquad (3.9\text{–}1)$$

For ideal dielectrics, $P = (\kappa - 1)\epsilon_0 E$, so $E_{eff} = E[1 + (\kappa - 1)/3]$ or

$$E_{eff} = \frac{\kappa + 2}{3} E \qquad (3.9\text{–}2)$$

and also, eliminating E,

$$P = \frac{3(\kappa - 1)}{\kappa + 2} \epsilon_0 E_{eff} \qquad (3.9\text{–}3)$$

This relation holds for a large enough sphere that the molecules in it have an average uniform behavior. If we let the sphere get smaller and smaller, we may come to a point where effects of local crystal structure produce a lack of spherical symmetry, and the relation ceases to be accurate. For gases and liquids, the average in both space and time of the electrical behavior of a single molecule is probably sufficiently symmetric that the equation continues to hold.   In this case, we can find the ratio α between the average moment $\mathbf{p} = \mathbf{P}/N$ for a single molecule, to $\mathbf{E}_{\text{eff}}$. This ratio, called the molecular polarizability, is given by

$$\alpha = \frac{\mathbf{p}}{\mathbf{E}_{\text{eff}}} = \frac{\mathbf{P}}{N\mathbf{E}_{\text{eff}}} = \frac{3(\kappa - 1)\epsilon_0}{(\kappa + 2)N} \qquad (3.9\text{-}4)$$

This relation is called the Clausius-Mossotti equation or sometimes (in works on optics) the Lorenz-Lorentz equation.   It is useful chiefly for gases in which κ is close to unity, and α can be written approximately as $(\kappa - 1)\epsilon_0/N = \chi\epsilon_0/N$.

The Field in a Spherical Cavity.   Now let us consider what would happen if the material in one of these spherical regions were removed. The field in the remainder of the material will include, in addition to the original $\mathbf{E}$, a contribution equal to that outside of a spherical polarized electret, which as we saw in section 3.6 is a dipole field.   The strength of this field near the sphere is of the same order of magnitude as $\mathbf{P}/\epsilon_0 = \chi\mathbf{E}$ (cf. problem 3.6g).   Thus if χ is not too small, this added field will change $\mathbf{P}$ substantially in the neighborhood of the cavity, and our calculation will be incorrect.

Let us try guessing what the correct field might be near such a spherical cavity, assuming the original $\mathbf{E}$ to be uniform.   The resultant surface distribution must produce a field and a polarization that maintains itself. Perhaps the resultant distribution makes a dipole field in the medium of different strength from that just mentioned.   Since it will act, if this is correct, as a dipole oriented in the opposite direction to $\mathbf{E}$, let us assume that the equivalent dipole is some vector $-\mathbf{p}$.   The combination of the field of $\mathbf{E}$ and $-\mathbf{p}$ must produce a surface charge density $P_n = -\mathbf{P} \cdot \mathbf{1}_r$ on the cavity whose resultant field is that of $-\mathbf{p}$.

From the spherical electret calculation, eq. 3.6–6, we see that $-\mathbf{P} \cdot \mathbf{1}_r$ must equal $-\mathbf{p} \cdot \mathbf{1}_r / \tfrac{4}{3}\pi a^3$.   On the other hand, we know that the radial component of electric field in the medium next to the boundary of the cavity is $-2\mathbf{p} \cdot \mathbf{1}_r / 4\pi\epsilon_0 a^3 + \mathbf{E} \cdot \mathbf{1}_r$, using eq. 3.1–7a for the dipole field. Then $-\mathbf{P} \cdot \mathbf{1}_r$ is $-\chi\epsilon_0$ times this, giving the radial component equation

$$-\frac{\mathbf{p} \cdot \mathbf{1}_r}{\tfrac{4}{3}\pi a^3} = -\chi\epsilon_0 \left(-\frac{2\mathbf{p} \cdot \mathbf{1}_r}{4\pi\epsilon_0 a^3} + \mathbf{E} \cdot \mathbf{1}_r \right)$$

which will be satisfied if the vectors are related by

$$\mathbf{p} = -\tfrac{2}{3}\chi\mathbf{p} + \tfrac{4}{3}\pi a^3 \chi\epsilon_0\mathbf{E}$$

Solving for **p**, we obtain

$$\mathbf{p} = \frac{\frac{4}{3}\pi a^3 \chi \epsilon_0 \mathbf{E}}{\frac{2}{3}\chi + 1} = \frac{4\pi a^3 \epsilon_0 \mathbf{E}(\kappa - 1)}{2\kappa + 1} \tag{3.9-5}$$

and the field in the cavity is

$$\mathbf{E}_{\text{sph cav}} = \mathbf{E} - \left(\frac{-\mathbf{p}}{\frac{4}{3}\pi a^3} \cdot \frac{1}{3\epsilon_0}\right) = \mathbf{E}\left(1 + \frac{\kappa - 1}{2\kappa + 1}\right)$$
$$= \mathbf{E}\left(\frac{3\kappa}{2\kappa + 1}\right) \tag{3.9-6}$$

For $\kappa = 1$, we see that the medium has no effect, whereas for very large κ, $\mathbf{E}_{\text{sph cav}} = \frac{3}{2}\mathbf{E}$.

We shall see in Chapter 4 (problem 4.3n) that the field found by this guesswork process is indeed the correct one. We have used a form of the image method, but the calculation can be carried out as in Chapter 4 by use of solutions of Laplace's equation with appropriate boundary conditions.

Problem 3.9a. Find α for diamond (see problem 3.8f).

Problem 3.9b. Two point charges q and q' are located in spherical cavities in a piece of dielectric material, far from any boundaries. The diameters of the cavities are small enough compared to the distances between their centers that the field of each charge and cavity may be treated as uniform at the other cavity. Find the forces on each charge, and account for them in terms of both bound and free charges.

3.10   Dielectric Relaxation, Breakdown, and Other Effects

Real dielectrics are characterized by various types of behavior that complicate the simple picture we have presented of ideal dielectrics. We have referred briefly to departures from homogeneity and isotropism and wish in this section to consider several other characteristics.

Dielectric Relaxation. It takes a finite time in many polar materials for the polarization to reach its maximum value. This is because the forces between adjacent molecules tend to prevent their being readily turned around under the action of $\mathbf{E}_{\text{eff}}$, so that they turn in individual "quantum jumps," occurring at random times. The average time for this "relaxation" varies from substance to substance over an enormous range, values from 10^{-10} sec to several thousand years having been reported.

One consequence of this effect is that a condenser containing such materials when suddenly connected to a potential difference V will acquire charge at a finite rate, much as if κ and C increased during the charging time from low values corresponding to polarization only by electron shift to final higher values corresponding to polarization by both electron shift and polar molecule rotation. On discharge, an inverse effect occurs. For instance, if a condenser is charged and quickly discharged and then left with terminals open, it will later be found to have acquired a potential difference between its plates (problem 3.10c).

Another consequence of the relaxation time is the phenomenon of hysteresis with alternating fields, namely, that the polarization lags behind the field in its variations. Because of the resulting heat transfer in the quantum jumps (a phenomenon that can properly be called "friction") there is a loss of electric energy, which is of considerable importance at high frequencies.

Finite Conductivity. Some dielectric materials have sufficient conductance for the resulting currents to produce noticeable energy loss in the form of heat. This loss and the hysteresis loss are referred to jointly as "dielectric losses." The term "condenser losses" may also include energy losses due to the resistance of the plates and connecting wires.

Another consequence of finite conductivity is the appearance of an absorption effect in condensers similar to the relaxation phenomenon. If a condenser contains two layers of material between its plates that have different conductivities (even if nominally the same substance), the currents in the two parts will in general be unequal at the start. As a result, charge will pile up at the interface between the two layers until the resulting additional field is enough to balance the currents. Even if the currents are too small to notice, the build up of charge appears as a change in C with time with an opposite effect at the time of discharge. (See problem 5.8a for details of a calculation.) This effect together with the similar one resulting from dielectric polarization, is called "dielectric absorption."[15]

Electret Behavior. Real electrets can be prepared by subjecting thin molten layers of various waxes to a high field ($\sim 10^6$ v/m) and allowing the material to solidify while the field is on. For some materials, a relatively constant polarization is thus frozen in. For others, what appears to be a complicated combination of dielectric relaxation and local ionic conduction results in a gradual loss of the original apparent polarization (called the "homocharge") and the building up of polarization of the opposite sign (the "heterocharge"). This latter polarization seems to be quite permanent, such disk electrets having been kept for three years or more without change of their characteristics.

---

[15] For details on dielectrics used in capacitors of various types, see M. Brotherton, *Capacitors*, D. Van Nostrand, Princeton, 1946; F. E. Terman, *Radio Engineering Handbook*, McGraw-Hill, New York, 1943, pp. 109–112 and 119–128. For standard condensers, see F. K. Harris, *Electrical Measurements*, John Wiley, New York, 1952, pp. 673–687.

However, if such a disk electret is allowed to stand uncovered, it appears to lose its surface charges $\pm\sigma_P$, an effect evidently due to the absorption of ions from the atmosphere. If metal plates are placed on the two sides and connected together, the absorbed charges will gradually migrate to the plates and neutralize each other, bringing the electret back to its original condition. Normally, an electret is stored with such "short-circuiting" plates in place. It is interesting to note that, if the plates are originally uncharged and then placed on opposite sides of the disk, a spark may be obtained when they are connected. However, energy cannot be drawn from the electret as from a battery. The reader will find it instructive to locate the source of energy in the spark. (Problem 3.10a.)

Variations of κ with Temperature and Pressure. It can be shown by use of statistical mechanics that the molecular polarizability α is the sum of a part independent of temperature, and one inversely proportional to the absolute temperature:

$$\alpha = \alpha_0 + p^2_{\text{perm}}/3kT \tag{3.10-1}$$

In this equation α_0 is the contribution to the polarizability of the electron shifting process, and $p^2_{\text{perm}}/3kT$ is that due to molecular rotation, which is clearly the temperature-dependent part. Careful experiments have verified both the form of eq. 3.10–1 and the constants.[16] The constant α_0 can be calculated in certain cases from atomic theory, and p_{perm} is the permanent dipole moment of the molecules, also calculable in some instances. The quantity k is the thermodynamic constant known as Boltzmann's constant and T is the absolute temperature. The value of p_{perm} for different substances ranges roughly from 0.10 to 2.0 $\times$ 10^{-18} electrostatic unit,[17] corresponding to the displacement of one electronic unit of charge by 0.02 to 0.4 $\times$ 10^{-8} cm.

Another way to change κ for a given piece of dielectric is to subject it to mechanical stress. Conversely, when dielectrics are polarized by external fields, a change in size is observed unless prevented by mechanical stress. This effect is known as "electrostriction" and must be taken into account in the proper study of the forces on charged conductors embedded in fluids.

Ferroelectricity. Ferroelectricity is a phenomenon that bears at least a superficial resemblance to ferromagnetism (sections 8.5 and 8.6), after which it takes its name. Typical materials exhibiting this behavior are

---

[16] F. Gutmann, *Revs. Mod. Phys.*, **20**, 487, 1948; W. F. G. Swann, *Journ. Frank. Inst.*, **255**, 513 (1953). Panofsky and Phillips, *op. cit.*, pp. 34–35; Van Vleck, *op. cit.*, Chapter III.

[17] Van Vleck, *op. cit.*, pp. 66, 67.

Rochelle salt and barium titanate.   The strong tendency in these materials for the elementary dipoles to hold each other in alignment is shown by hysteresis effects, in which changes in **D** tend to lag behind changes in **E**. Ferroelectric polarization tends to get masked by the absorption of free charge, just as with electrets, so that variations of **P** are more easily observed than absolute values.   The phenomenon of pyroelectricity, in which materials become polarized on heating, is an example of ferroelectric behavior in which only the temperature variation is detectable.

Ferroelectric materials, unlike electrets, obtain their behavior from their crystal structure, and have a so-called Curie temperature, above which they do not demonstrate their tendency for dipole alignment.   These materials can show very large polarizations for small applied fields, having effective dielectric constants of several thousand or more.   They often show a "domain" structure similar to that of ferromagnetic materials, with different regions in a crystal polarized in different directions.

There also exist materials called "antiferroelectric" which contain lines of ions all polarized in the same direction, but with neighboring lines alternating in their polarity, so that the over-all polarization is held to very low average values.[18]

Piezoelectricity.   This is an effect that occurs on the application of mechanical stress to certain anisotropic crystals.   Not only does κ change, but also a fixed polarization may result.   The mechanical stresses set up in such crystals by electric fields are not isotropic and are quantitatively different from ordinary electrostriction.   These last two effects are jointly referred to as "piezoelectricity."   Materials showing these effects to a marked degree are called "piezoelectric materials."   Quartz and Rochelle salt are the two most important.

Properly cut and ground crystals of quartz, for instance, will develop a polarization along a certain direction when compressed along another axis at right angles to the former.   Such crystals can be used to convert sound waves or the mechanical vibration of a phonograph needle into varying currents in and out of a condenser into which the crystal has been inserted.   A certain amount of electrical energy can be turned into mechanical energy of vibration by the inverse process, generating sound waves.   This process is particularly useful in the field of ultrasonics.[19]

Dielectric Breakdown.   This is the last property of real dielectrics we wish to discuss, and indeed the most important.   For any material there

[18] Further information on ferroelectricity may be found in G. Shirane, F. Jona, and R. Pepinsky, *Proc. Inst. Radio Engrs.*, **43,** 1738 (1955).   C. Kittel, *Introduction to Solid State Physics*, 2nd ed., John Wiley, New York, 1956, Chapter 8.

[19] For further details on piezoelectricity, see W. G. Cady, *Piezoelectricity*, McGraw-Hill, New York, 1946.

is a maximum field intensity beyond which damage occurs that results in conduction, sparking, and other breakdown phenomena.

At relatively high fields, the electrons in the filled bands (cf. section 2.1), as well as the few available conduction electrons or ions can gain enough

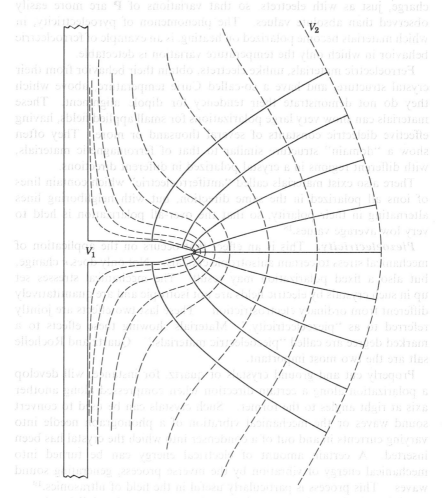

Fig. 3.10a. A conductor with a sharp point showing equipotentials and lines of force.

energy (by successive quantum jumps or single large ones) to be able to knock other charged particles loose and make them available for conduction. The process can in some instances reach a constant state of fairly steady current, but usually a multiplying or "cascading" process results, producing an "avalanche" of conducting particles that are produced along certain paths in the material. Local heating also occurs along these paths, and permanent damage results. Spark holes or punctures appear and the insulating qualities are greatly impaired.

Electrostatic apparatus that operates at high potentials, as most of it does, depends for its operation on the quality of the insulation with respect to breakdown (and of course with respect to conductivity). Air is the most common insulating material. Its breakdown occurs, when dry and at standard temperature and pressure (0° C and 760 mm Hg) at fields of about 3×10^6 v/m or 100 statv/cm. Fields somewhat less than this may produce some steady discharging currents known as "corona." The value quoted gives roughly the field for which disruptive sparking occurs.

The discharge of electricity is sometimes to be promoted rather than discouraged. For this purpose, conductors with sharp points can be used. We can show readily that the field near a sharp point is much larger than at other places on the conductor, so that corona and sparking most readily occur at these points. Consider the conductor shown in Fig. 3.10a, with a "point" which is a hemisphere of radius R on the tip of a cone.

It will be observed that the flux density at the surface of the point is much larger than elsewhere in the diagram. Consequently, when the field intensity is not unreasonably large over most of the region, it may nevertheless come to or above the breakdown value near the point. The lines of force near the point are like those for a sphere, and so we can use the result for a sphere (problem 2.3c) that just outside it, $E = V/a$ where a is the radius. If V is about 300 v, and $a = 0.1$ mm $- 10^{-4}$m, $E - 3 \times 10^6$ v/m, and breakdown will occur.

The operation of lightning rods and brush discharge points in electrostatic generators is based on this principle.

Problem 3.10a. Describe the charge and field distributions that occur when neutral metal plates are put on both sides of a disk electret. What happens when the plates are joined? What is the source of the energy in the spark that occurs?

Problem 3.10b. Show that the field in a depression on the outer surface of a conductor must be weaker than that at a nearby plane region, in contrast to the strengthening of the field at protuberances.

Problem 3.10c. Explain how the finite relaxation time for dielectric materials can lead to the appearance of a PD across a capacitor after it has been discharged.

Problem 3.10d. Use the result of problem 1.7n to justify more accurately the use of $E = V/a$ for the spherical tip in Fig. 3.10a.

Problem 3.10e. Calculate the maximum charge carried by a unit area of the belt of a Van de Graaff generator in air at atmospheric pressure if the field just outside the belt is 60% of the mean breakdown field for air.

Problem 3.10f. It is proposed to increase the charging rate of a Van de Graaff generator by using several belts that run inside one another. Show by use of the flux law that, if the belts are to be charged until the maximum field in air is just attained in their neighborhood, improvement can be obtained by neighboring belts running in alternate directions with alternate signs of charge, but not if they all run in the same direction.

Problem 3.10g.   The inside of the grounded tank of a Van de Graaff generator near the high voltage end is a spherical surface of radius R.   Show that the maximum PD between it and a concentric spherical high-voltage terminal inside the tank can be achieved, for a fixed value of the gas-breakdown field strength, if the high voltage terminal is a sphere of radius $R/2$.

4

Further
Topics
in
Electrostatics

4.1 Introduction

There are two general types of calculations in electrostatics that we have not yet discussed and wish to consider in this chapter. These are the question of how the charge is distributed on a given set of conductors when the potential or total charge on each is known and the question of the dependence of the potential energy of a system of charged conductors on their charges, potentials and positions. These problems are related because, first, the theory for each depends on the same general uniqueness theorem; second, in each case the potentials V and net charges Q of the conductors are taken to be the determining factors in the situation; and third, the coefficients of capacitance and potential that we shall introduce for the energy considerations must in general be calculated by the same methods that solve the distribution problem.

We shall start with a statement of the uniqueness theorem and a general survey of the methods of solving the distribution problem. Next we shall deal with some relatively simple but quite important distribution calculations. Finally we shall take up the general energy problem and arrive at useful methods for finding the forces on charged conductors.

4.2 The General Uniqueness Theorem for Electrostatics

In section 2.3, we proved that a given set of charges $Q_1, Q_2 \cdots Q_n$ applied to a set of conductors can distribute themselves in only one way. We wish to generalize this theorem because we frequently know the potential of a given conductor, rather than the charge on it. For simplicity, we may think that each conductor we have to consider is connected to one terminal of a set of batteries that have their other terminals grounded, so that the conductors are individually maintained at definite potentials $V_1, V_2 \cdots V_n$. The mechanism whereby batteries can maintain these potentials is irrelevant here (it will be discussed in sections 5.2 and 6.4).

The conditions for our general uniqueness theorem are that we are given the charges $Q_1, Q_2 \cdots Q_n$ on n conductors and the potentials $V_{n+1} \cdots V_{n+m}$ on m other conductors. We may further allow the presence of any number of fixed and known point charges $q_a, q_b \cdots$ and finally allow the space between the conductors to be filled in an arbitrary known way with ideal dielectric materials.[1] The theorem we wish to prove states that under these given conditions there is one and only one way in which charge is distributed over all the conducting surfaces, with therefore one and only one resulting field in the entire region under consideration.

Consider first the case in which we have the V's known for all the conductors, with empty space between them. Suppose we have two fields, the potential for each of which reduces to the appropriate value at the surface of each conductor. For instance, one field might have been obtained experimentally by connecting the conductors to the batteries in some arbitrary order and plotting the field by the straw needle or gypsum crystal line-of-force method, or the probe and electrostatic voltmeter method (see footnote on p. 47). The other field might then be a mathematically invented one—e.g., derived from a potential function $V(x, y, z)$ that was constructed in a mathematical fashion so as to yield the correct V's at each conductor, and at the same time to provide a field $-\nabla V$ in the intervening space that obeys the flux law. We can then calculate the corresponding local charge densities on each conductor from $\sigma = -\epsilon_0(\nabla V)_n$.

---

[1] The requirement that the materials be ideal is not necessary if the component of **D** parallel to **E** is restricted to being in the same sense as **E**, the materials are linear, and they show no significant relaxation or hysteresis phenomena.

Now, if the two fields differ from each other at any points in the intervening space, we subtract the two at each point to get a hypothetical third one. The potential of this hypothetical field will be zero on all conductors, but from the conditions given there may be non-vanishing charge densities $\sigma_1 \cdots \sigma_n$. However, application of the flux law will show that this is impossible. Both given fields obey this law, so the difference must. Flux cannot begin and end on a single conductor. In this case, it also cannot begin on one conductor and end on another or at infinity because all are at zero potential. So there can be no flux or field anywhere, and the two original fields and corresponding charge distributions are identical.

Now suppose we have m conductors with V's given and n with known Q's. Again consider two possible fields, of which one might be a mathematically constructed one, this time with $Q_i = \epsilon_0 \int_{S_i} \mathbf{E} \cdot \mathbf{dS}$ specified on the surface S_i of the ith conductor with known charge. The subtraction yields a set of m conductors of zero potential, and another set (of n conductors) with unknown potentials but zero net charges. The same argument used in section 2.3 applies here—namely, that there can be no highest or lowest potential among the n conductors, so that all $n + m$ must be at zero potential, and we can then use the argument of the previous paragraph to prove that the field is zero.

The addition of fixed point charges does not affect the arguments above because both the charges and the fields in their neighborhoods cancel on subtraction. The introduction of dielectric materials requires us to use the flux of $\mathbf{D}$ rather than of $\mathbf{E}$ in the arguments but makes no essential change. Thus we have proved the theorem in quite a general way.

By means of this theorem, we have reduced the distribution problem to that of finding by any mathematical means available a potential function whose gradient obeys the flux law and which satisfies the proper *boundary conditions*, namely:

1. The reduction to constant potential over the surface of each conductor.
2. The provision of the proper Q or V at each conductor.
3. The provision for the existence of whatever point charges are specified.
4. The proper conditions on $\mathbf{D}$ and $\mathbf{E}$ at any dielectric boundary or interface.

Three general methods for constructing such fields deserve mention here.

A. Fields may be constructed in "patchwork" fashion by finding simple arrangements of point charges that happen to have one or more equipotential surfaces of suitable shapes and then replacing the volumes inside or outside these particular equipotentials with regions of constant potential. A modification consists of matching two different free-space fields at a given surface in such a way as to fit the dielectric interface boundary conditions of the actual problem.   This approach is called the "method of images" and will be considered in the next three sections.

B. One may construct solutions by suitable use of the conditions that $-\nabla V$ must obey the flux law in the space outside the free charges, namely Laplace's equation $\nabla^2 V = 0$.   This approach involves a systematic study of solutions of this equation with various sorts of symmetry and then the selection of solutions that in proper combinations will satisfy the boundary conditions.   A brief introduction to it will be given in section 4.6.

C. In two dimensions, when V is for instance independent of the variable z, Laplace's equation becomes

$$\frac{\partial^2 V}{\partial x^2} + \frac{\partial^2 V}{\partial y^2} = 0 \qquad (4.2\text{--}1)$$

There exist some very powerful methods based on the theory of complex variables for the generation of solutions of eq. 4.2–1 that fit many different boundaries.   We shall not take up this method, however, and refer the reader to other books.[2]

4.3   Point and Plane Image Calculations

The simplest application of the method of images has in effect already been presented, namely, the case of the charged spherical conductor of radius R in a vacuum.   A field that fits the conditions for this conductor may be invented by taking the field of a point charge Q, placed at the location of the sphere's center, but using this field only at distances equal to or greater than R.   An interior region of constant potential (zero field) is patched on to the point charge field at the radius R.   The resultant field satisfies conditions 1, 3, and 4.   If the charge Q at the center equals the given charge on the conductor, or if $Q = 4\pi\epsilon_0 RV$ where V is the given potential, condition 2 is satisfied as we already know.

We could describe the situation by saying that we start with a point charge and then wipe out the field between it and one of its equipotentials, *transferring the charge to the equipotential surface* since we now must allow

[2] L. Page and N. I. Adams, Jr., *Principles of Electricity*, 3rd ed., D. Van Nostrand, Princeton, 1958, pp. 92–96; G. P. Harnwell, *Principles of Electricity and Electromagnetism*, 2nd ed., McGraw-Hill, New York, 1949, pp. 37–43; W. K. H. Panofsky and M. Phillips, *Classical Electricity and Magnetism*, Addison-Wesley, Cambridge, Mass., 1953, Chapter 4.

the same flux to end or begin there that originally went to or from the point.   The charge at the center that appears to be there from the outside, but really is not, is similar to a virtual image in optics, and we shall call it an "image charge."

The next simplest case is that of two equal and opposite point charges. One equipotential between them has a simple shape, namely, the plane of symmetry, for which $V = 0$.   Thus we can create a field that satisfies the

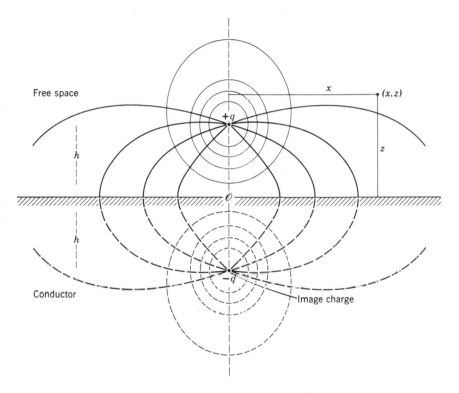

Fig. 4.3a.   A charge q outside a conducting plane, and its image.

conditions for a point charge outside an infinite plane conductor.   In Fig. 4.3a the charge outside the conductor is positive, and the original negative charge is the image.

The potential at a point (x, z) above the conductor may be found as in Chapter 1, namely

$$V(x, z) = \frac{q}{4\pi\epsilon_0[x^2 + (z - h)^2]^{\frac{1}{2}}} - \frac{q}{4\pi\epsilon_0[x^2 + (z + h)^2]^{\frac{1}{2}}} \qquad (4.3\text{--}1)$$

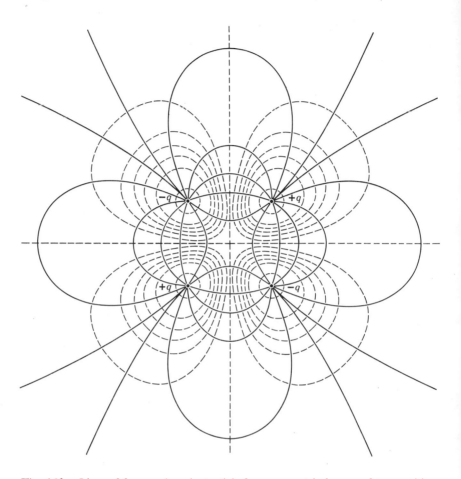

Fig. 4.3b. Lines of force and equipotentials for a symmetrical array of two positive and two negative charges. (Adapted from E. Durand, *Électrostatique et Magnétostatique*, Masson et Cie, Paris, 1953, Fig. 37.)

The value of σ on the surface of the conductor can be found from $\sigma = -\epsilon_0 \left(\dfrac{\partial V}{\partial z} \right)_{z=0}$. The result is

$$\sigma = -\frac{hq}{2\pi(x^2 + h^2)^{\frac{3}{2}}} \tag{4.3-2}$$

The charge density and potential are of course symmetric with respect to rotation about the line joining q and $-q$.

The force acting on q can be calculated immediately from Coulomb's law and the distance $2h$ between charge and image.   That is,

$$\mathbf{F} = -\mathbf{1}_z \frac{q^2}{16\pi\epsilon_0 h^2} \qquad (4.3\text{-}3)$$

This case is considered further in problems 4.3b, c, and d.

If we have two or more point charges outside a plane, we can solve the problem by adding the potentials of the corresponding charge pairs.   The images in this case make collectively a mirror image of the original distribution of charges.

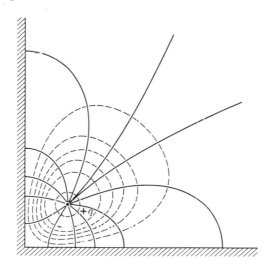

Fig. 4.3c.   Lines of force and equipotentials for a charge $+q$ in the space between two conducting planes that intersect at right angles (adapted from Durand, *loc. cit.*).

A more complicated case can be solved by use of the field of the four charges of Fig. 1.6f, shown with equipotentials in Figs. 4.3b and c.   The zero equipotential consists of two intersecting planes.   The field can be wiped out in three quadrants, leaving us with the case of two conducting half planes intersecting at right angles and having a single point charge located somewhere in the smaller angle between them—it does not have to be on a 45° line (problem 4.3e).

Images with Dielectrics.   Let us now show the application of this method to the problem of a point charge in a dielectric medium with a plane boundary.   We are given a point charge q embedded in a small spherical cavity in an ideal dielectric of constant κ, at a distance h from the infinite plane boundary (Fig. 4.3d; cf. Fig. 3.8a).   The other boundaries of the dielectric are at infinity. Positive bound charge will appear at the surface, because of the polarization, and lead to a field that is certainly more complicated than that of a simple point charge.

We shall try to construct a field that solves the problem in patchwork fashion, by guessing that in the vacuum, region 2, the field is given by a point image q_2 located at some distance h_2 from the boundary along the axis of symmetry as shown in Fig. 4.3e and that in region 1 the field is

Fig. 4.3d. A charge imbedded in   **Fig. 4.3e.** Image and field for
a dielectric near a boundary.   region 2.

produced both by q/κ at h in accordance with the calculation of section 3.8 and by an image q_1 in the vacuum at distance h_1 from the interface, as in Fig. 4.3f. (This latter image is to have effect only in the region in which it is not located.) We assume that only these particular point images are present—i.e., no polarization charges and no dielectric media add to our calculated fields. Then we can write for the potential at a point (x, y) in the plane of the paper

Region 1, $x < 0$: $\displaystyle V = \frac{q/\kappa}{4\pi\epsilon_0[(x + h)^2 + y^2]^{\frac{1}{2}}} + \frac{q_1}{4\pi\epsilon_0[(h_1 - x)^2 + y^2]^{\frac{1}{2}}}$

Region 2, $x > 0$: $\displaystyle V = \frac{q_2}{4\pi\epsilon_0[(x + h_2)^2 + y^2]^{\frac{1}{2}}}$

At the interface, we must have the same value of V from the two expressions, a more complicated statement of which is that $-\partial V/\partial y = E_t$ is the same on both sides. Setting the V's equal for $x = 0$ gives

$$\frac{q/\kappa}{(h^2 + y^2)^{\frac{1}{2}}} + \frac{q_1}{(h_1^2 + y^2)^{\frac{1}{2}}} = \frac{q_2}{(h_2^2 + y^2)^{\frac{1}{2}}} \qquad (4.3\text{–}4)$$

For very large y, we can neglect the h's, so that we must have

$$q/\kappa + q_1 = q_2 \qquad (4.3\text{–}5)$$

Furthermore, eq. 4.3–4 cannot hold for all y unless

$$h = h_1 = h_2 \qquad (4.3\text{–}6)$$

for otherwise we could write down an infinite number of inconsistent equations relating the three charges.

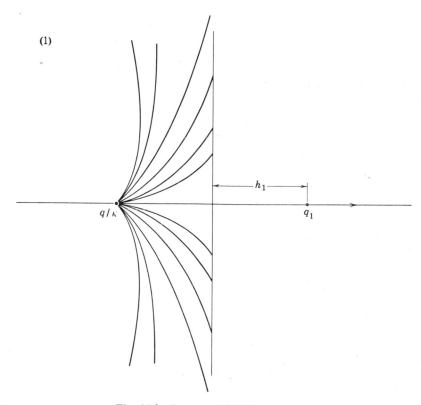

Fig. 4.3f.   Image and field for region 1.

The other boundary condition is that $D_{n1} = D_{n2}$, or $\kappa(\partial V/\partial x)_{x\to 0-} = (\partial V/\partial x)_{x\to 0+}$. We obtain from this equation after using eq. 4.3–6 and dividing out common terms

$$q - \kappa q_1 = q_2 \qquad (4.3\text{–}7)$$

From eqs. 4.3–5 and 4.3–7 we obtain finally

$$q_1 = \frac{\kappa - 1}{\kappa(\kappa + 1)} q \qquad (4.3\text{–}8)$$

$$q_2 = \frac{2}{\kappa + 1} q$$

so that the resultant expression for the potential is

$$\text{Region 1, } x < 0: \quad V = \frac{q}{4\pi\kappa\epsilon_0} \left[\frac{1}{[(x + h)^2 + y^2]^{\frac{1}{2}}} \right.$$

$$\left. + \frac{\kappa - 1}{(\kappa + 1)[(x - h)^2 + y^2]^{\frac{1}{2}}} \right] \tag{4.3-9}$$

$$\text{Region 2, } x > 0: \quad V = \frac{2q}{4\pi(\kappa + 1)\epsilon_0[(x + h)^2 + y^2]^{\frac{1}{2}}}$$

The reader can readily (problem 4.3h) verify that the surface density of polarization charge is

$$\sigma_P = \frac{(\kappa - 1)h}{2\pi\kappa(\kappa + 1)(h^2 + y^2)^{\frac{3}{2}}} q \tag{4.3-10}$$

We have thus found the solution to the distribution of polarization and field when a point charge is embedded in a large piece of dielectric near a plane surface, a solution anticipated near the end of section 3.8. More details for this case are taken up in problems 4.3*i* and *j*.

Problem 4.3a.   Consider the case of a conducting sphere of radius R surrounded by a spherical shell of ideal dielectric of bounding radii R and R' ($R' > R$) as a case to be solved by image charges at the center, and show how to obtain the appropriate field.

Problem 4.3b.   Prove by direct integration of σ that the total charge on the plane of Fig. 4.3*a* is $-q$.

Problem 4.3c.   Solve the problem of the point and conducting plane without using the method of images, using the division of fields near the conducting surface into local and distant, and considering that the *distant* field of the charge on the plane must have no component normal to the plane.

Problem 4.3d.   Discuss the point-and-conducting-plane image case when the entire space outside the conductor is filled with an ideal dielectric.

✓ **Problem 4.3e.**   Find the charge densities for an unsymmetrical case of Fig. 4.3*c* directly under the foot of the perpendicular from the charge q on each plane, where q is one electronic unit, distant 2×10^{-8} m from one surface and 3×10^{-8} m from the other.   What is the charge density at the intersection of the planes?

Problem 4.3f.   For what other angles than $90°$ can the method of images be used to find the field when a point charge is placed between two intersecting planes?   Discuss and give an example.

Problem 4.3g.   Make a sketch showing the images needed when two point charges are arbitrarily located in a $60°$ angle between two conducting planes.

Problem 4.3h.   Verify eq. 4.3–10.

Problem 4.3i.   Calculate the total polarization charge that appears on the surface in Fig. 4.3*d*, from eq. 4.3–10.   Verify this result from the flux theorem, considering that one-half the flux of the image q_2 appears to come through the plane and that this flux actually comes from q and the polarization charges near q and on the plane.

Problem 4.3j.   Calculate the angle through which a line of force is "refracted" at a point on the plane of Fig. 4.3d whose distance from the origin is 0.30 m, when $h = 0.50$ m, $q = 2 \times 10^{-9}$ coulomb, and $\kappa = 3.0$.

Problem 4.3k.   Find the distribution of polarization on the plane surface of a very large piece of ideal dielectric when a point charge q is located a small distance h from the plane, *outside* the material.

Problem 4.3l.   Find the force with which the dielectric material attracts q in problem 4.3k.

✓ **Problem 4.3m.**   Find the work necessary to take an electron from a point 1 Ångstrom unit (10^{-10} m) outside a metal surface to infinity.   Is a factor 2 needed because of the image charge?   What is the field E that acts on q?   What does the fact that E depends on q signify?

Problem 4.3n.   Verify that the solution given in section 3.9 for the field in a spherical cavity in a piece of dielectric is correct in accordance with the method of images.

Problem 4.3o.   Part of the work function of a metal is the work done against the image force with which an electron at a distance x outside a piece of metal is attracted inward.   Find that potential as a function of x that would give the same force on the electron (this effective potential is sometimes called the "motive").   If this potential is combined with that due to a uniform field E just outside the metal and directed toward it, a maximum of the total potential energy for the electron can be found somewhere outside the metal.   The work function in the presence of E is therefore reduced to the work necessary to get an electron from the Fermi level up to this maximum.   Prove that the amount $\Delta\phi$ by which ϕ is reduced is $e(eE/4\pi\epsilon_0)^{\frac{1}{2}}$.

4.4   Point and Sphere Image Calculations

Careful examination of the equipotential diagrams for pairs of opposite but unequal charges, such as Fig. 1.11e, will reveal that one equipotential surface has a simple shape.   Specifically, the surface for $V = 0$ is a sphere. To show this, consider the potential produced by charges q_1 and q_2 of opposite signs located on the x-axis at distances x_1 and x_2 from the origin. We have at the point (x, y, z)

$$V = \frac{q_1}{4\pi\epsilon_0[(x - x_1)^2 + y^2 + z^2]^{\frac{1}{2}}} + \frac{q_2}{4\pi\epsilon_0[(x - x_2)^2 + y^2 + z^2]^{\frac{1}{2}}} \quad (4.4\text{-}1)$$

When V is zero, this expression can be considerably simplified, the radicals disappearing with only one operation of squaring.   The result can be written

$$q_2^2[(x - x_1)^2 + y^2 + z^2] - q_1^2[(x - x_2)^2 + y^2 + z^2] = 0$$

which is the equation of a sphere, since the coefficients of x^2, y^2, and z^2

are all equal to $q_2{}^2 - q_1{}^2$. The center of the sphere will be at the origin if the coefficient of x is zero, that is, if $q_1{}^2 x_2 = q_2{}^2 x_1$ or

$$\frac{q_1{}^2}{q_2{}^2} = \frac{x_1}{x_2} \tag{4.4–2}$$

so for convenience we shall assume this to be true; furthermore since x_1 and x_2 are of the same sign, we will take them to be both positive and let $x_1 < x_2$ so that $q_1{}^2 < q_2{}^2$. The equation of the zero equipotential then becomes

$$x^2 + y^2 + z^2 = \frac{x_2{}^2 q_1{}^2 - x_1{}^2 q_2{}^2}{q_2{}^2 - q_1{}^2} = x_2 q_1{}^2 \frac{x_2 - x_1}{q_2{}^2 - q_1{}^2} = x_2{}^2 \frac{q_1{}^2}{q_2{}^2} \tag{4.4–3}$$

simplifying by means of eq. 4.4–2. The radius R of the sphere is

$$R = x_2 \left(-\frac{q_1}{q_2} \right) = (x_1 x_2)^{\frac{1}{2}} = x_1 \left(-\frac{q_2}{q_1} \right) \tag{4.4–4}$$

where the minus sign is needed to make R positive. Thus we have $x_2 = -R q_2/q_1$ and $x_1 = -R q_1/q_2$, with $x_1 < R$ and $x_2 > R$. We have therefore a spherical equipotential of radius R and potential value $V = 0$, produced by a charge q_1 at a distance $R(-q_1/q_2)$ from the center inside the sphere and a charge q_2 of opposite sign at a further distance $R(-q_2/q_1)$ along the same radius outside the sphere. We can wipe out the field inside and distribute q_1 on the surface of a spherical conductor of radius R, or wipe out the field outside and put q_2 on the inside surface of a spherical cavity of the same dimensions. (In this latter case the potential at "infinity" can be zero or any other value, namely the potential of the conductor in question.) The surface charge density can again be calculated from $\sigma = \epsilon_0 E$, with E at the conducting surface derived from q_1 and q_2. Calculations for these cases are asked for in problems 4.4b, c, and d.

A more general field with a spherical equipotential may be obtained with three point charges. Let us place q_3 at the center of the sphere of radius R discussed above. At the surface of the sphere we now have the sum of the original value $V = 0$ and the added value $V = q_3/4\pi\epsilon_0 R$. Thus we have, outside the sphere, a field which gives a constant potential $V = q_3/4\pi\epsilon_0 R$ over a sphere of radius R, implies a total charge on the sphere $Q = q_1 + q_3$, and involves a point charge q_2 at a distance $R(-q_2/q_1)$ from the center of the sphere. The field can be calculated from q_2 and the two images, q_3 at the center and q_1 at a radius $R(-q_1/q_2)$ from the center.

If we are given the radius of the sphere and the value and location of q_2, it remains to specify either Q or V on the sphere in order to locate both images and calculate the field and charge distribution.

The problem of two conducting spheres and that of a sphere and a plane, which are of considerable practical interest, can only be solved with an infinite series of images and will not be considered in this book.[3]

Problem 4.4a.   Discuss the reasons why spherical equipotentials can only exist in the case of two point charges when these are of opposite sign and why one charge must be inside and one out.

Problem 4.4b.   A point charge of 3×10^{-7} coulomb lies outside a grounded conducting sphere.   The sphere has a radius of 10 cm and the charge lies at a distance of 25 cm from the center of the sphere.   Find the magnitude and location of the image charge inside the sphere that yields the correct distribution, and find the value of σ at the two points of the conductor that are nearest and farthest from q.   Also find the value of σ at a point on the sphere midway between these two points.

Problem 4.4c.   Write a formula for the force exerted by the charge residing on a grounded conducting sphere of radius R on a point charge q at a distance r from its center ($r > R$).

Problem 4.4d.   Find a general expression for the field in a spherical cavity in a conductor when a single charge q is placed in the cavity but not at the center. Find the force on q.   Will q be in stable or unstable equilibrium if placed at the center?

✓ **Problem 4.4e.**   A point charge q resides at a distance $r > R$ from the center of an isolated conducting sphere with zero net charge and radius R.   Find the force on q.

✓ **Problem 4.4f.**   Consider an isolated conducting sphere and a point charge q outside it.   Allow q to recede from the sphere and increase in magnitude so that the field $\mathbf{E}$ it produces by itself at the center of the sphere remains constant. Find the limiting charge distribution and external field around the sphere, as $q \to \infty$, thus solving the problem of a conducting sphere placed into a fixed, homogeneous electric field.

Problem 4.4g.   A conducting sphere of radius 10 cm is maintained at a potential of $+100$ v by means of a battery.   A point charge of -1.0×10^{-9} coulomb resides at 10 cm from its surface.   Find the resultant electric field at a point on a radius 10 cm beyond the negative charge.

Problem 4.4h.   A conducting sphere of radius 1 m is given a charge of 3×10^{-7} coulomb.   Find the force exerted on a point charge of 5×10^{-7} coulomb 0.2 m outside its surface.

4.5   Image Calculations for Lines, Cylinders and Planes

In section 1.7, we calculated the potential due to two infinite, parallel filaments of charge of linear densities λ and $-\lambda$, namely eq. 1.7–15:

$$V = (\lambda/2\pi\epsilon_0) \ln (r_2/r_1) \qquad (4.5\text{--}1)$$

---

[3] See, for instance, Page and Adams, *op. cit.* section 31; Sir James Jeans, *Electricity and Magnetism*, Cambridge, 1908, sections 221, 222; J. C. Maxwell, *Treatise on Electricity and Magnetism*, 2nd and 3rd ed., Oxford, 1881 and 1904, articles 165–175.

In this equation, r_2 is the perpendicular distance from the negative line of charge to the point where V is evaluated, and r_1 is that from the positive.

The equipotentials are cylindrical surfaces; that is, they are surfaces composed of lines all parallel to the given lines of charge. We can readily show that they are *circular* cylinders. Figure 4.5a shows a plane perpendicular to the lines of charge.

The equation of an equipotential line in this plane is given by setting r_2/r_1 equal to a constant k. From the figure we have

$$\frac{r_2^2}{r_1^2} = k^2 = \frac{(x + x_0)^2 + y^2}{(x - x_0)^2 + y^2} \tag{4.5-2a}$$

which reduces after rearranging and completing the square to

$$\left[x - \left(\frac{k + \frac{1}{k}}{k - \frac{1}{k}} \right) x_0 \right]^2 + y^2 = \frac{4x_0^2}{\left(k - \frac{1}{k} \right)^2} \tag{4.5-2b}$$

Therefore each equipotential is a circular cylinder with center at $x = x_1$, where

$$x_1 = x_0 \frac{\left(k + \frac{1}{k} \right)}{\left(k - \frac{1}{k} \right)} \tag{4.5-3a}$$

and radius equal to

$$R = \frac{2x_0}{\left| k - \frac{1}{k} \right|} \tag{4.5-3b}$$

Furthermore, for each $k > 1$ belonging to a positive value of $V = (\lambda/2\pi\epsilon_0) \ln k$, we can find a corresponding equipotential for $-V$ by substituting $1/k$ for k in eqs. 4.5-2 and 4.5-3. Then R will be unchanged, and the location of the center will change from $x = x_1$ to $x = -x_1$. The resulting circles in Fig. 4.5a must each surround the appropriate line of charge. Several lines of force and equipotentials are shown in Fig. 1.11d, p. 47.

We have here a case, in contrast to that of the previous section, in which it is easy to deal with two conductors, and also in which the case of one conductor and an elementary charge distribution is of less physical interest. Hence we shall consider only cases with two conducting surfaces.

To show in general how we can apply the method of images, let us consider two long parallel circular-cylindrical wires of arbitrary diameters, placed an arbitrary distance apart and charged as a condenser to a potential difference V. We wish to find their capacitance. These two wires might be considered to correspond in Fig. 4.5a to the surfaces labeled α and β.

A field which satisfies the boundary condition for this pair of conductors can be constructed by using line images λ and $-\lambda$ if we can find their locations so that a pair of equipotentials α and β have the correct radii

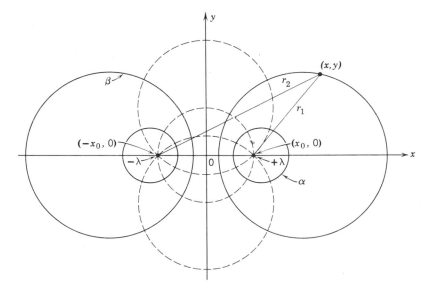

Fig. 4.5a. Variables used for the calculation of the equipotentials (solid) and lines of force (dashed) for two long parallel filaments of charge.

and positions to coincide with the surfaces of the wires and λ has such a value that the correct difference of potential V ensues.

We are given two radii R_α and R_β and a distance between the centers of the wires which we can call D. From eq. 4.5–3a, this distance must equal $x_{1\alpha} - x_{1\beta}$. Therefore we have enough equations to determine x_0, k_α and k_β. The potential difference $V = V_\alpha - V_\beta = (\lambda/2\pi\epsilon_0)\,[\ln k_\alpha - \ln k_\beta] = (\lambda/2\pi\epsilon_0)\ln (k_\alpha/k_\beta)$, so that we can solve for λ. Finally, the capacitance per unit length is then $C_l = \lambda/V$ and can readily be calculated. Note that the location of the zero equipotential cannot be freely taken for reasons concerned with the difficulty at infinity referred to in section 1.7 but that the final answer is independent of this difficulty. The answer, of course, is approximate for an actual finite pair of wires but may be considered accurate except for end corrections.

The results for two unequal wires are rather complicated and are reserved for those who wish to tackle problem 4.5h. Let us consider here the case of two wires of equal radii R.   (Fig. 4.5b.)   Let $k_\alpha = k > 1$, and $k_\beta = 1/k$.

Solving eq. 4.5–3b for k (taking the positive root of the resulting quadratic equation) we find

$$k = \frac{x_0 + (x_0^2 + R^2)^{\frac{1}{2}}}{R}$$

We have $D = 2x_1$, which is by eqs. 4.5–3a and 4.5–3b equal to

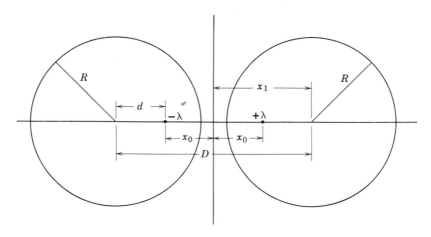

Fig. 4.5b.   Application to a pair of wires of radius R and separation D.

$R[k + (1/k)]$.   Using the value of k just obtained, $D = 2(x_0^2 + R^2)^{\frac{1}{2}}$ or

$$x_0 = \tfrac{1}{2}(D^2 - 4R^2)^{\frac{1}{2}}$$

so that

$$k = \frac{D + (D^2 - 4R^2)^{\frac{1}{2}}}{2R} \qquad (4.5\text{–}4)$$

Now, the potential difference between the wires is

$$V = (\lambda/2\pi\epsilon_0) \ln (k_\alpha/k_\beta) = (\lambda/2\pi\epsilon_0) \ln k^2 = (\lambda/\pi\epsilon_0) \ln k,$$

or $C_l = \lambda/V = \pi\epsilon_0/\ln k$, yielding finally

$$C_l = \frac{\pi\epsilon_0}{\ln \dfrac{D + (D^2 - 4R^2)^{\frac{1}{2}}}{2R}} \qquad (4.5\text{–}5)$$

for the capacitance per unit length of a parallel pair of wires of radii R and axis-to-axis separation D.

The potential at points in the region between the wires is given by eq. 4.5–1. The location of the images λ and $-\lambda$ from which the r's are measured is given by the distance d from the wire axis, where $d = \frac{1}{2}D - x_0$ or

$$d = \frac{1}{2}[D - (D^2 - 4R^2)^{\frac{1}{2}}] \qquad (4.5\text{-}6)$$

The surface charge density on either wire may then be found as in the previous sections.

The result just obtained can be immediately extended by using one-half the resulting field and applying it to the problem of the single wire parallel to a *plane* conductor. One of the two equal wires thus becomes an extended image. (Any other equipotential belonging to the same problem could of course be used for the image.) The only quantitative difference between this calculation and the preceding is that we must have one-half of the potential difference since V now means the PD from wire to central plane. It is convenient to write $D = 2h$ where h is the distance from wire to plane. The capacitance between a wire and a plane parallel to it is then twice the result of eq. 4.5–5 (inserting $D = 2h$ and simplifying)

$$C_l = \frac{2\pi\epsilon_0}{\ln \dfrac{h + (h^2 - R^2)^{\frac{1}{2}}}{R}} \qquad (4.5\text{-}7)$$

Note that in both eq. 4.5–5 and eq. 4.5–7, the logarithm becomes $\ln (D/R) = \ln 2h/R$ when $R \ll D$, and d becomes very small (approximately R^2/D).

We have not discussed the possible presence of dielectric materials, but it is obvious that, if an ideal dielectric fills all the relevant space, C_l is multiplied by κ.

Problem 4.5a. Show by calculation from eqs. 4.5–2 and 4.5–3 that the circles described by eq. 4.5–1 must surround the appropriate lines of charge.

Problem 4.5b. Prove that the lines of force for two parallel charged wires are circles. *Hints:* Calculate dy/dx from eq. 4.5–2b, eliminate k using 4.5–2a, and show that the equation obtained on replacing dy/dx by $-dx/dy$ is satisfied by any circle passing through ($\pm x_0$, 0).

Problem 4.5c. Find the capacitance per unit length of two parallel #18 (American Wire Gauge) copper wires 1 in. apart (cf. any convenient handbook with wire tables).

Problem 4.5d. Find the capacitance per centimeter between a #22 copper hook-up wire and a plane metal chassis if the wire runs parallel to the chassis and 0.5 cm away from it. Neglect the influence of any insulating material.

Problem 4.5e. Find a formula for the force per unit length on a charged wire parallel to a grounded conducting plane.

Problem 4.5f. Two long cylinders each of radius 4 cm lie parallel with their axes 10 cm apart. Find the charge densities on their nearest and farthest sides when charged to a PD of 1000 v.

Problem 4.5g. Discuss the application of section 4.5 to the case of a wire inside a long cylindrical cavity, parallel to the cavity axis but displaced from it.

Problem 4.5h. Find the capacitance of two parallel circular cylinders of radii R and R', with distance D between their axes. *Hint*: Prove first that

$$D = Rk + R'k' = (x_0{}^2 + R^2)^{\frac{1}{2}} + (x_0{}^2 + R'^2)^{\frac{1}{2}}.$$

4.6   The Use of Laplace's Equation

We wish now to consider briefly the method of constructing solutions to electrostatic problems by a systematic study of Laplace's equation. The most systematic and powerful methods always start by making a proper choice of a coordinate system.   We could make some progress with Cartesian coordinates, since the function $V = A/(x^2 + y^2 + z^2)^{\frac{1}{2}}$ is a solution of

$$\frac{\partial^2 V}{\partial x^2} + \frac{\partial^2 V}{\partial y^2} + \frac{\partial^2 V}{\partial z^2} = 0$$

as we saw in section 1.10 and since derivatives of V with respect to x, y, or z or any combination (and any order of derivative) are also solutions[4] (cf. problems 1.10*a* and 3.1*b*).

However, the most important and useful properties of the method we wish to discuss are not conveniently represented with Cartesian coordinates. We shall therefore consider other appropriate sets of coordinates.

By appropriate coordinate systems, we mean the following.   Any point $\mathscr{P}(x, y, z)$ is to be located by three new variables.   Just as allowing y and z to vary with x kept constant generates a plane, so also will there be sets of coordinate surfaces generated respectively by holding constant each of the three new variables.   We require that these surfaces always intersect each other at right angles (that is, are mutually orthogonal) and have shapes related to the types of conducting or dielectric surfaces we wish to study (spheres, cylinders, cones, ellipsoids, etc.).   Finally, and most important, Laplace's equation in the new coordinates shall be "separable," which means that it shall have solutions which are the products of three functions, each depending on one variable only.

Spherical Coordinates.   There are approximately eleven coordinate systems possible which have these properties (the number depends on how

---

[4] This is true because $\partial^2 V/\partial x\ \partial y = \partial^2 V/\partial y\ \partial x$ and so forth for all combinations of partial differentiations, so that $\nabla^2(\partial V/\partial x) = (\partial/\partial x)(\nabla^2 V) = 0$, etc.

they are classified).[5]   A simple example, and perhaps the most important, is that of spherical coordinates (r, θ, ϕ), in which r is the distance of $\mathcal{P}$ from the origin, θ is the angle between the line $\mathcal{OP}$ and a chosen axis, and ϕ represents rotation about this axis.   It is shown in the appendix (see Table A.2A) that in these coordinates, the Laplace equation becomes

$$\frac{\partial}{\partial r}\left(r^2 \frac{\partial V}{\partial r}\right) + \frac{1}{\sin \theta}\frac{\partial}{\partial \theta}\left(\sin \theta \frac{\partial V}{\partial \theta}\right) + \frac{1}{\sin^2 \theta}\frac{\partial^2 V}{\partial \phi^2} = 0 \qquad (4.6\text{-}1)$$

Let us now assume that V is a product of a function of r and a function of θ and ϕ:

$$V(r, \theta, \phi) = f(r)\,Y(\theta, \phi) \qquad (4.6\text{-}2)$$

Substitute this expression in eq. 4.6–1, and then divide by fY, noting that in each term one of the functions is a constant with respect to the differentiation.   We have then

$$\left[\frac{1}{f(r)}\frac{d}{dr}\left(r^2 \frac{df}{dr}\right)\right] + \left[\frac{1}{Y \sin \theta}\frac{\partial}{\partial \theta}\left(\sin \theta \frac{\partial Y}{\partial \theta}\right) + \frac{1}{Y \sin^2 \theta}\frac{\partial^2 Y}{\partial \phi^2}\right] = 0 \quad (4.6\text{-}3)$$

the first square bracket is a function only of r, and the second only of θ and ϕ.   Their sum cannot possibly add to zero for *all* the values of r, θ, and ϕ in the space between the given boundaries, unless each bracket is constant. The most convenient way to write this constant turns out to be to set the first bracket equal to $n(n + 1)$ and the second $-n(n + 1)$.

We have then the equations

$$\frac{d}{dr}\left(r^2 \frac{df}{dr}\right) = n(n + 1)f(r) \qquad (4.6\text{-}4)$$

$$\frac{1}{\sin \theta}\frac{\partial}{\partial \theta}\left(\sin \theta \frac{\partial Y}{\partial \theta}\right) + \frac{1}{\sin^2 \theta}\frac{\partial^2 Y}{\partial \phi^2} + n(n + 1)Y = 0 \qquad (4.6\text{-}5)$$

Solutions of eq. 4.6–5 are called "surface spherical harmonics" of degree n.   We shall not discuss them in general, but shall give some of their properties.   Proofs and further details may be found in standard texts in mathematics and mathematical physics.[6]   Let us remark in particular that

---

[5] A systematic discussion of them is given by E. Weber, *Electromagnetic Fields*, John Wiley, New York, 1950, Vol. I, pp. 445–446 and by P. M. Morse and H. Feshbach, *Methods of Theoretical Physics*, McGraw-Hill, New York, 1953, Vol I, p. 655ff.

[6] Cf. R. V. Churchill, *Fourier Series and Boundary Value Problems*, McGraw-Hill New York, 1941, Chapter IX; Morse and Feshbach, *loc. cit.*, pp. 1325–1330; Sir E. T. Whittaker and G. N. Watson, *Modern Analysis* 4th ed., Cambridge, 1943, Chapter XV; A. Erdélyi et al., *Higher Transcendental Functions*, McGraw-Hill, New York, 1953 Vol. I, Chapter III.

the solutions are finite and continuous for all θ and ϕ *only if n is an integer, positive, negative, or zero.*

Equation 4.6–4 can be solved by letting f be a power of r. Two such powers prove to be solutions, r^n and r^{-n-1}. By the general properties of second-order differential equations (see Appendix A.3) *any* solution of the equation must be an arbitrary sum of these two, namely

$$f(r) = Ar^n + Br^{-n-1} \qquad (4.6\text{–}6)$$

since such a sum contains two adjustable constants. It will be noted that eq. 4.6–5 is unchanged if we substitute $-n-1$ for n and $-n$ for $n+1$, so that the double choice for f is not reflected in a double choice for Y. A general solution for Y may be written $Y_n{}^m$, where m is an integer $(-n \leqslant m \leqslant n)$ that distinguishes the different possible solutions for a given n from each other. Thus we can write solutions of Laplace's equation in the form

$$V(r, \theta, \phi) = (Ar^n + Br^{-n-1})Y_n{}^m(\theta, \phi) \qquad (4.6\text{–}7)$$

Such functions are called "spherical harmonics."

A theorem of fundamental importance for the present method is the following, which we state without proof: Any arbitrary function of θ and ϕ, suitably well behaved in the mathematical sense, may be represented in a unique way by an infinite series of surface spherical harmonics. That is, given any $F(\theta, \phi)$ for the range of these angles over a sphere, we can write

$$F(\theta, \phi) = \sum_{n=0}^{\infty} \sum_{m=-n}^{n} C_{n,m} Y_n{}^m(\theta, \phi) \qquad (4.6\text{–}8)$$

where the $C_{n,m}$ are the coefficients in the expansion, that can be determined in a straightforward way from knowledge of F. Furthermore, any solution of the potential problem can be written in general as

$$V(r, \theta, \phi) = \sum_{n=0}^{\infty} \sum_{m=-n}^{n} (A_{n,m}r^n + B_{n,m}r^{-n-1})Y_n{}^m(\theta, \phi) \qquad (4.6\text{–}9)$$

Now, suppose we are given the value of V over the surface of a sphere of radius R, by a function $V = V_0(\theta, \phi)$. We can then find a function V that satisfies $\nabla^2 V = 0$ and reduces to V_0 on the sphere by writing either of two series

$$V_1 = \sum_{n=0}^{\infty} \sum_{m=-n}^{n} (r^n/R^n)C_{n,m} Y_n{}^m(\theta, \phi) \qquad (4.6\text{–}10a)$$

$$V_2 = \sum_{n=0}^{\infty} \sum_{m=-n}^{\infty} (R^{n+1}/r^{n+1})C_{n,m} Y_n{}^m(\theta, \phi) \qquad (4.6\text{–}10b)$$

The $C_{n,m}$'s are calculated for $F = V_0$, so that each of the series reduces to $V_0(\theta, \phi)$ when $r = R$. Thus V_1 has positive powers of r and will get very large as $r \to \infty$, so that it is in general only physically meaningful for small r, namely for points inside the sphere. On the other hand V_2 is infinite if $r \to 0$ and constitutes a solution outside the sphere. There are many other ways of solving boundary value problems, but this example will serve to show the general power of the method.

Table 4.6A

n	$P_n(\cos \theta)$	Zonal Harmonics	
0	1	1,	$\dfrac{1}{r}$
1	$\cos \theta$	$r \cos \theta,$	$\dfrac{1}{r^2} \cos \theta$
2	$\frac{1}{2}(3 \cos^2 \theta - 1)$	$\dfrac{r^2}{2}(3 \cos^2 \theta - 1),$	$\dfrac{1}{2r^3}(3 \cos^2 \theta - 1)$
3	$\frac{1}{2}(5 \cos^3 \theta - 3 \cos \theta)$	$\dfrac{r^3}{2}(5 \cos^2 \theta - 3 \cos \theta),$	$\dfrac{1}{2r^4}(5 \cos^3 \theta - 3 \cos \theta)$

Let us consider further only those cases with axial symmetry; namely, those in which V and Y do not depend on ϕ. The middle term of eq. 4.6–5 drops out, and we have an ordinary differential equation. It turns out that solutions of this equation that have no discontinuities are polynomials in $\cos \theta$. They are generally represented by the notation $P_n(\cos \theta)$ and are called "Legendre polynomials" or "surface zonal harmonics." The expansion theorem 4.6–8 applies to these functions also, for any F that is a function only of θ. Table 4.6A lists the P_n for $n = 0, 1, 2,$ and 3. The reader can readily verify that these functions satisfy eq. 4.6–5 (problem 4.6f). Corresponding solutions of eq. 4.6–1 are called "zonal harmonics" or "solid zonal harmonics" and are also listed.

Another general reason for the value of the present approach is that there are many useful ways of calculating or "generating" the functions P_n. For instance, if any two adjacent ones are known, the next may be found from a general formula (the "recurrence" formula). Also, values of $P_n(0)$ can be calculated, and the fact that $P_n(1) = 1$ can be proved from such formulas. There are also numerous ways of writing definite integrals which are equal to those functions.[6] The other coordinate systems also lead on separation to differential equations with sets of solutions that can be used to expand arbitrary functions, can be calculated by recurrence relations, and can be represented by definite integrals that are sometimes of use for computational purposes.

Let us construct a solution to the problem of a conducting sphere of radius R in a fixed, uniform external electric field. (Fig. 4.6a.) We expect to find V as a sum of zonal harmonics.   Our boundary conditions are that V is constant on the sphere—we can take the constant conveniently to be zero—and that far from the sphere E is constant, say in the z-direction so that $-(\partial V/\partial z) = $ constant $ = E_0$ and $V = -E_0 z + V_0$.   The extra constant V_0 arising from integration can be set equal to zero by noting that

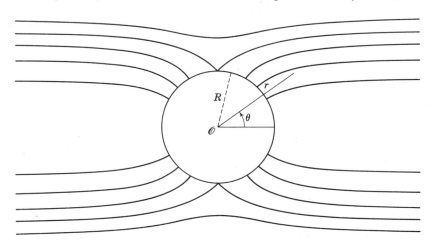

Fig. 4.6a.   A conducting sphere in a fixed, uniform external electric field.

by symmetry the plane through the center of the sphere normal to the z-axis must be an equipotential that intersects the sphere, so that at points far from the sphere in this plane we have $V = V_0 = 0$.

Taking the z-axis as the polar axis, we have $z = r \cos \theta$, so $V = -E_0 r \cos \theta$ for large r.   This is proportional to one of the zonal harmonics.   We can add to it only inverse powers of r that disappear when $r \to \infty$.   However, we must add terms that can yield a constant total V over the surface of the sphere, i.e., we must cancel the $\cos \theta$ variation in the harmonic we have already chosen.   There is thus only one other that can be used, namely, $(1/r^2) \cos \theta$, so we must have

$$V = -E_0 r \cos \theta + \frac{B}{r^2} \cos \theta$$

Setting $V = 0$ when $r = R$ yields $B = E_0 R^3$, and we have for the complete solution of the problem

$$V = E_0 \left(\frac{R^3}{r^2} - r \right) \cos \theta \qquad (4.6\text{--}11)$$

Problems 4.6a and b deal with this case; problems 4.6c and d apply the same considerations to spherical dielectric boundaries.

Let us give one more example of the general power of the spherical harmonic method. Problem 1.7e called for the potential of a uniformly charged disk of radius R at a point on its axis at a given distance from its center. The result is that

$$V = \frac{\sigma}{2\epsilon_0} [(r^2 + R^2)^{\frac{1}{2}} - r] \tag{4.6-12}$$

where r is the distance along the axis ($\theta = 0$). Now, can we find the potential at points off the axis ($\theta \neq 0$)? We know that V must be represented by a series of zonal harmonics with inverse powers of r, at least at fairly large distances from the disk. Let us use eq. 4.6–12 as a boundary condition for determining the coefficients. We need the result quoted above that $P_n(1) = 1$ for all n.

Let us expand eq. 4.6–12 in inverse powers of r.

$$V = \frac{\sigma}{2\epsilon_0} \left[r\left(1 + \frac{R^2}{r^2}\right)^{\frac{1}{2}} - r \right] = \frac{\sigma}{2\epsilon_0} \left[-r + r\left\{1 + \frac{R^2}{2r^2} - \frac{R^4}{8r^4} + \frac{R^6}{16r^6} \cdots \right\} \right]$$

$$= \frac{\sigma}{2\epsilon_0} \left[\frac{R^2}{2r} - \frac{R^4}{8r^3} + \frac{R^6}{16r^5} \cdots \right] \tag{4.6-13}$$

Now, if V is to be a series $\sum_{n=0}^{\infty} B_n P_n(\cos \theta)/r^{n+1}$, we must have this series fit the expansion just given along the axis where $\theta = 0$. Since $P_n(\cos 0°) = 1$, we see that each B_n can be immediately deduced from eq. 4.6–13, so that we have in general, for $r > R$

$$V(r, \theta) = \frac{\sigma}{2\epsilon_0} \left[\frac{R^2 P_0(\cos \theta)}{2r} - \frac{R^4 P_2(\cos \theta)}{8r^3} + \frac{R^6 P_4(\cos \theta)}{16r^5} \cdots \right] \tag{4.6-14}$$

A similar result could be written for $r < R$ by expanding in positive powers of r. The two solutions will "match" at the sphere of radius R drawn about the center of the disk.

Cylindrical Coordinates. Laplace's equation in cylindrical coordinates reads

$$\frac{1}{r} \frac{\partial}{\partial r} \left(r \frac{\partial V}{\partial r} \right) + \frac{1}{r^2} \frac{\partial^2 V}{\partial \phi^2} + \frac{\partial^2 V}{\partial z^2} = 0 \tag{4.6-15}$$

We can effect a separation of coordinates by writing the potential $V(r, \phi, z)$ as a product of three functions.

$$V(r, \phi, z) = f(r)\Phi(\phi)Z(z) \tag{4.6-16}$$

On substitution in the equation and dividing by V we have

$$\frac{1}{rf(r)}\frac{d}{dr}\left(r\frac{df}{dr}\right) + \frac{1}{r^2\Phi(\phi)}\frac{d^2\Phi}{d\phi^2} + \frac{1}{Z(z)}\frac{d^2Z}{dz^2} = 0 \qquad (4.6\text{--}17)$$

which can only be true for all r, ϕ, and z if in the first place the z-dependent term is a constant; let us call it k^2. Therefore we write

$$\frac{d^2Z}{dz^2} = k^2Z(z) \qquad (4.6\text{--}18)$$

and multiplying eq. 4.6–17 by r^2

$$\frac{r}{f(r)}\frac{d}{dr}\left(r\frac{df}{dr}\right) + \frac{1}{\Phi(\phi)}\frac{d^2\Phi}{d\phi^2} + k^2r^2 = 0 \qquad (4.6\text{--}19)$$

We see now that the ϕ-dependent term is constant; let us call it $-n^2$. We have then the two equations

$$\frac{d^2\Phi}{d\phi^2} = -n^2\Phi(\phi) \qquad (4.6\text{--}20)$$

$$r\frac{d}{dr}\left(r\frac{df}{dr}\right) + (k^2r^2 - n^2)f(r) = 0 \qquad (4.6\text{--}21)$$

If k is real and not zero, eq. 4.6–18 has solutions of exponential type, i.e., $Z(z) = e^{\pm kz}$. If n is real and not zero, eq. 4.6–20 has solutions of trigonometric type, $\Phi(\phi) = \sin n\phi$ or $\Phi(\phi) = \cos n\phi$. Such solutions will give the same result for the physically identical angles ϕ and $\phi + 2\pi$ if n is an integer.

Now, if k is not zero, eq. 4.6–21 is a form of Bessel's equation, which has as solutions the Bessel functions $J_n(kr)$ and $N_n(kr)$.[7] These functions are rather complicated oscillatory functions with many interesting properties, but it would take us too far afield to study them here.

Let us restrict ourselves to the case in which $Z(z)$ is constant, so that we have $k = 0$ and cylindrical symmetry (two-dimensional fields). Then it is clear that $f = r^n$ and $f = r^{-n}$ are solutions of eq. 4.6–21.

If $n = 0$, a solution of eq. 4.6–20 is $\Phi = A\phi + B$. Equation 4.6–21 reads then

$$\frac{d}{dr}\left(r\frac{df}{dr}\right) = 0$$

or

$$r\frac{df}{dr} = C$$

or

$$f = C\ln r + D$$

where A, B, C, and D are constants.

[7] All the references on p. 163 treat Bessel functions

We can then make a table of cylindrical harmonics for $V(r, \phi)$ (Table 4.6B).

Let us find the field and polarization in a long thin circular rod of ideal dielectric that is placed in an originally homogeneous field $\mathbf{E_0}$ at right angles to the field direction. As in the example of Fig. 4.6a, the potential far from the rod can be taken as $V = -E_0 r \cos \phi$. We can write V in

Table 4.6B

Cylindrical Harmonics

n		$f(r) \cdot \Phi(\phi)$	
0		$(A_0 \phi + B_0)(C_0 \ln r + D_0)$	
1	$r(A_1 \sin \phi + B_1 \cos \phi);$		$\dfrac{1}{r}(A_1 \sin \phi + B_1 \cos \phi)$
2	$r^2(A_2 \sin 2\phi + B_2 \cos 2\phi);$		$\dfrac{1}{r^2}(A_2 \sin 2\phi + B_2 \cos 2\phi)$
.	.		.
.	.		.
.	.		.
	$r^n(A_n \sin n\phi + B_n \cos n\phi);$		$\dfrac{1}{r^n}(A_n \sin n\phi + B_n \cos n\phi)$

general as a series of cylindrical harmonics, using positive powers of r inside the rod and negative powers, except for $-E_0 r \cos \phi$, outside the rod. The $\ln r$ solution is infinite for both $r = 0$ and $r \to \infty$ and so is not physically meaningful. Thus we write, tentatively, using suitable symbols for the various unknown constants:

$$V_{\text{outside}} = -E_0 r \cos \phi + \sum_{n=1}^{\infty} \frac{1}{r^n}(A_n \sin n\phi + B_n \cos n\phi) \tag{4.6–22}$$

$$V_{\text{inside}} = \sum_{n=1}^{\infty} r^n(a_n \sin n\phi + b_n \cos n\phi)$$

The boundary conditions $D_{1n} = D_{2n}$ and $E_{1t} = E_{2t}$ at the surface of the rod can be written

$$\frac{\partial V_{\text{outside}}}{\partial \phi} = \frac{\partial V_{\text{inside}}}{\partial \phi}; \qquad r = R$$

$$\frac{\partial V_{\text{outside}}}{\partial r} = \kappa \frac{\partial V_{\text{inside}}}{\partial r}; \qquad r = R \tag{4.6–23}$$

The two conditions 4.6–23 yield equations containing all the $\sin n\phi$ and $\cos n\phi$ which must hold for all values of ϕ, so that the coefficients for each of these functions must be the same on each side. For all values of n except 1, the two equations yield a pair of inconsistent equations for A_n and a_n or B_n and b_n that can only be satisfied by setting all these coefficients equal to zero. For $n = 1$, we find $A_1 = a_1 = 0$, and for B_1 and b_1,

$$E_0 R - \frac{B_1}{R} = -Rb_1$$

$$-E_0 - B_1/R^2 = \kappa b_1 \tag{4.6-24}$$

from which we readily find

$$b_1 = -\frac{2E_0}{\kappa + 1} \quad \text{and} \quad B_1 = E_0 R^2 \frac{\kappa - 1}{\kappa + 1} \tag{4.6-25}$$

so that we have

$$V_{\text{outside}} = E_0 \cos\phi\left(-r + \frac{\kappa - 1}{\kappa + 1}\frac{R^2}{r}\right)$$

$$V_{\text{inside}} = -\frac{2E_0 r \cos\phi}{\kappa + 1} \tag{4.6-26}$$

We can then find $\mathbf{E}$ inside the cylinder, setting $r\cos\phi = x$,

$$\mathbf{E} = -\frac{\partial V}{\partial x}\mathbf{1}_x = \frac{2E_0}{\kappa + 1}\mathbf{1}_x \tag{4.6-27}$$

and the rod is uniformly polarized according to

$$\mathbf{P} = (\kappa - 1)\epsilon_0 \mathbf{E} = \frac{2(\kappa - 1)\epsilon_0 E_0}{\kappa + 1}\mathbf{1}_x \tag{4.6-28}$$

Problem 4.6a. Show that eq. 4.6–11 agrees with the result of problem 4.4f, and describe the resulting field in suitable multipole terms.

Problem 4.6b. Find an expression for the charge density on the sphere whose potential is given by eq. 4.6–11, at an arbitrary angle θ.

Problem 4.6c. Find the potential inside and outside a sphere of ideal dielectric placed in a fixed, uniform electric field. Also find $\mathbf{P}$ at an arbitrary point in the sphere.

Problem 4.6d. Use the result of problem 4.6c to get a better approximation than that of eq. 3.8–7 for the force on a sphere of dielectric in an inhomogeneous electric field. (Assume the field to be homogeneous while calculating $\mathbf{P}$; then inhomogeneous for finding $\mathbf{F}$.)

Problem 4.6e. Use the zonal-harmonic method to find the field in a spherical cavity in an ideal dielectric which itself lies in a uniform external field.

Problem 4.6f.   Write eq. 4.6–5 with $\partial^2 Y/\partial\phi^2 = 0$ in terms of the independent variable $\mu = \cos\theta$, and verify that the functions $P_n(\mu)$ of Table 4.6A satisfy this equation.

Problem 4.6g.   Find a formula for the surface charge distribution on a long thin circular conducting rod placed at right angles to an originally uniform field.

Problem 4.6h.   Find the field in a long circular cylindrical cavity lying at right angles to an originally homogeneous field in a large piece of ideal dielectric.

Problem 4.6i.   Show by calculating the next term of eq. 3.3–3 that the first four terms of the expansion involve the first four Legendre polynomials in $\cos\theta = \mathbf{1}_r \cdot \mathbf{1}_{r0}$.

4.7   Energy in Systems of Conductors

The general problem of calculating forces in systems of electrostatic conductors—for instance in electrostatic potential-measuring devices—is

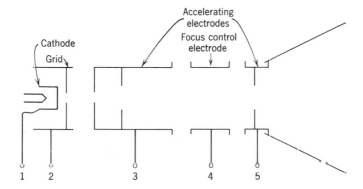

Fig. 4.7a.   Conductors in an electron-beam-forming apparatus.

best solved from the point of view of energy.   A number of our previous results could also have been derived from what follows, but we have preferred to emphasize direct use of the force concept, since it leads to a better development of physical intuition.   We wish now to derive several different expressions for the total potential energy in a system of conductors, relate these to each other, and show how they may be used to solve a number of force problems.

Let us begin with another expression of the superposition principle. Imagine a number of conductors in a given region that can be charged to arbitrary values of Q and V by means of appropriate batteries.   The region may or may not be filled with linear dielectric material.   Fig. 4.7a shows such a set (part of an electron-beam-forming apparatus).   We wish to show that the charge on any one is given by a linear combination of the potentials of all.   We shall number the conductors from 1 to n and write summations with letters $i, j, k, l, \cdots$, each of which is to run from 1 to n, also allowing any of these letters to denote a particular conductor. Our assertion is that

$$Q_i = \sum_{j=1}^{n} c_{ij} V_j \qquad (4.7\text{-}1)$$

where the constants c_{ij} are specific to the given arrangement of conductors and are called coefficients of induction when $i \neq j$, coefficients of capacitance when $i = j$. We can prove the validity of eq. 4.7-1 by adding the n separate fields produced by successively connecting only one conductor to a battery, leaving the rest grounded. When the kth conductor has a potential V_k with all $V_j = 0$ for $j \neq k$, the grounded conductors will in general all have induced charges on their surfaces whose total amounts (again by superposition) are proportional to V_k. The ith conductor will then have a charge which we can write $c_{ik} V_k$, the constant of proportionality having two subscripts to show that it gives the value of charge on the ith conductor when the kth is at unit potential and all others are at zero potential. Adding the fields and σ's for all the separate cases then yields the expression 4.7-1.

Let us now charge up the entire system from neutrality to the chosen set of potentials $V_1 \cdots V_n$ in uniform fractional steps. Specifically if V'_k is the potential on the kth conductor during the charging process, let $V'_k = \eta V_k$, where η (small Greek "eta") is the same for all conductors and varies from 0 to 1. For some particular value of η, we will have

$$Q'_i = \sum_{j=1}^{n} c_{ij} V'_j = \sum_j c_{ij} \eta V_j = \eta Q_i$$

Now consider the work done by the batteries in adding charge. The potentials of the batteries are imagined to be controllable and slowly varied as η is changed. When a charge $dQ_i = Q_i \, d\eta$ is transferred from ground to the potential V'_i, the work done will be[8] $V'_i \, dQ_i = V'_i Q_i \, d\eta = V_i Q_i \eta \, d\eta$ from the definition of potential and the assumption made above about the charging process. The total potential energy U is thus

$$U = \sum_{i=1}^{n} \int V'_i \, dQ_i = \sum_i V_i Q_i \int_0^1 \eta \, d\eta$$

or:

$$U = \tfrac{1}{2} \sum_{i=1}^{n} Q_i V_i \qquad (4.7\text{-}2)$$

[8] Strictly, the work done is dQ_i times the proper average of V in between V'_i and $V'_i + dV'_i$. The error made here is proportional to $dV'_i dQ_i = V_i Q_i (d\eta)^2$ and disappears in the limit on integration.

Since the potential energy does not depend on the order in which the conductors are charged, this expression must be true for any method of charging. (See problem 4.7*a* for an alternative proof of eq. 4.7–2.)

Using eq. 4.7–1, we have

$$U = \tfrac{1}{2} \sum_{i=1}^{n} \sum_{j=1}^{n} c_{ij} V_i V_j \qquad (4.7\text{–}3)$$

as another expression for the energy.

A third expression can be obtained by inverting the relations 4.7–1. This relation consists of *n* equations, one for each Q_i, and is therefore adequate to determine the *n* V's in terms of the Q's. If we imagine the equations to be solved, we can write[9]

$$V_l = \sum_{k=1}^{n} p_{lk} Q_k \qquad (4.7\text{–}4)$$

where the p_{lk} are called the coefficients of potential. Thus p_{lk} is the potential attained by conductor *l* when conductor *k* bears one unit of charge and all other conductors are neutral. Using this relation in eq. 4.7–2, we have

$$U = \tfrac{1}{2} \sum_{i=1}^{n} \sum_{k=1}^{n} p_{ik} Q_i Q_k \qquad (4.7\text{–}5)$$

A fourth expression for the energy differs from these three by referring the energy to fields rather than potentials. Let us include infinity or ground as a conductor in eq. 4.7–2 even though $V = 0$. Then we have all charge appearing in equal and opposite pairs, each pair being located at the two ends of a tube of displacement flux. We wish to associate parts of the terms in the sum of eq. 4.7–2 with each tube. Let each Q_i be considered an integral over dQ's spread over the conducting surfaces. For each positive dQ, say dQ_+, there is another negative dQ, say $dQ_- = -dQ_+$. The contribution to the over-all sum from the two is $\tfrac{1}{2} dQ_+(V_+ - V_-) = \tfrac{1}{2} dQ_+ \int \mathbf{E} \cdot \mathbf{dl}$, where we shall take the integral from V_+ to V_- along a line of displacement. The cross-sectional area of the tube associated with dQ_+ will be $dS = dQ_+/D$, where D is the magnitude of $\mathbf{D}$.

Thus the energy contribution is

$$\tfrac{1}{2} D \, dS \int \mathbf{E} \cdot \mathbf{dl} = \tfrac{1}{2} D \, dS \int \mathbf{E} \cdot \mathbf{1}_l \, dl = \tfrac{1}{2} \int_l (\mathbf{E} \cdot \mathbf{D}) \, dl \, dS$$

where the integral is over dl but *not* over dS, ($\mathbf{1}_l$ is a unit vector in the direction of $\mathbf{D}$) and where the variation of D is canceled out

---

[9] Equation 4.7–4 can be derived directly from the principle of superposition.

by a reciprocal variation of dS. If we finally integrate over all the dQ_+'s, we will add contributions from all tubes of flux and must then integrate the expression above over dS. But $dl\,dS = d\tau$, an element of volume, so that the integration now covers all the space outside the conductors,[10] and we arrive at the result

$$U = \tfrac{1}{2} \int_{\text{all space}} \mathbf{E} \cdot \mathbf{D} \, d\tau \tag{4.7-6}$$

which reduces in the case of ideal dielectrics to

$$U = \frac{\epsilon_0}{2} \int_{\text{all space}} \kappa E^2 \, d\tau \tag{4.7-7}$$

We can say, then, that each unit volume of an electrostatic field "contains" potential energy $\tfrac{1}{2}(\mathbf{E} \cdot \mathbf{D})$, bearing in mind that it is the system as a whole that really has the energy. Division of potential energy into parts has no strict operational meaning, although the example of problem 4.7e gives a considerable justification to this concept of energy per unit volume.

Let us apply the four expressions above to the simple case of an ideal condenser (cf. problem 2.7c). The energy is $U = \tfrac{1}{2}QV = \tfrac{1}{2}CV^2 = \tfrac{1}{2}(Q^2/C)$, as can be seen by direct integration, $U = \int_0^Q V\,dq = \int_0^Q (q/C)\,dq$. We have two conductors, so that

$$Q_1 = c_{11}V_1 + c_{12}V_2; \qquad Q_2 = c_{21}V_1 + c_{22}V_2$$

and since Q_1 is a function only of $V_1 - V_2$, we must have $c_{12} = -c_{11}$; $c_{21} = -c_{22}$. Furthermore, $Q_2 = -Q_1 = -Q$, so that $c_{11}(V_1 - V_2) = c_{22}(V_1 - V_2)$ or $c_{11} = c_{22} = C$, the ordinary capacitance. In this particular case, we cannot solve for the p's since only $V_1 - V_2$ enters the equations with the c's. However, we must have $V_1 = p_{11}Q_1 + p_{12}Q_2 = (p_{11} - p_{12})Q_1$, and similarly $V_2 = (p_{21} - p_{22})Q_1$, so that $V = V_1 - V_2 = (p_{11} + p_{22} - p_{12} - p_{21})Q_1$, resulting in $p_{11} + p_{22} - p_{12} - p_{21} = 1/C$. Thus $U = \tfrac{1}{2}[p_{11}Q_1{}^2 + (p_{12} + p_{21})Q_1Q_2 + p_{22}Q_2{}^2] = \tfrac{1}{2}[p_{11} + p_{22} - p_{12} - p_{21}]\,Q_1{}^2 = \tfrac{1}{2}Q^2/C$ as above.

Finally, if the condenser were an ideal plane-parallel condenser with area S, plate separation d, and dielectric constant κ, we would have

$$U = \tfrac{1}{2} \int \mathbf{E} \cdot \mathbf{D} \, d\tau = \tfrac{1}{2}\kappa\epsilon_0 E^2 Sd = \frac{\kappa\epsilon_0 S}{2d}(Ed)^2 = \tfrac{1}{2}CV^2$$

again corroborating our original result.

---

[10] Space inside the conductors can be included since $E = D = 0$ there.

If the condenser is not perfect but has stray flux from each plate to ground, we can write the charge on each plate as a sum of charge whose flux goes to the other plate and charge whose flux goes to ground, yielding

$$Q_1 = C(V_1 - V_2) + C'V_1 = (C + C')V_1 - CV_2$$

$$Q_2 = C(V_2 - V_1) + C''V_2 = -CV_1 + (C + C'')V_2$$

where C' and C'' are the measures of the stray capacitances. That is, we have $c_{11} = C + C'$; $c_{12} = -C$; $c_{21} = -C$; $c_{22} = C + C''$. These equations can be solved for V_1 and V_2, yielding

$$V_1 = \frac{(C + C'')Q_1 + CQ_2}{C(C' + C'') + C'C''}$$

$$V_2 = \frac{CQ_1 + (C + C')Q_2}{C(C' + C'') + C'C''}$$

from which relations the values of p_{11}, p_{12}, p_{21}, and p_{22} can be read.

The energy expression then reads

$$U = \tfrac{1}{2}Q_1V_1 + \tfrac{1}{2}Q_2V_2 = \tfrac{1}{2}[(C + C')V_1^2 - 2CV_1V_2 + (C' + C'')V_2^2]$$

$$= \tfrac{1}{2}[C(V_1 - V_2)^2 + C'V_1^2 + C''V_2^2]$$

with a corresponding expression in the Q's that does not however show so clearly that the effect of the stray capacitance is always to add to the energy.

Problem 4.7a. Consider a system of point charges that are brought into position from infinity one at a time, and prove that eq. 4.7–2 applies to them, where V_i is the potential at the ith charge produced by the other charges.

Problem 4.7b. Prove that the coefficients of capacitance are positive and the coefficients of induction are negative or zero.

Problem 4.7c. Prove that all the coefficients of potential p_{ij} are positive.

Problem 4.7d. Find the energy in the condenser of Fig. 3.7a if the dielectric slab has a constant κ, by the formula $\tfrac{1}{2}CV^2$ and by eq. 4.7–7.

Problem 4.7e. Find the change in energy when one plate of an insulated condenser with fixed charge is allowed to move a small distance toward the other plate, by use of the various formulas in the text. Compare the value you obtain with the work done, finding the force as in section 2.3.

Problem 4.7f. A 1 μf condenser is charged to 100 v, and a 2 μf condenser is charged to 50 v. The two are disconnected from their respective batteries and are connected to each other, positive terminal to positive and negative to negative. Find the original charges, the final charge, the original energy stored in each and the final energy in the combination. How do you account for the discrepancy?

Problem 4.7g. Use eq. 4.7–6 to find the potential energy of a uniformly charged spherical conductor. What result do we get if we imagine the conductor to be shrunk to a point, bearing a constant charge Q? Is there any physical meaning to be given to the resulting value for the potential energy of a single point charge?

Problem 4.7h. A condenser of 1200 μf is charged to 300 v and discharged through a photo-flash lamp. If one flash is produced every two seconds, what average power (joules/second) is needed to recharge the condenser?

Problem 4.7i. If the potential produced by a point charge follows a different power law than the minus first, show how the coefficients c_{ij} of a system of conductors will change when all dimensions are changed by the same factor k. Taking as an experimental fact that the c_{ij} always remain in constant ratio to each other when such a scale change by a factor k is made, show that any potential variation other than a power law is not possible.

4.8 Force Calculations

A general method of calculating forces in systems of conductors can readily be derived from the energy expressions of the last section, but there are a number of important properties of the coefficients that we must first discuss.

In the first place, the coefficients p_{ij} and c_{ij} with different subscripts are symmetrical, i.e., $p_{ij} = p_{ji}$, and $c_{ij} = c_{ji}$. To show this, imagine that we make small but *arbitrary* changes in the potentials and charges of each conductor by making small variations in batteries connected to each. Either the dV_i's or the dQ_i's can be taken as arbitrary, but then the other set is related to the chosen one by the c_{ij}'s or p_{ij}'s. The change in energy will then be given, as in the last section (p. 172), by

$$dU = \sum_{i=1}^{n} V_i \, dQ_i \tag{4.8-1}$$

However, the expression $U = \frac{1}{2}\sum_i V_i Q_i$ will continue to be valid as the V's and Q's change, so dU is also the differential

$$dU = \frac{1}{2} \sum_{i=1}^{n} (V_i \, dQ_i + Q_i \, dV_i) \tag{4.8-2}$$

Comparing eqs. 4.8–1 and 4.8–2, we see that

$$\sum_i V_i \, dQ_i = \sum_i Q_i \, dV_i \tag{4.8-3}$$

for all possible dQ's and dV's. Let us now use eq. 4.7–1 and its differential in eq. 4.8–3, obtaining

$$\sum_{i=1}^{n}\sum_{j=1}^{n} c_{ij} V_i \, dV_j = \sum_{k=1}^{n}\sum_{l=1}^{n} c_{kl} \, dV_k V_l \tag{4.8-4}$$

where we have used k in place of i and l in place of j on the right to emphasize the fact that all the summations are independent of each other and that the name given to each summation index is unimportant. Suppose now that all V's are zero except one—say V_3—and all dV's are zero except one other—say dV_2. Equation 4.8–4 will then reduce to $c_{32}V_3\,dV_2 = c_{23}\,dV_2V_3$, so that $c_{32} = c_{23}$. Similarly, every c_{ij} for $i \neq j$ is equal to c_{ji}. An exactly similar proof may be worked out for the p_{ij} by using eq. 4.7–4 instead of eq. 4.7–1 in eq. 4.8–3.

Now let us consider variations of the c_{ij} and p_{ij}. These coefficients depend on the *geometry* (size, shape, position) of the system of conductors and on the geometry and dielectric constants of any dielectric media present. Consequently they will vary if any conductor or piece of dielectric is moved, and in general we must assume that all the coefficients change when any one part of the system is displaced.

Let us focus our attention on the force on some part of the system and specifically on some component of this force. Any component of a force on an object at rest has a definite meaning only when we have defined the way in which it might move in the direction indicated, at least infinitesimally—that is, if we can consider the force in question to perform at least an infinitesimal amount of work. It may of course be in equilibrium under a balance of electric and mechanical forces; by motion we mean motion against the mechanical restraints. Suppose that the possible motion in the given direction is measured by a coordinate ξ (small Greek "xi"). Then the work done by the electrical force for a displacement $d\xi$ will be $F_\xi\,d\xi$. We shall use this expression as a means of finding F_ξ.

The force F_ξ will not depend on whether V's or Q's are determined on the conductors by batteries or insulation, since it could in principle be calculated from $f_S = \sigma^2/2\epsilon_0$ as in section 2.3. However, the energy change accompanying a displacement $d\xi$ will be different according to whether or not energy is available from batteries. Let us then calculate the energy changes for two possibilities—one, that all the charges Q_i are fixed and the other, that all the potentials V_i remain constant.

In the first case, all the energy $F_\xi\,d\xi$ that goes into work must come from the field (no batteries are present), so $dU = -F_\xi\,d\xi$, and

$$F_\xi = -\left(\frac{\partial U}{\partial \xi}\right)_Q$$

where the subscript Q indicates that all the Q's are kept constant in calculating $\partial U/\partial \xi$.

In the second case, some energy may come from the batteries. Let us calculate it by imagining that we first disconnect all the conductors, keeping Q's constant (all $dQ_i = 0$) and allowing the V's to vary, by amounts

dV_i, so that $dU = \frac{1}{2}\sum_i Q_i\, dV_i$.   Then reconnect the batteries, and bring all the conductors back to their original potentials by the addition of suitable dQ's, which we shall call dQ'_i, $i = 1, 2 \cdots n$.   This change is a special case of the arbitrary one we used in the first part of this section, so that

$$\sum_i V_i\, dQ'_i = \sum_i Q_i\, dV'_i = -\sum_i Q_i\, dV_i$$

where $dV'_i = -dV_i$ in order to restore the initial potentials.   But $\sum_i V_i\, dQ'_i$ is the energy supplied by the batteries and is seen to constitute an *increase* in U of twice the amount of the first decrease $\frac{1}{2}\sum_i Q_i\, dV_i$.

Thus the net change in U with constant potentials is equal and opposite to the change when the charges are constant, the batteries supplying exactly twice as much energy as is used up in mechanical work.   Hence we may write

$$F_\xi = -\left(\frac{\partial U}{\partial \xi}\right)_Q = +\left(\frac{\partial U}{\partial \xi}\right)_V \tag{4.8–5}$$

which may be written in the more explicit forms

$$F_\xi = -\frac{1}{2}\sum_{i=1}^n \sum_{j=1}^n \frac{\partial p_{ij}}{\partial \xi} Q_i Q_j \tag{4.8–6}$$

$$F_\xi = +\frac{1}{2}\sum_{i=1}^n \sum_{j=1}^n \frac{\partial c_{ij}}{\partial \xi} V_i V_j \tag{4.8–7}$$

We can also calculate torques in a similar way, since the work done during a small angular displacement $d\theta$ is $\mathscr{L}_\theta\, d\theta$ where $\mathscr{L}_\theta$ is the torque about the axis to which θ refers.   In fact, we need only to read $\mathscr{L}_\theta$ in place of F_ξ and θ in place of ξ in eqs. 4.8–5, 4.8–6, and 4.8–7 to get the proper torque equations.   For reference we shall write out the first one:

$$\mathscr{L}_\theta = -\left(\frac{\partial U}{\partial \theta}\right)_Q = +\left(\frac{\partial U}{\partial \theta}\right)_V \tag{4.8–8}$$

As a first example let us consider the force and torque on one plate of a condenser.   We have $U = \frac{1}{2}CV^2 = \frac{1}{2}Q^2/C$ so that

$$F_\xi = -\left(\frac{\partial U}{\partial \xi}\right)_Q = +\frac{Q^2}{2C^2}\frac{\partial C}{\partial \xi}; \qquad \mathscr{L}_\theta = \frac{Q^2}{2C^2}\frac{\partial C}{\partial \theta} \tag{4.8–9a}$$

and

$$F_\xi = +\left(\frac{\partial U}{\partial \xi}\right)_V = \frac{1}{2}V^2\frac{\partial C}{\partial \xi}; \qquad \mathscr{L}_\theta = \frac{1}{2}V^2\frac{\partial C}{\partial \theta} \tag{4.8–9b}$$

The two expressions are readily seen to be the same and show that the force and torque are in the direction of increasing capacitance. If the formula is applied to the "absolute" voltmeter discussed in section 2.7, we have $C = \epsilon_0 S/\xi$, where ξ is the plate separation, earlier called d. Then $\partial C/\partial \xi = -\epsilon_0 S/\xi^2$ and $F_\xi = -\epsilon_0 S V^2/2\xi^2$, which agrees with eq. 2.7–8, the minus sign indicating that the force is inward while ξ increases outwardly.

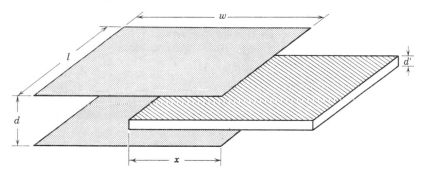

Fig. 4.8a. A slab of dielectric between two condenser plates.

Now suppose that a slab of dielectric of thickness d' is inserted part way between the condenser plates, as indicated in Fig. 4.8a. Let us calculate the force tending to pull the dielectric in when it is inserted a distance x, less than the width w of the plates. If V is the PD between the plates, the field in the space beyond the point to which the slab has been pushed is $E = V/d$. Above and below the slab, we will have a field E' and within it a field E'/κ (by the continuity of D_n) where $E'(d - d') + E'd'/\kappa = V$. The total energy in the condenser by eq. 4.7–7 is then $U = \frac{1}{2}\epsilon_0[E^2l(w - x)d + E'^2lx(d - d') + \kappa(E'/\kappa)^2lxd'] + U_{\text{corr}}$, where U_{corr} is the correction to the energy because of the necessary failure of our infinite-plane formulas at the edge of the slab. This term is difficult to calculate but will be independent of x as long as the edge of the slab is not near either edge of the condenser.[11]   In terms of V, we have

$$U = \tfrac{1}{2}\epsilon_0\left[\frac{V^2l(w - x)}{d} + lxE'V\right] + U_{\text{corr}}$$

$$- \tfrac{1}{2}\epsilon_0 V^2\left[\frac{l(w - x)}{d} + \frac{lx}{d - d' + d'/\kappa}\right] + U_{\text{corr}} \qquad (4.8\text{–}10)$$

and

$$F_x = \left(\frac{\partial U}{\partial x}\right)_V = \tfrac{1}{2}\epsilon_0 V^2 l\left[\frac{\kappa}{\kappa d - (\kappa - 1)d'} - \frac{1}{d}\right] = \frac{\tfrac{1}{2}(\kappa - 1)\epsilon_0 V^2 ld'}{\kappa d^2 - (\kappa - 1)dd'}$$

[11] The correction at the edges of the slab parallel to the motion has not been included but can be made small by a large ratio l/d'.

The force is always positive, and so the slab is always pulled *into* the condenser.

More complicated applications are to be found, for instance, in connection with the various forms of the quadrant electrometer, described in books on electrical measurements.[12]   The generalization of Earnshaw's theorem to the instability of a charged conductor in an electrostatic field is given in the footnote reference on page 40.

Problem 4.8a.   Write out the details of the proof that $p_{ij} = p_{ji}$.

Problem 4.8b.   Consider a system of conductors consisting of (1) a conductor with a totally enclosed cavity, (2) an insulated conductor in the cavity, and (3) an insulated conductor outside of (1) but in its vicinity (ground or infinity is not to be enumerated as part of the system but of course cannot be overlooked). Show that there are just four independent c_{ij}'s that do not vanish, and describe them in terms of ordinary capacitances.   This calculation expresses a more formal theory of electrostatic shielding than that given in Chapter 2.

Problem 4.8c.   Find the coefficients of potential from the c_{ij}'s of problem 4.8*b*.   Show that $p_{21} = p_{11}$ and $p_{31} = p_{32}$, and give a physical interpretation of these relations.

Problem 4.8d.   Prove that $(\partial U/\partial \xi)_r = -(\partial U/\partial \xi)_Q$ by differentiating both eq. 4.7–1 and eq. 4.7–3.

Problem 4.8e.   An air condenser has plates 12 cm square, separated by 1.0 cm. A $\frac{1}{2}$-cm thick slab of Corning 0080 glass, also 12 cm square is inserted halfway between the plates.   Find the electrostatic force on the slab when the condenser is charged to 1000 v.

---

[12] See, for instance, F. A. Laws, *Electrical Measurements*, 2nd ed., McGraw-Hill, New York, 1938, pp. 234–244; F. K. Harris, *Electrical Measurements*, John Wiley, New York, 1952, pp. 445–448; L. Page and N. I. Adams, Jr., *op. cit.*, pp. 65–68.

Steady
Currents

5.1 Steady-Flow Conditions in a Conducting Wire

The flow of charge in a conductor under the influence of a field was discussed in section 2.2, and two important facts governing this flow were asserted there. In the first place, the average velocity **v** of the electrons in any given region of a conductor is proportional to the average field **E** in the region but of course in the opposite direction. In the second place, any piling up of charge that results from the motion always has the effect of reducing the field. A steady velocity requires a steady field, and therefore there must be some mechanism that prevents the piling up of charge if steady currents are to be realized. We wish to discuss this mechanism and establish in general the conditions necessary for steady flow.

We describe the flow of charge with the concepts of *current* and *current density*. A current is a flow or streaming of charge, measured by the rate at which positive charge passes through any specified surface area (e.g., the cross section of a wire).   Current is a scalar quantity denoted by the letter i; its unit, the coulomb per second, is called the *ampere*.[1]   The charge that passes the surface area in time t will thus be $Q = it$.   The current density at a point in a conducting medium is defined to be a vector **J**, having the direction of the flow of positive charge and a magnitude equal to the current per unit area through an infinitesimal area normal to the direction of flow.   **J** is measured in amperes/meter² or

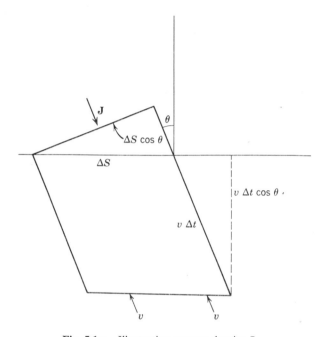

Fig. 5.1a.   Illustrating current density **J**.

coulombs/meter²-second.   The current through any small area is to be calculated by $\Delta i = \mathbf{J} \cdot \mathbf{\Delta S}$.   The current through ΔS in Fig. 5.1a, for instance, is the same as that through the area $\Delta S \cos \theta$ perpendicular to **J**, namely $J \Delta S \cos \theta$.   For large areas, clearly we must write an integral

$$i = \int_S \mathbf{J} \cdot \mathbf{dS}.$$

The sign convention just established maintains consistency with the signs for charge and charge density.   The confusion that sometimes results from the fact that electrons flow in the negative direction may be mitigated by borrowing the hole concept introduced in section 2.1.   If

[1] Other units are the milliampere (ma) which is 10^{-3} amp and the microampere (μa) which is 10^{-6} amp.

electrons are considered to move one after another, like a row of balls, the spaces ("holes") left behind by each electron successively move in the opposite direction.   These holes in the cloud of conduction electrons are regions of net positive charge.   As was said in Chapter 1, there is no easy experimental distinction between a treatment of current as a motion of electrons in the negative direction and as a motion of positive holes in the positive direction.

The first-mentioned property of conduction may be described now in terms of **J**.   If there are n conduction electrons per cubic meter, traveling with an average velocity **v**, each will travel a distance $l = v \, \Delta t$ in a time Δt, and all those in a cylinder of slant height $v \, \Delta t$ and base ΔS (Fig. 5.1a) will pass through ΔS in Δt.   The volume of the cylinder is $v \, \Delta t \cos \theta \, \Delta S$, so that $nv \, \Delta t \, \Delta S \cos \theta$ electrons will cross ΔS in the negative direction, involving a total charge of $-env \, \Delta t \, \Delta S \cos \theta$, where e is the numerical value of the electron charge.   Thus **J**, in the opposite direction to **v**, will have the magnitude

$$J = nev \qquad (5.1\text{-}1)$$

Since **v** is proportional to $-\mathbf{E}$ we can write

$$\mathbf{J} = \sigma\mathbf{E} = -\sigma \, \nabla V = \frac{\sigma}{e} \, \nabla \bar{\mu} \qquad (5.1\text{-}2a)$$

or

$$\mathbf{E} = \nabla \bar{\mu}/e = \rho\mathbf{J} \qquad (5.1\text{-}2b)$$

We write $\nabla V = -\nabla \bar{\mu}/e$ because as stated in section 2.4, it is properly the electrochemical potential $\bar{\mu}$ of the electrons that determines the current. For homogeneous isothermal materials, $\mathbf{E}$ and $\nabla \bar{\mu}$ are proportional.   The constant σ is a *scalar* constant called the *conductivity* of the conductor, and ρ its reciprocal, is called the *resistivity*.[2]   The dimensions of $\rho = 1/\sigma$ are (volts/meter) × (meter²/ampere) = meter-volts/ampere, which we shall shortly identify with meter-ohms.

Equation 5.1–2 holds whether or not $\mathbf{E}$ is constant (at least for times long compared with the mean free time t_m between electron collisions, about 10^{-14} sec).   Let us see how constant values of $\mathbf{E}$ and $\mathbf{J}$ can be maintained.   Consider first a particular piece of current-carrying material like the wire in Fig. 5.1b.   If at any instant, current is directed toward an insulated boundary of the conductor, charge must be piling up at the boundary, producing a steadily increasing added field.   Therefore constant $\mathbf{E}$ and steady flow requires $\mathbf{J}$ and $\mathbf{E}$ to be parallel to the conductor

---

[2] We have used bold-face Greek letters for σ (sigma) and ρ (rho), in order to retain conventional symbols while trying to avoid confusion with the also conventional σ and ρ for the charge densities of the previous chapters.

boundaries. If we consider any two surfaces S_1 and S_2 everywhere perpendicular to $\mathbf{J}$, each bounded by curves lying in the conductor boundaries, we will have currents $i_1 = \int_{S_1} \mathbf{J} \cdot d\mathbf{S}$ and $i_2 = \int_{S_2} \mathbf{J} \cdot d\mathbf{S}$ through them. Then i_1 must equal i_2, for otherwise charge must pile up in between. So the current must be the same through any surface that cuts across the wire. Current behaves mathematically like electric flux, and we can

Fig. 5.1b.   Current in a wire.

draw lines of flow (everywhere parallel to $\mathbf{J}$) that *do not begin or end anywhere in the conductor*. Since $\mathbf{J} = \sigma\mathbf{E}$, the lines of $\mathbf{E}$ must coincide with the current lines and must also not end in the conductor. (They could so end if σ were variable from point to point; cf. section 5.8.)

Before considering entire circuits, open or closed, let us consider the field and potential patterns in and near conducting wires. We shall assume in this chapter and the next, as we have up to now, that there is no source of electric field other than electrostatic charge distributions. We also assume that the conductors are stationary, so that no non-electric forces can act on the electron. (Magnetic sources of electric field, and non-electrostatic forces due to motion will be considered in Chapter 7.) Therefore there must reside on the surface of the conductor, and elsewhere in the external neighborhood, just the proper distribution of electric charge to produce a field inside the conductor with lines of force parallel to the edges.

We shall speak of the potential V in the conductor although we mean $-\bar{\mu}/e$ and not the cavity potential, since voltmeters and potentiometers actually measure the former. The charge flows through the conductor in the direction of decreasing potential. The two surfaces S_1 and S_2 in Fig. 5.1b are seen to be equipotentials, and the potential *decrease* between S_1 and S_2, commonly called "potential drop" and denoted by a positive number V, is

$$V = \int_1^2 \mathbf{E} \cdot d\mathbf{l} = \int_1^2 E\, dl = \int_1^2 \rho J\, dl$$

where the path of integration is along any line of flow from S_1 to S_2.

Let us consider for a moment the principle of superposition, which applies to eq. 5.1–2 because it is linear.   If we increase the field and potential everywhere in the same ratio, the flow lines will not change their pattern, but **J** will increase everywhere in the same proportion, as will i.   If we write

$$V = i \int_1^2 \rho(J/i)\, dl$$

we see that the resulting integral is independent of V and i.   Thus we can set:

$$V = Ri \qquad\qquad\qquad (5.1\text{–}3)$$

where R is a number that remains constant as V and i change but depends on the location of S_1 and S_2, on the flow pattern between these surfaces, and on the value of ρ (which we shall nearly always take as having the same value throughout the conductor, but which may vary in this case). The constant R is called the *resistance* of the piece of conductor and is measured in ohms ($=$ volts/ampere),[3] thus allowing us to measure ρ in meter-ohms.   Equation 5.1–3 is called *Ohm's law*; this name is also given to eq. 5.1–2.

If the wire is straight and long in comparison to its cross-sectional dimensions, the lines of current flow and of electric field will all be parallel, so that E will be constant along any one line and hence throughout the wire.   (The potential drop must be the same along a unit length of any line of flow, so that E must be the same on any line.)   With ρ constant, **J** is also uniform in direction and magnitude.   Thus we can write $i = JS$, where S is the cross-sectional area of the wire and $V = \int_1^2 \rho J\, dl = (\rho i/S) \int_1^2 dl = \rho l i/S$, where l is the length of wire between two cross sections S_1 and S_2.   We see that for this case,

$$R = \rho l/S \qquad\qquad\qquad (5.1\text{–}4)$$

The resistivities of materials are usually found from this equation by measuring R for samples of the materials in the form of wires.   This formula can also be used for curved wires if the radius of curvature is sufficiently large compared to the radius of the wire.[4]

Table 5.1*A* gives values of ρ for several elements and alloys.   The variation of resistance with temperature is comparatively large for pure

[3] A resistance of 10^6 ohms is called a megohm (M); 10^3 ohms is sometimes called a kilohm (K).   A common symbol for ohm is Ω (omega).   A value of 500,000 ohms can thus be written 500,000 Ω, 500 K or 0.500 M.

[4] For details on the construction of resistors, see F. Harris, *Electrical Measurements*, John Wiley, New York, 1952, Chapter 6.

Table 5.1A
Properties of Conducting Materials

	Conductivity (σ) Mhos/Meter at 20° C		Resistivity (ρ) Meter-Ohms at 20° C		Temperature Coefficient (α)*
Aluminum	3.54	$\times 10^7$	0.282	$\times 10^{-7}$	0.0039
Bismuth	0.083	$\times 10^7$	12	$\times 10^{-7}$	0.004
Brass (Cu 66%, Zn 34%)	1.39	$\times 10^7$	0.719	$\times 10^{-7}$	0.002
Carbon, 0°	0.00286	$\times 10^7$	349	$\times 10^{-7}$	−0.0005
Carbon, 500°	0.00370	$\times 10^7$	270	$\times 10^{-7}$	−0.0005
Constantan	0.20	$\times 10^7$	4.9	$\times 10^{-7}$	0.00001
Copper, annealed . . .	5.8	$\times 10^7$	0.172	$\times 10^{-7}$	0.00393
Copper, hard drawn . .	5.65	$\times 10^7$	0.176	$\times 10^{-7}$	0.00382
Iron, 99.98% pure . . .	1.0	$\times 10^7$	1.0	$\times 10^{-7}$	0.005
Lead	0.045	$\times 10^7$	22.2	$\times 10^{-7}$	0.004
Manganin (Cu 84%, Mn 12%, Ni 4%)	0.023	$\times 10^7$	43.5	$\times 10^{-7}$	0.000002
Mercury	0.0104	$\times 10^7$	96.2	$\times 10^{-7}$	0.00089
Nichrome	0.1	$\times 10^7$	10.0	$\times 10^{-7}$	0.0004
Silver	6.14	$\times 10^7$	0.162	$\times 10^{-7}$	0.0038
Sodium, 0° (solid) . .	2.3	$\times 10^7$	0.43	$\times 10^{-7}$	0.0044
Sodium, 116° (liquid) . .	0.98	$\times 10^7$	1.02	$\times 10^{-7}$	0.0033
Steel (4% Si)	0.161	$\times 10^7$	6.21	$\times 10^{-7}$	0.0008
Wolfram (tungsten) . .	1.81	$\times 10^7$	0.552	$\times 10^{-7}$	0.0045
Zinc	1.72	$\times 10^7$	0.58	$\times 10^{-7}$	0.0037
Amber	2	$\times 10^{-15}$	5	$\times 10^{14}$	
Sealing wax	1.3	$\times 10^{-14}$	8	$\times 10^{13}$	
Hard rubber	1×10^{-16}–5	$\times 10^{-14}$	2×10^{13}–1	$\times 10^{16}$	
Ordinary glass . . .	1.1	$\times 10^{-12}$	9	$\times 10^{11}$	
Mahogany	2.5	$\times 10^{-12}$	4	$\times 10^{11}$	
Commercial plate glass .	5	$\times 10^{-12}$	2	$\times 10^{11}$	
Maple wood	3.3	$\times 10^{-9}$	3	$\times 10^8$	
Red fiber	2	$\times 10^{-8}$	5	$\times 10^7$	
Blue Vermont marble . .	1	$\times 10^{-6}$	1	$\times 10^6$	
Bakelite	5×10^{-15}–5	$\times 10^{-6}$	2×10^5–2	$\times 10^{14}$	
Paraffin oil	1	$\times 10^{-14}$	1	$\times 10^{14}$	
Ethyl alcohol	3.3	$\times 10^{-5}$	3	$\times 10^4$	
Distilled water	2	$\times 10^{-4}$	5	$\times 10^3$	
Sodium chloride solution, 10% by weight . . .	12		8.33	$\times 10^{-2}$	
Sodium chloride, fused .	3.4	$\times 10^2$	2.94	$\times 10^{-3}$	

* Taken at 20° C unless otherwise indicated.

metallic elements, being approximately 0.4% per degree Centigrade in most cases. Specifically, we can say that, if R_{20} is the resistance of a piece of wire at 20° C, its resistance at $t°$ C is given approximately by

$$R_t = R_{20}[1 + 0.004(t - 20)] \qquad (5.1\text{-}5)$$

where the coefficient 0.004 is called the temperature coefficient, denoted by α in Table 5.1A. Equation 5.1-5 assumes that R_t varies linearly with t, which is not strictly true; for greater accuracy, quadratic terms should be used. For instance, for pure platinum, the relation is[5]

$$R_t = R_0(1 + 0.003985t - 0.000000586t^2) \qquad (5.1\text{-}6)$$

where R_t is given in terms of R_0, the resistance at 0° C.

Along any piece of wire of any shape, charge moves to lower values of potential, so that work is continually being done by the electric field. For each coulomb of charge that moves through one volt of potential drop, one joule of work is performed. The power expended (work per unit time) in a length of wire of resistance R is therefore

$$P = Vi = i^2R = V^2/R \qquad (5.1\text{-}7)$$

in joules/second or watts. Since, in steady flow, no kinetic energy is gained ($\mathbf{v}$ at any one point is constant in time) and no charges are redistributed, this power must all go into heat. It is in fact often called the "Joule heating."[6] It is easily understood in terms of our theory of conduction (section 2.1) as being the transfer of energy to heat in the downward quantum jumps of the electrons. Note that reversing i or V does not change the sign of P; the Joule heating is irreversible. We shall treat reversible energy changes in connection with steady currents, when we discuss the source of the energy that goes into heat in the next section.

For a small portion of a wire of cross-sectional area ΔS and length Δl, the Joule heating is $\Delta V J \Delta S$, where ΔV is the PD on the portion. Per unit area, then, we have, using a subscript S, the heating rate

$$P_S = J\,\Delta V = J(-\Delta\bar{\mu}/e) \qquad (5.1\text{-}8)$$

and per unit volume, using $\Delta V = E\,\Delta l$, the several expressions

$$P_\tau = J\,\Delta V/\Delta l = JE = \mathbf{J}\cdot\mathbf{E} = \sigma\mathbf{E}\cdot\mathbf{E} = \sigma E^2 \qquad (5.1\text{-}9)$$

The charges that reside on the surfaces of wires carrying steady currents may be discussed in relation to the potential. The amount of charge on

---

[5] H. F. Stimson, *National Bureau of Standards Journal of Research*, **42**, 209 (1949).

[6] Some of J. P. Joule's many experiments on the mechanical equivalent of heat were performed with this electrical effect.

any small portion of the surface of a wire is equal to the mean potential of that portion multiplied by its capacitance to ground or to the appropriate nearby conductor.   This distributed capacitance (the so-called stray capacitance) is seen to play a fundamental role in the production of steady currents, for it is the source of most of the field that makes the electrons flow.   The surface charges must of course be in motion as are those in the interior of the wire, but the amount at any one place must remain constant by replenishment, for steady state currents.

5.2   Complete Circuits and Emfs

Let us now ask where the lines of charge flow might begin or end. Any such place would be a location of the piling up or taking away of electrons (or, of course, of positive charge).   The field produced by the charge in these regions would then vary in time, so that for flow that is steady for a long or indefinite time there can be no such regions, and we shall not consider them here.   We shall come back in section 5.3 to the case of flow that is approximately steady for short times and in which charge is transferred from end to end of the flow lines.

Since wires are not infinitely long, the lines of flow must form closed loops if they are not to end.[7]   *Steady currents require closed circuits.* There may be branches in the circuit where three or more wires are connected together, but any given line of flow will close on itself without branching.   Such a closed flow line will be called a *current filament.*

If we follow a current filament along a wire, starting from one point in the circuit, we observe a continual decrease in potential.   This cannot go on indefinitely, since $\oint \mathbf{E} \cdot \mathbf{dl} = 0$ here as elsewhere where all fields are electrostatic.   There *must* be some portion of the circuit that does not behave like a conductor (does not obey Ohm's law) but where there is a *rise* in potential along the current.   There must also, of course, be some place where energy is available to be the source of the Joule heat, since the charge densities on the surfaces of the various conductors do not change and their potential energy cannot be the source.

The most common non-magnetic sources of energy and locations of potential rises are at the electrode-to-solution boundaries in chemical cells. We shall not consider such cells in detail, but we need to consider enough of their electrical properties to provide an explanation of their potential rises.

[7] It is possible to have, in an extended conducting medium, a spiraling or twisted system of non-closed current lines topologically similar to the **D** lines of Fig. 3.8d, but circuits with wires whose thickness is neglected cannot show such behavior.

Let us consider as an example the so-called dry cell. It consists of a zinc can filled with a paste-like solution of ammonium chloride (NH_4Cl) and zinc chloride ($ZnCl_2$) in water.   At the center there is a carbon rod surrounded by a mixture of insoluble manganese oxides, MnO_2 and Mn_2O_3.   The solution is a conductor because it contains negative chlorine ions (Cl^-) and positive zinc and ammonium ions (Zn^{++} and NH_4^+) that are free to move as charge carriers.

Now, the potential rise we are concerned with is actually a drop in $\bar{\mu}$. However, the solution in this cell contains no free electrons and cannot be said to have a $\bar{\mu}$.   Let us turn our attention then to the cavity potentials of the four parts, zinc can, solution, manganese oxide mixture, and carbon rod.

Zinc atoms can rather easily give up their two valence electrons (becoming zinc ions) and enter the solution.   Since water molecules are dipoles, their negative ends can turn to attract the positive zinc ions, so that the dipoles effectively pull zinc ions off the metal surface.   Thermal agitation of the zinc atoms assists this process.   Every ion that comes off will leave the metal negative, since two electrons are left behind.   The cavity potential of the solution becomes positive, and there will be a layer of positive ions just outside the metal, with a corresponding layer of negative charge (electrons) just inside the metal.   The process will stop when the electric field is just strong enough to balance the attraction of the water dipoles.   Such a pair of layers in a chemical cell is called a double layer. Its thickness is fixed by atomic dimensions, so the definite **E** at equilibrium corresponds to a definite cavity PD between metal and solution (see problem 1.7*i* for a numerical example).

· If the cavity PD were reduced, more zinc ions would pass into solution until the PD was restored to its equilibrium value. If electrons were continually removed from the zinc case so that the cavity PD were kept below the equilibrium value, zinc ions would enter into the solution steadily, at a rate depending on the change in PD.   Similarly, if the PD were kept larger than the equilibrium value, zinc ions would be continuously pulled back to the case.

By combining the work function of the zinc with the cavity PD between zinc and solution, we can arrive at a relation between the Fermi level in the zinc and the potential energy of an electron in an imaginary cavity in the solution.   Let us next describe the relation between the latter potential energy and the Fermi level in the carbon rod.

At the carbon rod, a fairly complex chemical reaction can occur, involving the transformation of ammonium chloride to ammonium hydroxide and of MnO_2 to Mn_2O_3, accompanied by a transfer of electrons from the carbon rod (the carbon itself is inert).   Without going into the chemical details,[8] we can treat the electron transfer as a passage from the Fermi level in the carbon to a certain level in the manganese oxide mixture. We can consider all the energy changes involved in the reaction to be lumped together and included in the electron energy jump, leading to a sort of effective $\bar{\mu}$ for the manganese oxide mixture.

The manganese oxide mixture is complex but will undoubtedly have an average contact PD with the solution, so its cavity PD and (taking into account its average work function) its $\bar{\mu}$ will come to definite levels with respect to a cavity in the solution.   The carbon $\bar{\mu}$ at equilibrium will equal the effective $\bar{\mu}$ of the manganese oxide and will therefore itself have a definite relation to the electron potential energy in a cavity in the solution. The main point to be emphasized is that the $\bar{\mu}$'s of the two electrodes will be *differently* related to this cavity, so they will be unequal; in fact, their difference is about 1.5 ev.

A cell, in simple terms, is a chemical device for putting two conductors into electrical contact while maintaining a difference of Fermi levels between them.

When an external circuit is established between the terminals of a dry cell, the difference of $\bar{\mu}$'s starts a current, which tends to reduce the cavity PD at each interface in the cell.   These reductions increase the rate of chemical reaction and hence of charge transfer in the cell.   A steady current will result for that difference of $\bar{\mu}$'s at the cell terminals that produces the same current inside and outside the cell.   (There will be a PD across the solution itself due to its ohmic conduction property.) The lines of J will then be continuous, but charge will be carried by electrons in the wires, by ions through the solution, by Zn^{++} ions at one double layer, and by electrons at the other.

The sources of energy for the cell are the energy changes that occur in the chemical reactions.   These changes are of electric origin and could be described as charge rearrangements, involving both electrostatic potential energy and molecular (electronic) kinetic energy.   A cell has an enormous reservoir of separated positive and negative charges which release energy as they re-arrange themselves but are limited by their atomic and wavelike (quantum) properties to rearranging by means of the relatively slow chemical reactions at the solid-liquid interfaces.

[8] The two reactions can be written

$$NH_4^+ + H_2O \rightarrow NH_4OH + H^+$$

$$2MnO_2 + 2H^+ + 2e^- \rightarrow Mn_2O_3 + H_2O$$

For details on this and other so-called primary cells, see the article by W. J. Hamer in the *Encyclopedia of Chemical Technology*, Interscience, New York, 1949, Vol. 3, pp. 292–342; also G. W. Vinal, *Primary Batteries*, John Wiley, New York, 1950.

Although we described the dry cell as having a difference in $\bar{\mu}$ at one interface only, it is possible to define one at each interface, and we shall refer to cells in general as each having two such PD's.

A most important property of chemical-cell potential differences is that they do not reverse with the current (that is, if an external source is arranged to make the current pass in the reverse direction). Therefore the power involved *does* reverse. Thus electric potential energy can either be produced or used up in a cell. (Actual reversal in many cells, such as the one described, leads to extraneous chemical reactions that interfere considerably with the primary ones, but ideal infinitesimal reversals will do for the arguments which follow.)

Any such reversible potential difference in a circuit is called "an electromotive force," abbreviated emf and written with the symbol $\mathscr{E}$. We shall use only the abbreviation, since the word "force" has come to mean something with definite dimensions different from those of potential difference. Let us now use the obvious fact that the net change of V or $\bar{\mu}$ around a circuit is zero and apply it to an unbranched circuit in which all the conduction is ohmic except at two double-layers in a cell, the sum of whose PD's is a constant $\mathscr{E}$. We shall assume the solution to be ohmic, with resistance r, which we shall call the "internal resistance" of the cell.[9] Then the entire potential drop V must equal the rise $\mathscr{E}$. Since V is the sum of terms iR for all the sections into which we wish to divide the ohmic part of the circuit, we can write

$$\mathscr{E} = i\left(\sum_j R_j + r\right) = i(R_{ext} + r) \tag{5.2 1}$$

where $\sum_j R_j = R_{ext}$ is the sum of the external resistances. The generalization of eq. 5.2–1 to branched circuits will be made in section 5.5.

From eq. 5.2–1 we can find the power relation for the circuit, for the power produced by the emf $\mathscr{E}$ is

$$\mathscr{E}i = i^2(R_{ext} + r) \tag{5.2-2}$$

How does the energy "travel" from the double layer where it becomes available to the conducting portions of the circuit where it appears as heat? The electric field that pushes the electrons can be said to perform the work, although any given charge that produces the field will acquire as much potential energy from charges of the same sign moving toward it as it will lose by charges moving away from it. These charges provide a sort

[9] If the PD's on the double layers are changed when the currents are established as mentioned above, the change will be approximately proportional to the current, and can be included in eq. 5.2–1 by assigning part of r to each double layer.

of guiding field for the current without actually performing net work. We shall see later (section 10.4) that we can account for the flow of energy in terms of both electric and magnetic fields.   It will suffice here to point out that since the moving electrons in the body of the wire do *not* push each other along or have any appreciable interactions with each other, other than the preservation of the average electrical neutrality in the metal, it would be incorrect to say that the energy flows along inside the wires.

5.3   The Establishment of Steady Flow, Condenser Charging, and Time Constants

Let us consider the following process of initiating a steady current in a conductor, in order to give a graphic picture of the fields and charges

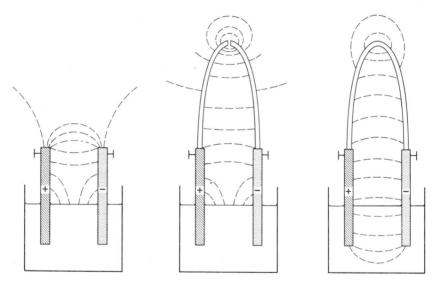

Fig. 5.3a-c.   Lines of force for a chemical cell.

involved in the establishment of steady flow.   We start with a cell that has two electrodes projecting at the top with no wires connected.   Two long wires are then connected to the two terminals.   After charges on them have come to rest, their ends are connected together and the current starts.

At first, there will be an electric field between the terminals and from terminals to solution, somewhat as in Fig. 5.3a.   (Remember that the solution as a whole lies at a potential somewhere between the potentials of the two electrodes.)   In the second case, Fig. 5.3b, the two wires become extensions of the equipotential volumes of each electrode. (There is, of course, nothing to prevent these wires being several miles long or having many bends and twists, etc.) Lines of force proceed from one to the other along their entire lengths, entering and leaving the wire surfaces at right angles. The field is strongest where the wires are closest. In each case, the PD between the electrodes is equal to the sum of the double-layer PD's, that is, to the emf $\mathscr{E}$ of the cell. (By making all the wires of the same material, the constant difference between the cavity PD and $-\bar{\mu}/e$ can be left out of consideration.)

When the ends of the wires are brought together, the field between the ends increases to a large value (same PD, small distance), often enough to make a spark-over just before they touch. At the instant of contact, electrons move very rapidly under the action of this large field, rapidly destroying the equipotential nature of the nearby wire interiors. Thus a current is initiated. Much of the flow is likely to have components toward the boundaries, so that charge rapidly gets to the boundaries and redirects the field along the wires. These effects will spread along the whole length of each wire, and readjustments will continue until the conditions of steady flow are reached, as in Fig. 5.3c.

Note that the lines of force meet the wires at angles other than 90° because there is now a component of field parallel to the wire. Also, note the lines of force in the solution between the electrodes.

The time taken for the establishment of steady flow is experimentally observed to be very short. To estimate this time, we shall take into consideration the distributed capacitance of the wires. The idea behind the calculation will be clearer if we first deal with the process of charging or discharging a single large condenser (a "lumped" rather than a "distributed" capacitance). Consider a condenser of capacitance C that is charged to a potential difference $V = V_0$ and connected to wires like those attached to the cell of Figs. 5.3a–c. A very similar set of diagrams can be made for (a) the isolated condenser, (b) the condenser with two pieces of wire connected to its terminals but not to each other, and (c) the situation shortly after the wires are joined. The condenser will begin to discharge, with lines of charge flow passing from the positive charges on one plate through the wire to the negatives on the other.

As a first estimate of the time it will take, let R be the total resistance of the two joined wires. Then the current, as soon as the very short time of establishment is over, will be $i = V_0/R$, or nearly so if V has decreased somewhat. If we assumed that V and i did not change, the charge $Q_0 = CV_0$ initially on the condenser would have passed through the wire from positive plate to negative in a time given by writing $Q_0 = it_0$, so that $t_0 = Q_0/i = CV_0/(V_0/R) = RC$.

Now we can specify the conditions of the experiment more carefully in order to make a better calculation. Let us choose C so that RC is very much larger than the experimentally observed time for the establishment of steady current with a *cell* of emf $\mathscr{E} = V_0$ and the same wires with the same R. The discharging can then be considered a slow process, with Q and $V = Q/C$ on the condenser changing slowly with time. In this case, the current will remain steady for any period of time short compared to RC, during which the potential V of the condenser does not change appreciably. We shall call such currents "quasi-steady." Thus we can write

$$V = Q/C = iR$$

and since the current is the rate at which the condenser discharges,

$$i = -dQ/dt$$

so that

$$R\frac{dQ}{dt} = -\frac{Q}{C} \tag{5.3-1}$$

which is a differential equation that can be written in a form suitable for integration:

$$\frac{dQ}{Q} = -\frac{dt}{RC}$$

We have

$$\int \frac{dQ}{Q} = \ln Q + \text{constant} = -\int \frac{dt}{RC} = -\frac{t}{RC} + \text{constant}$$

which we can write, letting a be the difference of the two constants,

$$\ln Q = -t/RC + a$$

and

$$e^{\ln Q} = e^{(-t/RC)+a}$$

or

$$Q = e^a \cdot e^{-t/RC}$$

The quantity e^a can be evaluated by setting $t = 0$, since we are given that the condenser starts with charge Q_0. Thus we have

$$Q = Q_0 e^{-t/RC} \tag{5.3-2}$$

and from $i = -dQ/dt$,

$$i = \frac{Q_0}{RC} e^{-t/RC} = \frac{V_0}{R} e^{-t/RC} = i_0 e^{-t/RC} \tag{5.3-3}$$

so that, since $V = iR$,

$$V = V_0 e^{-t/RC} \tag{5.3-4}$$

It is seen that Q, i, and V all decrease in the same way with time.   The exponential function $e^{-t/RC}$ is plotted in Fig. 5.3d.   The value RC is now seen to be the time it takes the potential, charge, or current to drop to $1/e = 0.368$ of its initial value and is called the "time constant" of the circuit containing the capacitance C and resistance R, being the only way in which a meaningful discharge time can be defined (of course a factor other than $1/e$ could be adopted).

Now if we charge up a capacitance with a cell of emf $\mathscr{E}$ and wires of

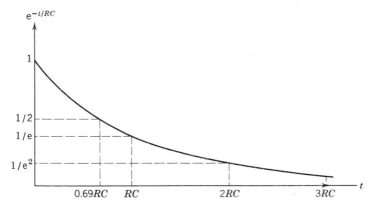

Fig. 5.3d.   Exponential-decay curve.

total resistance R (including the internal resistance r of the cell), we will also have quasi-steady flow.   In this case, there are three types of PD around the circuit (see Fig. 5.3e).   The rise is the emf $\mathscr{E}$; the potential

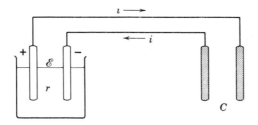

Fig. 5.3e.   Charging a capacitance from a cell.

difference in the condenser is down in the direction of the current (although no actual current exists between the condenser plates), as is the iR drop. Thus we have

$$\mathscr{E} = iR + \frac{Q}{C} = R\frac{dQ}{dt} + \frac{Q}{C} \qquad (5.3\text{–}5)$$

where $i = +dQ/dt$ since the current increases Q in this case. This is a more complicated differential equation than eq. 5.3–1. It can be reduced to a form similar to the latter if we define $q = \mathscr{E}C - Q$, the difference between the final charge $\mathscr{E}C$ on the condenser and its value Q at any time t. Then $Q = \mathscr{E}C - q$, and

$$\frac{dQ}{dt} = -\frac{dq}{dt}$$

so that eq. 5.3–5 reads

$$\mathscr{E} = -R\frac{dq}{dt} + \frac{\mathscr{E}C - q}{C} = -R\frac{dq}{dt} + \mathscr{E} - \frac{q}{C}$$

or

$$R\frac{dq}{dt} = -\frac{q}{C}$$

We can then repeat the earlier method of solution and obtain

$$q = q_0 e^{-t/RC}$$

Since in the charging case $Q_0 = 0$ and $q_0 = \mathscr{E}C$, we have

$$\mathscr{E}C - Q = \mathscr{E}Ce^{-t/RC}$$

which rearranges to

$$Q = \mathscr{E}C[1 - e^{-t/RC}] \tag{5.3–6}$$

from which we derive

$$i = \frac{\mathscr{E}}{R}e^{-t/RC} \tag{5.3–7}$$

and for the PD on the condenser

$$V = \mathscr{E}[1 - e^{-t/RC}] \tag{5.3–8}$$

The charge and potential on the condenser increase as shown by the graph of $1 - e^{-t/RC}$ in Fig. 5.3f, whereas the current decreases as in the previous case.

Note that in time $t = 2RC$ the functions in Figs. 5.3d and 5.3f are within $1/e^2$ of their final values, and so forth. Apparently one requires infinite times for complete charge and discharge. However, after sufficiently long times the discrete nature of charge will play a role, and fluctuations due to thermal agitation will end the process. Since the electron charge $e = 1.6 \times 10^{-19}$ coulomb, a typical charge of 10^{-6} coulomb would have to be reduced to about 10^{-13} of itself before the discreteness is important. However, $10^{-13} = e^{-13\ln 10} = e^{-13 \times 2.3} = e^{-30}$, so that a reduction of 10^{-13} occurs when $t = 30RC$. If RC is 1 sec, the process of charge or discharge is essentially through in one-half a minute ($t = 5RC$ or $6RC$ would generally give a *practically* complete discharge).

The time constant of a resistance–capacitance series circuit plays a fundamental role in alternating-current and pulse circuits, especially those involving vacuum tubes. We shall return to such matters later (section 9.8).

Let us reconsider the establishment of a current in a circuit with a cell and wires of resistance R. The capacitance is now distributed rather than lumped, which means that all parts of the circuit charge up simultaneously, and we can only calculate the time constant approximately.

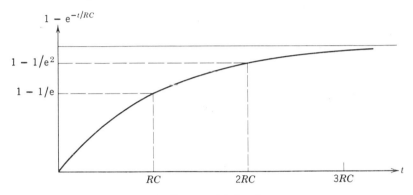

Fig. 5.3f.   Exponential-charging curve.

The capacitance of a wire parallel to a plane conductor—in particular a grounded conductor—is given by eq. 4.5–7. Any piece of our circuit will have approximately a capacitance of $2\pi\epsilon_0/\ln(2h/R_w)$ farads/m to ground, even though the latter only approximates a plane. Here, h is the distance from wire to ground, and R_w is the radius of the wire. The ratio $2h/R_w$ is likely to vary from about 4 (when $h \simeq 2R_w$) upwards to, say, 100 or 1000. Its logarithm will then vary from 1.4 to 7 or more. We can thus estimate the capacitance per meter of our circuit at 4×10^{-11} farads (if $\ln(2h/R_w) = 1.4$) down to 0.8×10^{-11} farads (if $\ln(2h/R_w) = 7$). Taking 1×10^{-11} farad/m as an average value, and a circuit of 2 m length, we have a total capacitance of the order of 2×10^{-11} farad $= 20\ \mu\mu$f. Now, the largest resistances in common use in laboratory circuits are of the order of 10^6 ohms. If $R = 10^6$ and $C = 2 \times 10^{-11}$, then $RC = 2 \times 10^{-5}$ sec. In many cases, R will be smaller and so will C, so that this time is an upper limit. In very long circuits—e.g., the miles of wire from a generating plant to a distant house—the resistance is kept low to reduce power losses, so that if we have, say, 10^4 m of wire we are likely to have only a few ohms, and the time will again be very short.

Calculations of a more exact nature that take into account the distributed nature of the capacitance in a circuit can produce more definite answers but will not change the order of magnitude of the results just obtained.

5.4 Simple Battery Circuits

In this section we shall consider in detail the current, voltage, and resistance relationships in simple circuits containing resistances and one or more electrochemical cells.   Consider first the case already discussed,

$$R_{ext} = R_a + R_b + R_c + R_d$$

Fig. 5.4a.   Potential-resistance diagram, simple circuit.

of one cell of emf $\mathscr{E}$ and internal resistance r, with an external conductor whose total resistance is R_{ext}.   Let us graph the potential V at points around the circuit as a function of the resistance measured along it from any arbitrary point, such as $\mathscr{P}$ in the schematic circuit in Fig. 5.4a. The potential falls along the resistive part of the circuit, with a slope $dV/dR = -i$, where i is the current.   At the first double layer, there is a sudden rise $\mathscr{E}'$ ($\mathscr{M}\mathscr{N}$ in the figure), then a fall in the solution between the plates ($\mathscr{N}\mathscr{S}$), another rise $\mathscr{E}''$, and then a steady fall back to the point $\mathscr{Q}$ which is at the same potential as $\mathscr{P}$ and represents the same point. The reader might imagine the graph to be wound around a cylinder so that $\mathscr{Q}$ and $\mathscr{P}$ coincide.   The dotted lines $\mathscr{N}\mathscr{U}$ and $\mathscr{U}\mathscr{T}$ complete a parallelogram that shows that $\mathscr{E}'$ and $\mathscr{E}''$ can be considered as acting at one place, with the internal resistance r added to R_{ext}, for purposes of studying the external behavior of the circuit.   Figures 5.4b and 5.4c show the results obtained when combining two cells into a battery, first in the usual way with emf's adding, and second with emf's opposing. The dotted lines again show that we may treat any such battery (or any series-connected group of cells) as having a simple emf and internal resistance. Figure 5.4c shows graphically the reversal of emf without reversal of internal-resistance drop when a cell is connected backwards.

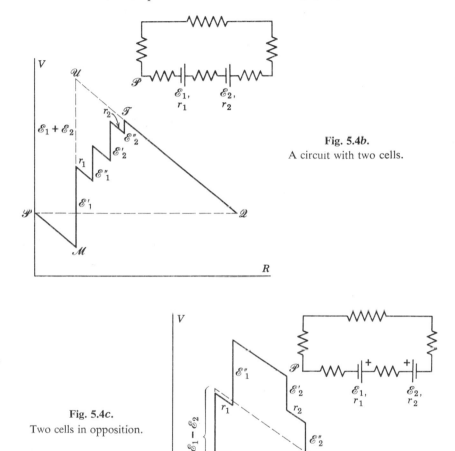

Fig. 5.4b.
A circuit with two cells.

Fig. 5.4c.
Two cells in opposition.

Figure 5.4d shows a diagram and graph for a circuit with two elements in parallel. The graph proceeds as in Fig. 5.4a from $\mathscr{P}$ to $\mathscr{X}$, where the current divides. The line $\mathscr{X}\mathscr{Y}_1$ shows the drop from $\mathscr{X}$ to $\mathscr{Y}$ in resistor R_1, and similarly for the line $\mathscr{X}\mathscr{Y}_2$ and resistor R_2. Here $\mathscr{Y}_1$ and $\mathscr{Y}_2$ have the same ordinate because they both represent the same point $\mathscr{Y}$ and the same potential. The rest of the graph could equally well be continued from $\mathscr{Y}_1$ instead of from $\mathscr{Y}_2$ as shown. The lines $\mathscr{X}\mathscr{Y}_1$ and $\mathscr{X}\mathscr{Y}_2$ must each have a less negative slope than $\mathscr{T}\mathscr{X}$ because the current is less in each branch than in the rest of the circuit. Furthermore, the sum of the slopes of $\mathscr{X}\mathscr{Y}_1$ and $\mathscr{X}\mathscr{Y}_2$ must equal that of $\mathscr{T}\mathscr{X}_1$ since $i_1 + i_2 = i$ in order that no charge continue to pile up at $\mathscr{X}$ and $\mathscr{Y}$.

Fig. 5.4d. A circuit with a parallel branch.

Any battery circuit with elements in series (no branches) can be represented schematically as in Fig. 5.4e, where we use R for R_{ext} to make the writing simpler. The current is given by

$$i = \frac{\mathscr{E}}{r + R} \tag{5.4-1}$$

and is a maximum when $R = 0$, a condition known as a "short circuit." When $R = \infty$, we have an "open circuit" and zero current.

The external potential drop is $V = iR$, or

$$V = \mathscr{E}\,\frac{R}{r + R} \tag{5.4-2}$$

in terms of R and

$$V = \mathscr{E} - ir \tag{5.4-3}$$

in terms of i. Thus we may think of V as being that proportion of $\mathcal{E}$ that R is of the total resistance in the circuit, or as being the emf reduced by the internal potential drop ir.

Equation 5.4–3 can be applied, for instance, to the case of a distant cell (or generator) furnishing power to some location through a long power line. The resistance of the line is fixed and can be considered as part of r, in fact often the major part. Thus the voltage available will depend on the current drawn by virtue of the "line drop" ir.

Fig. 5.4e.   A cell with a load and an internal resistance.

The power expended in the resistance R of Fig. 5.4e is

$$P = i^2R = \frac{\mathcal{E}^2R}{(r+R)^2} \tag{5.4-4}$$

Suppose we vary R keeping $\mathcal{E}$ and r fixed. Then P is zero if $R = 0$ and also if $R \to \infty$. It has a maximum which can be found by writing $dP/dR = 0$. It is left to the reader to show that this occurs when $R = r$ (problem 5.4a). The maximum power that a given battery can furnish to a variable resistance R is furnished when R equals the internal resistance of the battery.[10] This statement is the power-transfer theorem and is of extreme practical importance. We shall see later that it can be applied in the alternating-current case as well (section 9.6).

The efficiency of the power transfer may be defined as the ratio of the power expended in R to the power $\mathcal{E}i$ produced by the emf, so that

$$\text{efficiency} = \frac{P}{\mathcal{E}i} = \frac{iR}{\mathcal{E}} = \frac{R}{R+r} \tag{5.4-5}$$

a quantity that varies from 0 to 1 as R varies from 0 to ∞ and is equal to the fraction of the emf that appears as external PD. The efficiency is

[10] For low-resistance sources, such as storage batteries or generators, the maximum power cannot be drawn without serious overheating of connecting wires or damage to battery cells. The theorem as stated is of practical importance only for high-resistance sources.

50% under the condition of maximum power transfer, and the external voltage is $\mathscr{E}/2$.

The external resistance R is often called a "load" when power transfer is under consideration. The conductance $G = 1/R$ of the load may be taken as a measure of it, so that "no load" refers to an open circuit ($R = \infty$). The "regulation" of a source of power designed for a particular load G is a number expressing the internal drop (or line loss, or difference between PD at rated load and at no load) as a percent of the rated voltage on the load. In our terms, the regulation $= ir/V = (\mathscr{E} - V)/V$.

Fig. 5.4*f*.   Resistances in parallel.

We have indicated that when several resistance elements are connected in series, their total or overall resistance is their sum:

$$R = R_1 + R_2 + R_3 + \cdots \tag{5.4-6}$$

On the other hand, when we have several resistors connected in parallel, forming several branches, as in the circuit of Fig. 5.4*f*, we can treat the group as a single resistor by the following considerations. Let V be the common potential difference across all the resistors, and let $i_1, i_2 \cdots$ be the separate currents. Then $i_1 = V/R_1$, $i_2 = V/R_2$ etc; the separate currents are inversely proportional to the resistances. If i is the current in the rest of the circuit ($\mathscr{E}$ and r in the figure), then since charge does not collect at the junctions,

$$i = i_1 + i_2 + \cdots$$

or

$$i = V/R_1 + V/R_2 + \cdots = V\left(\frac{1}{R_1} + \frac{1}{R_2} + \cdots\right)$$

Thus i and V are proportional, and so the group of resistors acts like a single one. The reciprocal of its resistance, i/V is given by the symmetrical formula

$$\frac{1}{R} = \frac{1}{R_1} + \frac{1}{R_2} + \cdots \tag{5.4-7a}$$

The reciprocal of a resistance is called a conductance, and is measured in mhos.[11]   Thus eq. 5.4–7a can be written

$$G = G_1 + G_2 + \cdots \qquad (5.4\text{–}7b)$$

A discussion of voltmeter and ammeter measurements will not be out of place in this section, although the electromagnetic forces upon which such meters depend for their operation will not be taken up until Chapter 7, and their actual construction in section 8.8.   Both instruments may be described here in terms of their common, central feature—a device that gives a mechanical deflection to an indicating pointer that is proportional to the current through the instrument.   This device is generally called a "galvanometer."   Common forms require from 5×10^{-5} to 10^{-2} amp for full-scale deflection.

A voltmeter is made by placing a high resistance (called a "multiplier") in series with a galvanometer so that the full-scale current will flow through the instrument when some chosen PD exists between the terminals.   Then for any lower potential difference V the current and the deflection will change proportionately, so that the scale can be calibrated directly in volts.

A voltmeter is connected between the two points in a circuit whose PD is desired.   The current drawn by the voltmeter generally disturbs the circuit under test, however, and it is usually important to have this disturbance small.   It is customary to indicate the full-scale current, or sensitivity, for a given meter by indicating the ratio of the instrument's resistance to the full-scale voltage reading.   Thus for a full-scale current of 5×10^{-5} amp, the sensitivity is $1/(5 \times 10^{-5}) = 20,000$ ohms/v.

An ammeter is made by putting a small resistance, called a "shunt," in parallel with the galvanometer.   If the shunt resistance is considerably less than that of the galvanometer, most of the current that enters and leaves the terminals will pass through the shunt.   However, the small fraction that passes through the galvanometer will be proportional to the total, so that the scale can be calibrated directly in amperes.   It is desirable for an ammeter to have as low a resistance as possible, so as to interfere as little as possible with a circuit in series with which it is inserted.

Problem 5.4a.   Prove the statement in the text that the maximum power transfer for a cell with an external resistance R occurs when R is equal to the internal resistance r.

Problem 5.4b.   Write the ratio of power expended in a resistance R connected to a cell of emf $\mathscr{E}$ and resistance r, to the maximum available, in terms of the ratio $K = r/R$.   Show the slow variation of this ratio with K by calculating the ratio

[11] The word "mho" is the "reciprocal" of "ohm."   A conductance of $(1 \text{ megohm})^{-1}$ is called a "micromho."

for $K = 100, 20, 10, 2,$ and $1.25.$ Show also that the ratio for any value K' is the same as for $K = 1/K'.$

Problem 5.4c.   You are given three resistors, of values 1 ohm, 2 ohms, and 3 ohms.   Find all the resistance values obtainable by series and parallel arrangements of these resistors.

Problem 5.4d.   Two equal resistors R_1, and two others R_2 and R_3 are arranged as shown (Fig. 5.4g).   Find the relation that must hold between R_1 and R_2 if the resistance between $\mathscr{A}$ and $\mathscr{B}$ is to be equal to R_3.

Problem 5.4e.   Find the relation between the values R_1, R_2, and R_3 in Fig. 5.4g when an emf $\mathscr{E}$ and series resistance equal to R_3 is connected between $\mathscr{A}$ and $\mathscr{B}$, and the PD across the original R_3 is $\mathscr{E}/200$.

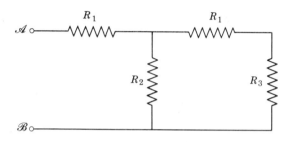

Fig. 5.4g.   (Problem 5.4d)

Problem 5.4f.   An emf $\mathscr{E}_1$ with resistance r_1 is in parallel with an emf $\mathscr{E}_2$ of resistance r_2.   The PD across the combination is V, and the net current entering and leaving is i.   Find the relation between V and i involving $\mathscr{E}_1, \mathscr{E}_2, r_1$ and r_2, and give a rule for constructing a series circuit with one $\mathscr{E}$ and one r that is equivalent to this parallel circuit (has the same relation between V and i).

Problem 5.4g.   A certain resistor is supposed to have a resistance of 11 K (11,000 ohms), but its value is actually 10% too high.   What resistance should be put in parallel to correct its value?   What tolerance is allowable in the added resistor if the resulting value can be in error by 2%?

Problem 5.4h.   Solve problem 5.4g, but a correction is to be made for a value that is 10% too low.

Problem 5.4i.   Find the current in each resistor in Fig. 5.4h.

Problem 5.4j.   A generator has an emf of 120 v and feeds a certain house with a line whose resistance is 0.13 ohm in each wire.   In the house there are three 60-watt, 120-volt lamps connected in parallel on the line.   Then an electric iron rated at 120 v and 1100 watts is connected in parallel.   Find the drop in voltage at the lamps when the iron is connected.   (Assume resistances of lamps and iron to be constant.)

Problem 5.4k.   A 500-v generator feeds a trolley line.   The overhead wire has a resistance of 0.10 ohm/mile.   The return rails have a combined resistance of 0.03 ohm/mile.   Two cars are on the line, one 1.0 mile from the power house, and one 3.0 miles away.   The motor in each is controlled so as to draw 100 amp.   Find the PD at each trolley car.

Problem 5.4l.   A battery of emf 120 v and internal resistance 4 ohms is

connected to a parallel combination of 20 ohms and a variable resistor R.   Find
the value of R that will result in an expenditure of 100 watts in itself.

Problem 5.4m.   A 20,000-ohm/volt voltmeter of range 300 v is used to test a
certain power supply.   It reads 270 v.   Then a resistance of 6000 ohms is placed
in parallel with the voltmeter, which now reads 234 v.   If the power supply can
be treated as an emf $\mathcal{E}$ with a resistance r in series, find $\mathcal{E}$ and r to 1 %.

Problem 5.4n.   A certain galvanometer deflects full scale when a PD of 50
millivolts is placed across it.   Its resistance is 1.0 ohm.   Tell how to construct
an ammeter of range 2 amp and a voltmeter of ranges 10 v and 100 v, with this
galvanometer.

Fig. 5.4h.   (Problem 5.4*i*)

Problem 5.4o.   A 3-v voltmeter of 100-ohms/volt resistance and an ammeter of
range 0.2 amp and resistance 0.25 ohm are used along with a 1.5-v cell to measure
a resistance whose value is about 9 ohms.   Calculate the percentage of error
made for each method of connecting the meters in taking the ratio of their
readings to be the correct value of the resistance.

Problem 5.4p.   A generator of emf $\mathcal{E} = 220$ v has an internal resistance of
0.040 ohm and is rated to deliver 100 kilowatts.   Find the percent regulation.

Problem 5.4q.   A 1.5-v dry cell is short-circuited through an ammeter whose
resistance is 0.0010 ohm.   If the ammeter reads 28 amp, find the internal
resistance of the cell.

5.5   The Method of Kirchhoff

The rules of the previous section for resistances in series and in parallel
can be used to solve a number of circuit problems for the pertinent currents
and voltages.   The circuit of problem 5.4*i* is a fairly complex example.

However, there are many more complicated cases that cannot be handled this way, and it is important to develop a more general method. For instance, if the connections between the resistances are complicated, as by the 400-Ω connection between two parallel branches in Fig. 5.5a, or if there are emf's in various parts of a circuit, as in Fig. 5.5b, we cannot use the ordinary series-parallel calculation for effective resistance.

The general method for handling such problems must evidently involve

Fig. 5.5a-b.   Circuits for which series-parallel calculations do not apply.

writing down suitable simultaneous equations for the various unknown currents and/or voltages. The method is called the method of Kirchhoff and the rules for obtaining equations are the conditions we have already discussed, namely, that no current lines end anywhere and the total potential drop around any closed path is zero.

Formal statements of the rules are known as "Kirchhoff's laws":

1. The sum of the currents entering any junction of three or more circuit elements equals the sum of the currents leaving that junction.

2. The sum of the emf's around any closed loop in a circuit, taken with due regard to signs, equals the sum of the ohmic potential drops around that loop.

There are several ways of writing equations from these rules. One may write them in terms of currents or of voltages and one may either construct sets of equations from both laws or define a set of unknowns that automatically satisfy one law, leading to a single set of equations derived from the other law. We shall illustrate by considering the branch-current and the loop-current methods. As an example, we shall take the circuit of Fig. 5.5c, which with certain simplifications will be important for the study of the Wheatstone's bridge in section 5.7 ($\mathscr{E}_g$ and R_g will become the galvanometer branch; $\mathscr{E}_b$ and R_b the battery branch of the bridge).

The branch-current method consists in assigning symbols and positive

directions for the currents in each distinct branch and writing two sets
of equations for these currents.   A branch is the complete set of series-
connected elements between two junctions, where by the word junction
we mean a point where three or more elements are connected together.
If the number of junctions is j, the first rule will provide us with j equations.
However, one of these equations must be derivable from the others, since,
if charge of either sign does not collect at any $j - 1$ of the junctions, it
cannot collect at the jth one.   (There cannot be one single point where

Fig. 5.5c. Branch current analysis.

flow lines begin or end.)   Thus we get $j - 1$ *independent* equations.   In
our example, $j = 4$, and the three equations are for junctions $\mathscr{A}$, $\mathscr{B}$, and
$\mathscr{C}$ respectively.

$$i_3 + i_1 = i_b \tag{5.5-1}$$

$$i_4 = i_3 + i_g \tag{5.5-2}$$

$$i_g + i_2 = i_1 \tag{5.5-3}$$

The equation for junction $\mathscr{D}$ is evidently just the sum of these three.

Now, if there are m branches in the circuit and m unknown currents,
we need $m - (j - 1)$ equations from the second rule, so we choose $m - j + 1$
loops for application of the rule.   For each one, a positive direction of
circulation is assumed, as indicated by the curved arrows in Fig. 5.5a,
where $m = 6$ and $m - j + 1 = 3$.   The equations become for this case,
taking loops in the order 1, 2, and b,

$$i_1 R_1 + i_g R_g - i_3 R_3 = \mathscr{E}_1 + \mathscr{E}_g \tag{5.5-4}$$

$$i_2 R_2 - i_g R_g - i_4 R_4 = \mathscr{E}_2 - \mathscr{E}_g \tag{5.5-5}$$

$$i_b R_b + i_4 R_4 + i_3 R_3 = \mathscr{E}_b \tag{5.5-6}$$

We now have six equations in the six unknowns i_1, i_2, i_3, i_4, i_g, and i_b, which can be solved by standard methods.

However, let us proceed with the loop-current method.   In this method, we consider that there are a set of independent closed currents flowing in $m - j + 1$ loops, so that the first rule of Kirchhoff is satisfied automatically, although we have the non-physical idea of two or more independent currents in some of the branches—frequently in both directions.   No difficulty actually results, however, if we add the PD's produced by each

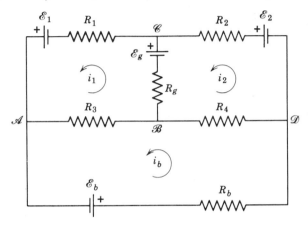

Fig. 5.5d. Loop-current analysis.

current in an element containing two or more, for this corresponds to the proper algebraic addition of the currents to give the actual physical value.[12]

In our example, we can assume that a current i_1 circulates around loop 1, i_2 around loop 2, and i_b around loop b, as in Fig. 5.5d.   Note that we have used for the loop currents the same symbols as we used above for those branch currents which appear in only one loop apiece.   This is done to show the equivalence but is of course not necessary, just as it is not necessary to use the particular loops we have chosen.   Current i_b for instance could have been assumed to pass through R_2 and R_1 instead of R_4 and R_3 as indicated, or it could follow a path through R_4, R_g, and R_1.   For our particular choice of loops, the equations from the second rule read

$$i_1(R_1 + R_3 + R_g) - i_2 R_g - i_b R_3 = \mathscr{E}_1 + \mathscr{E}_g \qquad (5.5\text{-}7)$$

$$-i_1 R_g + i_2(R_2 + R_4 + R_g) - i_b R_4 = \mathscr{E}_2 - \mathscr{E}_g \qquad (5.5\text{-}8)$$

$$-i_1 R_3 - i_2 R_4 + i_b(R_3 + R_4 + R_b) = \mathscr{E}_b \qquad (5.5\text{-}9)$$

[12] These loop currents were first introduced by J. C. Maxwell.   See article 282b in the reference on page 40, footnote 15.

Each equation in this group sets the iR drops equal to the potential rises in the emf's. For each loop, the drop due to the current belonging to that loop involves all the resistance around the loop. Other currents enter only through the resistances of the branches in common with the loop in question and involve potential rises if the currents are opposite to the chosen positive sense around the loop.

We have three equations in the three unknowns i_1, i_2, and i_b, written in the appropriate form for the determinant method of solution (determinants are discussed briefly in Appendix A.6). Note that these equations are just the same as eqs. 5.5–4, 5.5–5, and 5.5–6 after elimination of i_3, i_4, and i_g by eqs. 5.5–1, 5.5–2, and 5.5–3. The difference in the two methods lies in the directness with which the equations are obtained, a matter of considerable importance for especially complex circuits.

The determinant method for this case requires the calculation of the determinant Δ formed by all the coefficients of the i's and also of the determinants Δ_1, Δ_2, etc., found from Δ by replacing the column of coefficients of one of the currents by the column of $\mathscr{E}$'s that appears on the right hand side of the equations. Thus we have

$$\Delta = \begin{vmatrix} R_1 + R_3 + R_g & -R_g & -R_3 \\ -R_g & R_2 + R_4 + R_g & -R_4 \\ -R_3 & -R_4 & R_3 + R_4 + R_b \end{vmatrix} \tag{5.5–10}$$

$$\Delta_1 = \begin{vmatrix} \mathscr{E}_1 + \mathscr{E}_g & -R_g & -R_3 \\ \mathscr{E}_2 - \mathscr{E}_g & R_2 + R_4 + R_g & -R_4 \\ \mathscr{E}_b & -R_4 & R_3 + R_4 + R_b \end{vmatrix} \tag{5.5–11}$$

$$\Delta_2 = \begin{vmatrix} R_1 + R_3 + R_g & \mathscr{E}_1 + \mathscr{E}_g & -R_3 \\ -R_g & \mathscr{E}_2 - \mathscr{E}_g & -R_4 \\ -R_3 & \mathscr{E}_b & R_3 + R_4 + R_b \end{vmatrix} \tag{5.5–12}$$

$$\Delta_b = \begin{vmatrix} R_1 + R_3 + R_g & -R_g & \mathscr{E}_1 + \mathscr{E}_g \\ -R_g & R_2 + R_4 + R_g & \mathscr{E}_2 - \mathscr{E}_g \\ -R_3 & -R_4 & \mathscr{E}_b \end{vmatrix} \tag{5.5–13}$$

Then according to the theory of determinants, we have

$$i_1 = \Delta_1/\Delta$$
$$i_2 = \Delta_2/\Delta \tag{5.5–14}$$
$$i_b = \Delta_b/\Delta$$

We shall not evaluate these expressions without first setting certain terms equal to zero, but before so doing, there are two features of the complete solution we wish to point out.

In the first place, each current is a linear function of the four emf's—

e.g., $i_1 = k\mathcal{E}_1 + l\mathcal{E}_2 + p\mathcal{E}_g + q\mathcal{E}_b$, where k, l, p, and q are functions only of the R's. That is, each emf contributes separately and independently to all the currents. We can solve the problem separately for each emf, if we wish, setting the other emf's equal to zero but leaving their internal resistances in the circuit, and then adding the separate solutions for each current. This fact is the *superposition theorem* for d-c circuits.

In the second place, we can derive a result from the diagonal symmetry of Δ. Note that the element in the first row and second column is the resistance in common between the first and second loops and is equal to the element in the second row and the first column, and so forth. The result we wish to point out is that the current i_1, produced in branch 1 by a unit emf in branch 2 (with other emf's equal to zero) is equal to the current i_2 in branch 2 produced by unit emf in branch 1. Specifically, if we set $\mathcal{E}_2 = 1$ and the other $\mathcal{E}$'s equal to zero, the expression for i_1 becomes

$$i_1 = \frac{1}{\Delta} \cdot \begin{vmatrix} 0 & -R_g & -R_3 \\ 1 & R_2 + R_4 + R_g & -R_4 \\ 0 & -R_4 & R_3 + R_4 + R_g \end{vmatrix}$$

whereas if we set $\mathcal{E}_1 = 1$ with the others zero, we have for i_2

$$i_2 = \frac{1}{\Delta} \cdot \begin{vmatrix} R_1 + R_3 + R_2 & 1 & -R_3 \\ -R_g & 0 & -R_4 \\ -R_3 & 0 & R_3 + R_4 + R_b \end{vmatrix}$$

The two expressions are seen to be equal when we pick out the co-factor determinant of the 1 in each case (see Appendix A.6). The same symmetry considerations apply to any two branches in any circuit. This is a statement of the *reciprocity theorem*.

Now let us solve for the currents. We shall restrict ourselves to the case in which $\mathcal{E}_1 = \mathcal{E}_2 = 0$ and $R_b = 0$. We shall show later how to develop a solution for $R_b \neq 0$ from the results we shall now calculate.

Using the rule for evaluating third-order determinants that is given in the Appendix (Appendix A.6), we obtain the following results:

$$\Delta = R_1 R_2 R_3 + R_2 R_3 R_4 + R_3 R_4 R_1 + R_4 R_1 R_2$$
$$+ R_g(R_1 + R_2)(R_3 + R_4) \qquad (5.5\text{--}15)$$

$$i_1 = \frac{1}{\Delta}\{\mathcal{E}_b[R_g(R_3 + R_4) + R_3(R_2 + R_4)] + \mathcal{E}_g R_2(R_3 + R_4)\} \qquad (5.5\text{--}16)$$

$$i_2 = \frac{1}{\Delta}\{\mathcal{E}_b[R_g(R_3 + R_4) + R_4(R_1 + R_3)] - \mathcal{E}_g R_1(R_3 + R_4)\} \qquad (5.5\text{--}17)$$

$$i_b = \frac{1}{\Delta}\{\mathcal{E}_b[R_g(R_1 + R_2 + R_3 + R_4) + (R_1 + R_3)(R_2 + R_4)]$$
$$+ \mathcal{E}_g(R_2 R_3 - R_1 R_4)\} \qquad (5.5\text{--}18)$$

We can now find the currents in the other branches from eqs. 5.5–1, 5.5–2, and 5.5–3 or by inspection of Fig. 5.5*d*. We have

$$i_3 = i_b - i_1 = \frac{1}{\Delta} \{\mathscr{E}_b[R_g(R_1 + R_2) + R_1(R_2 + R_4)]$$
$$- \mathscr{E}_g R_4(R_1 + R_2)\} \quad (5.5\text{--}19)$$

$$i_4 = i_b - i_2 = \frac{1}{\Delta} \{\mathscr{E}_b[R_g(R_1 + R_2) + R_2(R_1 + R_3)]$$
$$+ \mathscr{E}_g R_3(R_1 + R_2)\} \quad (5.5\text{--}20)$$

$$i_g = i_1 - i_2 = \frac{1}{\Delta} \{\mathscr{E}_b(R_2 R_3 - R_1 R_4) + \mathscr{E}_g(R_1 + R_2)(R_3 + R_4)\} \quad (5.5\text{--}21)$$

Careful inspection of these results will show a complete symmetry of i_1, i_2, i_3, and i_4 with respect to R_1, R_2, R_3, and R_4 which reflects the symmetry of the circuit arrangement.   Another result to note is that in the expression for the current in any particular branch, the coefficient of the emf in the same branch will always be positive.

Let us finally show how to modify the solution just obtained so as to include a non-zero value of R_b.   We can imagine that, in setting up the determinants, we placed the term $i_b R_b$ of eq. 5.5–9 on the right-hand side and treated $-i_b R_b$ as if it were an emf added to $\mathscr{E}_b$.   Since the solution process is from the algebraic point of view simply an elimination of unknowns, eqs. 5.5–16 through 5.5–21 will still be valid if we replace $\mathscr{E}_b$ everywhere by $\mathscr{E}_b - i_b R_b$.   In eq. 5.5–18 we will have i_b appearing twice, so that we can solve for it, and then use this value in the other equations.   Problem 5.5*a* asks for a useful and not too tedious calculation with R_b.

This process uses what is frequently called the *compensation theorem*, which says that addition of a resistance δR to any branch is equivalent to adding an emf $-i' \delta R$ to the same branch instead, where i' is the *new* current in that branch.

Problem 5.5a.   Find i_b for the circuit of Fig. 5.5*d* with a battery resistance R_b included, but $\mathscr{E}_1$ and $\mathscr{E}_2$ still zero, by modifying the solution for the case without R_b, as suggested in the text.   Verify by inspection of eqs. 5.5–10 and 5.5–13. Use the solution so obtained and the reciprocity theorem to find the current in R_g when $\mathscr{E}_g = 0$, $\mathscr{E}_b \neq 0$, and $R_b \neq 0$.

Problem 5.5b.   Verify that eqs. 5.5–15, 5.5–16, 5.5–17, and 5.5–18 have the correct symmetry properties with respect to the exchanges (*a*) of R_1 with R_2 and R_3 with R_4 and (*b*) of R_1 with R_3 and R_2 with R_4.

Problem 5.5c.   Find the currents in each cell in the circuit of Fig. 5.5*e*.

Problem 5.5d.   Three Edison storage cells in different states of charge are shown in Fig. 5.5*f*, connected in parallel to a common load.   Find the current delivered by each and the PD on the load.

Problem 5.5e.   An east-west trolley line 10 miles long has an overhead wire whose resistance is 0.070 ohm/mile and a return rail of resistance 0.0080 ohm/ mile.   It is fed at the east end by a generator of emf 500 v and internal resistance 0.02 ohm and at the west end by a generator of emf 490 v and internal resistance

Fig. 5.5e.   (Problem 5.5c)

Fig. 5.5f.   (Problem 5.5d)

Fig. 5.5g.   (Problem 5.5f)

0.03 ohm.   At what point on the line would a car drawing 100 amp obtain a minimum of potential difference?   What is the value of this minimum PD?

✓ **Problem 5.5f.**   Find the current in each resistor in Fig. 5.5g.

✓ **Problem 5.5g.**   Eight resistors form a square as in Fig. 5.5h.   Find the resistance between 𝒜 and ℬ, 𝒜 and 𝒞, and 𝒜 and 𝒟.

Problem 5.5h. Twelve equal resistors lying on the edges of a cube are connected at the corners. Find the resistance between one corner and each of the three unlike other corners.

Problem 5.5i. Find the resistance between $\mathscr{A}$ and $\mathscr{B}$ in Fig. 5.5i. Is there a principle of symmetry you can use?

Fig. 5.5h. (Problem 5.5g)

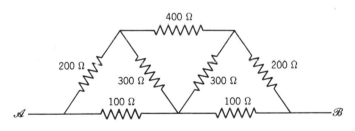

Fig. 5.5i. (Problem 5.5i)

5.6 Thévenin's Theorem

In the last section, we gave illustrations of three circuit theorems of rather general applicability. In this section, we shall prove and illustrate another circuit theorem of considerable interest and importance. The proposition is called "Thévenin's theorem" and asserts that any combination of emf's and resistors connected between two terminals acts like a single effective emf with an effective internal resistance in series.

To prove this theorem, let us consider an arbitrary network connected between two terminals, with some other equally arbitrary network connected externally to the same terminals.   One might imagine, for instance, that each network is enclosed in a box, with only the terminals projecting, as shown in Fig. 5.6a.

Fig. 5.6a.   Two arbitrary two-terminal networks in boxes.

Now let us imagine that we solve network N by Kirchhoff's laws, using the external potential difference V as if it were an emf, just as we treated $-i_b R_b$ as an emf on p. 211.   If $\mathscr{E}_1$, $\mathscr{E}_2$, $\cdots$ represent the various emf's in network N, the solution for the current i will be a linear expression in $\mathscr{E}_1$, $\mathscr{E}_2$, $\cdots$, and V with coefficients depending on the resistances $R_1, R_2, \cdots$ in N.   If V is taken as a potential drop when calculated in the direction chosen as positive for i, the coefficient of V will be negative, since the equivalent emf is $-V$.   Thus we shall write

$$i = g_1\mathscr{E}_1 + g_2\mathscr{E}_2 + \cdots - gV \tag{5.6-1}$$

where the g's all have the dimensions of mhos and represent a sort of conductance (called "transfer conductance").   Solving for V we obtain

$$V = \frac{g_1}{g}\mathscr{E}_1 + \frac{g_2}{g}\mathscr{E}_2 + \cdots - \frac{i}{g} \tag{5.6-2}$$

The relation between V and i becomes exactly that for a cell of emf $\mathscr{E}$ and internal resistance r, namely

$$V = \mathscr{E} - ir \tag{5.6-3}$$

if we set

$$\mathscr{E} = \frac{g_1}{g}\mathscr{E}_1 + \frac{g_2}{g}\mathscr{E}_2 + \cdots \tag{5.6-4}$$

and

$$r = \frac{1}{g} \tag{5.6-5}$$

thus proving the theorem.

We can also solve network N' for i in terms of its emf's $\mathscr{E}'_1$, $\mathscr{E}'_2$, $\cdots$ and resistances R'_1, $R'_2 \cdots$, and of V as an emf.   However, if V is defined as a drop for network N, it acts as a rise for network N', so we have

$$i = g'_1\mathscr{E}'_1 + g'_2\mathscr{E}'_2 + \cdots + g'V$$

or

$$V = \frac{i}{g'} - \frac{g'_1}{g}\mathscr{E}_1 - \frac{g'_2}{g}\mathscr{E}_2 \cdots$$

which may be written

$$V = ir' - \mathscr{E}' \tag{5.6-6}$$

where r' and $\mathscr{E}'$ depend only on R'_1, $R'_2 \cdots$ and $\mathscr{E}'_1$, $\mathscr{E}'_2 \cdots$

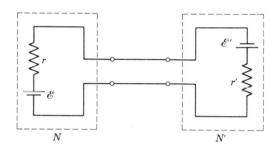

Fig. 5.6b.   An equivalent circuit for Fig. 5.6a.

The two eqs. 5.6–3 and 5.6–6 can now be combined to give an expression for the current i between the networks:

$$i = \frac{\mathscr{E} + \mathscr{E}'}{r + r'} \tag{5.6-7}$$

just as if two cells were connected in series, with a combined emf of $\mathscr{E} + \mathscr{E}'$ and a combined resistance of $r + r'$, as in Fig. 5.6b.

Let us see what meaning we can attach to $\mathscr{E}$ and r, or $\mathscr{E}'$ and r'.   If network N' is removed, so that there is an open circuit at the terminals of N, we will have $i = 0$ and $V = \mathscr{E}$.   Thus the effective emf of a two-terminal network is the open-circuit potential difference at the terminals.

Suppose now that all the emf's $\mathscr{E}_1$, $\mathscr{E}_2 \cdots$ are removed from N.   Any internal cell resistances are to be replaced by equal resistors, so that none of the values R_1, $R_2 \cdots$ are changed.   Choose for N' a single cell of emf $\mathscr{E}'$ and negligible resistance.   Then $\mathscr{E}$ and r' are zero, and since $i = \mathscr{E}'/r$, we see that the internal resistance of a two-terminal network is just the resultant resistance between the terminals when the emf's are set equal to zero.   Such a network without emf's is called a "passive network" as contrasted with an "active network" containing emf's.

The most important use of Thévenin's theorem comes from its use in the power-transfer theorem which was proved in section 5.4. If an active network N of equivalent emf $\mathscr{E}$ and resistance r feeds power to a passive network N' of variable effective resistance r', the maximum power transfer will occur when $r' = r$. This condition does not involve the emf's, so it holds true if they vary, as in the a-c case. An important application is to the transfer of a-c power in communication circuits. It is customary to design various pieces of apparatus such as amplifiers, test sources, microphones, loudspeakers, and transmission cables to have effective internal resistances[13] of one or another standard value, e.g., 500 ohms or

Fig. 5.6c. A T-section attenuator network with input and output circuits N and N'.

200 ohms. Then any active element (source of a communicative "signal") can be connected to any passive element (receiver) of the same design resistance. The proper matching of the elements not only provides for maximum power transfer, but also affects certain other properties, such as frequency response, linearity, maintenance of vacuum-tube currents within safe limits, etc. Problems 5.6a–f deal with attenuators that provide impedance matching along with reduction in voltage. Problems 5.6g and h call for treatment of two circuits of the previous section by Thévenin's theorem.

Problem 5.6a. A T-attenuator network, shown in Fig. 5.6c, is used to match two networks N and N' each to a resistance R, and at the same time to reduce the voltage on N' by the attenuation factor x_a over what it would be if N and N' were connected directly. Show that for proper matching, R_1 and R_2 are related by

$$R^2 = R_1{}^2 + 2R_1R_2 \tag{5.6–8}$$

and that

$$x_a = \frac{R_2}{R_2 + R_1 + R} \tag{5.6–9}$$

Find R_1 and R_2 in terms of R and x_a.

[13] In a-c circuits, the concept of impedance usually replaces that of resistance. But in the usual power-transfer case, the relevant impedances generally act like resistances.

Problem 5.6b.   Show that R_1 of problem 5.6a increases as x_a decreases from 1 to 0 and that R_2 decreases, when R is constant.   Sketch curves showing these variations.

Problem 5.6c.   The attenuation α_{db} in decibels is

$$\alpha_{db} = 10 \log_{10} (1/x_a{}^2)$$

Show that $R_1 = R \tanh (2.303\alpha_{db}/40)$ and $R_2 = R \operatorname{csch} (2.303\alpha_{db}/20)$, so that R_1 and R_2 can be calculated for a given R and α_{db} from a table of hyperbolic functions (these functions are defined in Appendix A.5).

Problem 5.6e.   Find R_1 and R_2 for T-section networks designed for 500-ohm input and output resistances, and attenuations of 1db, 3db, 10db, and 60db.

✓ **Problem 5.6f.**   Find the conditions on R_1 and R_2 in the π-section network of Fig. 5.6d so that it will match resistances R at each pair of terminals and provide a given attenuation α_{db}.

Fig. 5.6d.   (Problem 5.6f)

✓ **Problem 5.6g.**   Treat the circuit of Fig. 5.5d, with $\mathscr{E}_1$, $\mathscr{E}_2$, and R_b all equal to zero, by Thévenin's theorem, taking the network N' to be $\mathscr{E}_g$ and R_g, and thus check eq. 5.5–21.

Problem 5.6h.   Treat the circuit of Fig. 5.5d by Thévenin's theorem when N' is taken to be the resistor R_1, and $R_b = 0$.

5.7   Resistance Bridges and Potentiometers

Precision measurements in the field of steady-current circuits involve determinations of emf, current, and resistance.   Of these three, the measurement of resistance by comparison with known resistance standards is the most straightforward and direct.   Furthermore, accurate resistance values are required for emf and current measurements.   Resistance bridges are especially valuable because they allow comparison of resistance values without the necessity of known or constant emf's or currents.   The question of the determination of resistance in terms of mechanical units (so-called "absolute" determinations) will be discussed in section 7.10.

The Wheatstone Bridge.   The Wheatstone bridge circuit, shown in Fig. 5.7a, is similar to the circuit of Fig. 5.5d, with all batteries but one removed.   We take the case of negligible battery resistance (see problem 5.7d for the inclusion of R_b).   Three of the resistors shown are considered to be known and the fourth is to be found by adjusting one or more of the three until the galvanometer deflection is reduced to zero. By an elementary calculation, or from eq. 5.5–21, we see that a null result on the galvanometer occurs when $R_2 R_3 = R_1 R_4$ or

$$\frac{R_1}{R_2} = \frac{R_3}{R_4} = n \tag{5.7–1}$$

where n is called the bridge ratio across the galvanometer. This relation is of course valid for steady currents. If there are appreciable inductive or capacitive effects in the circuit, charge may flow in the galvanometer

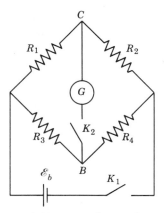

Fig. 5.7a. A Wheatstone bridge: K_1 = battery key, K_2 = galvanometer key; the galvanometer G has resistance R_g.

while the current in the rest of the bridge is being established, even if eq. 5.7–1 holds. Therefore it is necessary to test the balance by closing the battery key K_1 first, allowing the main currents to become established, and then pressing the galvanometer key K_2 to test for balance.

Satisfactory use of such bridges requires a sufficiently good sensitivity. By sensitivity is generally meant the smallest fractional deviation from the balance value of one of the resistance arms that leads to a detectable current in the galvanometer. The smallest detectable current depends on the particular galvanometer and the conditions of its use. We shall only calculate here a bridge sensitivity defined as the ratio of the current through (or PD across) the galvanometer to the fractional change away from balance of one of the resistors.

By eq. 5.5–21, the current through the galvanometer is in general

$$i_g = \mathscr{E}_b \frac{R_2 R_3 - R_1 R_4}{R_1 R_2 R_3 + R_2 R_3 R_4 + R_3 R_4 R_1 + R_4 R_1 R_2 + R_g (R_1 + R_2)(R_3 + R_4)} \tag{5.7–2}$$

Let us consider that $R_2 R_3 = R_1 R_4$ and that R_2 is replaced in eq. 5.7–2 by a variable R'_2 when the bridge is slightly out of balance. We shall write

$$R'_2 = R_2(1 + x)$$

or

$$x = \frac{R'_2 - R_2}{R_2}$$

so that x is the fractional deviation of resistor 2 from balance. When we substitute R'_2 in eq. 5.7–2, the numerator will reduce to $x R_2 R_3$. The presence of x in the denominator will on binomial expansion lead to terms in the numerator with x^2, x^3, $\cdots$ which we shall neglect, assuming x to be small (the simplest bridges are easily balanced to within 1%). Therefore we shall not substitute R'_2 for R_2 in the denominator of eq. 5.7–2.

The resulting expression can be easily simplified if we factor $R_2 R_3$ or its equal $R_1 R_4$ out of the first four terms of the denominator. We find

$$i_g \simeq \frac{x \mathscr{E}_b}{(R_1 + R_2 + R_3 + R_4) + R_g\left(\dfrac{R_1}{R_2} + 2 + \dfrac{R_2}{R_1}\right)} \qquad (5.7\text{–}3)$$

so that

$$\frac{i_g}{x} \simeq \frac{\mathscr{E}_b}{(R_1 + R_2 + R_3 + R_4) + R_g\left(n + 2 + \dfrac{1}{n}\right)} \qquad (5.7\text{–}4)$$

It is easily seen that the same result except for a possible minus sign results if R_1, R_3, or R_4 is taken as the adjustable resistor.

The expression $n + 1/n$ has a minimum value when $n = 1$. Thus the sensitivity ratio i_g/x is a maximum when we have, simultaneously, $n = 1$, the lowest permissible total resistance of the bridge, and the largest permissible emf $\mathscr{E}_b$. Both the upper limit on $\mathscr{E}_b$ and the lower limit on $R_1 + R_2 + R_3 + R_4$ are determined principally by the value of the unknown to be measured and the permissible power dissipation in the various resistors.

The choice of which galvanometer to use for a given bridge depends of course on the relation between i_g and the galvanometer deflection (cf. section 8.8). It also depends on R_g, and on the value of effective resistance to which it should be connected for proper damping. Sometimes, for instance, it is useful to place an external resistance in series with the galvanometer, or in parallel with it, to make a proper match. The influence of such resistors on the over-all sensitivity is not hard to compute.[14]

[14] Cf. Harris, *op. cit.*, Chapter 7, for details on precision resistance bridges.

Potentiometers.   The potentiometer method is the most important technique for comparing potential differences and has a number of applications.   It consists fundamentally in balancing two potential differences against each other and detecting their equality when a galvanometer in the circuit connecting them indicates no current flow.   Figure 5.7*b* shows two networks connected with a galvanometer.   When no current flows, the open-circuit PD's of the two networks must be equal.   One of the networks, say, network 2, contains a quantity to be measured in terms of the open-circuit PD V_2, and the other is a measuring circuit with a means for adjusting V_1 and knowing its value.

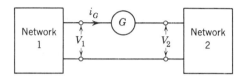

Fig. 5.7*b*.   Illustrating the potentiometer principle.   When $i_g = 0$, $V_1 = V_2$.

The types of PD's that can be measured with this method include the emf's of cells and of thermocouples, the PD on a voltmeter carrying sufficient current to make it read some convenient value, and the PD on a resistor carrying a current that passes through an ammeter to be calibrated or through another resistor to be compared with the first.   Since at balance no current is drawn from the cell or thermocouple, its external potential difference must equal its emf.   Any internal resistance thus does not enter into the measurement, although it may affect the sensitivity. It should be noted that in case the measured circuit contains more than one kind of material, it is always the difference in $\bar{\mu}/e$ that is actually measured.

The measuring network invariably uses an iR drop for V_1.   One method of adjusting V_1, known as Poggendorff's[15] first method, consists in keeping i fixed and varying the portion of the total resistance in network 1 that is connected to the terminals.   Poggendorff's second method consists in keeping a fixed resistance between the terminals and varying and measuring the current.

The variation in the amount of resistance required in the first method can be accomplished at one or at both connections.   A simple slide wire can be used as a potentiometer, with only one connection variable, but greater precision of reading can be obtained by making one terminal vary in steps and the other along a continuous wire.

[15] Poggendorff was the first to use the potentiometer principle.   *Ann. Phys. u. Chemie,* **54** (1841).

Figure 5.7c shows a circuit for comparing the emf $\mathcal{E}$ of a cell with the iR drop in a resistance R, which is the resistance between the taps $\mathscr{P}$ and $\mathscr{Q}$, with $\mathscr{P}$ movable in steps between $\mathscr{A}$ and $\mathscr{B}$, and $\mathscr{Q}$ a sliding tap movable between $\mathscr{B}$ and $\mathscr{C}$.   When G reads zero, $iR = \mathcal{E}$.   The value of i may be adjusted to a predetermined value by balancing a standard cell of known emf $\mathcal{E}_S$ against the drop in a predetermined resistance R_S between $\mathscr{A}$ and $\mathscr{Q}_S$.   Then if i remains constant, we have $i = \mathcal{E}/R = \mathcal{E}_S/R_S$, and $\mathcal{E}$ can be found.

Fig. 5.7c. A potentiometer circuit, showing a special slide wire for standard cell adjustment and a parallel circuit for range changing. Switch K_2 is closed to the right for balancing $\mathcal{E}$ and to the left for balancing $\mathcal{E}_S$.

The most serious problem in potentiometer measurements is that of maintaining a constant current in the tapped resistance R.   This problem is attacked partly by using a battery $\mathcal{E}'$ of much larger current capacity than actually needed and partly by a rapid switching from standard cell to unknown and back to standard cell.

Also shown in Fig. 5.7c is an arrangement for changing the range of the potentiometer.   Many ordinary potentiometers have a maximum range of 1.6 v and can be read to 0.0001 v.   Thermocouple measurements, however, involve emf's of a millivolt or so; accurate measurement of such emf's requires a smaller range, say 0.016 v.   If resistance R_3 is exactly 1/99 of that in the branch $\mathscr{A}\mathscr{B}\mathscr{C}$, then closing of K_3 and rebalancing the circuit will result in the same current i in $\mathscr{C}_S\mathscr{A}$ but only 1/100 as much in $\mathscr{A}\mathscr{B}\mathscr{C}$, so the potentiometer has 1/100 the range it had before.[16]

[16] For details, see Harris, *op. cit.*, Chapter 12.

Problem 5.7a. Can the power-transfer theorem be used in reverse? That is, if a galvanometer of a certain resistance R_g is available for a Wheatstone's bridge, will the most power be transferred into it if the internal resistance of the network is equal to R_g?

Problem 5.7b. What values of resistors are needed in series if a switch that successively makes contact with each junction between two resistors will divide the set into two parts of ratios successively 0.001, 0.01, 0.1, 1.0, 10, 100, and 1000, for use in a Wheatstone bridge, when the total resistance is 1011.01 ohms?

Problem 5.7c. Calculate the sensitivity $i_g/\Delta x$ for a slide-wire bridge where x is the relative displacement of the sliding contact from one end of the wire. If the position of the sliding contact can be read to the same accuracy at all points along the wire, prove that the contribution of this reading error to the error of the result is least if the bridge is balanced for $n = 1$.

Problem 5.7d. Use the result of problem 5.5a to derive an expression for i_g/x for a Wheatstone bridge circuit with appreciable battery resistance R_b.

Fig. 5.7d. (Problem 5.7i)

Problem 5.7e. Suppose the contact errors at the ends of a slide-wire bridge amount respectively to additional lengths of wire α and β. If the bridge is balanced with a resistor R_1 near the α end and R_2 near the β end, with wire lengths l_1 and l_2, and then rebalanced with R_1 and R_2 interchanged, yielding lengths l'_2 and l'_1, find α and β in terms of these measured lengths and the ratio $R_2/R_1 = n$. What happens when $n = 1$?

Problem 5.7f. Show that, if R_1 and R_2 are in parallel and an error dR_2 is made in R_2, an error $dR = dR_2[R_1/(R_1 + R_2)]^2$ is made in the value of the parallel resistance. If a switch has an unknown contact resistance of about 0.001 ohm, show how to make a variable resistor of values from 49.50000 to 50.50000 ohms for which the contact resistance error is less than 0.00003 ohm.

Problem 5.7g. Use Thévenin's theorem on a simple potentiometer circuit to find the current through the galvanometer when the setting between $\mathscr{P}$ and $\mathscr{Q}$ (see Fig. 5.7c) is out by ΔV volts. Hence find $i_g/\Delta V$. Show how measurements of i_g can eliminate the necessity of getting an exact balance (this is the principle of the "deflection potentiometer").

Problem 5.7h. What sensitivity must a galvanometer have if it is to be used in a potentiometer with a range of 1.6 v, standard current of 1.0 ma, main battery 6.0 v, when an emf of 1.0 v is to be measured to 0.001 %? Take the resistance of galvanometer and standard cell together to be 300 ohms.

Problem 5.7i. Tell how the circuit of Fig. 5.7d can be used to measure the emf of cell $\mathscr{E}$ without drawing current from it. Under what conditions could $\mathscr{E}'$ be measured instead?

Problem 5.7j.   Two standard cells differ in emf by about 300 μv.   Show how to measure this difference if you are given a galvanometer, a standard 0.1 ohm resistor, a 10-ma range ammeter, and a battery and controlling resistor.

Problem 5.7k.   A high-voltage supply produces between 1250 v and 1350 v and may provide up to 200 μa of current.   A battery of constant emf and a galvanometer calibrated to read ± 25 μa are available along with necessary resistors.   Show how to measure small variations in the high voltage from an originally set value of 1300 v, using a type of potentiometer.

5.8   Two- and Three-Dimensional Currents

We have restricted ourselves in the last few sections to currents in thin wires where the flow is one dimensional in character.   Let us now consider in more detail the flow of charge in extended media.   We treat **J** therefore as a type of field vector which can vary in magnitude and direction from point to point.

The current through any surface S will be given by the integral (cf. p. 182).

$$i = \int_S \mathbf{J} \cdot \mathbf{dS} \tag{5.8-1}$$

If S is a closed surface, the current out of S will be the rate of decrease of the charge inside (since charge can neither be created nor destroyed):

$$\int_{\text{closed } S} \mathbf{J} \cdot \mathbf{dS} = -\frac{\partial Q}{\partial t} ; \qquad Q = \int_\tau \rho \, d\tau \tag{5.8-2}$$

where τ is the volume bounded by S.   If any polarization charge is present, we will not include its motion in **J** and hence must understand ρ to mean free charge.   The surface integral can be rewritten by use of the divergence theorem, eq. A.2–22, and the time derivative can be taken inside the integral sign for the τ integration if the boundary of τ is fixed. Thus we have

$$\int_{\text{closed } S} \mathbf{J} \cdot \mathbf{dS} = \int_\tau \nabla \cdot \mathbf{J} \, d\tau$$

$$= -\int_\tau \frac{\partial \rho}{\partial t} \, d\tau \tag{5.8-3}$$

which must hold for any volume τ whatsoever.   It therefore holds for as small a volume as we please surrounding any arbitrary point $\mathscr{P}$ from which fact we can deduce that the integrals are equal, giving the result that

$$\nabla \cdot \mathbf{J} + \frac{\partial \rho}{\partial t} = 0 \tag{5.8-4}$$

This equation is called the "equation of continuity" and is an expression of the conservation of charge.

A steady state is one in which all time derivatives are zero, so we must have $\partial\rho/\partial t = 0$ and

$$\mathbf{V} \cdot \mathbf{J} = 0 \qquad \text{Steady state} \quad (5.8\text{--}5)$$

Now, if the medium obeys Ohm's law, we have as in eq. 5.1–2

$$\mathbf{J} = \sigma\mathbf{E} \qquad (5.1\text{--}2); \ (5.8\text{--}6)$$

If σ is a constant with respect to position in the medium, we must have div $\mathbf{J}$ proportional to div $\mathbf{E}$, for steady or unsteady states:

$$\mathbf{V} \cdot \mathbf{J} = \sigma\mathbf{V} \cdot \mathbf{E} \qquad (5.8\text{--}7)$$

and for a steady state we conclude that $\mathbf{E}$ has zero divergence, so that ρ vanishes.

$$\mathbf{V} \cdot \mathbf{E} = \rho/\epsilon_0 = 0 \qquad \text{Steady state} \quad (5.8\text{--}8)$$

(We replace ϵ_0 by ϵ if the material possesses a dielectric constant different from unity.)

On the other hand, if σ is a function of position, its variation must be considered in calculating div $\mathbf{J}$:

$$\mathbf{V} \cdot \mathbf{J} = \partial(\sigma E_x)/\partial x + \cdots$$

$$= \sigma\partial(E_x/\partial x) + \cdots + E_x(\partial\sigma/\partial x) + \cdots$$

where the dots indicate the y and z terms.   In vector form we have

$$\mathbf{V} \cdot \mathbf{J} = \sigma\mathbf{V} \cdot \mathbf{E} + \mathbf{E} \cdot \mathbf{V}\sigma = \frac{\sigma\rho}{\epsilon_0} + \mathbf{E} \cdot \mathbf{V}\sigma \qquad (5.8\text{--}9)$$

(cf. Appendix, Table A.2B, item 4) and the vanishing of $\mathbf{V} \cdot \mathbf{J}$ does not ensure the vanishing of ρ.   Volume charge density can exist in regions of variable conductivity, and its amount can be calculated from eq. 5.8–9. Such regions exist in thin layers at the boundary between two materials of different conductivity, and so we see that, even in the steady state, static charge will be found at such interfaces.

Rather than use eq. 5.8–9 for ρ in a thin boundary layer, let us assume as usual that the boundary is a surface of infinitesimal thickness, and consider the surface charge density and the "refraction" of flow lines at the boundary for the steady state (Fig. 5.8a).   Since charge can neither be piling up or disappearing at a boundary, the current toward the boundary on one side must equal that away from it on the other side;   that is, $\mathbf{J}_1 \cdot \mathbf{dS} = \mathbf{J}_2 \cdot \mathbf{dS}$ or

$$J_{n1} = J_{n2} \qquad (5.8\text{--}10a)$$

where J_{n1} and J_{n2} are the normal components of $\mathbf{J}$ in the two cases.   Just as in the dielectric case, the tangential component of **E** is the same on both sides, representing the common value of $-\nabla V$ along the boundary:

$$E_{t1} = E_{t2} \qquad (5.8\text{--}11a)$$

The two conditions just established can be rewritten by use of eq. 5.8-6:

$$\sigma_1 E_{n1} = \sigma_2 E_{n2} \qquad (5.8\text{--}10b)$$

and

$$\frac{J_{t1}}{\sigma_1} = \frac{J_{t2}}{\sigma_2} \qquad (5.8\text{--}11b)$$

By use of either the J's or the E's we can find the "law of refraction"

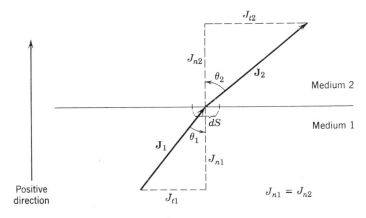

Fig. 5.8a.   Current directions at a boundary.

for the angles made by **E** and **J** with the normal.   For instance, divide eq. 5.8-11b by eq. 5.8-10a, getting

$$\frac{\tan \theta_1}{\sigma_1} = \frac{\tan \theta_2}{\sigma_2} \qquad (5.8\text{--}12)$$

The surface charge density σ can be found by the Gauss flux law:

$$E_{n2} - E_{n1} = \sigma/\epsilon_0 \qquad (5.8\text{--}13)$$

We notice that, if σ_2 is relatively very large (medium 2 is highly conducting, and medium 1 is poorly conducting) and θ_2 is some angle between 0 and 90°, $\tan \theta_1$ and θ_1 become very small, which means that the lines of flow in the poorly conducting medium are practically perpendicular to the surface. J_{t1} and E_{t1} hence become essentially zero.   Furthermore, from eq. 5.8-10b we see that the large σ_2 is accompanied by a very small E_{n2}—the field practically vanishes in the good conductor.

The surface charge density on a very good conductor surrounded by a poor one is then practically the same as for the static case with no current flow, eq. 2.3–1.   The total charge on an ideal conductor of zero resistivity is related to the current into it by a constant involving the conductivity of the surrounding medium (we use ϵ for the permittivity of the medium since some polarization effects are likely to accompany the conduction current):

$$Q = \int_S \sigma \, d\mathbf{S} = \epsilon \int_S \mathbf{E} \cdot d\mathbf{S} = \frac{\epsilon}{\sigma} \int_S \mathbf{J} \cdot d\mathbf{S} = \frac{\epsilon i}{\sigma} \qquad (5.8\text{–}14)$$

The Resistance-Capacitance Analogy. If current enters and leaves a poorly conducting medium via two good conductors (called "electrodes"), we can write the equivalent resistance in terms of the PD V between the two good conductors:

$$R = V/i \qquad (5.8\text{–}15)$$

which by use of eq. 5.8–14 becomes

$$R = \frac{\epsilon V}{\sigma Q} \qquad (5.8\text{–}16)$$

Now, Q/V is just the capacitance of the two conductors with a medium of permittivity ϵ between them.   The definition of this capacitance depends on the existence of static charge on the conductors that is proportional to V and is independent of whether or not current also exists.   It is however important that all (or practically all) of the flux, and therefore current, that leaves one conductor enters the other.

Suppose now that we have a pair of electrodes that can be placed either in a vacuum or in a conducting medium and that there are no boundary effects which will disturb the field and current patterns.   The field pattern must then be the same in the two cases, as charge resides in the same places in each case, and div $\mathbf{E}$ is zero in the space between.   Thus if we can find the capacitance $C_0 = Q_0/V_0$ for the vacuum case, which is ϵ_0/ϵ times that with the medium in place, we can calculate the resistance when the conducting medium is present, by the formula

$$R = \frac{\epsilon_0}{\sigma C_0} \qquad (5.8\text{–}17)$$

and vice versa.   If the capacitance is measured with the medium in place, we replace ϵ_0 by ϵ in eq. 5.8–17.

This formula is readily verified for the case of a slab of low-conductivity material of thickness l with parallel plane sides of area S and with plane electrodes in contact.   The resistance of this arrangement is given according to eq. 5.1–4 by $R = \rho l/S = l/\sigma S$, and the capacitance according to eq. 2.7–4 by $C_0 = \epsilon_0 S/l$, so that eq. 5.8–17 is seen to hold. The resistance between concentric spheres or cylinders can be found by use of eqs. 2.7–3 and 2.7–5.

In many cases, there is not only a boundary between a metal of negligible resistivity (with σ of the order of 10^7 mho/m) and a liquid or solid of fairly high resistivity (σ of the order of 1 mho/m), but there is also a boundary between the latter and a gas or other insulator of extremely high resistivity, (σ roughly of the order of 10^{-10} mho/m).

Let us consider the boundary condition for the latter. We have already considered this for thin wires, in which $\mathbf{J}$ is obviously parallel to the surface inside the more conducting substance, and $\mathbf{E}$ outside (together with the practically negligible $\mathbf{J}$) makes an angle of almost any magnitude with the normal in the poorly conducting medium. In a more general case, the normal component of $\mathbf{J}$ will be so small in the gas or other insulator that its equal in the other medium will be negligible in comparison to the parallel component.

For instance, if we have a thin layer of a conducting solution with plane parallel sides, all the current will be in the plane of the layer, and cylindrical symmetry will result without the necessity of infinitely long electrodes (perpendicular to the plane in question). Thus the capacitance formulas for two parallel, infinite circular wires or for two concentric cylinders can be used to find the resistance between disk-shaped or ring-shaped electrodes in a tray containing a conducting electrolyte whose depth is not greater than the height of the electrodes.

Cases of axial symmetry, for which the same pattern occurs in every plane through a given axis and no current flows through any of these planes (no ϕ or "hoop" component in spherical coordinates; cf. Appendix A.2) can be treated by placing a conducting liquid in a tray with a tilted bottom, so that a wedge-shaped piece of liquid results and the flow pattern within it will represent a fraction of the complete figure of revolution.

Lines of force and equipotentials can much more readily be located and graphed for a conducting solution than for a field in vacuo, because a small amount of current can be drawn by the measuring apparatus without making an appreciable disturbance of the field pattern; the usual method that uses the potentiometric-balance principle in fact draws current only when balance is not achieved. There are several different techniques for making such measurements, for a study of which the reader is referred elsewhere.[17]

Another application of this relation between capacitance and resistance is to the resistance between terminals inserted in the earth for purposes of measuring soil conductivity. If a small spherical electrode is inserted in

[17] E. Weber, *Electromagnetic Fields*, John Wiley, New York, 1950, Vol. I, pp. 189–192.

the ground and a much larger electrode of arbitrary shape is inserted some distance away, the capacitance is like that of a small isolated sphere, with "infinity" the other terminal. Most of the PD and the resistance is to be found in the neighborhood of the small sphere, so the total resistance between it and the distant group of electrodes is a measure of the soil conductivity in the neighborhood of the sphere.

The Relaxation Time. The approach of current in an extended medium to a steady state can be studied by using eqs. 5.8–4 and 5.8–7 together with $\mathbf{V} \cdot \mathbf{E} = \rho/\epsilon_0$, where ρ is the free charge density and ϵ the permittivity of the medium, assumed to be an ideal dielectric. We have then

$$\frac{\sigma\rho}{\epsilon} + \frac{\partial\rho}{\partial t} = 0 \tag{5.8–18}$$

which differential equation is satisfied by

$$\rho = \rho_0 e^{-\sigma t/\epsilon} \tag{5.8–19}$$

where ρ_0 is the free charge density, as a function of x, y, and z, at time $t = 0$.

We see that the time required for an initial charge density to fall to $1/e$ of its value is ϵ/σ. It is called the "relaxation time." If we assume that $\epsilon \simeq \epsilon_0$, and use values of σ from Table 5.1A, we see that for copper, the relaxation time is 1.5×10^{-19} sec, and for pure water it is 4×10^{-8} sec, whereas for plate glass it is about 2 sec and for amber it is about 4×10^3 sec. We see that for metals the time is far too short to measure or observe. It is in fact much shorter than the RC time constants we estimated in section 5.3 and is shorter than the mean free time $t_m \simeq 10^{-14}$ sec between electron collisions.

Current with Space Charge. Our considerations in this section have thus far dealt with current in ohmic materials. The law of conservation of charge, eq. 5.8–4, holds also for the motion of charges in empty space. In this case, we can write eq. 5.1–1 for any type of charge in motion as

$$\mathbf{J} = \rho\mathbf{v} \tag{5.8–20}$$

where ρ is the volume density of the moving charges and is the total or net density if there are no fixed charges present. Then eq. 5.8–4 reads

$$\mathbf{V} \cdot (\rho\mathbf{v}) + \frac{\partial\rho}{\partial t} = 0 \tag{5.8–21a}$$

which can be rearranged to give

$$\rho\mathbf{V} \cdot \mathbf{v} + (\mathbf{v} \cdot \mathbf{V})\rho + \frac{\partial\rho}{\partial t} = 0 \tag{5.8–21b}$$

The diode considered in section 1.10 is an example. In that case, **J** is in the x-direction and all quantities are functions of x only. For the steady state, $d(\rho v)/dx = 0$, so $J = \rho v$ is a constant, a fact that was used without proof in section 1.10. The existence of a minimum of potential at a point where v is reduced to zero is inferred from the fact that, if the PD between the electrodes is not too great, the current that reaches the anode is considerably less than that emitted. Therefore some but not all of the electrons must turn back. If we assume them all to have an initial velocity v_0, they will all slow down to rest together. At the rest point, some fraction must be able to drift beyond to a region where they are accelerated, and therefore this rest point is a minimum of V. Generally, the rest point is very near the cathode, so that one can take $x_1 \simeq 0$ in eq. 1.10–6. Since the constant a is proportional to J, we obtain from this equation the usual result of diode theory that the current is proportional to the $\frac{3}{2}$ power of the PD between the electrodes.[18]

Problem 5.8a. A parallel-plate condenser whose plates are 10 cm square and 0.5 cm apart contains two slabs of dielectric, one 0.3 cm thick with $\sigma = 7.0 \times 10^{-5}$ mho/m and the other 0.2 cm thick with $\sigma = 4.0 \times 10^{-5}$ mho/m. The dielectric constants are 2.0 and 2.5 respectively. Find the current and the free charge density at the interface between the two slabs when a PD of 100 v is applied between the plates and a steady state has been reached. The plate in contact with the thicker slab is positive. Also find the charge densities on each plate.

Problem 5.8b. Use the result of problem 2.7d to find approximately the resistance between two small metal hemispheres of radii a and b imbedded with their plane faces flush with the ground in level soil at a distance c apart large compared to their radii.

Problem 5.8c. Find the leakage conductance per meter of a cylindrical coaxial cable whose inner conductor has a radius of 0.125 in. and whose outer conductor has an inner radius of 0.375 in., if the space between is filled with material whose conductivity is 6.0×10^{-8} mho/m.

Problem 5.8d. Modify eq. 1.10–6 to apply to points $0 \leqslant x \leqslant x_1$. Assume that in this region $J = J_{em} - J_{ret}$, where J_{em} is the emitted current density and J_{ret} that which returns from the rest point. Then find the constant a in terms of the J's for each region, and finally find $V(x_2)$ in terms of J and x_2, where x_2 is the distance from cathode to anode, and x_1 in terms of J, J_{em}, and v_0. Assume that x_1 is very small in comparison to x_2. *Hints:* J_{em} and J_{ret} are each independent of x, and v is the same at a given x for each direction of motion.

[18] For a good discussion of space-charge-limited current, see L. B. Loeb, *Basic Processes of Gaseous Electronics*, University of California, Berkeley, 1956, pp. 620–625.

6

Phenomena Related to Electron Levels

6.1 Introduction

We have seen that the concept of the Fermi level, U_F or $\bar{\mu}$, of the electrons in a metal is essential for explaining the properties of conductors, chemical cells, and contacts between different materials. There are two other sets of phenomena whose electrical aspects may be adequately understood only in terms of electron levels and which in these aspects form a proper part of our subject, namely, semiconduction and thermoelectricity. This chapter is devoted to the electrical principles of these phenomena and to aspects of chemical cells that were not taken up in Chapter 5. Only the basic elements of the physics of each topic will be given; complications such as thermoelectric effects in semiconductors, the effects of magnetic fields on thermoelectricity, and thermodynamic aspects of electrochemistry are beyond the scope of this book. The three following sections are independent of each other; the omission of any or all of them will not interfere with the continuity of the rest of the material.

6.2   Semiconductors

The energy-level schemes of semiconducting materials were treated in a simplified, brief way in section 2.1.   In terms of that picture, we can describe the principal electrical properties of semiconductors.

In the first place, their conductivity is low because the available carriers, whether electrons or holes, are present in very much smaller density than in metals.   This fact, however, means that their conductivity is quite sensitive to factors that tend to change the carrier density. Raising the temperature, for instance, will cause more electrons to jump the appropriate gap ($U_C - U_V$ in intrinsic material, $U_C - U_D$ in n-type, and $U_A - U_V$ in p-type), and the conductivity will show a marked temperature dependence, increasing with T rather than reducing as for most metals. Semiconducting devices called thermistors make use of this effect for numerous control purposes.[1]

Luminous energy falling on a semiconductor can increase the charge carrier density by a photoelectric effect, in which electrons in the conduction band or in donor levels absorb photons and are excited to the conduction band.   This property is called photoconductivity and has numerous applications.[2]

As we indicated in section 2.1, the height of the Fermi level in a semiconductor is considerably dependent on the impurity concentration.   It can also be modified by changing the temperature or temporarily adding excess charge carriers of one sign or the other.   Rectification properties can be derived from these facts. We shall use as a single illustration the so-called p–n junction, or boundary between a piece of p-type semiconductor and a piece of n-type (both usually of germanium).   We can suppose that there is a certain density N_0 of acceptors in the p-type material, and (for simplicity) the same density of donors in the n-type material.   The junction will then be assumed to be a region of width $2x_0$, in which the acceptor density N_A varies linearly from N_0 at, say, $x = -x_0$, to 0 at $x = x_0$, whereas the donor density N_D varies linearly from 0 at $x = -x_0$ to N_0 at $x = x_0$.

Because there are no conduction electrons in the p-type material and no conduction holes in the n-type, holes and electrons will pass across the boundary, making the p-type material more negative and the n-type material more positive.   This will raise the electron energy levels in the

---

[1] See J. A. Becker, C. B. Green, and G. L. Pearson, *Bell Sys. Tech. Journ.*, **26**, 170–212 (1947) and *Trans. Amer. Inst. Elec. Eng.*, **65**, 711–725 (1946), for details on thermistors.

[2] K. R. Spangenberg, *Fundamentals of Electron Devices*, McGraw-Hill, New York, 1957, pp. 408–414; L. P. Hunter, *Handbook of Semiconductor Electronics*, McGraw-Hill, New York, 1956, section 5.

former and lower them in the latter; in fact, equilibrium will set in when the Fermi levels come to equilibrium, which requires just this sort of change.

Figure 6.2a illustrates this state of affairs, showing the level variation as a function of x.

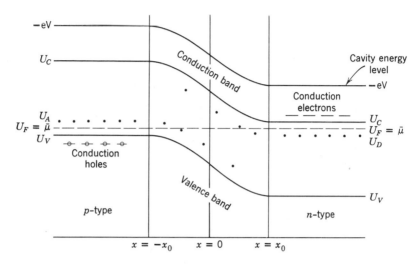

Fig. 6.2a. Level diagram for a p–n semiconductor junction.

Because the Fermi level drops considerably below the conduction band for x just less than x_0, we can assume that the donors in this region are all ionized and have delivered their electrons to the p-type material. Similarly, on the p side we can assume that for $x > -x_0$, all the acceptor levels are filled. This means that there is a charge density in the transition layer given by

$$\rho = -eN_A + eN_D = eN_0(x - x_0)/2x_0 + eN_0(x + x_0)/2x_0$$

or

$$\rho = eN_0 x/x_0 \tag{6.2--1}$$

It then follows from the one-dimensional Poisson equation (section 1.10) that

$$\frac{d^2V}{dx^2} = \frac{-eN_0 x}{\epsilon_0 x_0} \tag{6.2--2}$$

Integrating once and using the vanishing of dV/dx for $|x| \geqslant x_0$, we have

$$\frac{dV}{dx} = -\frac{eN_0(x^2 - x_0^2)}{2\epsilon_0 x_0} \tag{6.2--3}$$

A second integration now gives, letting $V(0) = 0$,

$$V(x) = \frac{-eN_0}{2\epsilon_0 x_0}(\tfrac{1}{3}x^3 - xx_0^2) \tag{6.2--4}$$

which shows that the cavity potential varies in a cubic fashion between $x = -x_0$ and $x = x_0$. The energy of each electron level will vary in accordance with $-eV(x)$, since the levels are located below the cavity potential-energy value by amounts depending on the local atomic structure, which we assume to be approximately homogeneous throughout.

Let us show that such a junction acts as a rectifier. Evidently, current is easily passed in the direction that brings the majority carriers in each material toward the junction. This case can be seen more clearly if we consider the barrier that prevents electrons from going to the p-type material and vice versa, when the system is in equilibrium. There are relatively few levels available for the conduction electrons of the n-type material to occupy in the p-type.[3] Only if they are thermally excited to a considerable energy above the U_C level on the p side can they then pass over easily. Holes on the p side are similarly situated but need to be "excited downwards" (have electrons from lower levels come up to them). When we make the n-type material more negative and the p-type more positive, the levels will shift so as to reduce these barrier heights and make the transfer easier. In statistical mechanics, it is shown that the resulting currents vary in an exponential way with the applied PD (difference in $\bar{\mu}$'s).

When current is passed the other way, the levels are depressed, and there are very few carriers available to make the transition. What current there is usually derives from the continual thermal production of carriers in the transition layer and is largely independent of the applied PD. Thus it comes about that the current in many semiconductor rectifiers can be approximately given as a function of applied potential difference V by a formula of the type (called the "diode characteristic").

$$i = i_0(e^{bV} - 1) \tag{6.2--5}$$

where the first term represents the forward exponentially-varying current and the second the constant reverse current.

Metal-to-semiconductor interfaces can also be rectifying, in case a so-called barrier layer is formed by virtue of electrons leaving the bulk material and residing on the surface. (Cf. problem 1.10h.) Formulas similar to the diode characteristic hold in these cases as well. Copper-oxide, selenium, germanium, and silicon plate rectifiers are made by using

---

[3] The conduction holes are not easily available as levels into which electrons crossing the junction can fall because of their relative paucity and the way they move around.

one such rectifying junction with a metal electrode, and another junction treated so as to avoid the production of a barrier layer.

Photovoltaic cells are sources of emf using p–n junctions or barrier layers. Luminous energy falling on such a junction will produce electron-hole pairs, each of which will move under the action of the electric field toward the material for which it is a majority carrier. Consequently the n-type will become more negative and the p-type more positive. A difference of $\bar{\mu}$'s is created which is, of course, an emf. The so-called solar battery, using silicon, is an example.

Another aspect of the action of a p–n junction is that as current is passed in the forward direction, holes enter the n-type material and electrons enter the p-type material. These minority carriers are said to be "injected" on each side. It takes a finite time for holes and electrons to meet and recombine on each side—it usually takes an intermediate stage of trapping of the minority carrier at an impurity or dislocation where it waits for a majority carrier to come along and neutralize it. Thus it happens that injected carriers can travel some distance in the material of opposite character.

Transistor action uses a combination of rectification and injection. A thin layer of p-type material, for instance, is sandwiched between two pieces of n-type. A current is then passed through one of these p–n junctions, called the "collector," in the reverse direction. If a forward current is passed through the other junction, called the "emitter," electrons injected into the p-type material may diffuse all the way to the reverse-biased junction and act to increase the reverse current by providing the carriers that are otherwise missing for that direction of conduction. Thus a current in the low-resistance forward-biased circuit of the emitter can modulate or control a similar magnitude of current in the high-resistance collector circuit. If external and internal resistances are matched, more power (i^2R) will be developed in the collector circuit than was provided in the emitter circuit.

For many further details on semiconductors, the reader is referred elsewhere.[4]

6.3 The Peltier, Seebeck, and Thomson Thermal Effects

If there is a difference in temperature between two metallic conductors in contact, there will be a tendency for electrons to pass from the warmer

[4] Spangenberg, *loc. cit.*; Hunter, *loc. cit.*, H. K. Henisch, *Rectifying Semi-conductor Contacts*, Clarendon Press, Oxford, 1955; W. Shockley, *Electrons and Holes in Semi-conductors*, D. Von Nostrand, Princeton, 1950; C. Kittel, *Introduction to Solid State Physics*, 2nd ed., John Wiley, New York, 1956, Chapters 13 and 14.

conductor to the cooler one even when the electrochemical potentials are equal, for electrons excited to higher levels in the warmer piece will jump to lower empty levels in the cooler piece more frequently than the reverse will happen. Thus Ohm's law for homogeneous or inhomogeneous materials, eq. 5.1–2a, needs further modification when the temperature is not uniform.

In fact, differences of temperature T act mathematically like differences of $\bar{\mu}$. The current density depends linearly on ∇T as well as on $\nabla \bar{\mu}$.

Fig. 6.3a. A thermocouple circuit, illustrating the Seebeck effect.

Such linear dependence is generally to be expected for small gradients and is found experimentally to hold over all temperature gradients normally met with. We shall write the modified form of Ohm's law as follows:

$$\mathbf{J} = \frac{1}{\rho e}\,(\nabla \bar{\mu} + S^* \, \nabla T) \tag{6.3--1}$$

where S^* is the new constant of proportionality and is called, for reasons to be mentioned later, the "entropy transport per electron" or more briefly the "S-star." It is always positive. It is a property of the metal in question and is a function of the temperature T.

The Seebeck Effect. Equation 6.3–1 has the consequence that when $\mathbf{J} = 0$ in a conductor, a difference of temperature implies a difference of $\bar{\mu}$. This difference leads to the appearance of an emf, called the Seebeck emf,[5] in a circuit containing wires of two different materials with the two junctions at different temperatures. Figure 6.3a shows such a circuit, opened at a place where the temperature is T_p and connected into a

---

[5] Named after its discoverer, T. J. Seebeck, *Abh. d. Konigl. Acad. d. Wiss. Berlin*, 1822–1823, p. 265.

potentiometer which measures the difference in $\bar{\mu}$ between the opened ends. If $\mathbf{J} = 0$, we will have

$$\nabla \bar{\mu} = -S^* \, \nabla T \tag{6.3-2}$$

which for any displacement $\mathbf{dl}$ along the conductor implies $d\bar{\mu} = -S^* \, dT$. The net emf around the circuit we shall call $\mathscr{E}_{BA}(T', T'')$ with the positive current direction and the labeling of the materials related as in the figure. We have

$$\mathscr{E}_{BA}(T', T'') = -\frac{1}{e}(\bar{\mu}_4 - \bar{\mu}_1) = -\frac{1}{e}\int_{\mathscr{P}_1}^{\mathscr{P}_4} d\bar{\mu} = \frac{1}{e}\int_{\mathscr{P}_1}^{\mathscr{P}_4} S^* \, dT \tag{6.3-3}$$

Since the terminals $\mathscr{P}_1$ and $\mathscr{P}_4$ are at the same temperature and since S^* depends only on the kind of material and the temperature, we can write the emf as an integral over the temperature range of the values of S^* around the circuit.   We have

$$\mathscr{E}_{BA}(T', T'') = \frac{1}{e}\oint_{\text{circuit}} S^* \, dT \tag{6.3-4}$$

or the equivalent

$$\mathscr{E}_{BA}(T', T'') = \frac{1}{e}\int_{T'}^{T''} (S_A{}^* - S_B{}^*) \, dT \tag{6.3-5}$$

The former of these equations is clearly quite general and can be used for any number of materials and any temperature distribution.   The latter equation is in a form to help us remember the sign convention of Fig. 6.3a: if $S_A{}^*$ is greater than $S_B{}^*$, electrons are transferred more rapidly along metal A toward lower temperatures than along metal B, and the positive current goes from A to B at the hot junction (i.e., holes go uphill toward higher temperatures, and faster in metal A). The symbol $\mathscr{E}_{BA}(T', T'')$ can be read "emf from B to A at temperature T' less than T''."

When $\mathbf{J}$ is not zero, as in a circuit carrying a steady current, $\nabla \bar{\mu}$ will be equal to $-S^* \, \nabla T + \rho e\mathbf{J}$. The circulation integral of the second term is just the ordinary potential drop of Ohm's law, and the integral of the first term is still the thermal emf, so that our expression for this emf is correct with or without the presence of currents.

A pair of wires connected as in Fig. 6.3a is called a thermocouple; thermocouples are very widely used for temperature measurement and control.   The emf of a thermocouple depends on the properties of two materials and on two temperatures, but it is very easy to show from eq. 6.3–5 that a tabulation of emf's of various substances each paired with one particular standard and each with the same lower temperature $T' = T_0$ (usually $0°$ C) will allow the prediction of the emf for all the possibilities (see problem 6.3a).

The quantity $S_A{}^* - S_B{}^*$ for any particular pair of metals is often useful. It can be found by differentiating the emf $\mathscr{E}_{BA}$ with respect to the warmer temperature T'' (here we set $T'' = T$). The derivative $d\mathscr{E}_{BA}/dT$ is called, for historical reasons, the "thermoelectric power" or "thermopower." We have

$$\frac{d\mathscr{E}_{BA}}{dT} = \frac{1}{e}[S_A*(T) - S_B*(T)] \qquad (6.3\text{–}6)$$

It is to be observed that the thermopower depends only on one temperature. Graphs of thermopowers of several substances A with one reference B

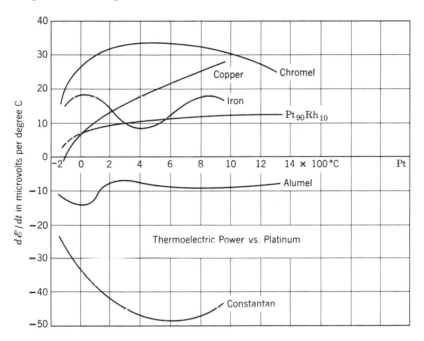

Fig. 6.3b. Thermopowers of various metals referred to platinum. (Taken from P. M. Dike, *Thermoelectric Thermometry*, Philadelphia, 1954, courtesy of Leeds and Northrup, Inc.)

(usually taken as platinum) present information about the emf's of many possible material and temperature pairs in a very compact way. Figure 6.3b is an example.

For details on the operation of thermocouples, the measurement of thermal emf's, and the reduction of unwanted thermal emf's in other measurements, the reader is referred elsewhere.[6]

[6] R. L. Weber, *Heat and Temperature Measurement*, Prentice-Hall, Englewood Cliffs, 1950, Chapter 5; P. H. Dike, *Thermoelectric Thermometry*, Leeds and Northrup, Philadelphia, 1954; F. K. Harris, *Electrical Measurements*, John Wiley, New York, 1952, pp. 431–443.

The Peltier Effect.   The Peltier and Thomson effects involve heat transfer, and so we must consider heat conduction briefly before taking them up.   Heat is energy transferred without the performance of any macroscopic work and is thus to be ascribed to the transfer of thermal energies by molecular and electronic collisions.   In the absence of electric current, a heat current $\mathbf{J}_Q$ joules/m²-sec will be produced by a temperature gradient ∇T, in accordance with the heat-conduction equation

$$\mathbf{J}_Q = -\kappa_Q \nabla T \tag{6.3-7}$$

This equation is studied in an elementary way in beginning courses in physics and is called Fourier's law.   The constant κ_Q is called the "coefficient of heat conductivity."

It is shown in books on solid-state physics[7] that the electrons in a metal play a major role in heat conduction, their jumps from higher to lower levels in adjacent pieces of material at different temperatures accounting for their activity in this regard.   Since without electric current a gradient of $\bar{\mu}$ exists, this gradient also contributes to $\mathbf{J}_Q$ in eq. 6.3–7.

Now, if there is a current in a wire, $\nabla\bar{\mu}$ and ∇T are differently related than when $\mathbf{J} = 0$, and we must write the dependence of $\mathbf{J}_Q$ on the two gradients separately.   Because the same processes are involved in heat conduction and charge transfer, the quantity S^* appears in the general equation for $\mathbf{J}_Q$.[8]   This equation reads

$$\mathbf{J}_Q = -\frac{S^*T\,\nabla\bar{\mu}}{\rho e^2} - \left(\kappa_Q + \frac{S^{*2}T}{\rho e^2}\right)\nabla T \tag{6.3-8}$$

When $\nabla\bar{\mu} = -S^*\nabla T$, eq. 6.3–8 clearly reduces to eq. 6.3–7.

If we use eq. 6.3–1, we can write $\mathbf{J}_Q$ in terms of $\mathbf{J}$ and ∇T:

$$\mathbf{J}_Q = -\frac{S^*T\mathbf{J}}{e} - \kappa_Q\nabla T \tag{6.3-9}$$

Since $-\mathbf{J}/e$ is the number of electrons passing through a unit area in unit time, we see that the heat transferred for each electron involved in a flow of charge is S^*T.   Since entropy, usually denoted by S, is defined in thermodynamics as heat transfer divided by the absolute temperature at

---

[7] See, e.g., C. Kittel, *op. cit.*, pp. 138–153.

[8] The fact that S^* relates both $\nabla\bar{\mu}$ to $\mathbf{J}_Q$ and ∇T to $\mathbf{J}$ is a special case of Onsager's theorem that forms the basis for the theory of the thermodynamics of irreversible processes.   Cf. L. Onsager, *Phys. Rev.*, **37**, 405 (1931); *Phys. Rev.*, **38**, 2265 (1931); *Ann. N.Y. Acad. Sci.*, **46**, 241 (1945); H. D. Callen, *Phys. Rev.*, **73**, 1349 (1948); S. R. DeGroot, *Thermodynamics of Irreversible Processes*, Interscience, New York, 1951. C. A. Domenicali, *Rev. Mod. Phys.*, **26**, 237 (1954) has given a detailed review of the applications of this theorem and the concepts of electrochemical potential, etc., to thermoelectricity.

the point of transfer, we see the reason for calling S^* the entropy transported per electron.

Now consider a junction between two metals with a steady current across it.   If the contact resistance is negligible, $\bar{\mu}$ will be the same in both metals and no electrical energy is expended at the junction.   Both $\mathbf{J}$ and $\mathbf{J}_Q$ will be the same on each side of the junction, for neither charge nor energy will collect there in a steady state.   If the two values of S^* are different, the heat transport by the electrons on the two sides will be unequal, and therefore there must also be a difference between the two $\kappa_Q \nabla T$ terms.

As far as the external surroundings are concerned, heat can be absorbed or emitted by the junction only through temperature-gradient conduction, for the electrons do not get out of the wires.   The difference between the values of $\kappa_Q \nabla T$ on each side will in fact lead to such absorption or emission.   Specifically, if the two metals are denoted by the letters A and B as before, and S_A^* is greater than S_B^*, then when positive current passes from A to B, electrons carry more heat away from the junction in A than bring it up in B, so that the $\kappa_Q \nabla T$ terms must combine to show an absorption of heat from the surroundings.   The amount of this absorption per unit charge is denoted by Π_{BA} (Π is a Greek capital "pi") and is given by

$$\Pi_{BA} = \frac{T}{e} [S_A^*(T) - S_B^*(T)] \qquad (6.3\text{--}10)$$

The rate of absorption per unit time is then $\Pi_{BA}i$, where i is the current. It becomes an emission of heat when the current is reversed.   This rate of absorption is called the Peltier heat.[9]   Since it is a reversible heat exchange, it may also be called the Peltier emf, although because $\bar{\mu}$ is the same in each metal, we cannot properly ascribe any emf to the junction itself.

The Thomson Effect.   Finally, let us consider the heat flow along a wire.   If there is a temperature gradient in the wire, we expect the heat current, and of course S^* and T, to vary along the wire.   Also $\mathbf{J}_Q$ will in general have components into or out of the wire.   The heat transported by the electrons will not be constant along the wire, and its variation will give rise to compensating changes in the ∇T term that, as in the Peltier effect, result in the absorption or emission of heat.   Let us write the component of eq. 6.3–9 along the wire with ordinary light-face type and calculate the difference of J_Q at the two ends of a uniform piece of wire of length Δl.   We have, since S^* is a function of T and J is constant,

$$\Delta J_Q = \Delta l \frac{\partial J_Q}{\partial l} = -\frac{J}{e} \left(T \frac{dS^*}{dT} \Delta T + S^* \Delta T \right) - \frac{\partial}{\partial l} (\kappa_Q \nabla T) \Delta l \qquad (6.3\text{--}11)$$

ΔT represents the temperature difference between the ends of the piece.

[9] J. C. A. Peltier, *Ann. Chim. Phys.*, **56,** 371 (1834).

From eq. 6.3–1, we see that $S^* \Delta T/e = J\rho \Delta l - \Delta\bar{\mu}/e$. The quantity $J^2\rho \Delta l$ is clearly the Joule heat produced per unit cross section of the segment of wire, and the product $J\Delta\ \bar{\mu}/e$ represents the net potential energy carried into the segment of wire by the electrons. The last term in eq. 6.3–11 is part of the heat-conduction pattern that carries away the net heat generated in the wire. Let us examine the first term on the right in eq. 6.3–11.

This term evidently represents another component of heat generation, beside the Joule heat, of amount $T \Delta T (dS^*/dT)$ per electron, or $(-1/e)T \Delta T (dS^*/dT)$ per unit charge, or $(-i/e)T \Delta T (dS^*/dT)$ per unit time. This heat is called the Thomson[10] heat. It is usually described in terms of the Thomson coefficient σ_{Th}, given by

$$\sigma_{\text{Th}} = -\frac{T}{e}\frac{dS^*}{dT} \qquad (6.3-12)$$

which is the rate of Thomson heat generation per unit current and per unit temperature difference. If a current i is established in a wire, the heat generated in a portion with a temperature difference ΔT between its ends is $\sigma_{\text{Th}}i \Delta T$, and the rate of heat generation over the entire wire is

$$\frac{dQ_{\text{Th}}}{dt} = i \int_{T'}^{T''} \sigma_{\text{Th}}(T) \, dT \qquad (6.3-13)$$

This heat generation is reversible like the Peltier heat. Its amount per unit charge is often called the Thomson emf, $\mathscr{E}_{\text{Th}}$, so we can write for a single piece of wire

$$\mathscr{E}_{\text{Th}}(T', T'') = -\frac{1}{e} \int_{T'}^{T''} \sigma_{\text{Th}} \, dT \qquad (6.3-14)$$

Relations between the three thermoelectric effects are readily obtained. If we integrate eq. 6.3–5 by parts and use eqs. 6.3–10 and 6.3–13, we can write

$$\mathscr{E}_{BA}(T', T'') = \frac{1}{e} T''[S_A^*(T'') - S_B^*(T'')] - \frac{1}{e} T'[S_A^*(T') - S_B^*(T')]$$

$$- \frac{1}{e} \int_{T'}^{T''} T\left[\frac{dS_A^*(T)}{dT} - \frac{dS_B^*(T)}{dT}\right] dT$$

$$= \Pi_{BA}(T'') - \Pi_{BA}(T') + \int_{T'}^{T''} [\sigma_{\text{Th},A}(T) - \sigma_{\text{Th},B}(T)] \, dT$$

or

$$\mathscr{E}_{BA}(T', T'') = \Pi_{BA}(T'') - \Pi_{BA}(T') + \mathscr{E}_{\text{Th},A}(T', T'') - \mathscr{E}_{\text{Th},B}(T', T'')$$
$$(6.3-15)$$

[10] W. Thomson (Lord Kelvin), *Trans. Roy. Soc. Edinb.*, **21**, 153 (1847); also *Math. Phys. Papers.*, **1**, 232 and 266 (1882).

We see that the Seebeck emf can be written as a sum of the Peltier and Thomson emf's. Mathematically this is accomplished by integration by parts; physically it is the heat transported by the electrons that accounts for the different locations of the Seebeck emf and the two heating effects.

Using eq. 6.3-6 with eqs. 6.3–10 and 6.3–12, we can readily derive Kelvin's two relations:

$$\Pi_{BA}(T) = T\frac{d\mathscr{E}_{BA}(T_0, T)}{dT} \tag{6.3–16}$$

and

$$\sigma_{\text{Th},A}(T) - \sigma_{\text{Th},B}(T) = -T\frac{d^2\mathscr{E}_{BA}(T_0, T)}{dT^2} \tag{6.3–17}$$

where the derivatives do not depend on the value of T_0.

The Peltier heat is useful for controlling the heat supply in certain calorimetric effects and of course can be measured in such experiments. Like the Seebeck emf, its measurement always involves the difference between the appropriate quantities for two metals. The Thomson heat is harder to measure but involves a single substance only. It can be measured by establishing a current in a uniform bar of material which is hotter in the middle than it is at the two ends. Then in one half of the bar the current and temperature gradient are in the same direction, and in the other half they are not. Therefore symmetrically situated points on the bar can be found where Joule heating is the same but the Thomson heats are equal and opposite. A thermocouple temperature-difference measurement, coupled with heat conduction information, will suffice to determine σ_{Th}. Careful measurements made on one substance can be used with Seebeck emf measurements and eq. 6.3–17 to obtain other Thomson coefficients.

For measurement details[11] and for a discussion of the various effects that enter when magnetic fields and crystalline inhomogeneities are present,[12] the reader is referred elsewhere.

Problem 6.3a. Show from eq. 6.3–5 that the emf of a thermocouple between temperatures T' and T'' can be found from its values between T' and T_0 and between T'' and T_0 and that $\mathscr{E}_{CA} = \mathscr{E}_{BA} + \mathscr{E}_{CB}$ where A, B, and C denote three different materials.

Problem 6.3b. Materials A, B, and C are connected in a circuit, with junctions at temperature $T_{BC} = T_1$, $T_{CA} = T_2$ and $T_{AB} = T_3$. Write the emf as the sum of the emf's of two ordinary thermocouples, using material C as one member of each pair.

[11] Dike, *loc. cit.*; Weber, *loc. cit.*; W. Meissner, *Handbuch der Experimentalphysik*, Leipzig, 1935, Vol. XI, Part 2, pp. 458.
[12] See Domenicali, *loc. cit.*; Callen, *loc. cit.*; and De Groot, *loc. cit.*

Problem 6.3c.   Find approximately the emf of a copper-constantan thermo-couple operating between 200° C and 600° C, by estimating the appropriate area in Fig. 6.3*b*.

Problem 6.3d.   Find the Peltier heat at the hot junction of the thermocouple in problem 6.3*c*.   If the thermocouple circuit has a resistance of 2.0 ohms, find how much heat is absorbed at the hot junction owing to the current produced by the Seebeck emf.   How much current should be supplied by an external emf, to absorb 0.01 watt at the hot junction?

6.4   Electrochemical Effects

All of the principal electrochemical effects occur with electrolytes,[13] which are solutions of ions[13] in water or other solvents, in contact with metallic conductors known as electrodes.[13]   The study of such systems is a major item in physical chemistry, and we shall not try to present here a discussion appropriate to texts in that field.   However, there are certain fundamental electrical principles involved in these effects, whose elucida-tion aids materially in the understanding of electrical conduction in solutions and of the operation of electrical cells.   Hence we shall give them brief attention in this section.

Ions in Solution.   The first consideration concerns the existence of ions in solution.   A pair of ions, like Na^+ and Cl^- or Cu^{++} and $SO_4^=$, would be more easily pulled apart in the gaseous state if they were neutral than if they were charged.   That is, if they had enough energy to move around freely and independently, they would neutralize each other sooner or later.   Why do they not do so in solution?   One way of answering this is to say that, owing to the large dielectric constant of water, the attraction between two oppositely charged ions is very weak in water solution.

A better but lengthier answer for our purposes is in terms of energy levels.   When an atom is ionized, the electron most easily removable is taken away.   We say that the highest occupied level has been emptied. Thus the highest occupied level of a neutral atom becomes the lowest vacant level of a singly charged positive ion.   If the atom can be ionized twice, the highest occupied level of the singly charged atom becomes the lowest vacant level of the doubly charged atom.   Similarly, the highest occupied level of a negative ion that has gained an extra electron is the same as the lowest vacant level of the neutral atom, and so on.

Now, the energies of these various levels are changed when the ions are in solution, for each ion will be surrounded by water molecules, these being

---

[13] The words "electrolyte," "ion," and "electrode" were introduced by M. Faraday *Experimental Researches in Electricity*, Bernard Quaritch, London, 1839, Vol. I, §§ 661–665.

permanently polarized. The dipoles will line up so as to weaken the field and therefore reduce the amount of energy gained when an electron comes in to neutralize a positive ion or goes out of a negative ion. The energies of the empty levels of positive ions are raised in solution, and the energies of the filled levels in negative ions are lowered.

Any ions that can exist in solution make frequent collisions with each other and with other molecules present. In a steady state, we can be sure that there are no vacant electron energy levels in some atoms, molecules, or ions that are below any filled levels in the same or other entities, for otherwise electrons would shift into these vacant levels from the higher filled ones.

We therefore answer our question by saying that pairs of ions that can exist in solution satisfy the condition that all the vacant levels of the positive ions lie above all the occupied levels of the negative ions. It must also be true that the vacant levels referred to are above any filled levels in the water molecules (or molecules of whatever solvent is used) and similarly the occupied levels of the ions must all be below any vacant levels in the solvent.[14] There are no conduction electrons in solutions, and so there are no levels of the metallic sort to consider. Figure 6.4a shows some typical levels for water solutions.

The quantity of interest for any electron level, vacant or occupied, is obviously the energy required to take an electron from that level on any particular ion, to a cavity in the solution. This could be called the work function for the level, but is customarily called the solvated ionization potential and is denoted by $\mathscr{J}_{\pm z}$ where $\pm z$ is the number of electron charges on the ion in question. If V again denotes the cavity potential, we can write for the electrochemical potential of an electron in any particular level an equation like eq. 2.4–2:

$$\bar{\mu} = -\mathscr{J}_{\pm z} - eV \qquad (6.4–1)$$

Sometimes an electron transfer to or from a molecule is followed immediately by another energy change such as a dissociation or a combination process. In this case, we can define $\mathscr{J}_{\pm z}$ so as to include the overall energy change.

This formula 6.4–1 for the effective Fermi level is strictly correct only at absolute zero. As the temperature rises and higher levels become partially occupied, $\bar{\mu}$ will also rise. At ordinary temperatures however, eq. 6.4–1 is a fairly good approximation.

Another factor governing the existence of ions in solution is that of the energy with which pairs of ions of opposite sign may come together to

[14] For details on this and other parts of this section, see R. W. Gurney, *Ions in Solution*, Cambridge University Press, Cambridge, 1936.

form a crystalline solid.   If the potential energy per ion pair is less in the crystalline solid than the energy of the same pair in solution, the ions will not remain in the dissolved state.

Electrodes.   If a piece of metal is inserted into a solution, there are four elementary possibilities for charge transfer.   Electrons may pass from the metal to vacant levels in ions or molecules in the solution, or second,

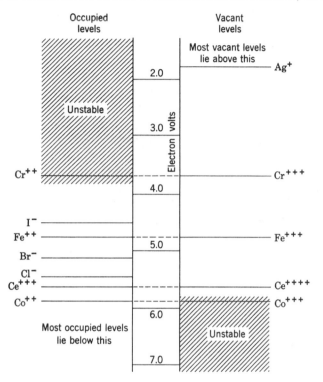

Fig. 6.4a.   Electron energy levels in aqueous solutions. (After R. W. Gurney, *Ions in Solution*, Cambridge Univ. Press, Cambridge, 1936, Fig. 43.)

they may pass from filled solution levels into the metal.   Third, atoms at the surface of the metal may leave their conduction electrons behind and pass as ions into the solution, and finally ions of the same atomic species may leave the solution and become attached to the surface of the metal. (We say they are "adsorbed" on the surface.)   The possibility of a different sort of atoms becoming adsorbed is complicated, because when enough "foreign" atoms have arrived, the surface becomes plated with them and further arrivals find a surface of their own kind.   Such cases along with other cases of two-step chemical reactions, etc., will not be treated here.

We can treat these four possibilities all in terms of energy levels.   If electrons transfer between the metal and a certain electron level in the solution, this level and the Fermi level in the metal will come to equality at equilibrium in the same way as for metal-to-metal contacts.   In fact, we can write

$$\bar{\mu}_m = -\phi - eV_m = \bar{\mu}_s = -\mathscr{J}_{\pm z} - eV_s \qquad (6.4\text{--}2)$$

where the subscripts m and s refer to metal and solution.   As a consequence, the cavity potential difference becomes

$$V_m - V_s = \frac{1}{e}(\mathscr{J}_{\pm z} - \phi) \qquad (6.4\text{--}3)$$

(Strictly, a term of the form (kT/e) times the logarithm of a certain concentration ratio must be added on the right side of eq. 6.4–3.)

The transfer of an ion from solution to metal can, for the purposes of energy-balance calculations, be thought of as the transfer of an electron from the metal to the ion when it comes near the metal, followed by the adsorption of the neutral atom onto the surface.   As indicated above, we can represent the combined action by a single quantity $\mathscr{J}_{\pm z}$.

The principal transfer that occurs in any particular case is determined by whether the Fermi level of the metal is initially above the lowest vacant level in the solution, below the highest occupied level, or in between these two.   In the first two cases, transfers will occur when uncharged metal is put into contact with uncharged solution.   In the last case, no change can occur unless $V_m - V_s$ is first adjusted; electrodes in this condition when no transfer can occur are called "ideally polarized electrodes."   Many electrolytic processes will not take place until a certain minimum PD is established.

A chemical cell is a combination of a solution and two electrodes or two solutions and two electrodes.   In the latter case, the two solutions are either kept from mixing by a porous diaphragm which allows ions to pass through to establish electrical equilibrium or are separated by a vessel or tube containing a third solution whose mixing with either of the other two does not produce unwanted difficulties. If the charge transfers that occur at the two electrodes are of different types the $\bar{\mu}$'s in the electrodes will at equilibrium be at different levels, so that an emf will be produced, as we indicated in section 5.2.

When a current is passed from electrode to solution or vice versa, there will be a small shift of the cavity PD from the equilibrium value, for, in order to have a finite rate of charge transfer, there has to be a finite difference $\Delta\bar{\mu}$ in the $\bar{\mu}$'s.   The relation between $\Delta\bar{\mu}$ and the resulting current density J in one direction across the interface is exponential in nature, generally of the form

$$J = c \exp\left[\alpha \, \Delta\bar{\mu}/kT\right] \tag{6.4-4}$$

where c depends on the concentrations and α is a constant between 0 and 1 called the transfer coefficient. Thus it only takes a small shift in the cavity PD to produce a considerable current across the interface. This added PD is called the "overvoltage" or "overpotential." For most circuit applications, it can be approximately included in the internal potential drop ir. The exponential character of the current-voltage relation holds only so long as some other process that limits the current does not take effect, such as processes restricting the rate at which ions can get to the interface from the body of the solution. This exponential character accounts for the asymmetrical or rectification properties of certain cells and of electrolytic condensers.

Electrolytic capacitors are formed by choosing appropriate electrodes and solutions with one rectifying and one non-rectifying pair and running current in the direction of low conductivity long enough to build up a suitable layer of chemical-reaction products at the interface of the rectifying electrode. This will require a large overpotential. If then a considerably smaller overpotential is applied, almost no current will be passed, and the deposited chemical layer will act as a layer of dielectric between the electrode and the solution. On a macroscopic scale, this layer can be extremely thin, leading to very large capacitance values in a small space.

Faraday's Laws. When current passes across a metal-solution boundary, a chemical change occurs. If a current i passes for a time t, then it coulombs pass through, or it/e electrons. If each atom, molecule, or ion involved has a valence z (i.e., carries z electrons), the number of such chemical entities transferred will be it/ze. The mass of each in grams is the molecular weight M divided by Avogadro's number N_0, which is defined as the number of oxygen atoms which have collectively a mass of 16.0000 g ($M = 16.0000$ for oxygen). Therefore the total mass m deposited or dissolved in the chemical action is

$$m = \frac{it}{ze} \cdot \frac{M}{N_0} = \frac{itM}{z\mathscr{F}} = \frac{Q}{\mathscr{F}} \cdot \frac{M}{z} \tag{6.4-5}$$

in grams, where M/z is called the "chemical equivalent" of the molecular species in question, $Q = it$ is the charge in coulombs passed between electrode and solution, and the quantity $\mathscr{F}$, called the "faraday," is given by

$$\mathscr{F} = N_0 e = 6.0230 \times 10^{23} \times 1.60209 \times 10^{-19}$$
$$= 96{,}493 \pm 2 \text{ coulombs}$$

Accurate measurements of the faraday using eq. 6.4–5 are taken together with a determination of N_0 from X rays to provide one of the most accurate values of e now available.

The two laws of electrolysis discovered by Faraday[15] are both embodied in eq. 6.4–5—namely, that (1) the mass deposited or dissolved is proportional to the chemical equivalent, for several cells through which the same Q is passed and (2) m for any one cell is proportional to Q.

Electrolytic Conduction. Although current at a metal-solution interface is usually carried by one type of transfer, current in the body of a solution is transported by all the ionic types that are present. Any ionic species will move under the influence of an electric field at a constant speed proportional to the field strength. We write for the magnitude of the speed of any ion

$$v = uE \qquad (6.4\text{–}6)$$

where the proportionality constant u is called the "mobility." When there are, as in a simple case, one species each of positive and negative ion, the total current density J is given by a sum of terms for each species

$$J = n_+ z_+ e u_+ E + n_- z_- e u_- E \qquad (6.4\text{–}7)$$

where $z_+ e$ and $z_- e$ are the magnitudes of the charge on each species of ion, and n_+ and n_- are the numbers of each per unit volume. Since the solution must be neutral at any interior point, $n_+ z_+ = n_- z_-$. The conductivity $\sigma = J/E$ is thus given by

$$\sigma = n_+ z_+ e(u_+ + u_-) \qquad (6.4\text{–}8)$$

The fraction of J carried by either ionic species is called the transference number τ for that species. We have clearly

$$\tau_+ = \frac{u_+}{u_+ + u_-} \; ; \qquad \tau_- = \frac{u_-}{u_+ + u_-} \; ; \qquad \tau_+ + \tau_- = 1 \qquad (6.4\text{–}9)$$

How can it be that the current is carried by two carrier types in the interior of the solution and by one type only in a discharge process at an electrode? Part of the answer is that the concentration of positive and negative ions near each electrode must change to make up for the difference. Let us call a region near the positive electrode (i.e., the one toward which the negative ions move) within which all the concentration changes occur R_+, and the corresponding region at the other electrode R_-. Then of the current i that enters R_+ from the main body of the solution, a fraction τ_+

---

[15] M. Faraday, *op. cit.*, §§ 713–821.

is carried by the positive ions. If all of the current passing to R_+ from the electrode is carried by the particular positive ions in question, an amount of ions corresponding to the current difference $(i - \tau_+ i)$ is removed from R_+. This difference, however, is equal to $\tau_- i$, the amount of negative charge carried out of R_+ by the negative ions. Hence the net result is to reduce the quantity of positive and negative ions in R_+ by equal amounts. Measurement of this reduction in quantity constitutes one way of determining τ_+ and τ_-.

This is not all the answer to our question, however. We do not expect τ_+ and τ_- to change very much as the concentration varies, so that, except right next to the electrode, the positive and negative ion currents will be uniform and cause no concentration changes. Next to an electrode, however, ions of the same sign as the electrode move away and their concentration near it will get small very rapidly. If this is the negative ion, the region near the electrode then becomes positively charged.

Unless negative ions move back into this region, the positive charge there will make the positive ions that enter slow down and pile up, so that the current cannot be maintained. Actually, as soon as any species of ion varies considerably in concentration from place to place, thermal diffusion, resulting from random thermal motion, will cause ions to enter the region where the concentration is weak. This diffusion plays an essential, and needless to say complicated, role in readjusting the current at an interface. The exact mechanism of this readjustment is very difficult to calculate even in ideally simplified cases.

Above all, it should be noted that a true steady state is never attainable in electrolysis, because of these progressive concentration changes, as well as the using up of electrode materials. The methods used to maintain a relatively constant emf and internal resistance in practical cells will not be discussed here.

The diffusion tendency just mentioned will produce an emf between different solutions, as in the two-solution cells referred to above. However, a judicious choice of the solution used for connecting two halves of a cell can reduce this emf to almost negligible proportions.

The Lead and Weston Cells. There are three types of cells most commonly encountered in experimental physics; one of these, the dry cell, was discussed in section 5.2.

The lead storage cell involves reversible processes at each plate, there being no secondary reactions to remove the products found when the cell delivers energy. Hence chemical energy can be restored by reversing the current. The reaction at one electrode involves the change of a lead atom with four units of positive charge, Pb^{++++}, to the divalent ion Pb^{++}; at the other plate the reaction is from neutral lead, Pb, to Pb^{++}. For the chemical details, the reader is referred elsewhere.[16]   Such a cell is generally characterized in an electrical sense by the charge it can deliver at a standard current.   The ampere-hour (3600 coulombs) is used for reference to charge capacity.

The Weston standard cell is used as a reproducible laboratory source of emf for standardization purposes.   It contains a solution, saturated or unsaturated, of cadmium sulfate ($CdSO_4$).   The positive electrode consists of mercury metal covered with crystals of the nearly insoluble salt mercurous sulfate (Hg_2SO_4).   When a mercury ion leaves the metal, it picks up a sulfate ion from the solution and the two deposit together on the salt crystals.   Thus the effective reaction is the deposition of $SO_4^=$.

The negative electrode is a solution of cadmium metal in mercury.   In the saturated form of the cell, crystals of cadmium sulfate, $CdSO_4$, are placed on the mercury-cadmium solution.   As at the other electrode, a transfer of Cd to Cd^{++} results in Cd^{++} and $SO_4^=$ joining the crystal, so the electrode is essentially another form of $SO_4^=$ electrode, involving a different energy change.

The resulting emf turns out to be nearly independent of concentration because the same ion is deposited or dissolved in the two different reactions, so that new cells can be made up to have very closely the same emf as an originally calibrated one.   This value, which is temperature dependent, has been determined to be, at $t°$ C,

$$\mathscr{E}(t) = 1.018646 - 0.0000406(t - 20)$$
$$- 0.00000093(t - 20)^2 + 0.00000001(t - 20)^3 \text{ v} \qquad (6.4\text{--}10)$$

The unsaturated cell is more portable and has a lower temperature coefficient, but the emf of each new cell has to be calibrated against a standard.[17]

Problem 6.4a.   Let the ionization potential (energy necessary to remove one electron) of an atom be $\mathscr{I}$ in vacuo and $\mathscr{J}$ in solution. Let the work done in removing the ion from the solution into a cavity be W and the work of removing a neutral atom be W_0.   Find the relation between these four quantities, and give arguments to show that $\mathscr{J} < \mathscr{I}$.

Problem 6.4b.   Let the work done in removing an ion of charge $\pm ze$ from the surface of a metal into a cavity within that metal be $\mathscr{I}_{\pm z}$, and the work done in removing the same ion from the solution to a cavity within the solution be $W_{\pm z}$. Write expressions for the ionic electrochemical potentials $\bar{\mu}_{m,\text{ionic}}$ and $\bar{\mu}_{s,\text{ionic}}$ for the ion on the metal and in the solution, and so find the cavity PD at equilibrium.

[16] Cf. G. W. Vinal, *Storage Batteries*, John Wiley, New York, 4th ed. 1955 or a short account in H. J. Creighton and W. A. Koehler, *Principles and Applications of Electrochemistry*, 2nd ed., John Wiley, New York, 1944, Vol. II, Chapter IV.

[17] See references on p. 190.

Problem 6.4c.   Find the number of ampere-hours per cm^2 required to plate a coating of silver 0.1 mm thick on an electrode, if the density of the silver layer is 10.50 g/cm^3. (At. wt of silver = 107.88; valence = 1.)

Problem 6.4d.   Suppose that at the negative electrode of a cell, the current is all carried by the passage of negative ions into the solution. Find out what happens to the number of ions in region R_- as described in the text.

Problem 6.4e.   Tell qualitatively why a Daniell cell, consisting of zinc, a solution of zinc sulfate, a porous membrane, a solution of copper sulfate, and copper, will produce an emf with the copper *positive*, whereas when zinc and copper are in direct contact the contact potential difference between them is such as to make the copper *negative*. Assume the solutions on the two sides of the membrane to have negligible cavity PD.

Problem 6.4f.   It is observed that, if sulfuric acid is dissolved in water to give H^+ and $SO_4^=$ ions, along with a very small concentration of OH^- ions from thermal dissociation of the H_2O water molecules, and a current is passed through the solution between platinum electrodes, H_2 is discharged at the negative electrode in accordance with $2H^+ + 2e \rightarrow H_2$, whereas at the positive electrode, we have $4OH^- \rightarrow 2H_2O + O_2 + 4e$. Nothing appears to happen to the $SO_4^=$. What fact can you infer about the solution that would explain this observation?

Problem 6.4g.   Chemists call positive ions "cations" because they migrate toward the electrode that is made negative when an external emf is applied and is hence called the "cathode" in accordance with standard usage. Similarly, negative ions that proceed toward the positive "anode" are called "anions." Explain why cations migrate toward the positive electrode of a cell that is a source of emf, and vice versa for anions.

The
Magnetic
Field

7.1 Introduction

Magnetic forces are forces between currents or moving charges. The most fundamental approach in studying them might be to inquire into the force between a pair of moving charges. However, the expression for this force is too complicated to be made the basis of a simple definition of a magnetic field quantity. We shall take the simpler approach of studying first the forces on a moving charge produced by any unspecified external agent. This force is given by the Lorentz force law, which is not only a physical law but at the same time constitutes a definition of a magnetic-field quantity. Several straightforward applications of this law will be discussed, some of which will provide us with convincing evidence of its validity.

Our next step will be to specify the way in which magnetic fields are produced, introducing the law due primarily to Ampère, but in certain special forms also to Laplace, Biot, and Savart. Faraday's law for induced emf's will then be taken up as an experimentally verified extension of the Lorentz force law.   These laws and their applications will prepare the way for the straightforward development of the fictional but useful pole concept in Chapter 8 and lead to a discussion of ferromagnetic materials.

7.2   The Force on a Moving Charge and the Definition of B

In Chapter 1, we considered the force on a charge at rest; we saw that we can write the force in a way that separates the properties of the charge, i.e., the magnitude q, and the properties of the surroundings—the vector $\mathbf{E}$. In writing eq. 1.2–2, $\mathbf{F} = q\mathbf{E}$, we not only express the definition of $\mathbf{E}$, but also state a law of physics, namely, that the force on a charge at rest at a given point in the vicinity of other charges at rest is proportional to its magnitude q and has a direction that is the same for all positive values of q, being opposite for all negative q's.

Now, if the surroundings contain moving charges (currents) but the test charge q is still at rest, the same law is found to hold, and we make the same definition of $\mathbf{E}$.   In this case, however, $\mathbf{E}$ may be no longer given by Coulomb's law, as in eq. 1.2–3, and of course it may vary in time (section 7.9 will give the law according to which $\mathbf{E}$ is produced by moving charges).

If, on the other hand, the surrounding charges are stationary and q moves, $\mathbf{F} = q\mathbf{E}$ again holds and $\mathbf{E}$ is of necessity found from Coulomb's law.   That is, the expression $q\mathbf{E}$ gives a force that is independent of the velocity $\mathbf{v}$ of the charge.   Problem 1.6a in Chapter 1 and the diode calculation in sections 1.10 and 5.8 dealt with moving charges in an electrostatic field.

Let us consider the case now in which both the charge q and its neighbors are moving.   In order to separate again the effects of the surroundings and the properties of the charge, we shall focus our attention on a particular point $\mathscr{P}$ at a particular time t and ask what force is exerted on q when it is passing through $\mathscr{P}$ at t with some given velocity $\mathbf{v}$.   We can imagine an experiment in which particles (electrons and ions) carrying various charges are accelerated by some apparatus which allows them to pass through $\mathscr{P}$ at time t with various speeds and directions.   Study of the resulting deflections of these particles will allow a determination of their accelerations when at $\mathscr{P}$ and the force on each can be found by $\mathbf{F} = m\mathbf{a}$.[1]

---

[1] To be accurate, our experiments require that the test charges not react appreciably on the surroundings (see section 1.2, p. 5) and that the experimental errors in locating the positions of particles near $\mathscr{P}$ and their times of passage be small in comparison to the space and time variations of the effects under study.

⸱ The results can all be expressed in a compact form using vector notation. However, this notation may conceal, from the reader unfamiliar with it, the physical meaning of the law.   In particular, it hides a basic symmetry inherent in the situation.   Hence we shall begin with an elementary although somewhat lengthy description.

As we have said, the force $\mathbf{F} = q\mathbf{E}$ which acts on a charge at rest is found to act unchanged on the moving charges.   However, there is an additional force that depends on $\mathbf{v}$.   We should expect the direction of

Fig. 7.2a.   Velocity-dependent forces on charges moving at $\mathscr{P}$.

such a velocity-dependent force to depend not only on the direction of $\mathbf{v}$, but also on the nature of the surrounding charge and current distributions that are presumably the "cause" of this force.   This is in fact the case. Part of the dependence on $\mathbf{v}$ consists in the circumstance that the velocity-dependent forces on ions of different charges, speeds, and directions lie in a certain plane through $\mathscr{P}$ ($\mathscr{MN}$ in Fig. 7.2a).   To use an equivalent expression, the forces are all perpendicular to a certain definite line $\mathscr{QR}$ (Fig. 7.2a).   This line will be taken as determining the direction of the magnetic field at $\mathscr{P}$ which gives rise to the velocity-dependent force. The magnitude of the force is zero if the charge is moving along the line $\mathscr{QR}$, in either direction.   In fact, the magnitude turns out to be proportional to the projection of $\mathbf{v}$ on the plane $\mathscr{MN}$, as well as being proportional to q in analogy to the electric force qE.   We can write, therefore,

$$F = Bqv_{\text{proj}} \qquad\qquad \text{MKS} \quad (7.2\text{-}1)$$

where v_{proj} is the magnitude of the projection $\mathbf{v}_{\text{proj}}$ of $\mathbf{v}$ on the plane $\mathcal{M}\mathcal{N}$ and B is the proportionality constant that depends on the surroundings and not on the charges under observation.

It remains only to specify the direction of the force in the plane $\mathcal{M}\mathcal{N}$. It is always perpendicular to the vector $\mathbf{v}_{\text{proj}}$. In specifying which way along the perpendicular it acts, we find that for all vectors $\mathbf{v}$ through $\mathcal{P}$, $\mathbf{F}$ and $\mathbf{v}_{\text{proj}}$ are related in the same sense of circulation or rotation. That is, if as in Fig. 7.2*b* we draw a circulating arrow showing the direction

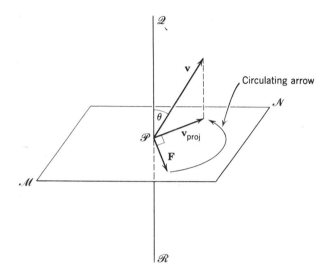

Fig. 7.2*b*.   A charge q moves with velocity $\mathbf{v}$ through point $\mathcal{P}$ and experiences a force $\mathbf{F}$ perpendicular to $\mathbf{v}_{\text{proj}}$ in plane $\mathcal{M}\mathcal{N}$.

through which $\mathbf{F}$ should be rotated by 90° to get to $\mathbf{v}_{\text{proj}}$, this circulating arrow applies to all possible pairs of vectors, except that negative values of q reverse the relationship. We might say that the space has a certain circulating property set up in it. (We shall see in section 7.4 that this circulation direction is just the direction of circulation of the current that produced it.)

We could try to describe the magnetic field in terms of some type of circulation entity, with a magnitude B and a direction specified by means of a plane and a circular arrow in the plane. But such a description is awkward, is historically unconventional, and does not make use of the relative simplicity of vector analysis. Hence we shall introduce a vector $\mathbf{B}$ directed normally to the plane, and specify its direction in relation to the circulation by the right-hand-screw rule—if the fingers are curled to

match the circulating arrow, the thumb points along the normal chosen
for **B** (cf. Fig 7.2c). This convention is of course arbitrary, but has
arisen historically because it fits, as we shall see, the custom of calling
the north-seeking end of a compass needle positive. This latter convention
is related to the choice of map makers in putting north at the top of maps,
and of the mathematicians' habit of making the upward direction rather
than the downward the positive one for graphs.

There is of course complete symmetry between the two sides of the plane

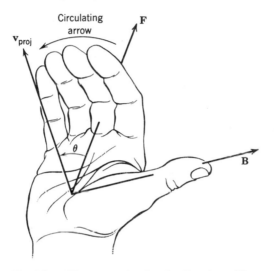

Fig. 7.2c. The convention for the direction of **B**.

$\mathscr{M}\mathscr{N}$ (**v** can be on either side for a given $\mathbf{v}_{proj}$), so that the assignment of
a vector to one of the normals ($\mathscr{P}2$ in Fig. 7.2b) conceals this symmetry.
There is no physical reason that connects one direction along the line $\mathscr{Q}\mathscr{R}$
with the sign of a charge as there is for the vector **E**. (The electric field
intensity **E** is often called a "polar vector," whereas vectors like **B** are
called "axial vectors" or "pseudovectors"; cf. Appendix A.4.)

For historical reasons, **B** is called the "magnetic induction." We shall
use it as our fundamental magnetic-field quantity. The force vector
which has the direction specified above and the magnitude $qv_{proj} B$ may
be written in vector notation by use of the vector product (cf. Appendix
A.2),

$$\mathbf{F} = q\mathbf{v} \times \mathbf{B} \tag{7.2-2}$$

We can finally write a general expression for the entire force on a given
charge at a given place and time:

$$\mathbf{F} = q\mathbf{E} + q\mathbf{v} \times \mathbf{B} \qquad \text{MKS} \quad (7.2\text{--}3a)$$

an equation known as the Lorentz force law.[2] (The entire expression on the right is called the Lorentz force; the second term is called the magnetic force.) This law has been experimentally verified over a wide range of values of q and $\mathbf{v}$ and for a wide variety of values of $\mathbf{E}$ and $\mathbf{B}$. The only limitations on its validity arise from the omission of additional terms due to radiation that depend on the *acceleration* rather than on the velocity of q. We shall limit ourselves whenever necessary to small accelerations so that eq. 7.2–3 may be considered strictly valid.

In our MKS absolute practical units, we measure F in newtons, q in coulombs, and v in meters/second. Hence B has the units newton-second/coulomb-meter=newton/ampere-meter. This unit is also called the weber/meter², which is the more conventional name (the weber is a flux unit to be introduced shortly) and the tesla,[3] a name adopted by the International Electrotechnical Commission in June, 1956.

We shall also express the magnetic force law in Gaussian units, for which F is in dynes, q in statcoulombs, v in centimeters/second, and B is measured in the electromagnetic unit (emu), known as the gauss[4] or the oersted. (The reason for two names being given to one unit will be discussed in Chapter 8.) In this case, the Lorentz law becomes

$$\mathbf{F} = q\mathbf{E} + \frac{q}{c}(\mathbf{v} \times \mathbf{B}) \qquad \text{Gaussian} \quad (7.2\text{–}3b)$$

where c is an experimental constant related to the experimental constant ϵ_0 in the MKS form of Coulomb's law. In fact, $c = 1/(4\pi\epsilon_0 \cdot 10^{-7})^{\frac{1}{2}}$ $= 2.99793 \times 10^{10}$ cm/sec (i.e., the velocity of light). It enters both here and in Ampère's law (cf. section 7.4).

One weber/m² $= 1.00$ tesla $= 10^4$ gauss; this conversion factor is fairly easy to remember from the fact that 10,000 gauss or 1.00 weber/m² is a round number expressing approximately the largest practicable magnetic field obtainable in ordinary laboratory electromagnets.

Particle Motions. The value of $\mathbf{B}$ will in general vary from point to point. Let us consider as a first example the special case in which $\mathbf{B}$ is uniform over a certain region in space and is constant in time. Let us also assume that $\mathbf{E}$ is zero in this region. The magnet of a cyclotron provides

---

[2] This law which we now take as fundamental was derived by H. A. Lorentz from theories of Clausius and others and first published in *Archiv. Néerl.* **xxv** 363 (1892), especially Chapter IV, pp. 432 ff.

[3] Named after Nikola Tesla (1856–1943), an electrical engineer with many inventions to his credit.

[4] Gaussian units are those in which the electrostatic system is used for electric charge, field, potential, and capacitance, and electromagnetic units are used for $\mathbf{B}$ and the other magnetic quantities to be introduced later. See Appendix A.7.

an example of such a region that is familiar nowadays to most students of elementary physics.

Then there are two simple cases:

a.   If the charge starts to move in the direction of the field **B**, there will be no force and hence the particle will continue to move in this direction without acceleration.

b.   If the particle is started in a plane perpendicular to **B**, its acceleration will lie in the same plane, and the particle's path will all be contained in

Fig. 7.2d.   Motion of ions in uniform **B**. (*a*) **v** is parallel to **B**, leading to straight line motion. (*b*) **v** is perpendicular to **B**, leading to circular motion.

this plane.   Further, since the force is at right angles to the velocity, no work will be done and the speed will remain constant.   (This property is true for the work done by the magnetic force in all cases of motion of charged particles, and not only for this special case.)   Thus as the particle moves, it will change its direction under the action of a *constant* force at right angles to its path.   It will, in short, move in a circle, and if positive will circulate in the opposite direction to that of the arrow of Fig. 7.2*b*.[5] We may find the radius of this circle from **F** = *m***a** by writing

$$F = qvB = mv^2/R$$

or

$$R = \frac{mv}{qB} \qquad\qquad \text{MKS} \quad (7.2\text{-}4a)$$

$$R = \frac{mvc}{qB} \qquad\qquad \text{Gaussian} \quad (7.2\text{-}4b)$$

R is the radius of the circular path (Fig. 7.2*d*) and *m* is the mass of the

[5] This oppositeness is related to Lenz's law.   Cf. section 7.9.

particle that bears the charge q.   If relativistic effects are important, the relativistic value of mv is to be used (problem 7.2d).

Equations 7.2–4 describe the motion of particles in cyclotrons, betatrons, synchrotrons, mass spectrometers, and numerous other devices that involve the magnetic deflection of moving particles.   In fact, the success of any of these devices constitutes a verification of the Lorentz force law. Another use of eqs. 7.2–4 consists in measuring the momentum of particles that make visible tracks in a Wilson cloud chamber.   Frequently, the density or origin of the tracks provides sufficient evidence to establish the value of q, whereupon the momentum $mv = RBq$ may be found from measurements of R and B (by methods to be discussed later).

If a particle has an initial velocity at some angle other than 90° or 0° with the direction of **B**, the motion resolves itself into a combination of a constant velocity component in the direction of **B** and a circular motion in the perpendicular plane: i.e., the path is a helix of constant radius and pitch.   More complicated motions occur when **B** is non-uniform or when both electric and magnetic fields are present together.[6]

Problem 7.2a.   What would happen to eq. 7.2–3 if (a) the south direction was taken as positive for compasses; (b) the left hand was used to define the vector product; (c) the left hand was used to relate the circulatory arrow in Fig. 7.2b to **B**; (d) the circulating arrow was turned around; (e) electrons were called positive?   Consider these alternatives both separately and in combinations.

Problem 7.2b.   Find the radius of curvature of an electron in a magnetic field of 4000 gauss if the electron has a kinetic energy of (a) 10 ev, (b) 1000 ev.

Problem 7.2c.   Show that the magnetic force per unit volume on a collection of moving charges with current density **J** is $f_\tau = \mathbf{J} \times \mathbf{B}$.

Problem 7.2d.   Deduce from the formula $F = d(mv)/dt$, which is used in special relativity, that eq. 7.2–4 is correct for the relativistic value of mv. *Hint*: Prove first that $d(mv)/dt = mv\omega$ for circular motion, where ω is the angular velocity.

Problem 7.2e.   Find **B** so that an electron will have a frequency of rotation of 10^6 cycles per sec, if **B** is uniform.

7.3   The Motor and Generator Rules

The operation of electric motors and generators follows rules derivable from eq. 7.2–2.   The *motor rule* deals with the force on a thin wire carrying a current.   Suppose we consider a section of a straight wire of length L at rest in a uniform magnetic field of strength **B**, at an angle θ with the wire.   (Fig. 7.3a.)   Let a current i pass through the wire, and let q denote

[6] See, e.g., J. R. Pierce, *Theory and Design of Electron Beams*, D. Van Nostrand, Princeton, 1954, and Zworykin, Morton, Ramberg, Hillier, and Vance, *Electron Optics and the Electron Microscope*, John Wiley, New York, 1945.

the total charge on the conduction electrons in the section of the wire under consideration.   If t is the time required for one electron or electron hole to travel a distance L in the wire (and therefore the time for charge q to pass the end of the wire), we see that the speed of each electron is $v = L/t$ and also that the current is equal to $i = q/t$ from which we can conclude that $qv = iL$.   The total force on the charges in the wire is therefore

$$F = qvB \sin \theta = iLB \sin \theta \qquad \text{MKS} \quad (7.3\text{-}1)$$

The force is transmitted to the wire itself by the metallic binding forces.

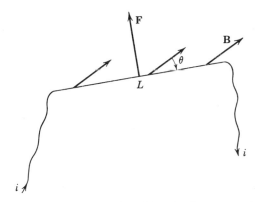

Fig. 7.3a.   A current in a wire of length L in a magnetic field
B experiences a force **F**.

It is directed at right angles to wire and magnetic induction as in Fig. 7.3a (remember that i is positive in the direction of flow of positive charges).

This direction can be easily remembered by any one of several possible three-finger rules, of which the following is suggested as particularly mnemonic.[7]   The sentence "a *current* in a *magnetic field* experiences a *force*" is applied to the thumb, forefinger, and middle finger of the right hand, the underlined words applying to the fingers in the order named (see Fig. 7.3b).   The three mutually perpendicular fingers then give the mutual relations of the three quantities when $\theta = 90°$, and by simple extension for any θ.

In the more general case that the wire is not straight and the induction not uniform, we must replace $q\mathbf{v}$ by $i\,\mathbf{dl}$ and the force as an integral:

$$\mathbf{F} = i \int_{\text{wire}} \mathbf{dl} \times \mathbf{B} \qquad \text{MKS} \quad (7.3\text{-}2)$$

This expression assumes a thin single wire of any shape carrying a current

[7] The difficulty of memorizing any rule may be appreciated when one realizes that, utilizing both right and left hands, there are twelve ways of associating the three elements with three fingers, of which six ways give correct results.

of i amperes.   The element **dl** is a vector representing a small portion of the wire, directed along the wire in the sense chosen as positive for i. The integral is taken over the piece of wire on which the force **F** is being sought.   Electric motors are arrangements for utilizing this force to produce torques in rotating machinery.

We have so far considered the wire to be at rest.   If the wire moves, the charges it contains will have added velocity components in addition

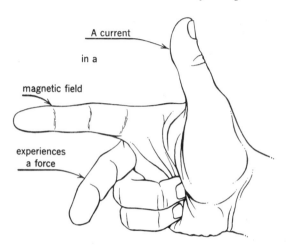

Fig. 7.3b.   A three-finger right-hand rule.

to that due to the current (i.e., convection will occur).   The additional force they experience is an example of the generator effect.   It will be simplest to deal with this latter effect separately before combining the two.

Let a thin wire of any shape move through a region where there is a magnetic field.   Let a given element of the wire **dl** have a velocity **v** (Fig. 7.3c).   The positive and negative charges contained in the wire will thus move at velocity **v** and experience magnetic forces.   An amount q of these charges will experience a force $\mathbf{F} = q(\mathbf{v} \times \mathbf{B})$, and in general there will be a component of **F** along the wire, oppositely directed for positive and negative charges.

There may also be electric fields present, producing an additional force on q.   If the wire obeys Ohm's law, it will be the total force that determines the quantum jumps of the electrons and their average speed.   In fact, Ohm's law in the form of eq. 5.1–2b becomes now[8]

$$\mathbf{E} + \mathbf{v} \times \mathbf{B} = \rho\mathbf{J} \qquad\qquad \text{MKS} \quad (7.3\text{--}3)$$

[8] We have here a different modification of Ohm's law from that expressed in eq. 6.3–1.   We still identify **E** in the wire with $\nabla\bar{\mu}/e$.

where **v**, the wire velocity, must not be confused with the electron velocity
J/ne.   The current will be parallel to the sides of the wire.   Whatever the
direction of **v** ✕ **B**, **E** will become adjusted (in a very short time) so that
the resultant **E** + **v** ✕ **B** is a vector directed along the wire.

Suppose the two ends of a generator wire form a closed circuit with an
external resistor that is stationary or at least is located outside the magnetic field (e.g., connected by means of a sliding switch or commutator).

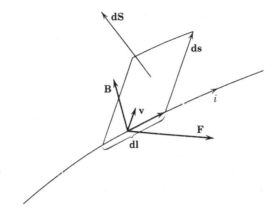

Fig. 7.3c.   Illustrating the work done on charges in a wire when
the wire is moved through a field **B** with velocity **v**.

Since current will flow from a more positive potential to a more negative
one in this resistor, we deduce that the potential is higher at the end toward
which the charge moves inside the generator wire.   The charge therefore
moves against **E** in this latter wire, which means that **v** ✕ **B** must be
opposite to **E** and greater in magnitude.   The integral $\oint$**E** · **dl** around the
entire circuit is zero here as in the case of the chemical cell, and we again
have a situation in which work is done on charges in addition to that
calculable from the field **E**.   Since $J = i/S$ and $\rho J\,dl = i\rho\,dl/S = i\,dR$,
where S, dl, and dR are the area, length, and resistance of a small section
of the wire, we can write

$$0 = \oint \mathbf{E} \cdot \mathbf{dl} = \oint \rho \mathbf{J} \cdot \mathbf{dl} - \oint \mathbf{v} \times \mathbf{B} \cdot \mathbf{dl}$$

$$= \oint i\,dR - \int_{\text{gen wire}} \mathbf{v} \times \mathbf{B} \cdot \mathbf{dl}$$

or

$$\int_{\text{gen wire}} \mathbf{v} \times \mathbf{B} \cdot \mathbf{dl} = iR_{\text{total}} \qquad \text{MKS} \quad (7.3\text{-}4)$$

and R_{total} is the total resistance around the circuit.

The quantity $\mathscr{E} = \int_{\text{gen wire}} \mathbf{v} \times \mathbf{B} \cdot \mathbf{dl}$ is the work done per coulomb on the charges as they move around the circuit and is called the *motional induced emf*. It is the quantity in terms of which the generator effect is usually expressed. Let us write it in a more useful form. Letting the work done when a charge q moves a distance $\mathbf{dl}$ be dW, we have

$$dW = \mathbf{F} \cdot \mathbf{dl} = q(\mathbf{v} \times \mathbf{B}) \cdot \mathbf{dl} \qquad \text{MKS} \quad (7.3\text{--}5)$$

By the rules for the "triple scalar product" (see Appendix A.2–30), $\mathbf{v} \times \mathbf{B} \cdot \mathbf{dl} = (\mathbf{dl} \times \mathbf{v}) \cdot \mathbf{B}$. Write $\mathbf{v} = \mathbf{ds}/dt$; then $\mathbf{dl} \times \mathbf{v} = (\mathbf{dl} \times \mathbf{ds})/dt = \mathbf{dS}/dt$ where $\mathbf{dS}$ is the vector representing the area swept out by the element $\mathbf{dl}$ when it moves a distance $\mathbf{ds}$. (See Fig. 7.3c.) We then can write for the work done

$$dW = q(\mathbf{dS} \cdot \mathbf{B})/dt \qquad \text{MKS} \quad (7.3\text{--}6a)$$

$$dW = (q/c)(\mathbf{dS} \cdot \mathbf{B})/dt \qquad \text{Gaussian} \quad (7.3\text{--}6b)$$

The quantity $\mathbf{dS} \cdot \mathbf{B} = \mathbf{B} \cdot \mathbf{dS}$ is mathematically similar to an element of electric flux $d\Phi_E = \mathbf{E} \cdot \mathbf{dS}$ and will be written $d\Phi$, where Φ is called the "flux of induction" or the "magnetic flux". Its MKS unit is called the "weber," and the Gaussian unit is the gauss-centimeter^2 or maxwell. (1 weber = 1 tesla-m^2 = 10^8 maxwells.) From eq. 7.3–6a, we can readily see that 1 weber = 1 joule/amp = 1 v-sec.

We see that the work done when a charge moves through $\mathbf{dl}$ is proportional to the rate at which flux is "swept out" by the wire in its motion. Now let us divide the wire into elements $\mathbf{dl}$ such that in dt the same charge q moves through each $\mathbf{dl}$. The total work done is obtained by integrating eq. 7.3–6 over the wire. The integration amounts to adding the $(d\Phi/dt)$'s for each dl, obtaining a $d\Phi/dt$ that applies to the entire wire, with the constant factor q in front. Hence

$$W = -q\frac{d\Phi}{dt}$$

The minus sign has to do with a convention as to which side of the wire in Fig. 7.3c is taken as positive and will be explained later (section 7.9). The motional induced emf is then

$$\mathscr{E} = \oint \mathbf{v} \times \mathbf{B} \cdot \mathbf{dl} = -\frac{d\Phi}{dt} \qquad \text{MKS} \quad (7.3\text{--}7a)$$

$$\mathscr{E} = \frac{1}{c}\oint \mathbf{v} \times \mathbf{B} \cdot \mathbf{dl} = -\frac{1}{c}\frac{d\Phi}{dt} \qquad \text{Gaussian} \quad (7.3\text{--}7b)$$

We calculated this result assuming that the charges move through the wire, but slowly enough that we can temporarily disregard the motor effect.   Let us suppose now that the electrons are prevented from moving by a suitable electrostatic field in addition to the magnetic induction. For instance, suppose the wire is part of an open circuit with capacitance so small that no appreciable motion of charge can occur.   No motion of charge in a conductor implies no force; hence we must have

$$\mathbf{E} = -\mathbf{v} \times \mathbf{B}$$

at every point of the wire.   Consequently the electric potential difference

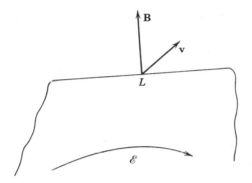

Fig. 7.3d.   Motional emf $\mathscr{E}$ generated in wire L.

between two points $\mathscr{A}$ and $\mathscr{B}$ is just equal to the induced emf between those two points:

$$V_{ab} = -\int_{\mathscr{A}}^{\mathscr{B}} \mathbf{E} \cdot d\mathbf{l} = \int_{\mathscr{A}}^{\mathscr{B}} \mathbf{v} \times \mathbf{B} \cdot d\mathbf{l} = \mathscr{E} \quad \text{MKS} \quad (7.3\text{--}8)$$

Note that the line integral of the electric field yields the same results regardless of the path, whereas the motional emf must be calculated along the wire at the given instant.

If the wire is straight, has a length L, and is moved in a uniform field of induction $\mathbf{B}$ at right angles to itself and to $\mathbf{B}$ (Fig. 7.3d) we have the simple expression

$$\mathscr{E} = vBL \qquad\qquad\qquad \text{MKS} \quad (7.3\text{--}9a)$$

$$\mathscr{E} = \frac{v}{c} BL \qquad\qquad\qquad \text{Gaussian} \quad (7.3\text{--}9b)$$

The direction of $\mathscr{E}$ can be found either from the vector product rule in the Lorentz law or from the same three-finger rule given above.   The current in this case involves the motion of positive charges along $\mathbf{v}$, so that the thumb represents the motion of the wire, the forefinger the field, and the middle finger the resulting electromotive force.

It must be emphasized here that eq. 7.3–7 applies only to emf's generated by the *motion of the wire* and not (as yet) to a possible variation of **B** with time.   Note that $d\Phi/dt$ in eqs. 7.3–6 and 7.3–7 has not yet been defined as a true derivative of a function Φ.   We must study some properties of **B** and in particular a theorem concerning magnetic flux, before we can generalize eq. 7.3–7.

A simple type of generator that can produce steady currents is the Faraday disk.   A copper disk is arranged to rotate in a uniform magnetic field, with its axis parallel to **B**.   A circuit is established in the disk between its center and a point on its circumference, by using a sliding contact on the axle and another on the periphery (a cup of mercury into which the disk is inserted a few millimeters is one arrangement).

Then if the disk is rotated at an angular velocity ω, an emf $\mathscr{E}$ will be developed between axle and periphery, given by

$$\mathscr{E} = \tfrac{1}{2}BR^2\omega \qquad (7.3\text{–}10)$$

where R is the radius of the disk (cf. problem 7.3*a*).   Such a disk can also be run as a motor (problem 7.3*b*).   Practical motors and generators, including commercially useful Faraday-disk machines, are described in books on electrical engineering.

Now let us consider the generator effect as it occurs in a motor.   If the wire of Fig. 7.3*a* with $\theta = 90°$ moves with a velocity **v** under the action of the force **F**, an emf will be induced in the wire, of magnitude $\mathscr{E} = vBL$, and in a direction opposite to that of the current (for this reason it is called a back emf).   Some external source of power must thus provide energy at a rate $\mathscr{E}i = ivBL$ to make the charge flow against this back emf. The power exerted mechanically on the wire from the force **F** on the charges inside it is $\mathbf{F} \cdot \mathbf{v}$ which is also equal to $ivBL$, since $F = iLB$. Hence we see that the power supplied by a motor is just that which is required by the generator effect occurring in the motor.   Of course, the power expended in ohmic heating of the wire must also be supplied by the external sources.

In the general case of variable **B** and curved wires, we can write for the force on a piece **dl**

$$d\mathbf{F} = i\,\mathbf{dl} \times \mathbf{B}$$

and for the power

$$d\mathbf{F} \cdot \mathbf{v} = i\,\mathbf{dl} \times \mathbf{B} \cdot \mathbf{v} = -i\mathbf{v} \times \mathbf{B} \cdot \mathbf{dl} = -i\,d\mathscr{E}$$

leading to the same conclusion as for the straight wire.

Conversely, for the generator, a current i leads to the generation of power at the rate $\mathscr{E}i$; the current i produces a motor force on the wire oppositely directed to its velocity **v**, so that work must be done by an external agent (diesel engine, turbine, etc.) to turn the generator. The reader can easily show that again the two expressions for the power are equal.

The Hall Effect. This effect is the production of transverse electric fields and potential differences in a conductor carrying current across a magnetic field. If in a flat rectangular wire, as in Fig. 7.3*e*, there is a current density **J** in the *x*-direction passing through a magnetic field **B** in the *y*-direction, then, regardless

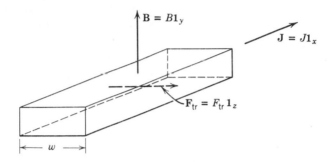

Fig. 7.3*e*. Illustrating the Hall effect.

of the sign of the current carriers, there will be a force in the positive *z*-direction as shown.

The carriers will then be deflected toward the positive *z* side of the bar and will there build up a charge of their own sign, until the resulting transverse electric field E_{tr} across the bar is enough to balance out the magnetic force and restore the flow lines to parallelism with the sides of the bar. That is, the net transverse force in the steady state will be zero:

$$\mathbf{F}_{tr} = q(\mathbf{E}_{tr} + \mathbf{v} \times \mathbf{B}) = 0$$

or

$$\mathbf{E}_{tr} = -\mathbf{v} \times \mathbf{B} = -vB\,\mathbf{1}_z$$

and a PD will be developed across the width *w* of the bar equal to

$$V = E_{tr}w = vBw \tag{7.3–11}$$

so that the sign of *V* measures the sign of v_x and hence of the charge carriers. A combination of **E** and **B** can thus provide a distinction which neither can provide while acting alone on a conductor.

Although *V* and the current *i* are the quantities actually measured, it is most convenient to describe the Hall effect in terms of E_{tr}, *J*, and *B*. Since $J = nqv$ where *n* is the number of charge carriers per unit volume and *q* is the charge on each, we have

$$E_{tr} = \frac{JB}{nq} \tag{7.3–12a}$$

The constant $1/nq$ is generally called the Hall coefficient R_H, so we write

$$E = R_H JB; \quad R_H = 1/nq \tag{7.3-12b}$$

(Detailed studies of the dynamics of electron motion in metals lead to values for R_H from $1.0/nq$ to $1.5/nq$ or so.[9])

Measurements of R_H have shown that for most metals, R_H is negative, and if we assume $q = -e$, we find for n the expected value of one or two times the number of atoms present. However, for some metals R_H is positive, and in some cases n appears to be unusually small. For semiconductors, R_H may be of either sign. Table 7.3A gives a few typical values (from Kittel).[9]

The explanation of these anomalies has to do with the behavior of electron holes in acting like actual positive charges when certain conditions hold for the electronic wave motions. The reader is referred to texts on solid-state physics for details.[9]

Table 7.3A
Hall Coefficients for Various Metals*

	Hall coefficient (R_H) volt-meter^3/ampere-weber
Bismuth	-1000×10^{-11}
Beryllium	$+24.4 \times 10^{-11}$
Cadmium	$+6.0 \times 10^{-11}$
Copper	-5.5×10^{-11}
Gold	-7.2×10^{-11}
Lithium	-17.0×10^{-11}
Silver	-8.4×10^{-11}
Sodium	-25.0×10^{-11}
Zinc	$+3.3 \times 10^{-11}$

* Taken from C. Kittel, *loc. cit.*, p. 298.

Problem 7.3a. Derive eq. 7.3–10 for the emf of a Faraday disk.

Problem 7.3b. Find the torque delivered to a Faraday disk of radius R if a current i is fed in at the periphery and taken out at an axle radius R'. Assume **B** to be constant over the disk and perpendicular to it.

Problem 7.3c. A vertical, rectangular U-shaped piece of wire, with the horizontal part 2 cm long and the vertical sides 10 cm long hangs in a magnetic field whose direction is perpendicular to the plane of the U. The field has a value $B = 0.3$ weber/m^2 within a circle in this plane of diameter 5 cm and is essentially zero outside of this circle. If a current of 6 amp is passed through the loop, find the force on it when the horizontal section is symmetrically located in the center of the circle. Show that if this force is down, a displacement of the loop to either side will result in a force tending to bring the loop back to the center but that the reverse is true if the force on the horizontal path is upward.

[9] C. Kittel, *Introduction to Solid State Physics*, 2nd ed., John Wiley, New York, 1956, pp. 296–298; W. Shockley, *Electrons and Holes in Semiconductors*, D. Van Nostrand, Princeton, 1950. The effect was discovered by E. H. Hall, *Phil. Mag.*, **9**, 225 and **10**, 301 (1880).

Problem 7.3d. The armature of a direct-current motor carries 24 equally spaced coils, each with ten turns, connected in series with their connection points at the 24 segments of the rotating commutator. Sliding carbon "brushes" make contact with the commutator to admit current to the coils; the arrangement of the brushes and the geometry of the magnetic field in which the armature rotates are such that each wire parallel to the axis turns in an average field of 8500 gauss and the torques all are in the same sense. If at any instant all the coils are connected to the brushes in such a way that there are two equal parallel paths through the combination, and a current of 12 amp is delivered to the brushes, find the average torque developed in the armature. Take each coil as a square 8 cm on each side, with the wires parallel to the axis of the motor at a distance of 5 cm from the axis.

Problem 7.3e. The machine described in problem 7.3d is run as a generator, with the same field. If the armature is turned at 3600 revolutions per minute, find the average emf produced. If a resistance of 12 ohms is connected between the brushes and each ten-turn armature coil has a resistance of 0.100 ohm, find how much power is generated.

✓ **Problem 7.3f.** The magnetic field of the earth at a certain locality has a strength of 0.50 gauss, directed downward at an angle of 69° with the vertical. Find the force on a straight wire three meters long carrying 100 amp which is (a) vertical, (b) parallel to the horizontal component of the earth's field, and (c) horizontal and perpendicular to the horizontal component of the earth's field.

✓ **Problem 7.3g.** A bar of annealed copper is used to study the Hall effect and is placed across a magnetic field of 0.80 weber/m^2. Using values from Tables 5.1A (p. 186) and 7.3A, find the angle which the resultant electric field makes with the sides of the bar. If the bar is 2.0 cm wide (in the direction normal to **B** and **J**), by what distance along the bar must the terminals of a galvanometer circuit be displaced so as to give a null deflection on the galvanometer?

7.4 Ampère's Law

We now turn to a consideration of Ampère's law,[10] which gives the way in which the magnetic induction **B** at a given point is produced by the external surroundings—that is, by the moving charges in the neighborhood of the point. The law has been experimentally verified by innumerable measurements of the induction produced by coils similar to those we shall consider in section 7.5.

We start with currents which are steady or slowly varying.[11] Experiment shows that the principle of superposition holds here as in the electric-field case, and so we can consider any current to be composed of suitable

[10] Given in the memorable work of A. M. Ampère, *Memoires de l'Academie*, **6**, 175 (Paris, 1823).

[11] The currents may be variable if the time taken for an appreciable variation is large compared with the time necessary to charge up the distributed capacitance of the circuit and also large compared with r/c, where r is the maximum distance from any part of the circuit to points where the magnetic induction is to be computed and c is the velocity of light. (See section 10.3.)

current elements. Furthermore, any steady current involves a closed circuit, so that we shall first take as a current element a thin filament that makes a closed loop. Complex circuits or current distributions may always be resolved into a sum of such closed filaments. An alternative would be to take a short length dl of a filamentary current as an element, and we shall also state the law in a form using this type of element. However, the experiments referred to verify the closed-loop form directly;

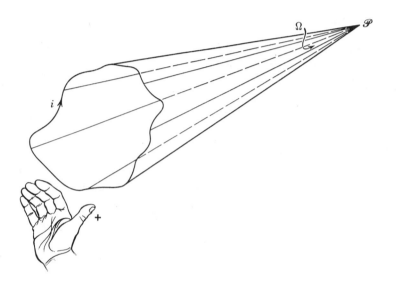

Fig. 7.4a. The solid angle subtended at $\mathscr{P}$ by a current loop.

the differential form involves a certain indefiniteness that can only be removed by a further assumption to be discussed later in this chapter.

The Solid-Angle Form. The closed-loop form of Ampère's law can be expressed in terms of the solid angle subtended by the loop of current at the point where the induction **B** is sought. Let the point $\mathscr{P}$ (Fig. 7.4a) have the coordinates (x, y, z); the solid angle Ω is then a function $\Omega(x, y, z)$ of these coordinates. The induction **B** at $\mathscr{P}$ is proportional to the current i and to the gradient of Ω so that the x, y, and z components of **B** are thus proportional to i and respectively to the x, y, and z partial derivatives of $\Omega(x, y, z)$.

In order to specify the direction of **B**, we need a sign convention for i and Ω. We shall define the positive side of a current loop by the right-hand screw rule. If the fingers of the right hand are directed along the wire pointing in the direction chosen as positive for the current i, the thumb points toward the positive side of the loop.   Point $\mathscr{P}$ in Fig. 7.4*a* is shown as on the positive side of the loop.   Then Ω is taken as the interior solid angle subtended at $\mathscr{P}$.   More generally, when a line drawn from the interior of the loop toward $\mathscr{P}$ leaves the former in the positive direction, the solid angle on the loop side of the cone is considered positive and that

Fig. 7.4b.   Variations of Ω as $\mathscr{P}$ moves through a loop.

on the far side negative.   If the line to $\mathscr{P}$ leaves the loop in the negative direction, the interior solid angle is negative and the exterior positive.

As $\mathscr{P}$ recedes indefinitely from the loop in the positive direction (to "$+\infty$"), Ω passes from some positive value less than 2π to zero.   If $\mathscr{P}$

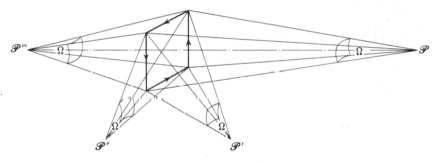

Fig. 7.4c.   Variations of Ω as $\mathscr{P}$ moves around a loop.

approaches the inside of the loop, Ω approaches 2π.   If we let $\mathscr{P}$ pass through the loop, Ω will continue to increase and become an exterior angle greater than 2π, approaching 4π as $\mathscr{P}$ goes to "$-\infty$."   (Fig. 7.4b.)

On the other hand, if $\mathscr{P}$ is allowed to go around the outside of the loop (Fig. 7.4c) and approach it from the negative side, Ω goes to 0 and must take on negative values, since we shall not allow it or its derivative to have a discontinuous jump.   As $\mathscr{P}$ approaches the loop from the back, Ω thus approaches -2π.   It will be seen therefore that Ω is not a single-valued function of position.   In fact, if $\mathscr{P}$ makes a series of circuits through the loop, Ω will change to $\Omega + 4\pi n$, where n is some positive or negative integer.

The magnetic induction **B** depends on the gradient $\nabla\Omega$, and this quantity is single-valued, since Ω and $\Omega + 4\pi n$ have the same derivatives. (In section 7.6 we will identify Ω with the magnetic scalar potential.)   It will be noted that at a point $\mathscr{P}$ on the positive side of the loop, $\nabla\Omega$ is a vector pointing toward the loop.

We now can write the solid angle form of Ampère's law for the magnetic induction at a point near a current loop:

$$\mathbf{B} = -\frac{\mu_0}{4\pi}\, i\, \nabla\Omega \qquad\qquad \text{MKS} \quad (7.4\text{--}1a)$$

$$\mathbf{B} = -\frac{i}{c}\, \nabla\Omega \qquad\qquad \text{Gaussian} \quad (7.4\text{--}1b)$$

The direction of **B** is that of $-\nabla\Omega$, so that **B** points away from the loop toward its positive side.   This fact is in agreement with the assertion in section 7.2 that the sense of circulation of the current is the same as that of the rotation of **F** to $\mathbf{v}_{\text{proj}}$.   As implied earlier, the induction produced by several current loops is given by summing eq. 7.4–1 for all the loops.

The quantity μ_0 is introduced in the MKS system to lead later to a symmetry between electric and magnetic quantities when dealing with the magnetic-pole fiction.   The value of the coulomb as used in the Lorentz force law and also in the current in Ampère's law is defined so as to make μ_0 exactly equal to $4\pi \times 10^{-7}$ weber/meter-ampere, units which may also be called henrys per meter and newtons per ampere^2 (cf. section 7.2).[12] In the Gaussian system, the esu of charge is defined by Coulomb's law, so that i is measured in statamperes, or statcoulombs/second.   One statampere is equal to 3.335×10^{-10} amp.   The experimental constant c is defined so as to appear equally in eqs 7.2–3b and 7.4–1b; identification with the velocity of light will be made in Chapter 10.   An experimentally simpler formulation of the MKS definition of the coulomb and the Gaussian-system definition of c will appear in the next section.

Laplace's Rule.   Let us now state the differential form of Ampère's law known as Laplace's rule.   According to this rule, the field **dB** produced

---

[12] μ_0 is called the "permeability of free space" but the question of whether it represents a real property of "free space" will not be pursued as it is irrelevant to our present study.   (The same comments apply to ϵ_0, the "permittivity of free space.") It is, for instance, permissible but not necessary to consider μ_0 a pure dimensionless number (it is after all a defined and not a measured quantity), in which case webers have the same dimensions as meter-amperes, and amperes^2 are dimensionally the same as newtons.   We shall for the most part not treat μ_0 this way, however; giving μ_0 dimensions is an aid to clarity in the rest of our subject.

at $\mathscr{P}$ by an element dl of a current i at another point $\mathscr{Q}$ is given by

$$dB = \frac{\mu_0}{4\pi} i \frac{dl \times 1_r}{r^2} \qquad \text{MKS} \quad (7.4\text{--}2a)$$

and

$$dB = \frac{i}{c} \frac{dl \times 1_r}{r^2} \qquad \text{Gaussian} \quad (7.4\text{--}2b)$$

where r is the distance $\overline{\mathscr{Q}\mathscr{P}}$, 1_r is a unit vector directed from $\mathscr{Q}$ to $\mathscr{P}$, and of course we can add the fields of any number of such elements. (Fig. 7.4d.)

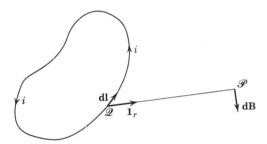

Fig. 7.4d.   Illustrating Laplace's rule.

The vector-product rule can be used to verify yet another use of the right hand for directional purposes. If the hand grasps the wire in the neighborhood of **dl** with the thumb pointing along the positive current direction, the fingers go around the wire in the general direction of **B**.

Now that we have stated the rule, let us show that the solid-angle form of Ampère's law can be derived from it.

Since the gradient of Ω is a type of derivative, we can rewrite eq. 7.4–1a in terms of a differential increment $d\Omega$ in the solid angle which corresponds to a displacement **ds** of $\mathscr{P}$:

$$\mathbf{B} \cdot \mathbf{ds} = -\frac{\mu_0}{4\pi} i \, d\Omega \qquad (7.4\text{--}3)$$

Conversely, if this expression is known to be true for all **ds**, we can derive eq. 7.4–1a from it by letting **ds** be, successively, $1_y \, dx$, $1_y \, dy$, and $1_z \, dz$.

Now let us calculate **B · ds** for a closed loop of current from Laplace's rule. We have

$$\mathbf{B} = \frac{\mu_0 i}{4\pi} \oint \frac{dl \times 1_r}{r^2} \qquad (7.4\text{--}4)$$

and therefore

$$\mathbf{B} \cdot \mathbf{ds} = \frac{\mu_0 i}{4\pi} \oint \frac{dl \times 1_r \cdot \mathbf{ds}}{r^2} \qquad (7.4\text{--}5)$$

where the second integral represents a summation around a closed loop over elements **dl** but not **ds**; r and $\mathbf{1}_r$ both vary along the wire. By the rules of the triple scalar product the integrand may be written $\mathbf{ds} \cdot \mathbf{dl} \times \mathbf{1}_r/r^2 = \mathbf{ds} \times \mathbf{dl} \cdot \mathbf{1}_r/r^2$. This expression can be interpreted in terms of solid angles; the interpretation is clearest if we keep $\mathscr{P}$ fixed and move the entire current through the negative displacement $-\mathbf{ds}$. Then the circuit sweeps out a ribbon-shaped surface as shown in Fig. 7.4e. In this figure, a vector $\mathbf{r} = r\mathbf{1}_r$ has been drawn from a point within a piece of the

Fig. 7.4e.   A method of deriving the Ω rule from Laplace's rule.

Fig. 7.4f.   A view of part of the solid angle subtended by a ribbon.

ribbon dS bounded by **dl** and **ds** to a point $\mathscr{P}$. The location of $\mathscr{P}$ and the direction of $-\mathbf{ds}$ are here taken so that the vector leaves the inside of the ribbon. The quantity $\mathbf{dl} \times (-\mathbf{ds})$ is a vector representing the small area $\mathbf{dS}$, directed to the inside of the ribbon; the projection of this area on a plane normal to $\mathbf{r}$ is then $\mathbf{dl} \times (-\mathbf{ds}) \cdot \mathbf{1}_r$ so that the element of the solid angle subtended at $\mathscr{P}$ by the small piece of ribbon is $\mathbf{ds} \times \mathbf{dl} \cdot \mathbf{1}_r/r^2$. Thus the integral over the closed loop gives the entire solid angle subtended by the ribbon. This solid angle is shown in a partial view in Fig. 7.4f. It represents the *decrease* of Ω that occurs when $\mathscr{P}$ moves a distance **ds** away from the loop or the loop moves $-\mathbf{ds}$ away from $\mathscr{P}$. We therefore write $\oint \mathbf{ds} \times \mathbf{dl} \cdot \mathbf{1}_r/r^2 = -d\Omega$, and eq. 7.4–5 is seen to be the same as eq. 7.4–3. We have therefore derived the solid angle form of Ampère's law from the differential.

Laplace's rule is not the only expression which on integration yields eq. 7.4–3. Any expression which is proportional to i and integrates to zero around an arbitrary closed loop can be added to eq. 7.4–2 without influencing the results. An example of such an expression would be any vector whose separate components are each differentials with respect to **dl** of scalar functions of r.[13] Thus we see that we cannot hope to derive Laplace's rule from the experimentally verified closed-loop rule. We can only assert that the former gives the correct results when applied to any closed circuit. This is the indefiniteness referred to at the beginning of this section. In spite of this indefiniteness, however, the differential form of the law is perhaps the easiest on the imagination, for it describes the actions at a point $\mathscr{P}$ in terms of specific occurrences at each of a series of points around a circuit. This type of formula may be called "a point-to-point action-at-a-distance" formula similar to Coulomb's law for electrostatic fields.

The Circuital Form. We now wish to derive from eq. 7.4–1 a formula for the circulation of **B**, $\oint \mathbf{B} \cdot \mathbf{ds}$, that is commonly known as the circuital form of Ampère's law. Let us add up the increments $\mathbf{B} \cdot \mathbf{ds}$ obtained by considering a series of points $\mathscr{P}$ along some arbitrary closed path in space. (Such paths are analogous to the Gaussian surfaces of section 1.4. They are introduced in locations convenient for calculation and usually do not coincide with any material wires. They can be called Stokesian paths, because of Stokes' theorem, A.3–39.) If the path does not encircle the current, $\oint d\Omega$ is clearly zero, and we have $\oint \mathbf{B} \cdot \mathbf{ds} = 0$. If the path links the current once, the discussion of solid angle earlier in this section shows that Ω must change by 4π. (See Figs. 7.4b, c, and g.) The sign of the change depends on which way the path goes, i.e., on the directions of the various elements **ds**, so that we must specify a positive direction on our arbitrary path. Let us take this path as passing through the loop toward the positive side, which is seen to be the same as passing around the wire in the direction given by the right-hand rule for eq. 7.4–2. Then the increment of Ω around the path is -4π and using eq. 7.4–3 we find for the circulation

$$\oint \mathbf{B} \cdot \mathbf{ds} = \mu_0 i \qquad\qquad \text{MKS} \quad (7.4\text{–}6a)$$

$$\oint \mathbf{B} \cdot \mathbf{ds} = \frac{4\pi i}{c} \qquad\qquad \text{Gaussian} \quad (7.4\text{–}6b)$$

[13] In symbols, $\mathbf{dB'} = i(\mathbf{dl} \cdot \nabla)\mathbf{f}(r)$ or $dB'_x = i\,\nabla f_x(r) \cdot \mathbf{dl}$; $dB'_y = i\,\nabla f_y(r) \cdot \mathbf{dl}$, etc.

The Stokesian paths can be considered flexible and be moved around without changing the integrals, as long as no currents are cut across. In the general case of a path that links several current loops (or the same one several times), we have

$$\oint \mathbf{B} \cdot d\mathbf{s} = \mu_0 \sum_k i_k \qquad \text{MKS} \quad (7.4\text{-}6c)$$

$$\oint \mathbf{B} \cdot d\mathbf{s} = \frac{4\pi}{c} \sum_k i_k \qquad \text{Gaussian} \quad (7.4\text{-}6d)$$

The summations here include each current once for each time it is linked in the positive sense, and once with the negative sign for each time it is linked in the reverse sense.

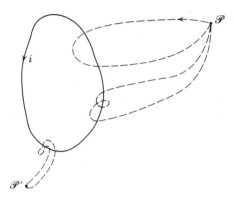

Fig. 7.4g. Stokesian paths linking a current once, twice, and zero times.

Although the formulas thus far given for **B** all refer to its value at points not occupied by currents—i.e., at points not *on* any elementary filament—the circuital form allows calculations involving **B** to be made at points within continuous current distributions.   The current i in eq. 7.4-6 can for instance be replaced by $\int \mathbf{J} \cdot d\mathbf{S}$ over a surface bounded by the path for $\oint \mathbf{B} \cdot d\mathbf{s}$.   An example is given in the next section.

Problem 7.4a.   Show that the dimensions of the quantity $(\mu_0 \epsilon_0)^{-1}$ are (meter/second)^2 regardless of whether μ_0 is taken to be dimensionless.

7.5 Applications of Ampère's Law

There are a limited number of cases in which the calculation of magnetic fields is elementary.   A number of these will now be given as examples of the three forms of Ampère's law we have just introduced.

The circuital form can be used easily in those cases in which the field has an appropriate symmetry.   Let us consider first a long, straight, thin wire, and find **B** at a point sufficiently near it that it may be treated as having infinite length (e.g., the effect of the distant return portion of the circuit can be neglected; cf. problem 7.5c for a proof that this neglect is legitimate).   Then **B** at a point $\mathscr{P}$ must by symmetry be tangent to a circle through $\mathscr{P}$ coaxial with the wire.   Let us use such a circle for calculation of the circulation.   The magnitude of **B** must be the same all

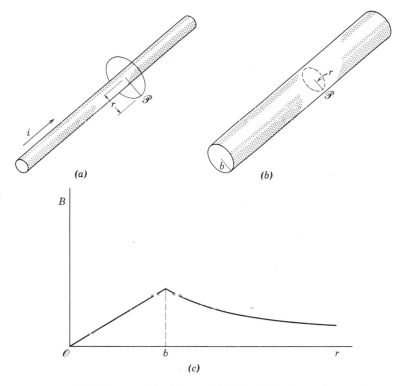

Fig. 7.5a–c.   Calculation of **B** inside and outside a long straight wire by the circuital method.

around the circle, so that $\oint \mathbf{B} \cdot \mathbf{ds} = 2\pi r B$ where r is the distance of $\mathscr{P}$ from the center of the wire.   (Fig. 7.5a and b.)

Hence we have the result, due originally to Biot and Savart,[14] for the field outside an infinite straight thin wire:

$$B = \frac{\mu_0 i}{2\pi r} \qquad\qquad \text{MKS} \quad (7.5\text{–}1a)$$

$$B = \frac{2i}{cr} \qquad\qquad \text{Gaussian} \quad (7.5\text{–}1b)$$

[14] J.-B. Biot and F. Savart, *Ann. Chimie et Phys.*, **15**, 222 (1820).

If the wire has a radius b and the current density J is uniform throughout its interior, the current within a circular cylinder of radius $r < b$ will be $\pi r^2 J = i(r^2/b^2)$ and we have

$$2\pi r B = \mu_0 i(r^2/b^2)$$

or

$$B = \frac{\mu_0 i r}{2\pi b^2}, \qquad r \leqslant b \qquad \text{MKS} \quad (7.5\text{-}2)$$

This is the only simple case in which the dimensions of the wire can be taken into account. Our other examples all assume wires of negligible cross section (cf. section 7.11 for cases in which consideration of wire dimensions is both necessary and complicated). However, this case does show explicitly how Ampère's law can be used in regions of non-vanishing J. Figure 7.5c shows graphically the variation of B with radius.

The force between two long, thin, parallel, current-bearing wires can be found from the law of Biot and Savart. If the wires have currents i_1 and i_2 and are separated by a distance r, the induction at the second one produced by the first is $B = \mu_0 i_1/2\pi r$ and by eq. 7.3–1, the force on a length L of the second is

$$F = i_2 B L = \mu_0 i_1 i_2 L/2\pi r \qquad \text{MKS} \quad (7.5\text{-}3a)$$

$$F = 2i_1 i_2 L/c^2 r \qquad \text{Gaussian} \quad (7.5\text{-}3b)$$

The reader can readily verify the fact that, if the currents are in the same direction, the force is one of attraction, whereas in the case of opposite currents the force is a repulsion. In many cases, this rule is simpler to use for getting directions or signs than the use of two right-hand rules. Equation 7.5–3a can be used as an experimental definition of the ampere, since μ_0 is an exactly defined constant and F and r are measurable in terms of newtons and meters.[15] Similarly, eq. 7.5–3b enables us to evaluate the constant c by measuring the force in dynes, the distance in centimeters, and the current in statamperes. The quantity i/c is the measure of current in electromagnetic units (emu) or abamperes. Thus 1 abampere = c statamperes. Actually, as we shall see later, a current balance using the force between circular coils is a more practical device for establishing the unit of current than is a pair of parallel wires.

Another symmetrical case is that of the toroidal solenoid,[16] shown in Fig. 7.5d and e. Regardless of the shape of the cross section of the coil,

[15] Cf. footnote on p. 270.
[16] A pipelike coil, named from the Greek "solen," a pipe.

B will be the same at all points on a circle coaxial with the toroid,[17] so that again we can use such a circle for calculation.   Through consideration of the solid angles subtended at a point on such a circle by symmetrically placed coils, one can prove that **B** is tangent to the circle (problem 7.5*b*). Let us first take a circle that lies inside the coil.   If the coil has N turns

Fig. 7.5d.   A toroidal coil.

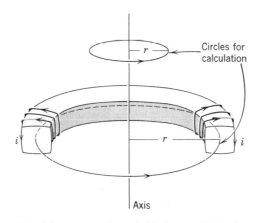

Fig. 7.5e.   View of one-half of a toroidal coil.

and each carries the same current i by virtue of the continuous, helical winding, the integral path in eq. 7.4–6 surrounds the current Ni and

$$2\pi r B = \mu_0 N i$$

so that

$$B = \frac{\mu_0 N i}{2\pi r} \qquad\qquad \text{MKS} \quad (7.5\text{–}4a)$$

Sometimes it is convenient to describe the coil in terms of the number of

[17] Provided the winding is sufficiently uniform and closely packed.   We neglect here the helical nature of solenoid windings, assuming each coil to be in a plane containing the axis (see problem 7.5*q*).

turns per unit length n_l measured along a circle drawn through the center of the cross section.   If this circle has a radius b, then $N = 2\pi b n_l$ and

$$B = \frac{\mu_0 b}{r} n_l i \qquad\qquad \text{MKS} \quad (7.5\text{-}4b)$$

If now the dimensions of the cross section are small compared to b, then r differs from b at most by a small amount, and the value of B at the center may be taken as the value throughout the coil,

$$B = \mu_0 n_l i \qquad\qquad \text{MKS} \quad (7.5\text{-}5)$$

The field outside the coil is everywhere zero (cf. footnote on p. 277). This is readily proved by calculating the circulation of **B** around a coaxial circle that lies outside the coil and therefore links no current.

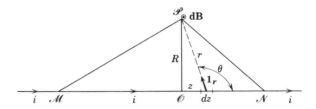

Fig. 7.5f.   Illustrating the calculation of **B** at $\mathcal{P}$ produced by a wire segment $\mathcal{MN}$ carrying a current i.   **dB** is a vector coming out of the page.

The induction produced by a circuit made up of a number of segments of straight lines, (i.e., a polygon) may be found by the use of Laplace's rule.   Let us consider a single segment.   In Fig. 7.5f, a segment $\mathcal{MN}$ of a circuit carries a current i.   The field at $\mathcal{P}$ produced by this segment is given by integrating eq. 7.4–2 from $\mathcal{M}$ to $\mathcal{N}$.   Let us set $d\mathbf{l} = \mathbf{1}_z\, dz$; then $\mathbf{1}_z \times \mathbf{1}_r = \sin\theta \mathbf{1}_\varphi$ where $\mathbf{1}_\varphi$ is a unit vector at $\mathcal{P}$ perpendicular to the plane $\mathcal{MPN}$ coming out of the paper.   Letting z be measured from $\mathcal{O}$, positively toward $\mathcal{N}$, we have $z = -R\cot\theta$ and $r = R\csc\theta$, so that $dz/r^2 = R\csc^2\theta\, d\theta/R^2\csc^2\theta = d\theta/R$.   Hence, the induction at $\mathcal{P}$ produced by the segment $\mathcal{MN}$ is

$$\mathbf{B} = \mathbf{1}_\varphi \frac{\mu_0 i}{4\pi} \int_{\theta_1}^{\theta_2} \sin\theta\, d\theta/R = \mathbf{1}_\varphi \frac{\mu_0 i}{4\pi R}(\cos\theta_1 - \cos\theta_2) \qquad \text{MKS} \quad (7.5\text{-}6)$$

from which we can derive eq. 7.5–1a by letting $\theta_1 \to 0$ and $\theta_2 \to 180°$. For a circuit made up of several straight segments, calculation of the field at any point in the neighborhood is a straightforward problem in the addition of vectors.

Let us now use the solid-angle form to find the field produced by a

circular loop, at points on the axis of the loop.   We need the formula
(problem 1.5e) for the solid angle subtended by a circle of radius a at a
point $\mathscr{P}$ on its axis a distance z from its plane (see Fig. 7.5g):

$$\Omega = 2\pi(1 - \cos\theta) = 2\pi\left(1 - \frac{z}{(a^2 + z^2)^{\frac{1}{2}}}\right)$$

where θ is the angle indicated in the figure.   By symmetry, the field at $\mathscr{P}$
must be along the axis; thus we can find B from $-\mu_0 i\,\nabla\Omega/4\pi$ even though

Fig. 7.5g.   Calculation of B on the axis of a circular loop.

we know Ω only on the axis and not at any other point and so cannot
calculate derivatives with respect to x and y.   We find on differentiating
Ω that

$$B_z = \frac{-\mu_0 i}{4\pi}\frac{\partial\Omega}{\partial z} = \frac{\mu_0 i a^2}{2(a^2 + z^2)^{\frac{3}{2}}} \qquad \text{MKS} \qquad (7.5\text{--}7a)$$

At the center of the circle,

$$B = \frac{\mu_0 i}{2a} \qquad \text{MKS} \qquad (7.5\text{--}7b)$$

If the loop consists of N turns of wire close together, of average radius a,
then i in the last two equations is to be replaced by Ni.

   The field inside a circular-cylindrical solenoid[16] may be readily derived
from the solid-angle rule.   Let us find the component parallel to the axis
of the coil.   In Figs. 7.5h and i point $\mathscr{P}$ has a coordinate z, measured
from the center $\mathcal{O}$.   Let the coil have n_t turns per unit length, and consider the contribution at $\mathscr{P}$ produced by the turns in a length dz' of the
coil at distance z' from $\mathcal{O}$.   The solid angle Ω is a function of $z - z'$, and

$$dB_z = \frac{-\mu_0 i n_t\, dz'}{4\pi}\frac{\partial\Omega}{\partial z} = \frac{\mu_0 i n_t\, dz'}{4\pi}\frac{\partial\Omega}{\partial z'}$$

since $\partial\Omega/\partial z = -\partial\Omega/\partial z'$.   Now the differential $(\partial\Omega/\partial z')\,dz'$ is just the
difference between the solid angles subtended by the front and back sides
of the group of turns in dz'.   Adding the contributions of all turns thus

amounts to adding the respective differences; the result on integration is that

$$B_z = \frac{\mu_0 i n_l}{4\pi} \int_{\text{coil}} \frac{\partial \Omega}{\partial z'} \, dz' = \frac{\mu_0 i n_l}{4\pi} (\Omega_2 - \Omega_1) \quad \text{MKS} \quad (7.5\text{-}8)$$

(Note that we can only get B_z this way; not B_x or B_y.) Now if the coil is long and thin and we consider points $\mathscr{P}$ inside and near the center, Ω_2

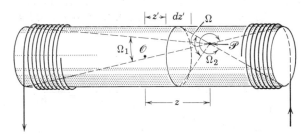

Fig. 7.5h.   Calculation of B_z in a solenoid.

is nearly 4π and Ω_1 is nearly 0.   Hence for a long thin solenoid, the axial field anywhere inside far from the ends is

$$B_z = \mu_0 n_l i \qquad\qquad \text{MKS} \quad (7.5\text{-}9a)$$

or

$$B_z = \frac{4\pi n_l i}{c} \qquad\qquad \text{Gaussian} \quad (7.5\text{-}9b)$$

Thus the field inside a long thin solenoid is constant throughout the central region.

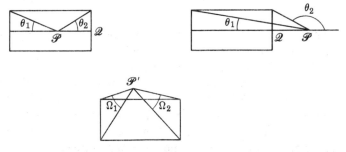

Fig. 7.5i.   Plane and solid angles for different positions in a solenoid.

For coils of any length, we can evaluate Ω_1 and Ω_2 by eq. 7.5-5 for points on the axis.   The reader will verify that the result is

$$B_z = \tfrac{1}{2}\mu_0 n_l i(\cos \theta_2 + \cos \theta_1) \qquad \text{MKS} \quad (7.5\text{-}10)$$

where θ_2 and θ_1 are the angles indicated in Fig. 7.5i.   This formula is valid for points both inside and outside the coil.   At the center of a long coil, $\cos \theta_1 = \cos \theta_2 \cong 1$, so we get eq. 7.5–9a again.   At the end of a long coil, point $\mathscr{2}$ in Fig. 7.5i, $\cos \theta_2 = 0$ and $\cos \theta_1 \cong 1$, so the field is one-half the value at the center.

Let us finally consider points outside the solenoid near its center ($\mathscr{P}'$ in Fig. 7.5i).   Here Ω_1 of Fig. 7.5h will be a small, positive solid angle, while Ω_2 will be a small negative solid angle, as can be seen by following the variation of Ω from one end to the other of the coil.   For an infinitely long solenoid, the field is zero anywhere outside.   An approximation for long but finite solenoids is considered in problem 7.5k.

Problem 7.5a.   Two flat rectangular current-bearing coils, one slightly larger than the other, are mounted on a common axis which lies in the plane of each. If their sides parallel to the axis are long compared to the other sides, find the torque of each on the other in terms of the dimensions, numbers of turns per coil, and angle of displacement.

Problem 7.5b.   Prove as suggested in the text that **B** for a toroidal coil is everywhere tangent to a circle coaxial with the coil.   *Hint*: Divide the coil into pairs of symmetrically placed coils and show that for each pair, the sum of the solid angle gradients has vanishing components in a plane containing the axis.

Problem 7.5c.   Find **B** in the plane of a square wire loop of side a, carrying current i, at a point which is on the perpendicular bisector of one side and at a distance r from the wire toward the center of the square.   Show that if $a \to \infty$ while r remains constant, we get as the result eq. 7.5–1.

Problem 7.5d.   Find the acceleration of an electron moving with a speed of 2.0×10^5 m/sec along a radius outside a long straight wire carrying a current of 3.0 amp, when the electron is at a distance of 2.5 cm from the wire.

Problem 7.5e.   How close must two parallel wires be if they each carry 20 amp and repel each other with a force of 10 dynes/cm?

✓**Problem 7.5f.**   Calculate the first and second derivatives of B_z in eq. 7.5–7a with respect to z, and state a general rule for the symmetry of any derivative with respect to a change from z to $-z$.   If two identical coils of N turns each, with axes coinciding, are placed a distance apart equal to their common radius a, show that the first three derivatives of the combined field of the two coils vanish at the axial point that is equidistant from the two.   Such a pair of coils is called a Helmholtz pair.   Show that B at this point is equal to $8\mu_0 iN/5^{\frac{3}{2}}a$.

Problem 7.5g.   Show why eq. 7.5–5 can be expected to be the same as eq. 7.5–9.   Find B at the center of a solenoid 70 cm long, 8 cm in diameter, wound uniformly with a total of 300 turns, carrying a current of 6.0 amp.

✓**Problem 7.5h.**   Use the circuital form of Ampère's law to relate the values of B_z just inside and just outside any point on the winding of a solenoid.   Write this result in terms of J_S, the current crossing a unit length of surface.   Use this result to show that B_z outside the winding near the center of a very long solenoid is equal to zero.

Problem 7.5i.   Use a symmetry argument on the variation of Ω in the plane midway between two equal symmetrically placed circular coils to show that **B** in this plane is everywhere perpendicular to it, and hence show that **B** is everywhere parallel to the axis in the perpendicular bisecting plane of a solenoid.

Problem 7.5j. A long straight wire carries a current of 2 amp. A rectangular coil 3 cm × 5 cm lies in a plane containing the long wire, with the 5-cm sides parallel to the wire and the nearest side 2 cm away. Find the force on the rectangle if it carries 10 amp.

Problem 7.5k. An approximation to the solid angle subtended by a small circular area at a point a distance r from the axis of the circle, when the axial distance z is large compared with its diameter, is given by multiplying the solid angle for $r = 0$ by the cosine of the angle between the axis and the line from the center of the area to the point in question, and by the appropriate factor for the increased distance. Use this approximation to obtain a formula for **B** in the mid-plane of a long solenoid at a distance r from the center, both inside and outside the coil.

Problem 7.5l. A solenoid of not especially great length has a single layer of n_l turns per meter over its entire length L and an extra layer covering a short length L' from each end toward the middle. Assuming no increase in diameter for the extra windings, find how to determine L' so that the field at the center will be equal to that for an infinitely long, single-layer coil.

Problem 7.5m. A wire 5 cm long is moved parallel to a long straight wire carrying 15 amp, the motion being in the plane of the two wires. If the short wire moves away from the long wire at 10 m/sec, what is the emf induced in the former when the distance between the wires is (a) 1 cm, (b) 1 m?

Problem 7.5n. A square coil 1 cm on a side, with 15 turns, is hung inside the center of a long solenoid with 2000 turns per meter, carrying 300 ma. If the plane of the square coil makes an angle of 20° with the axis of the solenoid and the coil carries 1 ma, find the torque on it.

Problem 7.5o. A steady current of 1000 amp is established in a long, straight, hollow, aluminum conductor of inner radius 0.500 in. and outer radius 0.750 in. Assuming uniform resistivity, calculate **B** as a function of the distance r from the axis of the conductor.

Problem 7.5p. By comparing eq. 7.5–3b with Coulomb's law written in electrostatic units, show that c has the dimensions of centimeter/second and that a statampere has the dimensions of dyne$^{\frac{1}{2}}$-centimeter/second.

Problem 7.5q. Show that the field on the axis of a toroidal coil, caused by the fact that the winding is helical and not a series of plane loops, is approximately that of a single, coaxial, circular loop of radius b, carrying current i. Discuss the field outside a straight solenoid arising from the helicity of the winding.

7.6 Magnetic Potential

We have discussed the production of magnetic fields and the forces they exert without using so far the concepts of potential, lines of force, and flux that were so useful in the case of electric fields. These concepts are indeed useful in the magnetic case, and we turn to them in this section and the next. We shall reverse the order from the electric case, however, and discuss potential before flux, for the reason that the basic flux theorem will be derived from one of the magnetic potential expressions.

The Scalar Potential.   One aspect of the greater complexity of the magnetic field over the electrostatic field lies in the existence of two quite different forms of magnetic potential—the scalar and the vector.   We start with the scalar potential as it is the simpler to derive and discuss, although it is of less fundamental importance than the vector potential. We have, in fact, already stated the appropriate formula—eq. 7.4–1.

The induction **B** is the gradient of a scalar function, which is analogous to the electrostatic potential V from which **E** can be derived.   For convenience in later pursuing the analogy between electric- and magnetic-field quantities, we shall write **B** in MKS units as μ_0 times the gradient of a new function V_m, called the "magnetic scalar potential;" in Gaussian units, a constant factor will not be introduced.   Thus we write

$$\mathbf{B} = -\mu_0 \nabla V_m \qquad\qquad \text{MKS} \quad (7.6\text{–}1a)$$

$$\mathbf{B} = -\nabla V_m \qquad\qquad \text{Gaussian} \quad (7.6\text{–}1b)$$

Then using eq. 7.4–1 we can write the magnetic scalar potential for a collection of current loops

$$V_m = \frac{1}{4\pi} \sum_k i_k \Omega_k \qquad\qquad \text{MKS} \quad (7.6\text{–}2a)$$

$$V_m = \frac{1}{c} \sum_k i_k \Omega_k \qquad\qquad \text{Gaussian} \quad (7.6\text{–}2b)$$

Unlike the electrostatic potential, the potential V_m is not single-valued, as we have seen in section 7.4.   If we wish to restrict ourselves to the consideration of points well outside the current circuits under consideration, we can choose that value of Ω and hence of V_m which goes to zero at infinity.   Hence V_m can be defined by an equation similar to eq. 1.7–1 with a reference point chosen at infinity for simplicity:

$$V_m = -\frac{1}{\mu_0} \int_\infty^{\mathscr{P}} \mathbf{B} \cdot d\mathbf{s} \qquad\qquad (7.6\text{–}3)$$

V_m will be multiple-valued unless the path in the integral is not allowed to pass through any current circuits, although it is otherwise arbitrary. Neither unit for V_m is commonly given a name, although by eq. 7.6–2a the MKS unit has the dimensions of amperes.   The Gaussian unit is called merely the emu of magnetic scalar potential.

We have not interpreted V_m as representing energy for the reason that **B** does not directly represent a force on a real entity.   If single magnetic poles really existed, then as we shall show in section 8.2, $\mathbf{B}/\mu_0$ would be the force on a unit pole at the point in question.   Hence we may speak of V_m as a sort of fictional "potential energy per unit pole."   This type of energy is not conserved with respect to closed-path motions, as is the genuine electrostatic potential energy, because of the multiple-valued nature of V_m.

This multiple-valuedness results in the complete absence of a scalar potential in a region with a volume current distribution **J**, for in such regions we have to imagine an infinite number of infinitesimal loop filaments, each of which involves multiple values of V_m. (The existence of V_m requires **curl B** $= 0$, and we shall show in section 7.8 that where **J** is not zero, neither is **curl B**.)

The Vector Potential.   The vector potential does not suffer from the multiple-valuedness of V_m and is of great use in deriving certain general and fundamental properties of electromagnetic fields. It is most readily introduced by writing a fourth formulation of Ampère's law. We shall start with eq. 7.4–4, summed over all current loops that contribute to B in a given region.

$$\mathbf{B} = \frac{\mu_0}{4\pi} \sum_k i_k \oint_k \frac{d\mathbf{l} \times \mathbf{1}_r}{r^2}$$

Let us denote the coordinates of the point where **B** is to be calculated by (x, y, z), and the coordinates of the varying integration point (the location of **dl**) by (x', y', z'). Then $r^2 = (x - x')^2 + (y - y')^2 + (z - z')^2$; **dl** can be written $\mathbf{1}_x \, dx' + \mathbf{1}_y \, dy' + \mathbf{1}_z \, dz'$, and we have

$$\mathbf{1}_r = \frac{x - x'}{r} \mathbf{1}_x + \frac{y - y'}{r} \mathbf{1}_y + \frac{z - z'}{r} \mathbf{1}_z$$

Now by eq. 3.1–3, $\mathbf{1}_r/r^2 = -\nabla(1/r)$, where the derivatives in the gradient are taken with respect to the unprimed coordinates. Let us write **dl** $\times$ $[-\nabla(1/r)]$ which is the same as $\nabla(1/r) \times$ **dl** in the determinant form for the vector product and then rearrange it:

$$\nabla\left(\frac{1}{r}\right) \times \mathbf{dl} = \begin{vmatrix} \mathbf{1}_x & \mathbf{1}_y & \mathbf{1}_z \\ \dfrac{\partial}{\partial x}\left(\dfrac{1}{r}\right) & \dfrac{\partial}{\partial y}\left(\dfrac{1}{r}\right) & \dfrac{\partial}{\partial z}\left(\dfrac{1}{r}\right) \\ dx' & dy' & dz' \end{vmatrix} = \begin{vmatrix} \mathbf{1}_x & \mathbf{1}_y & \mathbf{1}_z \\ \dfrac{\partial}{\partial x} & \dfrac{\partial}{\partial y} & \dfrac{\partial}{\partial z} \\ \dfrac{dx'}{r} & \dfrac{dy'}{r} & \dfrac{dz'}{r} \end{vmatrix}$$

The latter form is the symbolic operator that represents the curl (Appendix, eq. A.2–38) and follows from the former because the derivatives do not act on dx', dy', and dz', so that, for instance, $(\partial/\partial y)(dz'/r) = dz'(\partial/\partial y)(1/r)$, and so forth. Hence we may write

$$\nabla\left(\frac{1}{r}\right) \times \mathbf{dl} = \nabla \times \left(\frac{\mathbf{dl}}{r}\right) = \mathbf{curl}\,\frac{\mathbf{dl}}{r} \qquad (7.6\text{--}4)$$

The operation **curl** can be interchanged with the integration over x', y', z', so we have

$$\mathbf{B} = \frac{\mu_0}{4\pi} \sum_k i_k \oint_k \nabla\left(\frac{1}{r}\right) \times \mathbf{dl}$$

$$= \nabla \times \left[\frac{\mu_0}{4\pi} \sum_k i_k \oint_k \frac{\mathbf{dl}}{r}\right] \qquad \text{MKS} \quad (7.6\text{-}5)$$

The expression in brackets is called the "vector potential" and will be denoted by **A**. Thus, finally,

$$\mathbf{B} = \text{curl } \mathbf{A} = \nabla \times \mathbf{A} \qquad \text{MKS and Gaussian} \quad (7.6\text{-}6)$$

$$\mathbf{A} = \frac{\mu_0}{4\pi} \sum_k \left(i \oint \frac{\mathbf{dl}}{r}\right)_k \qquad \text{MKS} \quad (7.6\text{-}7a)$$

$$\mathbf{A} = \frac{1}{c} \sum_k \left(i \oint \frac{\mathbf{dl}}{r}\right)_k \qquad \text{Gaussian} \quad (7.6\text{-}7b)$$

In terms of components we have

$$A_x = \frac{\mu_0}{4\pi} \sum_k i_k \oint_k \frac{dx'}{r}$$

$$A_y = \frac{\mu_0}{4\pi} \sum_k i_k \oint_k \frac{dy'}{r} \qquad \text{MKS} \quad (7.6\text{-}7c)$$

$$A_z = \frac{\mu_0}{4\pi} \sum_k i_k \oint_k \frac{dz'}{r}$$

We see by comparison with eq. 1.7–5 that each component of **A** is mathematically similar to the electrostatic potential due to a linear distribution of charge along the various current circuits, with a linear density λ that varies in accordance with the orientation of **dl**.

If we think of the current in each conductor as having a finite lateral distribution, each current element i **dl** can be written $J \, dS \, \mathbf{dl} = \mathbf{J} \, dS \, dl = \mathbf{J} \, d\tau$, since the unit vector along a filament can be associated with **dl** or with **J**. Thus we can write the vector potential as a volume integral over all parts of space in which **J** is not zero:

$$\mathbf{A} = \frac{\mu_0}{4\pi} \int_\tau \mathbf{J} \frac{d\tau}{r} \qquad \text{MKS} \quad (7.6\text{-}8a)$$

$$\mathbf{A} = \frac{1}{c} \int_\tau \mathbf{J} \frac{d\tau}{r} \qquad \text{Gaussian} \quad (7.6\text{-}8b)$$

A has the dimensions of $\mu_0 i$ or i/c; the MKS unit is the weber/meter, and the Gaussian unit (emu) is the maxwell/centimeter or the gauss-centimeter.

The vector potential is readily defined for points in, as well as outside of, a region of continuous current density (cf. problem 1.7o on the convergence of the integral for V at a point in a medium of continuous charge density). Thus the $\mathbf{B} = \mathbf{curl}\ \mathbf{A}$ form of Ampère's law can be applied to such cases more easily than can the solid angle rule. Problem 7.6e gives an example of the calculation of $\mathbf{A}$ in such a region by the use of a limiting process.

We have defined $\mathbf{A}$ uniquely by eq. 7.6–7. However, there is more than one vector potential corresponding to a given $\mathbf{B}$ if we use eq. 7.6–6 to define $\mathbf{A}$. For let $\psi(x, y, z)$ be any suitably continuous function, and calculate **curl** $(\mathbf{A} + \nabla\psi)$:

$$\nabla \times (\mathbf{A} + \nabla\psi) = \nabla \times \mathbf{A} + \nabla \times \nabla\psi = \mathbf{B} + 0 \qquad (7.6\text{–}9)$$

since $\nabla \times \nabla\psi = 0$ for all ψ $\left(\text{the }x\text{-component is } \dfrac{\partial^2\psi}{\partial y\,\partial z} - \dfrac{\partial^2\psi}{\partial z\,\partial y} \equiv 0, \text{ etc.}\right)$. So the gradient of any function can be added to $\mathbf{A}$ without affecting $\mathbf{B}$. Some authors use the symbol $\mathbf{A}$ for such a generalized function, but we shall stick to the definition eq. 7.6–7.

The vector potential $\mathbf{A}$ as just defined has the property that its divergence is identically zero:

$$\nabla \cdot \mathbf{A} = \frac{\mu_0}{4\pi} \sum_k i_k \left[\frac{\partial}{\partial x} \oint_k \frac{dx'}{r} + \frac{\partial}{\partial y} \oint_k \frac{dy'}{r} + \frac{\partial}{\partial z} \oint_k \frac{dz'}{r} \right]$$

$$= \frac{\mu_0}{4\pi} \sum_k i_k \left[-\oint \frac{(x - x')\,dx' + (y - y')\,dy' + (z - z')\,dz'}{r^3} \right]$$

$$= \frac{\mu_0}{4\pi} \sum_k i_k \left[\oint_k \frac{r\,dr}{r^3} \right] = 0 \qquad (7.6\text{–}10)$$

where dr means the differential of r for variations in x', y', and z'.[18] The integral is equal to the variation of $(-1/r)$ around a closed circuit and thus vanishes.

The vector potential is a type of vector field quantity, for which we can draw field lines. The vanishing of the divergence means that the field lines have no beginnings or endings but only in cases of ideal symmetry will they form closed loops (cf. the discussion of lines of $\mathbf{D}$ in section 3.6). The general direction of the lines is parallel to the currents, since the vector elements of $\mathbf{A}$ are proportional to current elements.

[18] Since $r^2 = (x - x')^2 + (y - y')^2 + (z - z')^2$, $r\,dr = -(x - x')\,dx' - (y - y')\,dy' - (z - z')\,dz'$.

Although the calculation of **A** is somewhat more complicated than the corresponding calculation of V, there are a few cases in which the vector potential can be calculated fairly easily and which are quite instructive.

The contribution to **A** of any straight segment of a circuit is a vector parallel to this segment, and can be readily calculated.   Let the z-axis be taken parallel to the segment in question ($\mathcal{MN}$ in Fig. 7.6a) and find **A** at a point located by the perpendicular R and the distances z_1 and z_2, taking the foot of the perpendicular $\mathcal{O}$ as origin.   (It is convenient in this

Fig. 7.6a.   Calculation of **A** produced at $\mathcal{P}$ by a wire segment $\mathcal{MN}$ carrying a current i.

calculation to deal with positive numbers for both distances.)   Then $dl = \mathbf{1}_z\, dz$, and remembering that r is always a positive number we have

$$\mathbf{A} = \mathbf{1}_z \frac{\mu_0 i}{4\pi} \int_{-z_1}^{z_2} \frac{dz}{(R^2 + z^2)^{\frac{1}{2}}} = \mathbf{1}_z \frac{\mu_0 i}{4\pi} \left[\int_0^{z_1} \frac{dz}{(R^2 + z^2)^{\frac{1}{2}}} + \int_0^{z_2} \frac{dz}{(R^2 + z^2)^{\frac{1}{2}}} \right]$$

$$= \mathbf{1}_z \frac{\mu_0 i}{4\pi} \left[\ln \frac{z_1 + (R^2 + z_1^2)^{\frac{1}{2}}}{R} + \ln \frac{z_2 + (R^2 + z_2^2)^{\frac{1}{2}}}{R} \right]$$

$$= \mathbf{1}_z \frac{\mu_0 i}{4\pi} \ln \frac{[z_1 + (R^2 + z_1^2)^{\frac{1}{2}}][z_2 + (R^2 + z_2^2)^{\frac{1}{2}}]}{R^2} \qquad (7.6\text{--}11)$$

The reader should be able to show that this result still holds when $\mathcal{O}$ lies outside of $\mathcal{MN}$ (problem 7.6a).

The vector potential for any circuit made up of straight segments can be calculated at any point by a straightforward vector addition (problem 7.6b).   On the other hand, we get an infinite result for an infinitely long wire, exactly as for the electrostatic potential discussed in section 1.7. However, we found there that the potential V for an oppositely charged pair of wires is finite, and we should expect a similar result here.   Consider two parallel segments each of length $2z$ carrying equal and opposite currents, and calculate **A** at a point $\mathcal{P}$ in the perpendicular bisecting plane, a distance R_1 from the positive current and R_2 from the negative. (Fig. 7.6b.)   Then **A** at $\mathscr{P}$ becomes, setting $z_1 = z_2 = z$,

$$\mathbf{A} = \mathbf{1}_z \frac{\mu_0 i}{4\pi} \left[\int \frac{dz}{r_1} - \int \frac{dz}{r_2} \right]$$

$$\mathbf{A} = \mathbf{1}_z \frac{\mu_0 i}{4\pi} \left[\ln \frac{[z + (R_1^2 + z^2)^{\frac{1}{2}}]^2}{R_1^2} - \ln \frac{[z + (R_2^2 + z^2)^{\frac{1}{2}}]^2}{R_2^2} \right]$$

$$= \mathbf{1}_z \frac{\mu_0 i}{2\pi} \ln \left[\frac{R_2}{R_1} \cdot \frac{z + (R_1^2 + z^2)^{\frac{1}{2}}}{z + (R_2^2 + z^2)^{\frac{1}{2}}} \right]$$

where the exponent 2 has been removed from the logarithm in the last step.   Now if z is allowed to approach infinity (that is, if z is sufficiently

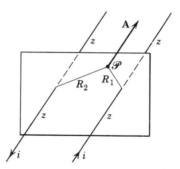

Fig. 7.6b.   Calculation of **A** for two infinite parallel wires.

large compared to R_1 and R_2), we have a result that is analogous to that of eq. 1.7–15:

$$\mathbf{A} = \mathbf{1}_z \frac{\mu_0 i}{2\pi} \ln \frac{R_2}{R_1} \qquad \text{MKS} \quad (7.6\text{–}12)$$

[19]Thus the equipotentials of eq. 1.7–15, section 4.5, and Fig. 1.11d, p. 47, become here the surfaces of constant A_z.   Since $\mathbf{B} = \mathbf{curl\ A}$ and A_x and A_y are zero, we have

$$B_x = \partial A_z / \partial y$$

$$B_y = -\partial A_z / \partial x \qquad\qquad (7.6\text{–}13)$$

$$B_z = 0$$

Now, the vectors **B** and **A** are clearly perpendicular.   We can interpret

[19] This paragraph may be omitted if section 4.5 has not been taken up.

eq. 7.6–13 simply if we compare **B** with **grad** $A_z = \mathbf{\nabla}A_z$ whose components are

$$\left.\begin{array}{l} \text{grad}_x\, A_z = \partial A_z/\partial x \\ \text{grad}_y\, A_z = \partial A_z/\partial y \\ \text{grad}_z\, A_z = \partial A_z/\partial z = 0 \end{array}\right\} \qquad (7.6\text{–}14)$$

We see that $B^2 = B_x{}^2 + B_y{}^2 = |\mathbf{\nabla}A_z|^2$ and that $\mathbf{B}\cdot\mathbf{\nabla}A_z = B_x\,\text{grad}_x(A_z) + B_y\,\text{grad}_y(A_z) = 0$.   Hence **B** has the magnitude of the gradient of A_z— proportional to E in the electric case—but is perpendicular to $\mathbf{\nabla}A_z$ as seen by the vanishing of the scalar product.   Since $\mathbf{\nabla}A_z$ at any point is normal to the surface A_z = constant through that point, **B** lies on this

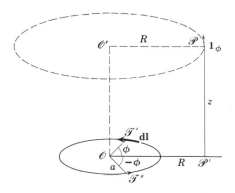

Fig. 7.6c.   Calculation of A for a circular loop.

surface along the circle cut on it by a plane normal to the wires.   These circles are therefore the magnetic lines of force.   In the electric case, their spacing was shown to be proportional to the gradient of V, so that by the analogous calculation they are seen to be properly spaced in this case, i.e., proportional to B (Cf. section 7.7.)

This case affords an excellent example of varying magnitude and orientation of the circulation density or curl of a vector quantity which is itself everywhere parallel to a given line.

In order to illustrate the difficulty in making exact calculations in cases of even moderate complexity, we shall write an expression for the vector potential produced by a single circular loop of current at an arbitrary point off the axis of the loop.

Consider a loop of current of radius a, and a point $\mathscr{P}$ located at a distance z from the plane of the loop and at a distance R from its axis. (Fig. 7.6c.)   Let us locate **dl** at a point $\mathscr{T}'$ by an angle ϕ measured from the line $\mathscr{O}\mathscr{P}'$ in the figure, where $\mathscr{P}'$ is the foot of the perpendicular from

$\mathscr{P}$ to the plane of the current. The distance $r = \overline{\mathscr{T}'\mathscr{P}}$ can be found from the law of cosines in triangle $\mathscr{T}'\mathcal{O}\mathscr{P}'$, and the Pythagorean theorem in triangle $\mathscr{T}'\mathscr{P}'\mathscr{P}$, yielding

$$r = (z^2 + a^2 + R^2 - 2aR \cos \phi)^{\frac{1}{2}}$$

Another element **dl** located at $\mathscr{T}''$, at an angle $-\phi$ in the figure, will be at the same distance from $\mathscr{P}$. The contributions of the two elements to **A** at $\mathscr{P}$ will cancel in the direction $\mathcal{O}'\mathscr{P}$ and add in the direction normal to the plane $\mathscr{P}'\mathcal{O}\mathcal{O}'\mathscr{P}$, the component of dl in this direction being $a\, d\phi \cos \phi$. Thus we can write

$$\mathbf{A} = \frac{\mu_0 i}{4\pi} \mathbf{1}_\phi \cdot 2 \int_0^\pi \frac{a \cos \phi \, d\phi}{(z^2 + a^2 + R^2 - 2aR \cos \phi)^{\frac{1}{2}}} \qquad \text{MKS} \quad (7.6\text{-}15)$$

where $\mathbf{1}_\phi$ is a unit vector normal to the plane $\mathscr{P}'\mathcal{O}\mathcal{O}'\mathscr{P}$, in the direction corresponding to increasing ϕ.

This integral cannot be evaluated in elementary terms. It belongs to a class of expressions called "elliptic integrals," so called because one of them arises in the calculation of the circumference of an ellipse. The reader is referred to texts on advanced calculus and to mathematical tables, where integrals of this type are reduced to standard forms and tabulated numerically.[20]

There are certain approximately calculable cases. If z is considerably larger than a, the radical can be written by neglect of a^2,

$$\sqrt{z^2 + R^2}\, [1 - (2aR \cos \varphi)/(z^2 + R^2)]^{\frac{1}{2}}$$

and the second factor expanded by the binomial theorem. The results will turn out to agree with a calculation to be made in section 8.2 (see problem 8.2a). On the other hand, if z is much smaller than a and R is nearly equal to a, a different expansion can be used, and will be given in section 7.11 for $z = 0$. It is also possible to make an expansion in terms of Legendre functions, that were considered in section 4.6.

The Vector Potential for an Infinite Solenoid. When we come to consider an infinite, uniformly wound solenoid, we find that we can make an explicit calculation using eq. 7.6–15. If the solenoid has n_l turns per meter, the contribution to **A** produced by the turns in length dz can be obtained by assuming these turns to act like $n_l\, dz$ circular loops. We have

$$A_\phi = \int_{\text{all loops}} dA_\phi = \frac{\mu_0 a n_l i}{2\pi} \int_{-\infty}^\infty dz \int_0^\pi \frac{\cos \phi \, d\phi}{(z^2 + a^2 + R^2 - 2aR \cos \phi)^{\frac{1}{2}}}$$

[20] Cf. *Handbook of Chemistry and Physics*, Chemical Rubber Publ. Co., Cleveland, mathematical section, any recent edition. W. Kaplan, *Advanced Calculus*, Addison-Wesley, Cambridge, Mass., 1952, pp. 179–181; B. O. Pierce, *A Short Table of Integrals*, Ginn, Boston, 1929, p. 121; W. F. Osgood, *Advanced Calculus*, Macmillan, New York, 1925, Chapter IX.

This integral can be evaluated by dividing it into two parts, writing $\pi/2 - \phi$ for ϕ in the angular range between $\pi/2$ and π and then interchanging the order of integration.   We have, using the method followed for eq. 7.6–12 where the z integration is mathematically the same,

$$A_\phi = \frac{\mu_0 a n_i i}{2\pi} \int_{-\infty}^{\infty} dz \int_0^{\pi/2} d\phi \left[\frac{\cos\phi}{(z^2 + a^2 + R^2 - 2aR\cos\phi)^{\frac{1}{2}}} \right.$$

$$\left. - \frac{\cos\phi}{(z^2 + a^2 + R^2 + 2aR\cos\phi)^{\frac{1}{2}}} \right]$$

$$= \frac{\mu_0 a n_i i}{2\pi} \int_0^{\pi/2} \cos\phi \, d\phi \ln\left(\frac{a^2 + R^2 + 2aR\cos\phi}{a^2 + R^2 - 2aR\cos\phi} \right)$$

Let us denote the ratio $2Ra/(R^2 + a^2)$ by α, and use integration by parts, the one part being $\cos\phi \, d\phi$ and the other the logarithm.   The integrated part vanishes, and except for the factor $\mu_0 a n_i i/2\pi$, the integral becomes

$$2\alpha \int_0^{\pi/2} \frac{\sin^2\phi \, d\phi}{1 - \alpha^2 \cos^2\phi} = \frac{2}{\alpha}\left[\phi - (1 - \alpha^2)^{\frac{1}{2}} \tan^{-1}\left\{ \frac{\tan\phi}{(1 - \alpha^2)^{\frac{1}{2}}} \right\} \right]_0^{\pi/2}$$

as the reader can readily verify by differentiation.   The expression $\tan^{-1}\{(\tan\phi)/(1 - \alpha^2)^{\frac{1}{2}}\}$ approaches $\pi/2$ as $\phi \to \pi/2$.   Using

$$(1 - \alpha^2)^{\frac{1}{2}} = (R^4 - 2R^2a^2 + a^4)^{\frac{1}{2}}/(R^2 + a^2) = |R^2 - a^2|/(R^2 + a^2)$$

we have

$$A_\phi = \frac{\mu_0 a n_i i}{2\pi} \cdot \frac{R^2 + a^2}{Ra} \cdot \frac{\pi}{2}\left[1 - \frac{|R^2 - a^2|}{R^2 + a^2} \right]$$

We have for convenience chosen $(1 - \alpha^2)^{\frac{1}{2}}$ to be positive, but the expression $|R^2 - a^2|$ must be taken as positive regardless of which sign is chosen for $(1 - \alpha^2)^{\frac{1}{2}}$.   If $R > a$ we have finally

$$A_\phi = \frac{\mu_0 n_i i a^2}{2R} \qquad\qquad \text{MKS} \quad (7.6\text{–}16a)$$

whereas for $R < a$

$$A_\phi = \tfrac{1}{2}\mu_0 n_i i R \qquad\qquad \text{MKS} \quad (7.6\text{–}16b)$$

It will be left to the reader to show (problem 7.6c) that inside the solenoid, when $R < a$, **curl A** yields the value of **B** found earlier and that outside, **curl A** $= 0$.   It is especially important to note that we have here a case in which **B** is zero throughout a certain region in which **A** does not vanish. We shall see later (section 7.9) that this non-vanishing of **A** has considerable physical significance.

Problem 7.6a.   Show that eq. 7.6–11 is correct when O lies to the left or right of segment $\mathcal{MN}$ in Fig. 7.6b.

Problem 7.6b.   Find the vector potential at the same point in the square of problem 7.5c for which **B** was sought.   Show that $\mathbf{A} \to \infty$ as $a \to \infty$.   Find its magnitude in webers/meter when $a = 0.50$ m, $r = 0.20$ m, and $i = 15.0$ amp.

Problem 7.6c.   Show from eq. 7.6–16 that $\mathbf{B} = \mu_0 n_l i$ inside the solenoid and $\mathbf{B} = 0$ outside it.   Show also that although the circulation of **A** does not vanish for a path surrounding the solenoid, its value is independent of the shape of this path (with what restriction?).

Problem 7.6d.   Show that $\nabla^2 V_m = 0$ in any region free of current, by using the results of problem 1.10f.   Then show that div **B** is zero in every such region.

Problem 7.6e.   Find the vector potential at the center of a cylindrical pipe of length L and inner and outer radii r_1 and r_2, that carries a uniform current density J parallel to its axis.   Calculate only that part of **A** produced by the current in this piece of pipe, disregarding the rest of the circuit.   Show that as $r_1 \to 0$, **A** remains finite.

Problem 7.6f.   Write the vector potential **A** in eq. 7.6–15 as the sum of two complete elliptic integrals, using a suitable reference work for these integrals if necessary.

Problem 7.6g.   Discuss **A** outside an infinite solenoid when the winding is taken as helical rather than as a series of true circles.

7.7   Magnetic Flux

The fact that **B** is the curl of another vector leads immediately to a very important conclusion, namely that the divergence of **B** is zero.

We have $\nabla \cdot \mathbf{B} = \nabla \cdot \nabla \times \mathbf{A}$ which has the form of the triple scalar product (Appendix A.2–30) and vanishes for the same algebraic reasons of cancellation as does any such product with two equal factors.   Hence

$$\text{div } \mathbf{B} = \nabla \cdot \mathbf{B} = 0 \qquad (7.7\text{–}1)$$

everywhere, including points within continuous current density distributions.

In accordance with study of divergence and flux in Appendix A.2, we see that the flux of **B** through any closed surface is zero.

$$\int_{\text{closed } S} \mathbf{B} \cdot \mathbf{dS} = 0 \qquad (7.7\text{–}2)$$

It is this fact that allows us to talk of the magnetic flux

$$\Phi = \int_S \mathbf{B} \cdot \mathbf{dS} \qquad (7.7\text{–}3)$$

through any loop or circuit as a definite quantity, for the integral that defines Φ can be taken over any surface bounded by the loop in question.

The flux through any loop can also be calculated from the vector potential.   Substituting eq. 7.6–6 into eq. 7.7–3 and using Stokes' theorem (Appendix A.2–39), we have

$$\Phi = \int_S \mathbf{curl\ A} \cdot \mathbf{dS} = \oint_{\text{boundary of } S} \mathbf{A} \cdot \mathbf{dl} \qquad (7.7\text{–}4)$$

The fact that the flux of induction through any closed surface is zero allows us to construct tubes of magnetic flux, each containing some unit or sub-unit of flux, exactly as in the electric case (section 1.6).   Magnetic

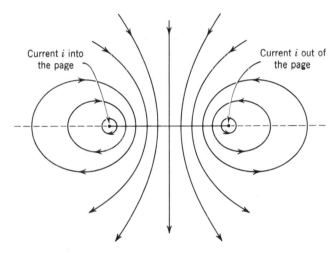

Fig. 7.7a.   Lines of **B** for a circular loop.   (Adapted from Durand, Electrostatique et Magnétostatique, Masson et Cie, Paris, 1953.)

lines of induction can, of course, be drawn without the necessity of proving the flux-conservation theorem;   however, we have now shown that we can draw lines in such numbers that their density is everywhere proportional to B.

As a simple application of the magnetic-flux law, consider a slender solenoid of cross-sectional area S.   The induction at the center is $\mu_0 n_i i$ and is constant over the entire cross section.   The induction at one end is one-half this value and is also constant over the cross section.   Thus we see immediately that of the flux $\Phi = \mu_0 n i S$ in the center of the coil, one-half (nearly) must pass out through the side, leaving one-half to pass out through the end.   This result would be awkward to calculate directly from the field at the sides of the solenoid.

Figures 7.7a, b, c, and d show the magnetic lines of induction for a single loop of wire, a pair of Helmholtz coils (problem 7.5f), a short

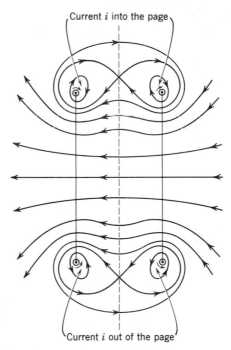

Current i into the page

Current i out of the page

Fig. 7.7b. Lines of **B** for two circular loops, currents parallel.
(Adapted from Durand, *op. cit.*)

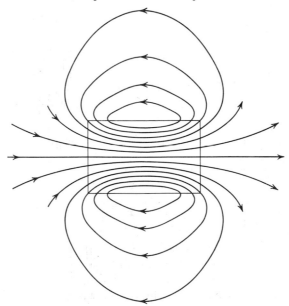

Fig. 7.7c. Lines of **B** for a short solenoid.   (Adapted from Durand, *op. cit.*)

solenoid, and a long solenoid. The fact that **div B** = 0 everywhere is equivalent to saying that there are no beginnings or ends to lines of induction. This of course was implied in our assertion that **B** is produced by current loops. The existence of free magnetic poles would contradict this statement, but no convincing experimental evidence has ever been found for such poles.

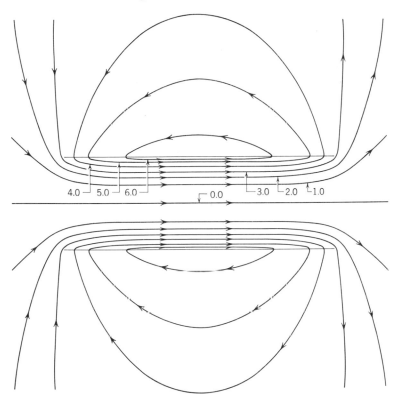

Fig. 7.7d. Lines of **B** for a long solenoid. The numbers represent flux Φ contained in surfaces of revolution (arbitrary scale).

In ideally symmetrical cases such as those of the long straight wire or the circle, the lines of **B** obviously form closed loops. But this is not always or even generally so. As a simple example, consider a circular current and in addition a long straight wire on the axis of the circle. The field of the straight wire when superimposed on that of the circular one will make the lines near the latter go around it in spiral fashion. Only for very special values of the currents will any of these spiral lines come back to the same point after going around the central wire. (Fig. 7.7e.) The lines of **B** in general are infinitely long! The concept of the number of lines through a given area becomes complicated in such cases (cf. the discussion for **D** produced by electrets, p. 121).   In fact, it can only be kept meaningful if arbitrary ends and beginnings of lines are introduced.[21]

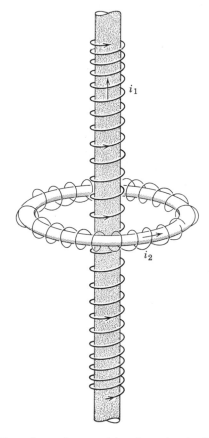

Fig. 7.7e.   Magnetic lines about a long straight wire and a circular loop, each carrying a current.   Lines of **B** in the vicinity of i_2 do not meet after one turn about i_1.   (Adapted from K. L. McDonald, *"Topology of Steady Current Magnetic Fields," American Journal of Physics*, **22**, 588 (1954), Fig. 1.)

Actual physical coils cannot have the ideal symmetry needed to make the lines close.

Let us note finally that eq. 7.7–1 is the second of Maxwell's equations

[21] See K. L. McDonald "Topology of Steady Current Magnetic Fields," *Am. Journ. Phys.*, **22**, 586 (1954), and Joseph Slepian "Lines of Force in Electric and Magnetic Fields," *Am. Journ. Phys.*, **19**, 87 (1951).

for electromagnetic radiation that we have derived, the first one being eq. 1.5–1 for div **E**.

Flux and Energy.   We now wish to show that the externally produced flux through a circuit can be interpreted as an energy function from which forces and torques can be calculated.   Let us consider a closed loop *l* carrying a current *i*, situated in an external magnetic field of induction **B**. The induction produced by the current *i* will not be considered, as we are not trying to calculate the force of a circuit on itself.   Let us displace

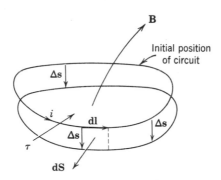

Fig. 7.7f.   Calculation of the work done on displacement of a loop.

the circuit by a small amount **Δs**, which need not be a constant around the circuit, (Fig. 7.7*f*).   The work done by the magnetic force **dF** on an element **dl** of the wire is then

$$dW = \mathbf{dF} \cdot \mathbf{\Delta s} = i\, \mathbf{dl} \times \mathbf{B} \cdot \mathbf{\Delta s} = i\mathbf{B} \cdot \mathbf{\Delta s} \times \mathbf{dl} = i\mathbf{B} \cdot \mathbf{dS} = i\, d\Phi$$

where **dS** is the rectangular element of area whose sides are **Δs** and **dl**, with its normal directed to the outside of the ribbon-shaped area swept out by the circuit during its displacement, and $d\Phi$ is the flux through **dS**. Therefore the work done on the entire circuit is $\Delta W = i\, \Delta\Phi$ where $\Delta\Phi$ is the outward flux through the ribbon swept out by the circuit.

In our figure, the positive direction through the current circuit is upward.   For the initial position of the loop, the positive direction is therefore outward from the volume τ bounded by the ribbon and a surface placed across each loop; for the final position upward is *into* the volume. If Φ_1 and Φ_2 are the values of the flux through the circuit in its initial and final positions, the equality of inward and outward flux means that

$$\Phi_2 = \Delta\Phi + \Phi_1 \qquad\qquad \text{MKS} \quad (7.7\text{–}5)$$

or

$$\Delta W = i\, \Delta\Phi = i(\Phi_2 - \Phi_1)$$

The function

$$U' = -i\Phi \qquad\qquad \text{MKS} \quad (7.7\text{–}6a)$$

which becomes in Gaussian units

$$U' = -\frac{i}{c}\,\Phi \qquad\qquad \text{Gaussian} \quad (7.7\text{–}6b)$$

is therefore a potential energy function whose decrease gives the work done by magnetic forces for any displacement of the circuit. We shall see in section 7.12 that when the energy of the sources of current is considered, the true potential energy turns out to be $U = -U' = +i\Phi$.

If Δs is a constant around the circuit, the work done can be written in terms of the component F_s in the direction of Δs of the total force $\mathbf{F}$ on the current loop

$$\Delta U' = -F_s\,\Delta s$$

If Δs is successively chosen to be in the x-, y-, and z-directions and the proper limit is taken, we can construct $\mathbf{F}$:

$$\mathbf{F} = -\nabla U' = i\,\nabla\Phi \qquad\qquad (7.7\text{–}7)$$

The variables x, y, and z of ∇ refer to the coordinates of some chosen point on the current loop.

By considering a rigid rotation of a loop, we can in a similar way calculate the torque (cf. problem 7.7c).

We are assuming here that i remains constant, which will be true if the emf producing the current does not change and the motion is slow enough that induced emf's are negligible. (We shall deal with changing currents in section 7.12, as well as with the contributions to W of the flux produced by i itself.)

Equation 7.7–6a can be written in terms of $\mathbf{A}$ by 7.7–4:

$$U' = -i\oint \mathbf{A}\cdot\mathbf{dl} \qquad\qquad \text{MKS} \quad (7.7\text{–}8)$$

If now the external field is produced by a second circuit with current i_2, we can use eq. 7.6–7 and obtain a symmetric formula for the energy:

$$U' = -\frac{\mu_0 i_1 i_2}{4\pi} \oint_1 \oint_2 \frac{\mathbf{dl}_1\cdot\mathbf{dl}_2}{r_{12}} \qquad\qquad \text{MKS} \quad (7.7\text{–}9a)$$

$$U' = -\frac{i_1 i_2}{c^2} \oint_1 \oint_2 \frac{\mathbf{dl}_1\cdot\mathbf{dl}_2}{r_{12}} \qquad\qquad \text{Gaussian} \quad (7.7\text{–}9b)$$

in which we have set $i = i_1$, and denoted by r_{12} the distance from an element $\mathbf{dl}_1$ of circuit 1 to an element $\mathbf{dl}_2$ of circuit 2. The double line integral is extended over both circuits, as indicated. The symmetry of these expressions shows that the force on either circuit can be found from changes in W. Note that r_{12} never becomes zero if the two circuits do not actually intersect.

The coefficient of $i_1 i_2$ is known as the *mutual inductance* M_{12} of the two circuits:

$$M_{12} = \frac{\mu_0}{4\pi} \oint_1 \oint_2 \frac{dl_1 \cdot dl_2}{r_{12}} \qquad \text{MKS} \qquad (7.7\text{--}10a)$$

$$M_{12} = \frac{1}{c^2} \oint_1 \oint_2 \frac{dl_1 \cdot dl_2}{r_{12}} \qquad \text{Gaussian} \qquad (7.7\text{--}10b)$$

This formula is known as Neumann's formula.[22]   The mutual inductance may be defined as the flux through either circuit produced by unit current in the other.   The MKS unit of mutual inductance is the henry.[23]   We shall return to a calculation of forces and inductances after we have introduced the general law for induced emf's.

The fact that $\nabla \cdot \mathbf{B} = 0$ and that in current-free regions $\mathbf{B}$ may be derived from a scalar potential V_m means that $\nabla \cdot \nabla V_m = 0$, so that V_m obeys Laplace's equation.   If the values of V_m (and thus of $\mathbf{B}$) are wanted in the neighborhood of any particular point, such as a center of symmetry (e.g., the center of a solenoid or the central point of the Helmholtz coils of problem 7.5f), the result can be written as a series expansion in spherical harmonics, in accordance with section 4.6.   In particular, if the coil system has axial symmetry, an expansion in Legendre functions can be used:

$$V_m = a_0 + a_1 r P_1(\cos\theta) + a_2 r^2 P_2(\cos\theta) + \cdots + a_n r^n P_n(\cos\theta) + \cdots \tag{7.7--11}$$

Thus the variation of V_m along the axis ($\theta = 0$) determines the a_n's and hence the variation of V_m for all r and θ.   The Helmholtz pair of problem 7.5f has a field B_z on the axis whose first three derivatives vanish at its central point. Setting $\theta = 0$ and $r = z$ in eq. 7.7–11 and differentiating to get B_z, we see that a_2, a_3, and a_4 must vanish.   Since $P_1(\cos\theta) = \cos\theta$ and $r\cos\theta = z$, the terms $a_0 + a_1 z$ are seen to give the potential for a uniform field.   The corrections to this potential involve only the terms $a_5 r^5 P_5(\cos\theta)$ and beyond, so it is clear that the uniformity of the field extends in all directions from the center, to the extent that this first correction term is small.

The various possible arrangements of coils that may be used to produce a uniform field may be classified according to the number of terms beyond a_1 in eq. 7.7–11 that vanish and may be characterized in detail by the values of the first one or two non-vanishing coefficients.   For a survey of various coil arrangements and also of the application of this method to a description of fields at large distances, the reader is referred elsewhere.[24]

[22] F. E. Neumann, *Berlin Abhandlungen*, 1845, p. 1; 1848, p. 1. Neumann was also the first to introduce the vector potential, in the same publications.

[23] A henry is dimensionally the same as a meter if we assume that μ_0 is dimensionless. Compare this result with the identity of the dimensions of the statfarad and the centimeter in the electrostatic and Gaussian systems of units.

[24] M. W. Garrett, *Jour. Appl. Phys.*, **22**, 1091–1107 (1951).

Problem 7.7a.   Write the field B_z on the axis of a solenoid of finite length as a series in powers of z, where z is measured from the center of the coil.   Use this series to identify the constants $a_1, a_2, \cdots$ of eq. 7.7–11 giving two non-vanishing coefficients beyond a_1.

Problem 7.7b.   Find the constants a_1 and a_5 for the field at the central point of the Helmholtz pair of problem 7.5*f*.

Problem 7.7c.   By writing the flux through a rigid plane loop in a uniform field as $\Phi = \mathbf{B} \cdot \mathbf{S}$, show that the torque on the loop can be written as the vector $\mathscr{L} = i\mathbf{S} \times \mathbf{B}$.

Problem 7.7d.   Prove eq. 7.7–7 by use of the vector theorem A.2–43 and a suitable argument about interchanging the order of the operations ∫ and ∇.

Problem 7.7e.   Find the flux through a square 3 cm on a side produced by a current of 15 amp in a long straight wire if one side of the square is parallel to the wire and 5 cm from it, and the opposite side is (*a*) 8 cm from the long wire and (*b*) 6 cm from the long wire.

Problem 7.7f.   What is the work required to turn the square coil in problem 7.5*n* from a position in which the positive normal to the coil is parallel to the direction of **B** in the solenoid to a position reversed by 180°?

Problem 7.7g.   A solenoid 50 cm long and 2 cm in diameter has 300 turns and carries 14 amp.   A circular coil of 5 turns with an average diameter of 2.5 cm carries a constant current of 0.50 amp.   Find the work done when the latter coil is brought up from infinity to a position over the solenoid at its center. Relate the sign of the work done to the relative orientation of the coils.

7.8   Differential-Equation Form of Ampère's Law

We have so far presented four forms[25] of the law by which currents produce magnetic fields.   These are all of the nature of "action-at-a-distance" formulas, in which the field at one point is related to currents elsewhere.   Now, just as we did for Coulomb's law in section 1.5, we can write a differential equation that expresses Ampère's law in terms of currents and fields at a single point.   This form is useful in cases of volume distributions of current and also in showing how **B** can be thought of as being "propagated" point by point from the immediate neighborhood of a current to any particular distant point in space.   The equation we are to derive is, in fact, the third of Maxwell's equations for electromagnetic radiation.

A volume current distribution is to be described in terms of the current density **J** as stated in section 5.8.   We have first to consider the case in which each current filament is a closed loop, as indicated at the beginning of section 7.4, so that there can be no points at which charge collects. This means that $\partial \rho / \partial t = 0$ and $\nabla \cdot \mathbf{J} = 0$ (eq. 5.8–5).   The case when $\partial \rho / \partial t$ does not vanish will be taken up shortly.

[25] The solid-angle form 7.4–1, the Laplace rule 7.4–2, the circuital form 7.4–6, and the vector-potential form 7.6–5.

Let us calculate the circulation of **B** around a single loop (Stokesian path) in terms of current density across a surface bounded by the loop. We have, using (7.4–6) and Stokes' theorem,

$$\oint \mathbf{B} \cdot d\mathbf{s} = \mu_0 i = \mu_0 \int_S \mathbf{J} \cdot d\mathbf{S}$$

$$= \int_S \mathbf{\nabla} \times \mathbf{B} \cdot d\mathbf{S}$$

This result must hold for any loop and surface, which can only mean that the integrands are equal:

$$\mathbf{\nabla} \times \mathbf{B} = \mu_0 \mathbf{J} \qquad\qquad \text{MKS} \quad (7.8\text{–}1)$$

The fact that $\mathbf{\nabla} \cdot \mathbf{J} = 0$ is corroborated by noting as we did in section 7.7 that the divergence of the curl of any vector is identically zero.

In case $\partial\rho/\partial t$ is not everywhere negligible—for instance, if there is appreciable capacitance in the circuit and the current is not constant— eq. 7.8–1 must be modified, for in the equation as it stands, the divergence of one side is zero and that of the other is not. We shall attempt a modification by adding some quantity to **J** so that the divergence of the right side of the resulting equation will vanish and shall justify our results later by reference to experiment. This added term will have the dimensions of a current density, and we shall label it, temporarily, **J′**. Thus we require for **J′** that

$$\mathbf{\nabla} \cdot (\mathbf{J} + \mathbf{J}') = 0$$

or since $\mathbf{\nabla} \cdot \mathbf{J} = -\partial\rho/\partial t$,

$$\mathbf{\nabla} \cdot \mathbf{J}' = \frac{\partial\rho}{\partial t}$$

The quantity ρ in this equation is the density of free charge and does not include bound or polarization charge, which does not participate in the currents we are considering. Hence we have $\rho = \mathbf{\nabla} \cdot \mathbf{D}$ (eq. 3.5–4) so that

$$\mathbf{\nabla} \cdot \mathbf{J}' = \mathbf{\nabla} \cdot \frac{\partial\mathbf{D}}{\partial t}$$

The simplest value to take for **J′** is evidently $\partial\mathbf{D}/\partial t$, although it should be clear to the reader that the curl of any arbitrary vector could be added to $\partial\mathbf{D}/\partial t$. Maxwell's most important contribution to electromagnetic theory was his assumption that $\partial\mathbf{D}/\partial t$ by itself is the proper correction to add to eq. 7.8–1, and we shall make the same assumption. He called it the "displacement-current density" and this name is still used, although it does not represent a current in the ordinary sense.[26]

---

[26] $\partial\mathbf{D}/\partial t$ represents a current density not only because it is added to **J** in eq. 7.8–2 and has the correct dimensions, but also because if we write $\mathbf{D} = \epsilon_0\mathbf{E} + \mathbf{P}$ the term $\partial\mathbf{P}/\partial t$ represents the current due to the motion of charge when the polarization changes (problem 7.8b). The term $\epsilon_0 \partial\mathbf{E}/\partial t$ does not admit of such a direct interpretation. See Maxwell's Treatise, articles 607–610 (reference in footnote 15, p. 40).

Thus we have as Maxwell's differential-equation form of Ampère's law:

$$\nabla \times \mathbf{B} = \mu_0\left(\mathbf{J} + \frac{\partial \mathbf{D}}{\partial t}\right) \qquad \text{MKS} \quad (7.8\text{–}2a)$$

$$\nabla \times \mathbf{B} = \frac{4\pi \mathbf{J}}{c} + \frac{1}{c}\frac{\partial \mathbf{D}}{\partial t} \qquad \text{Gaussian} \quad (7.8\text{–}2b)$$

This equation has been verified by many successful applications involving electromagnetic radiation, a subject to which we shall later return.

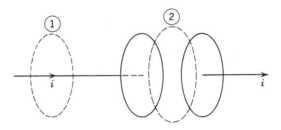

Fig. 7.8a.   Two paths 1 and 2 for the circulation of **B**.

We can use Stokes' theorem to write a circuital equation for the generalized case of non-closed current circuits:

$$\oint \mathbf{B} \cdot d\mathbf{s} = \int_S \nabla \times \mathbf{B} \cdot d\mathbf{S} = \mu_0 \int_S \left(\mathbf{J} + \frac{\partial \mathbf{D}}{\partial t}\right) \cdot d\mathbf{S}$$

or

$$\oint \mathbf{B} \cdot d\mathbf{s} = \mu_0\left(i + \frac{\partial \Phi_D}{\partial t}\right) \qquad \text{MKS} \quad (7.8\text{–}3)$$

where i is the total current through a surface S bounding the circuital path in question, and Φ_D is the flux of displacement through the same path.   (The path and surface must be stationary in time to allow $\partial/\partial t$ to be taken outside the integral sign.)

As an illustration of this equation, consider the simple case of a parallel-plate condenser during a charging-up period. The circulation of **B** around a path such as (1) in Figs. 7.8a and b can be calculated in terms of either a surface (S) passing through the wire or a distorted surface (S') passing between the condenser plates. Since $i = dQ/dt$ and $Q = \Phi_D$ inside the condenser, we see immediately that i through S and $d\Phi_D/dt$ through S' are equal. Similarly, the circulation of **B** around a path such as (2) that is just outside the electric field of the condenser should have the same value and of course it does.

Let us now use eq. 7.8–2 to calculate the magnetic induction produced by a single moving charge.   Let a charge q move with a speed $\mathbf{v}$ along a straight line.   At a fixed point $\mathscr{P}$ a distance r from q (Fig. 7.8c), $\mathbf{B}$ is by symmetry tangent to a circle $\mathscr{C}$ of radius r' coaxial with $\mathbf{v}$ and has the same magnitude everywhere on $\mathscr{C}$. Calculating the circulation on $\mathscr{C}$, we have $\oint B \cdot ds = 2\pi r' B$.

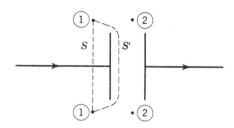

Fig. 7.8b. Two surfaces S and S' whose boundary is path 1 of Fig. 7.8a.

Taking any surface S bounded by $\mathscr{C}$ and not passing through or beyond the charge, we have $i = 0$ and Φ_D equal to q times the ratio of the solid angle subtended at q by $\mathscr{C}$, to 4π: $\Phi_D = (q/4\pi)2\pi(1 - \cos\theta) = \frac{1}{2}q\{1 - [z/(r'^2 + z^2)^{\frac{1}{2}}]\}$. Φ_D varies because z varies, with $dz/dt = -v$.

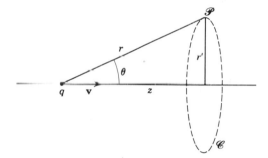

Fig. 7.8c. Calculation of $\mathbf{B}$ at $\mathscr{P}$ produced by a charge q moving with a velocity $\mathbf{v}$.

Hence

$$d\Phi_D/dt = \tfrac{1}{2}q\,\frac{d}{dz}\left(1 - \frac{z}{(r'^2 + z^2)^{\frac{1}{2}}}\right)\cdot\frac{dz}{dt} = \frac{qr'^2 v}{2(r'^2 + z^2)^{\frac{3}{2}}}$$

yielding from eq. 7.8–3

$$B = \frac{\mu_0 q r' v}{4\pi(r'^2 + z^2)^{\frac{3}{2}}}$$

which we may rewrite as

$$B = \frac{\mu_0}{4\pi}\frac{qv\sin\theta}{r^2} \quad \text{or} \quad \mathbf{B} = \frac{\mu_0 q}{4\pi}\frac{\mathbf{v}\times\mathbf{1}_r}{r^2} \quad \text{MKS} \quad (7.8\text{-}4)$$

The product $q\mathbf{v}$ is equivalent to an element of current $i\,\mathbf{dl}$ (see discussion on p. 259), so that eq. 7.8–4 is the same as formula 7.4–2, written for an isolated charge. The assumption of Maxwell concerning displacement currents is thus seen to remove the indefiniteness associated with the differential form of Ampère's law, and allows us to treat Laplace's rule, eq. 7.4–2, as being definite and correct.

It is important to note that a given current filament or isolated charge contributes only to one of the two terms in eqs. 7.8–2 and 7.8–3. We have seen how the circulation of $\mathbf{B}$ can be found from either term, depending on the location of the surface S. Simultaneous contributions from both terms can only occur when several current filaments or moving charges are involved.

The vector potential for an open current filament, or a distribution of such filaments, can be found using Laplace's rule as before (section 7.6). The difference caused by the non-closing of the current loops is simply that the paths for the integrals $i \int \mathbf{dl}/r$ are not closed but end where currents end. If the calculation of div $\mathbf{A}$ on p. 286 is repeated, the integral will not vanish. We will still have the variation of $1/r$ around the circuit, multiplied by $i = dq/dt$. The reader can show (problem 7.8e) that since $V = q/4\pi\epsilon_0 r$, the equation div $\mathbf{A} = 0$ is to be replaced by

$$\nabla \cdot \mathbf{A} + \mu_0\epsilon_0 \frac{\partial V}{\partial t} = 0 \qquad (7.8–5)$$

where the electrostatic potential V varies in time because of the open-circuit flow. Since $\mathbf{B}$ is still equal to **curl** $\mathbf{A}$, div $\mathbf{B}$ is still zero.

Problem 7.8a. Show explicitly how to deduce from the statement that $\mu_0 \int \mathbf{J} \cdot \mathbf{dS} = \int \nabla \times \mathbf{B} \cdot \mathbf{dS}$ for any surface, the statement that $\mu_0 \mathbf{J} = \nabla \times \mathbf{B}$.

Problem 7.8b. Show that in the expression $\partial\mathbf{D}/\partial t = \epsilon_0 \partial\mathbf{E}/\partial t + \partial\mathbf{P}/\partial t$, the term $\partial\mathbf{P}/\partial t$ represents a current associated with the motion of polarization charge as $\mathbf{P}$ varies.

Problem 7.8c. Verify the constants in eq. 7.8–2b.

Problem 7.8d. Suppose we add the curl of some vector $\mathbf{C}$, which is a function of x, y, z, and t, to $\partial\mathbf{D}/\partial t$ in the expression for $\mathbf{J}$. How will eqs. 7.8–2 and 7.8–4 be modified?

Problem 7.8e. Prove eq. 7.8–5.

Problem 7.8f. Verify that the induction inside and outside a long straight wire, given by eqs. 7.5–1 and 7.5–2, satisfies eq. 7.8–1.

7.9   Induced Electric Fields

We are now prepared to generalize the results of section 7.3 for magnetically induced emf's. We have studied the sources of $\mathbf{B}$ and deduced the conservation of flux, so that we can partially extend the induction law with this study as a basis.   The principal generalization, however, is to a type of induction which cannot be deduced from our previous results although it can be made plausible and can like them be described in terms of flux changes.   We shall also discuss the law of induction in terms of non-static electric fields.

The theorem of flux conservation allows us to rephrase the generator rule of section 7.3.   The rate at which flux is swept out by the motion of all parts of a closed circuit is equal to the rate of change of the flux through the circuit (if due regard is paid to signs), since by the conservation theorem, the latter is a definite number determined only by the location of the circuit.   Thus Φ in eq. 7.3–7 can be taken as the total flux through the circuit.   Once a positive direction has been assigned to Φ, there is a positive sign for the motion of current around the circuit according to the conventions of section 7.4.   The emf $\mathscr{E}$ in eq. 7.3–7 is taken as positive if a current produced solely by its action would run in the positive direction.   The reader can readily verify that the negative sign in this equation follows from the Lorentz force law and the above-mentioned right-hand rule for the signs of current and emf.

This negative sign is embodied in the theorem known as Lenz's law: the induced emf is always in such a direction as to produce a current and resulting flux change that counteracts the original flux change responsible for the induction.[27]   It will be seen later that this law is a particular case of the law of the conservation of energy.

Now let us ask what happens if the currents that are the sources of **B** move and the circuit whose emf is being studied is held still.   The result is clearly the same as if the circuit moved and the source remained still. In fact, all our experience in the laboratory and on moving vehicles, airplanes, etc., indicates that it is only relative motion that plays a role in electromagnetic phenomena.   We do not need to consider at this point any effects involving speeds comparable to the speed of light.

As a matter of fact, any large effects due to "absolute motion," with respect to the "fixed stars" or any other astronomical frame of reference, would show up most strongly in daily and annual variations or strongly directional variations associated with the earth's speed of 19 mi/sec around the sun and tangential velocity of 0.3 mi/sec at the equator due to rotation on its axis.   No such effects have ever been found.

This elementary fragment of the theory of relativity[28] leads us to some interesting consequences for the theory of electricity.   The first one is

---

[27] H. F. E. Lenz, *Ann. der Phys.*, **31**, 483 (1834).

[28] Properly called "Galilean" or "Newtonian" relativity rather than "Einsteinian." Einsteinian relativity is considered briefly in section 10.8.

that an emf may be produced in a stationary circuit by moving a source of magnetic induction.   Since the circuit is stationary, there can be no force of the type $q(\mathbf{v} \times \mathbf{B})$ on the charges in the wire, and the emf must involve a new electric field $\mathbf{E}$.   This $\mathbf{E}$ is to be calculated from the changing flux of $\mathbf{B}$; but before we calculate it, let us use its existence to complete our generalization of the law for induced emf's.

Faraday, in 1831, discovered by experiment that the emf induced in a closed circuit is given by the negative rate of change of flux through the circuit regardless of how this change is made—whether by motion of the circuit, motion of the source or change in strength of the source.[29]   Faraday's law is the law of induced emf's written with complete generality as

$$\mathscr{E} = -\frac{d\Phi}{dt} \qquad \text{MKS} \quad (7.9\text{–}1a)$$

$$\mathscr{E} = -\frac{1}{c}\frac{d\Phi}{dt} \qquad \text{Gaussian} \quad (7.9\text{–}1b)$$

The motional part of the emf can be deduced as above, but the emf produced in one circuit by changing the current in another cannot.   It might seem that the change of $\mathbf{B}$ in and around a circuit caused by changing the current in a source coil could be simulated by some complicated type of motion of the source, and there are some cases in which this is so, but there are cases in which it is clearly impossible.

For instance, we showed in section 7.5 that the magnetic fields outside a toroid and an infinite solenoid are everywhere zero.   Yet if a wire is looped around either of these, an emf will be induced when the current in the toroid or solenoid is changed.   Since there is at no time any induction $\mathbf{B}$ at any point on the wire loop, the emf could not be found by relative motion considerations and the generator rule of section 7.3.   How can magnetic flux that never touches a wire have an effect on the charges in it?

This question can be properly answered if we now consider the induced electric field.   Let us first take up a case of emf induced by relative motion and apply our elementary relativity to one of the charges in the wire. When the source of magnetic field is stationary and the charge moves with velocity $\mathbf{v}$, we have for the force on the charge

$$F = q(\mathbf{E}' + \mathbf{v} \times \mathbf{B})$$

where $\mathbf{E}'$ represents whatever electrostatic field may be present.   Now if we observe the force on the charge while we ourselves move with it, so that we observe q to be at rest and the source to move with velocity $-\mathbf{v}$,

[29] M. Faraday, *Experimental Researches in Electricity*, Bernard Quaritch, London, 1839, Vol. I, Series I, §§ 1–59.

we will have only an electric force, although it will clearly be the same magnitude and direction of force as before, since **F** is measured by $m\mathbf{a}$ and an acceleration is unchanged by addition of a constant velocity.   Let us write now $$\mathbf{F} = q\mathbf{E}$$ so that we have a new value for the electric field strength[30]

$$\mathbf{E} = \mathbf{E}' + \mathbf{v} \times \mathbf{B}$$

A moving source of magnetic field produces an electric field.   Since the emf will be the same, being defined as $\oint(\mathbf{F}/q) \cdot \mathbf{dl}$, we must have $\oint\mathbf{E} \cdot \mathbf{dl} = \oint\mathbf{v} \times \mathbf{B} \cdot \mathbf{dl} = -d\Phi/dt$.   This new electric field is not derivable from a potential, since its circulation does not vanish, so that it cannot be called an *electrostatic* field (see section 1.8).   To carry the matter a bit further, we may note that since the wire containing q is at rest, we do not need it. The product $q\mathbf{E}$ is always the force that *would* be exerted *if* a charge q were put at the point in question (and did not disturb the surroundings). Hence we see that everywhere in the neighborhood of a moving source of **B** there is an induced field **E**.

By use of Stokes' theorem, in a similar fashion to its use in sections 1.8 and 7.8, we can derive a differential equation for **E**.   Around any closed path we have

$$\mathcal{E} = \oint \mathbf{E} \cdot \mathbf{dl} = \int_S \mathbf{\nabla} \times \mathbf{E} \cdot \mathbf{dS} = -\frac{d\Phi}{dt} = -\frac{d}{dt} \int_S \mathbf{B} \cdot \mathbf{dS}$$

and again the integrands of the surface integrals must be equal, yielding

$$\mathbf{\nabla} \times \mathbf{E} = -\frac{\partial \mathbf{B}}{\partial t} \qquad \text{MKS} \quad (7.9\text{-}2a)$$

$$\mathbf{\nabla} \times \mathbf{E} = -\frac{1}{c}\frac{\partial \mathbf{B}}{\partial t} \qquad \text{Gaussian} \quad (7.9\text{-}2b)$$

This equation is the last of Maxwell's equations to be developed—the others being eqs. 1.5–1, 7.7–1, and 7.8–2.   They will be considered together in Chapter 10.

We have shown that **B** and **E** have a particularly intimate relationship beyond that expressed by their both acting on charges and being produced by charges.   One seems to turn into the other when we change our velocity relative to the system under observation.   Another instance of this relationship is given by considering the magnetic field produced by a moving charge.   If we consider the Coulomb law for the field of a stationary charge

$$\mathbf{E} = \frac{q}{4\pi\epsilon_0}\frac{\mathbf{1}_r}{r^2} \qquad \text{MKS} \quad (7.9\text{-}3)$$

---

[30] Compare with eq. 7.3–3 where we consider a conductor to be present but do not use Galilean relativity.

we see that eq. 7.8–4 can be written

$$\mathbf{B} = \mu_0\epsilon_0\mathbf{v} \times \mathbf{E} \qquad\qquad \text{MKS} \quad (7.9\text{–}4)$$

where $\mathbf{E}$ and $\mathbf{B}$ are both measured at the same point. We can consider eq. 7.9–4 to apply to the fields produced by a collection of charges with a common velocity $\mathbf{v}$ and thus assert that *a moving source of electric field produces a magnetic field.* This statement is, of course, a partial statement of Ampère's law.

Let us take a numerical example. Consider a generator with an induction $\mathbf{B}$ of 0.1 weber/m^2, an armature radius of 0.1 m, and a revolution rate of 1800 rpm or 30 rps. The speed of one of the armature wires will then be $30(2\pi)(0.1) = 19$ m/sec and the force per unit charge will then be $vB = 1.9$ newtons/coulomb. If the magnet rotates instead and the armature is stationary, the induced electric field will then be 1.9 v/m.

Now suppose that we have an electrostatic field of 1.9 v/m ·and that we move with respect to its source with a velocity of 19 m/sec at right angles to $\mathbf{E}$. By eq. 7.9–4, the induction will be $\mu_0\epsilon_0 vE = (4\pi \times 10^{-7})$ $(4\pi \times 9 \times 10^9)^{-1}(19)(1.9) = 36.1/(9 \times 10^{16}) = 4 \times 10^{-16}$ weber/m^2, an extremely small value. Sizable values of B only arise from currents in metallic conductors; in this case, the enormous electrostatic field produced by the moving charges is cancelled by that of stationary charges of opposite sign.

On the other hand, a single moving charge is a moving source of $\mathbf{B}$ and an *induced* electric field should also be present. This in turn may be expected to give rise to another component of $\mathbf{B}$ and so on. In other words, the fields of a moving charge are rather complicated. As the example above indicates, eqs. 7.9–3 and 7.9–4 are adequate for all small velocities. More explicitly, let us consider a velocity of 1 m/sec. Then the order of magnitude of the first B we calculate is $1/(9 \times 10^{16})$ times the initial E; the second E is about the same as the first B; the second B is $1/(9 \times 10^{16})$ times the second E and so on. The successive components decrease rapidly for speeds of the order of 1 m/sec. Only for speeds of the order of $1/(\mu_0\epsilon_0)^{\frac{1}{2}} = (9 \times 10^{16})^{\frac{1}{2}} = 3 \times 10^8$ m/sec are all the successive components of importance. This speed is the speed of light, so we can say that when charged particles move with speeds comparable with that of light, the formulas 7.9–3 and 7.9–4 are not accurate, but that for much lower speeds such as are ordinarily encountered, the errors involved in their use are negligible. For calculation at high velocities, other procedures must be used and are considered in section 10.8.

We still have one problem to solve. How do we calculate the induced electric field in cases in which relative motion considerations do not work?

We make use for this purpose of eq. 7.7–4

$$\Phi = \int_S \mathbf{B} \cdot \mathbf{dS} = \oint_{\text{boundary of } S} \mathbf{A} \cdot \mathbf{dl}$$

This equation is quite general.   It comes from the general relation $\mathbf{B} =$ **curl A** and the use of Stokes' theorem, and holds when the currents are variable.[31]   Faraday's law then reads, for fixed circuits,

$$\mathcal{E} = \oint \mathbf{E} \cdot \mathbf{dl} = -\frac{\partial \Phi}{\partial t} = -\oint \frac{\partial \mathbf{A}}{\partial t} \cdot \mathbf{dl}$$

so that

$$\oint \left(\mathbf{E} + \frac{\partial \mathbf{A}}{\partial t} \right) \cdot \mathbf{dl} = 0$$

for any closed path.   Now the vanishing of this integral implies, according to the arguments used in section 1.8, the existence of a potential V whose negative gradient gives the sum $\mathbf{E} + \partial \mathbf{A}/\partial t$.   Thus

$$\mathbf{E} + \frac{\partial \mathbf{A}}{\partial t} = -\nabla V$$

or

$$\mathbf{E} = -\frac{\partial \mathbf{A}}{\partial t} - \nabla V \qquad\qquad \text{MKS} \quad (7.9\text{–}5a)$$

$$\mathbf{E} = -\frac{1}{c} \frac{\partial \mathbf{A}}{\partial t} - \nabla V \qquad\qquad \text{Gaussian} \quad (7.9\text{–}5b)$$

The quantity $-\nabla V$ appears to represent any electrostatic field that is present. To test whether this is so, let us calculate $\nabla \cdot \mathbf{E}$ using eq. 7.8–5:

$$\nabla \cdot \mathbf{E} = -\frac{\partial}{\partial t} (\nabla \cdot \mathbf{A}) - \nabla^2 V = \mu_0 \epsilon_0 \frac{\partial^2 V}{\partial t^2} - \nabla^2 V \qquad (7.9\text{–}6)$$

If $-\nabla V$ is the electrostatic field, we must have $-\nabla^2 V = \rho/\epsilon_0$, by eq. 1.10–1, which means that $\nabla \cdot \mathbf{E}$ cannot equal ρ/ϵ_0.   This in turn would mean that the electric field of magnetic origin has a non-vanishing divergence even though the field is not produced by charge density.   We cannot settle the question without a further assumption (again to be justified in Chapter 10), which is that $\nabla \cdot \mathbf{E}$ is always equal to ρ/ϵ_0.   This means that $-\nabla V$ includes some magnetically induced field along with the electrostatic field.

However, this last effect is small if the time variations are slow enough. Since $\mu_0 \epsilon_0 = 1/c^2$, we can compare the time and space derivatives in eq. 7.9–6 by first considering a variation of V with respect to ct and then with respect to x. If time variations of appreciable amount only occur during times long compared to r/c where r is the maximum distance over which V is of interest, we can take

---

[31] The application of our equations to cases of *rapidly* varying currents will be discussed in Chapter 10.

$\Delta(ct)$ as much larger than r and Δx as much smaller than r, so that $\partial V/\partial(ct)$ is much less than $\partial V/\partial x$. The second time derivatives will be even smaller in comparison to $\nabla^2 V$. We shall refer to the induced part of ∇V as a radiation term.

For the present we shall assume that ∇V represents any electrostatic field present and omit its consideration here. Except for radiation terms, the induced electric field produced by motion and/or by change of a current is given by

$$\mathbf{E} = -\frac{\partial \mathbf{A}}{\partial t} \qquad\qquad \text{MKS} \quad (7.9\text{-}7a)$$

$$\mathbf{E} = -\frac{1}{c}\frac{\partial \mathbf{A}}{\partial t} \qquad\qquad \text{Gaussian} \quad (7.9\text{-}7b)$$

This formula expresses Faraday's law for fixed circuits in terms of fields and the directly calculable vector potential $\mathbf{A}$ and is the solution of our problem. In fact, eq. 7.9–7 is seen to satisfy eq. 7.9–2. Problem 7.9b involves the calculation of the emf induced in a wire surrounding an infinite solenoid and illustrates our solution of the paradox of the induced emf when $\mathbf{B}$ at the wire is always zero. It remains true that the use of the flux of induction is the easiest way to calculate the emf (cf. problem 7.9e), but a detailed mental picture of the production of this emf is the clearest if the producing current is considered to generate a vector potential $\mathbf{A}$ which acts directly on the charges in the wire through the field of eq. 7.9–7.

Lines of $\mathbf{E}$ as given by eq. 7.9–7 can have no ends if ρ is zero. They will not however be closed except in cases of ideal symmetry (see footnote 21 on p. 296). We have been considering here only fixed circuits. It is possible to write formulas for fields in moving circuits taken with respect to observers moving with the velocities of the various parts of the circuits. Such formulas are sometimes useful but are unnecessarily complicated for our purposes. A similar notion that is sometimes used but is misleading and occasionally quite wrong is that of considering the fields *themselves* as moving. This idea should by now appear absurd to the reader, for it is not forces that move, but objects (e.g., charges) under the influence of the forces. The reader will be on safest ground if he always considers first some convenient "frame of reference"—e.g., the laboratory—with respect to which he can define $\mathbf{E}$ and $\mathbf{B}$ and measure velocities of the various charges.

Problem 7.9a. Repeat the calculations of $\mathbf{B}$ and $\mathbf{E}$ in the numerical example in the text involving a generator, using Gaussian units.

Problem 7.9b. Suppose the current in the infinite solenoid whose vector potential is given in eq. 7.6–16 varies with the time in accordance with $i = f(t)$.

Calculate the emf induced in a loop of wire that (a) has n turns inside the solenoid and (b) surrounds the solenoid n times.

Problem 7.9c.   The earth's magnetic induction at a certain place is 0.500 gauss, directed downward in a north-south vertical plane, at an angle of 69° with the horizontal.   A square coil of 100 turns that is 35 cm on each side is rotated about a vertical axis that bisects two opposite sides of the coil.   If the coil turns at 15 revolutions per second, write the induced emf as a function of the time.

Problem 7.9d.   Show that Lenz's law can be used to determine the sense of circulation of a charged particle moving normally to a magnetic field **B**.

Problem 7.9e.   Show that the radiation term in ∇V in eq. 7.9–5 cannot influence any emf calculations.

7.10   Mutual Inductance

In this section, we wish to consider the calculation of emf's induced by one circuit in another and of the currents resulting from them.   It will be convenient to take the second aspect first.

Consider a circuit containing a loop of wire in a variable magnetic field and a series resistor R which for definiteness we shall take to be outside the field, as in the case of the generator circuit of section 7.3. Let the resistance of the loop itself be r, so that $R + r$ is the total resistance in the circuit.   Let us assume that a current i flows in the circuit at a given instant when the rate of change of flux is $d\Phi/dt$ and that the time constant of the distributed capacitance of the circuit is small enough that i is constant at any instant throughout the circuit, even though its magnitude may vary with time.   For simplicity, we shall consider the loop to be at rest, but similar considerations to those in section 7.3 will apply if all or part of it is in motion.

There must be a PD across R of magnitude $V = iR$, produced by an ordinary electrostatic field.   In the wire of the loop there will be two fields acting, the electrostatic one $\mathbf{E}_{stat}$ just mentioned and the field $\mathbf{E} = -\partial \mathbf{A}/\partial t$ associated with the magnetic field.   The two fields together act to make the current flow, so that Ohm's law becomes for the loop

$$\int_a^b \left(\mathbf{E}_{stat} - \frac{\partial \mathbf{A}}{\partial t} \right) \cdot \mathbf{dl} = ir$$

where a and b represent the connection points between the loop and the external resistor R.   The integral $\int_a^b \mathbf{E}_{stat} \cdot \mathbf{dl}$ is equal to $-\int_b^a \mathbf{E}_{stat} \cdot \mathbf{dl}$ taken over R, which is $-V = -iR$.   The integral of $-\partial \mathbf{A}/\partial t$, on the other hand, is the induced emf $\mathscr{E}$, so that we have

$$-\int_a^b \frac{\partial \mathbf{A}}{\partial t} \cdot \mathbf{dl} = \mathscr{E} = V + ir = i(r + R) \qquad (7.10–1)$$

This equation is exactly similar to that for a cell with internal and external resistances.

If an external emf $\mathscr{E}'$, say that of a chemical cell, is present in the circuit, then V for the external part of the circuit will be $iR - \mathscr{E}'$, and we have as to be expected

$$\mathscr{E} + \mathscr{E}' = i(r + R) \tag{7.10-2}$$

Now let us consider the induction of an emf in one circuit by a current in another. The flux Φ_{12} through circuit 1 produced by circuit 2 may be written in terms of the mutual inductance (cf. section 7.7):

$$\Phi_{12} = M_{12}i_2 \tag{7.10-3}$$

where M_{12} is given in eq. 7.7–10.

Then the emf $\mathscr{E}_{12} = -d\Phi_{12}/dt$ becomes

$$\mathscr{E}_{12} = -d(M_{12}i_2)/dt \tag{7.10-4a}$$

and if both circuits are fixed in position

$$\mathscr{E}_{12} = -M_{12}\,di_2/dt \tag{7.10-4b}$$

Equation 7.10–4b may be taken as an alternative definition of the mutual inductance M_{12}. The complete symmetry of eq. 7.7–10 shows that the emf $\mathscr{E}_{21}$ induced in circuit 2 by a changing current in circuit 1, when the circuits do not move, is given by

$$\mathscr{E}_{21} = -M_{21}\,di_1/dt = -M_{12}\,di_1/dt \tag{7.10-5}$$

The mutual inductance between two circuits is the same, regardless of which circuit is considered to be the inducing agent and which the circuit acted upon.

The calculation of mutual inductance is quite complicated, even in cases of considerable symmetry. We shall have to restrict ourselves here to three practical applications and one case that illustrates the computational difficulty. The formula 7.7–10 is valuable for showing the symmetry of M_{12} and M_{21}, but rather than start with this formula, we shall use previous calculations of **B** and the formula $\Phi = \int\mathbf{B} \cdot d\mathbf{S}$.

Consider first a long solenoid of cross-sectional area S_1 and n_{l1} turns per meter, with a short secondary winding on its outside containing n_{l2} turns per meter, of area S_2 and length l_2 (Fig. 7.10a). If we were to assume unit current in the secondary and to calculate the flux linking the primary, we would have a complicated calculation, for the secondary field will look like Fig. 7.7b, and different amounts of flux will link each different turn of the primary. (The sum of the amounts of flux linking each turn of a coil is called the "flux linkage" in that coil.) On the other hand, if the primary is long and the secondary is located far from the ends of the primary, a unit current in the latter will produce a uniform field through the secondary, and the flux linkage will be easy to calculate. In fact, the flux in the primary when it carries i_1 amperes will be $\mu_0 i_1 n_{l1} S$, by eq. 7.5–9a. Each turn of the secondary will be linked by this flux,

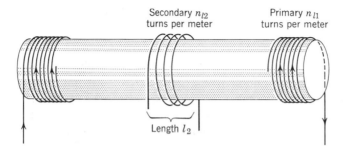

Fig. 7.10a.   A solenoid with a secondary winding for mutual inductance.

so that the total flux linkage will be $n_{l2} l_2 \mu_0 i_1 n_{l1} S_1$. Setting $n_{l2} l_2 = N_2$, the mutual inductance of a long solenoid and a short secondary coil outside it far from its ends is

$$M_{12} = \mu_0 n_{l1} N_2 S_1 \qquad\text{MKS} \quad (7.10\text{–}6)$$

Note that the formula involves the turns per unit length and the cross section of the long inside coil and the total number of turns only of the short outside coil.

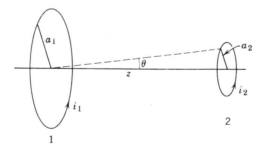

Fig. 7.10b.   Illustrating M_{12} between large and small coaxial coils.

As a second example, consider two circular loops of wire with a common axis as in Fig. 7.10b. We shall let one of the loops be small enough that the variation of the field produced by the other over its area is negligible. Let the large circle have a radius a_1, the small one have radius a_2, their distance apart be z, and the positive directions for both be defined in the same sense.

By eq. 7.5–7, the field of loop 1 at the center of coil 2 is

$$B = B_z = \frac{\mu_0 i_1 a_1{}^2}{2(a_1{}^2 + z^2)^{\frac{3}{2}}}$$

Since a_2 is small enough, we may assume B_z to have a constant value over the area $\pi a_2{}^2$ of coil 2, so that the mutual inductance is

$$M_{12} = \frac{\pi \mu_0 a_1{}^2 a_2{}^2}{2(a_1{}^2 + z^2)^{\frac{3}{2}}} \qquad \text{MKS} \quad (7.10\text{–}7)$$

The criterion for a_2 being small may be approximately obtained by noting that Ω subtended by loop 1 at a point on the circumference of loop 2 differs from that subtended by the center of loop 2 by roughly a factor $\cos \theta$ because of inclination, and another factor of $\cos^2 \theta$, because the distance to the center of loop 1 increases by $1/\cos \theta$ (as long as z is not too small compared with a_1). Since $\cos^3 \theta \simeq 1 - 3\theta^2/2$ and $\theta \simeq a_2/z$, Ω will vary by less than 1 % if $3\theta^2/2 < 1/100$ or $a_2/z \lessapprox \frac{1}{12}$.

If a_1 is small ($a_1/z < \frac{1}{12}$, for instance) we can find M_{12} by finding the flux through loop 1 produced by a unit current in loop 2.   The result is

$$M_{12} = \frac{\pi \mu_0 a_1{}^2 a_2{}^2}{2(a_2{}^2 + z^2)^{\frac{3}{2}}}$$

This latter formula differs from eq. 7.10–7 in assuming a_1 small instead of a_2. If both a_1 and a_2 are sufficiently small compared to z, the two formulas for M_{12} give the symmetrical result

$$M_{12} = \frac{\pi \mu_0 a_1{}^2 a_2{}^2}{2z^3} \qquad \text{MKS} \quad (7.10\text{–}8)$$

A method for deriving eq. 7.10–7 by calculating the flux through a large loop 1 produced by a small loop 2 is considered in problem 8.2a. If loop 1 has N_1 closely wound turns and loop 2 N_2 turns, formulas 7.10–7 and 7.10–8 are to be multiplied by $N_1 N_2$.

Finally, note that M_{12} becomes negative if the positive senses of the two coils are oppositely defined. Negative values of mutual inductance are frequently required for consistency in the analysis of the circuits associated with the coils.

The Absolute Measurement of Resistance.   As a third example, consider a small rotatable circular coil of N_2 turns and mean radius a_2 located at the center of a pair of Helmholtz coils of N_1 turns each, with mean radius a_1, with an angle θ between the two axes (problem 7.5f and Fig. 7.10c). To a good approximation the flux through coil 2 will be given by using the result of problem 7.5f, along with the area of coil 2 and $\cos \theta$:

$$M_{12} = \frac{8 \pi \mu_0 N_1 N_2 a_2{}^2 \cos \theta}{5^{\frac{3}{2}} a_1} \qquad \text{MKS} \quad (7.10\text{–}9)$$

This arrangement can be used to measure a resistance in terms of length and time.   Suppose that a current i_1 is passed through the Helmholtz pair and also through a series resistor R.   Let the inner coil be rotated at constant angular velocity ω, so that $\cos\theta = \cos\omega t$.   Then suppose that an intermittent contact arrangement allows a connection to be made to coil 2 when the induced emf is a maximum.   Since $\mathscr{E} = -(d/dt)(M_{12}i_1)$, we have

$$\mathscr{E} = \frac{8\pi\mu_0 N_1 N_2 a_2{}^2}{5^{\frac{3}{2}}a_1}\, i_1\omega\,\sin\omega t$$

and $\mathscr{E}$ will have its greatest value $\mathscr{E}_{max}$ when $\sin\omega t = 1$ or $\theta = 90°$, $450°$, etc.   If we balance the drop on the resistor R against $\mathscr{E}_{max}$, we can

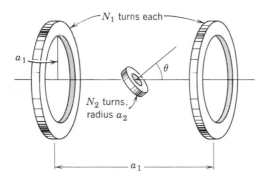

Fig. 7.10c.   A variable mutual inductance used in absolute resistance measurements.

get a null result, detectable as usual with a galvanometer, when $i_1 R = \mathscr{E}_{max}$ or

$$R = \frac{8\pi\mu_0 N_1 N_2 a_2{}^2\omega}{5^{\frac{3}{2}}a_1} \qquad\qquad \text{MKS}\quad (7.10\text{--}10a)$$

$$= \frac{32\pi^2 N_1 N_2 a_2{}^2\omega}{5^{\frac{3}{2}}c^2 a_1} \qquad\qquad \text{Gaussian}\quad (7.10\text{--}10b)$$

which formulas only involve length and time measurements.   In fact, if μ_0 is taken to be dimensionless, we can write the dimensions of ohms as joule-seconds/coulomb^2 = joules/ampere^2-second = joules/newton-second = meters/second in conformity with eq. 7.10–10a.   Otherwise we have volts/ampere = (webers/second)/(coulombs/second) = webers/coulomb. This type of resistance measurement is commonly called "absolute."   (A more accurate method of measuring a resistance is to compare it with the impedance of a known inductance at a known frequency, using an a-c bridge (section 9.6).)

   The Absolute Measurement of Current.   The mutual inductance of two coaxial circular loops (solid and dashed circles in Fig. 7.6c) can be written from eq. 7.6–15, since $A = A_\phi$ is a constant around a circle of radius R centered on the axis,

$$M_{12} = 2\pi R A_\phi/i = \mu_0 a R \int_0^\pi \frac{\cos \phi \, d\phi}{(z^2 + a^2 + R^2 - 2aR \cos \phi)^{\frac{3}{2}}} \qquad (7.10\text{–}11)$$

(cf. problem 7.6d).

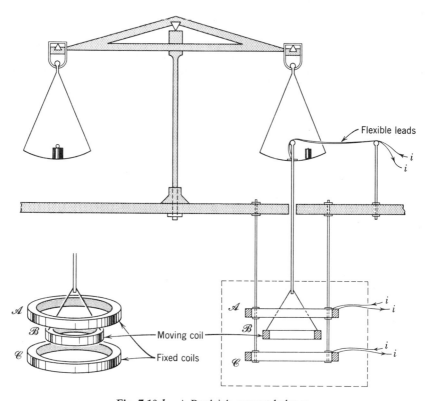

Fig. 7.10d.   A Rayleigh current balance.

We have shown in section 7.7 that the force between two circuits can be calculated from the mutual inductance. We have, in fact,

$$F_\xi = -\frac{\partial U'}{\partial \xi} \qquad (7.10\text{–}12)$$

where F_ξ is the force in the direction of an arbitrary displacement $\Delta \xi$, and U' is given by

$$U' = -M_{12} i_1 i_2 \qquad (7.10\text{–}13)$$

The best way of calibrating an ammeter directly in terms of amperes—i.e., the best way of making an absolute current calibration—is by means of a current balance.   Figure 7.10*d* shows an arrangement for measuring the force exerted on a movable coil between two fixed ones.   Coil $\mathscr{B}$ is suspended from the arm of a sensitive balance, between two fixed coils $\mathscr{A}$ and $\mathscr{C}$.   The same current i is made to flow through all three coils. The current leads from coil $\mathscr{B}$ must be carefully brought out through flexible leads so as not to disturb the balance, and they must be properly twisted so as not to affect the mutual inductance.   If i runs in the same direction in $\mathscr{B}$ and $\mathscr{C}$, and in the opposite direction in $\mathscr{A}$, $\mathscr{C}$ will attract $\mathscr{B}$, and $\mathscr{A}$ will repel $\mathscr{B}$.

The resultant force on $\mathscr{B}$ will be the sum of two.   In fact, $\mathscr{A}$ and $\mathscr{C}$ can be treated as parts of the same coil, so that the force can be written

$$F = i^2 \frac{dM_{12}}{dz}$$

where z is measured downward.   A precise calculation of M_{12}, then, will allow a standard ammeter to be constructed in the form of a current balance.   The details of such calculations are quite involved; the use of eq. 7.10–11 would give only a first approximation, since the windings on each coil are spaced out.   The reader is referred elsewhere for further details.[32]

Problem 7.10a.   Calculate the induced emf from the Lorentz force law for a moving loop of wire, when **E** includes magnetically induced electric fields, and show explicitly, by considering the rule for the time derivative of an integral over a region with a moving boundary, that $\mathscr{E} = -d\Phi/dt$.

Problem 7.10b.   A long solenoid which has 15 turns per centimeter and a radius of 8 cm has a short secondary winding of 50 turns that has (*a*) a radius of 10 cm and (*b*) a radius of 5 cm.   Find the mutual inductance in each case.

Problem 7.10c.   Calculate M_{12} from eq. 7.10–11 for the case that z is much larger than either a or R, by using three terms in the binomial expansion of $[1 + (a^2 + R^2 - 2aR \cos \phi)/z^2]^{-\frac{1}{2}}$, and use the result to check eq. 7.10–7 together with the remarks on the criterion for a_2 being small.

Problem 7.10d.   Find the force exerted by the small coil in Fig. 7.10*b* on the large one.

---

[32] For measurements of the absolute ampere, see R. W. Curtis, R. L. Driscoll, and C. L. Critchfield, *Jour. Res. Nat. Bur. Stds.*, **28**, 133 (1942) and H. L. Curtis, R. W. Curtis, and C. L. Critchfield, *Jour. Res. Nat. Bur. Stds.*, **22**, 485 (1939).   For the absolute ohm, see H. L. Curtis, C. Moon, and C. M. Sparks, *Jour. Res. Nat. Bur. Stds.*, **21**, 375 (1938) and **16**, 1, (1936), and J. L. Thomas, C. Peterson, I. L. Cooter, and F. R. Kotter, *Jour. Res. Nat. Bur. Stds.*, **43**, 291 (1949).   A review of both measurements is given by H. L. Curtis, *Jour. Res. Nat. Bur. Stds.*, **33**, 235 (1944).   For inductance calculations in general, see E. B. Rose and F. W. Grover, *Bull. U.S. Bur. Stds.*, **8**, 1 (1912) and *Nat. Bur. Stds. Circular* 74.

7.11   Self-inductance

Any closed circuit will be linked by a magnetic flux produced by its own current in addition to any flux produced by neighboring circuits. This flux will be proportional to the current, so that we can write

$$\Phi = Li \qquad (7.11\text{-}1)$$

where L is the constant of proportionality, known as the *self-inductance*, or more briefly, as the inductance.

If there are several loops in the circuit, as in a solenoid, Φ is taken to mean the total flux linkage or the sum of the fluxes through each loop. It is, of course, the quantity whose time derivative gives the emf. By Lenz's law, the emf must be written with a negative sign if current and emf are both assigned the same positive direction. Thus we have

$$\mathscr{E} = -L\frac{di}{dt} \qquad (7.11\text{-}2)$$

which because of the minus sign is often called a "back emf." Self-inductance, like mutual inductance, is measured in henries.

When an external source of emf $\mathscr{E}'$ is used to establish current in a circuit containing, say, a *total* resistance R and an inductance L, we can write as we did in the last section

$$\mathscr{E} + \mathscr{E}' = iR$$

or

$$\mathscr{E}' = iR - \mathscr{E} = iR + L\frac{di}{dt} \qquad (7.11\text{-}3)$$

We may thus treat the induced emf as a potential drop with the positive sign.

Any circuit whatsoever has inductance. Before proceeding to two simplified but nevertheless still complicated calculations of L, let us consider its effect in retarding the establishment of a current. We shall only consider circuits in which this inductive effect is more influential than the effect of the distributed capacitance considered in section 5.3 so that we can neglect the latter. A typical circuit is conventionally represented as in Fig. 7.11a, where the symbol $\curvearrowright\!\!\text{OOOO}\!\!\curvearrowleft$ refers to the entire inductance of the circuit, and the resistance is correspondingly the total resistance. From eq. 7.11–3 we see that we may treat these two distributed quantities as if they were two separate series elements, since the potential drops are seen to be additive. Such separated elements are called "lumped" elements. In practical circuits, large values of L and R are generally physically lumped, at least in an approximate sense, whereas small values appear distributed throughout.   In ignoring capacitive effects in eq. 7.11–3 we are assuming that i is the same throughout the circuit at any given instant.

Let us now imagine that at time $t = 0$ the switch K of Fig. 7.11a is closed.   The current cannot increase with infinite rapidity since $L \, di/dt$ must be finite.   Therefore we can assume that $i = 0$ at $t = 0$ and that after the initial instant, eq. 7.11–3 must hold.   This equation is mathematically identical with eq. 5.3–5 if we replace Q by i, $1/C$ by R, and R

Fig. 7.11a.   Circuit with self-inductance.

by L.   Hence we can use the solution eq. 5.3–6 for the charging of a condenser to express the rise of current in a self-inductive circuit.   The result is

$$i = \frac{\mathscr{E}'}{R} \left(1 - e^{-(R/L)t}\right) \qquad\qquad (7.11\text{–}4)$$

The current rises in accordance with a curve like that of Fig. 5.3f where now for the time constant we have L/R instead of RC.

For a typical battery circuit without any especially inductive elements in it, L might be of the order of 10^{-6} henry.   If R were as low as 1 ohm, the time constant would be 10^{-6} sec, so that the current will be rapidly established.   If the capacitance is also important, the equations become more complicated, and must be referred to a later chapter (section 9.8).

When K is opened, a very large negative di/dt will ensue.   If the resulting back emf is large enough (as it frequently is), an arc will be struck across the switch terminals as they are separated, and the current will flow through this arc for a short time.   On the other hand, if the key is a rapidly opening kind, for example a toggle or spring-operated switch, or if it is operated in a vacuum so that no arcing can start, the large back emf will lead to the building up of a substantial charge on the condenser formed by the two switch contacts.   In either case, the current will not die out instantaneously but rather in a complicated way which we shall not consider further here (a modified way of turning off the current is considered in the next section).

Calculations of L.   The arguments that led to the mutual-inductance formula 7.7–10 can be seen to give a similar value for L, differing only in that the double integral must be taken twice around the single circuit under consideration.   However, a serious difficulty arises.   The r in the denominator of the integrand becomes zero when dl_1 and dl_2 coincide. The integral turns out on examination to become infinite because of this fact.   This can be seen from eq. 7.6–12 for the vector potential of two long parallel wires.   The magnitude of **A** becomes infinite at the center of one wire and so does that of **J**, if we imagine the wire to be an infinitely thin current filament in order to make the equation apply to points as close as we please to its center.

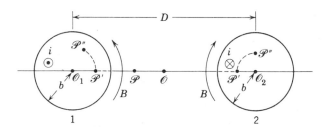

Fig. 7.11b.   Calculation of L for two parallel wires.

We can describe this result by saying that our theory does not allow us to calculate the inductive effect of a single filament on itself but only that of the various filaments of a current on each other.   Self-inductance is thus seen to be a special case of mutual inductance.   Any further discussion of this difficulty would involve discussing the action of the individual slowly accelerated electrons on each other and is beyond the scope of this book.

If we take into account the current distribution in a wire, we find that the infinity referred to above reduces to a small and sometimes quite insignificant contribution.   We shall illustrate with the case of two long parallel circular wires of equal radius b.   In order to avoid end effects, we shall calculate the flux linking a unit length of the circuit far from the ends of the wires.   The two wires are shown in cross section in Fig. 7.11b. We assume here that the current is uniformly distributed throughout the wire and shall consider later the extent to which this assumption is justified.

Let us calculate the flux per unit length passing between the wires by an integral of B along a line joining their centers.   Because of symmetry, we can calculate twice the flux on one side of the figure.   In terms of the distance r from $\mathscr{O}_1$, the field produced by wire 1 is given inside the wire by eq. 7.5–2

$$B_1 = \frac{\mu_0 i r}{2\pi b^2} \qquad\qquad r \leqslant b$$

and outside the wire by eq. 7.5–1a

$$B_1 = \frac{\mu_0 i}{2\pi r} \qquad\qquad r \geqslant b$$

The field of wire 2 may be written

$$B_2 = \frac{\mu_0 i}{2\pi(D - r)} \qquad\qquad r \leqslant D - b$$

Now it will be observed that the flux linking any particular current filament, like that shown entering and leaving the figure at the point pairs $\mathscr{P}'$, is generally not the same as for other filaments.   However, if the wires are small, so that $b \ll D$, the amount of flux of wire 2 that passes inside wire 1 will be of insignificant amount.   Its average effect on all the filaments in wire 1 can with small error be calculated by integrating from $\mathscr{O}_1$ to $\mathscr{O}$, yielding (note that dS is replaced by dr because we deal with unit length only)

$$\Phi_2 = \int_0^{D/2} \frac{\mu_0 i\, dr}{2\pi(D - r)} = \frac{\mu_0 i}{2\pi} \ln \frac{D}{(D/2)} = \frac{\mu_0 i}{2\pi} \ln 2$$

On the other hand, the contribution of B_1 to the flux will vary considerably over the wire.   It will be necessary to calculate it for arbitrary points, like $\mathscr{P}''$ in the figure and then make a proper average, which is done by considering that the average power is what can be readily measured in such a circuit.   Hence we write

$$\mathscr{E}_{av} i = \int_S \mathscr{E} J\, dS \qquad\qquad (7.11\text{–}5)$$

where S is the cross-sectional area of the wire and $\mathscr{E}$ and J are the emf and current density respectively at a variable point in that cross section.

The contribution to Φ_1 from B_1 outside the wire is the same for all points inside the wire, namely

$$\Phi_{1\,outside} = \int_b^{D/2} \frac{\mu_0 i\, dr}{2\pi r} = \frac{\mu_0 i}{2\pi} \ln \frac{D}{2b}$$

For $\Phi_{1\,inside}$, linking a filament through a point $\mathscr{P}''$ inside the wire, we can find the flux through a surface composed of a piece of a cylinder coaxial with the wire, connecting $\mathscr{P}''$ with a point $\mathscr{P}'$ on the line $\mathscr{O}_1\mathscr{O}$, and the plane surface $\mathscr{P}'\mathcal{O}$. No flux from wire 1 passes through the cylinder, so that the flux linking the filament through $\mathscr{P}'$ is the same as that through $\mathscr{P}''$, namely

$$\Phi_{1\ inside}\ (r) = \int_r^b \frac{\mu_0 i r'\ dr'}{2\pi b^2} = \frac{\mu_0 i (b^2 - r^2)}{4\pi b^2} \qquad (7.11\text{-}6)$$

where r is the distance $\overline{\mathcal{O}_1 \mathscr{P}'} = \overline{\mathcal{O}_1 \mathscr{P}''}$. Averaging the emf as in eq. 7.11–5 amounts to averaging the flux over the area, since we are assuming that J is constant (and equal to $i/\pi b^2$). In fact, we only need to average the quantity $(b^2 - r^2)$. For this average, we find

$$\text{average of } (b^2 - r^2) = \frac{1}{S} \int (b^2 - r^2)\ dS$$

$$= \frac{1}{\pi b^2} \int_0^b (b^2 - r^2) 2\pi r\ dr = \frac{\pi b^4}{\pi b^2} \left(1 - \frac{1}{2} \right) = \frac{b^2}{2}$$

yielding

$$\text{average of } (\Phi_{1\ inside}) = \frac{\mu_0 i}{8\pi}$$

Now we can find the total flux linking the circuit by combining Φ_2, $\Phi_{1\ outside}$, and $\Phi_{1\ inside}$, and multiplying by 2. If we finally divide out i, we have the inductance per unit length of a pair of equal parallel wires, separated by many times their radii:

$$L_l = \frac{\mu_0}{\pi} \left(\ln \frac{D}{b} + \frac{1}{4} \right) \qquad (7.11\text{-}7)$$

For a battery circuit without lumped inductance, in which the wires while not parallel are separated by say 100 times their radii, this formula will still give the correct order of magnitude. The logarithm will be of the order of 5, and we have, roughly, 10^{-6} henry or 1.0 microhenry per meter, accounting for the estimate given above in discussing time constants.

As a second example, let us calculate the inductance of a single circular loop that has a radius a and is made of wire of radius b. We shall suppose that b is so much less than a that the field inside the wire is the same as that for a straight wire, allowing us to find the local inside contribution from the average $\Phi_{1\ inside}$ just calculated. In fact, since the wire has a length $2\pi a$ the inside contribution will be $\frac{1}{4}\mu_0 i a$. We shall neglect the contribution inside the wire of the distant portions of the circuit and calculate the external flux by use of the expression for A_ϕ in section 7.6.

We need A_ϕ for points in the plane of the loop, where $z = 0$, and specifically at the inside edge of the wire where $R = a - b$. Equation 7.6–15 was calculated for a filamentary current, and we shall assume that outside our finite-radius wire we can approximate A_ϕ by considering all the current to be concentrated at the axis of the wire. The error made in this assumption will not be greater than the errors made by the approximate expansion we wish to give of eq. 7.6–15.

Putting $z = 0$ and $R = a - b$ in this equation, we have

$$A_\phi = \frac{\mu_0 i a}{2\pi} \int_0^\pi \frac{\cos \phi \, d\phi}{[(a - b)^2 + a^2 - 2a(a - b) \cos \phi]^{\frac{1}{2}}}$$

Now let us write $\phi/2 = \beta$ and $1 - \cos \phi = 2 \sin^2 \beta$. The expression can then be rearranged to give

$$A_\phi = \frac{\mu_0 i a}{\pi} \int_0^{\pi/2} \frac{(1 - 2 \sin^2 \beta) \, d\beta}{[b^2 + 4a(a - b) \sin^2 \beta]^{\frac{1}{2}}}$$

$$= \frac{\mu_0 i a}{2\pi[a(a - b)]^{\frac{1}{2}}} \int_0^{\pi/2} \frac{(1 - 2 \sin^2 \beta) \, d\beta}{[b^2/4a(a - b) + \sin^2 \beta]^{\frac{1}{2}}}$$

Let us shorten the writing by setting

$$\frac{b}{2[a(a - b)]^{\frac{1}{2}}} = k$$

The last integral can be evaluated easily but approximately for two ranges of β. If $\sin^2 \beta$ is sufficiently larger than k^2 that we can neglect k^2 altogether the denominator becomes $\sin \beta$ and the integral can be readily evaluated. On the other hand, if $\sin^2 \beta$ is small enough that it may be replaced by β^2, the integral can also be evaluated simply. If k is small enough, the ranges of β in which the two methods apply will overlap. Since $b \ll a$, $k \sim b/2a$ and can be considered small.

Let us choose a particular value of β, say β_1, in the region in which both methods overlap. Then for $\beta \geqslant \beta_1$, we can omit k^2 from the integral, and for $\beta \leqslant \beta_1$, we can write $\sin^2 \beta = \beta$. To be specific, suppose that 1% is set as the limit of error. Since $\sin \beta \simeq \beta - (\beta^3/6) = \beta[1 - (\beta^2/6)]$ and 1% in $\sin^2 \beta$ means $\frac{1}{2}\%$ in $\sin \beta$, we can take $\beta_1{}^2/6 \simeq 0.005$ or $\beta_1 \simeq 0.17$ radian $= 10°$. Then we wish k^2 to be not greater than $0.01 \sin^2 \beta_1 \simeq 0.01\beta_1{}^2$, or $k \lessgtr 0.1\beta_1 \simeq 0.017$, yielding $b/a \lessgtr 0.034$ or $1/30$.

Now we can evaluate our integral. We have

$$\int_0^{\pi/2} \frac{(1 - 2 \sin^2 \beta) \, d\beta}{(k^2 + \sin^2 \beta)^{\frac{1}{2}}} = \int_0^{\beta_1} \frac{(1 - 2\beta^2) \, d\beta}{(k^2 + \beta^2)^{\frac{1}{2}}} + \int_{\beta_1}^{\pi/2} \frac{(1 - 2 \sin^2 \beta) \, d\beta}{\sin \beta}$$

$$= \left\{ (1 + k^2) \ln [\beta + (\beta^2 + k^2)^{\frac{1}{2}}] - \beta (\beta^2 + k^2)^{\frac{1}{2}} \right\}_0^{\beta_1} + \left[\ln \tan \frac{\beta}{2} + 2 \cos \beta \right]_{\beta_1}^{\pi/2}$$

as the reader may verify directly by differentiation. When we substitute the limits, we should remember that we have assumed $k^2 \ll \beta_1^2 \ll 1$ so that it would be misleadingly complicated not to omit k^2 from $(\beta_1^2 + k^2)^{\frac{1}{2}}$ or from $(1 + k^2)$ or to retain $\tan(\beta_1/2)$ instead of $\beta_1/2$, and $\cos \beta_1$ instead of $1 - \beta_1^2/2$. (We cannot omit k from the first logarithm when $\beta = 0$, however!)   We obtain a result independent of β_1, which further justifies its use.   The integral is

$$\left[\ln 2\beta_1 - \beta_1^2 - \ln k + \ln \tan \frac{\pi}{4} - \ln \frac{\beta_1}{2} - 2(1 - \beta_1^2/2)\right] = \ln(4/k) - 2$$

so that, since $\Phi_{\text{outside}} = \oint \mathbf{A} \cdot \mathbf{dl} = 2\pi(a - b)A_\phi,$

$$\Phi_{\text{outside}} = \mu_0 i [a(a - b)]^{\frac{1}{2}} \left\{\ln \frac{8[a(a - b)]^{\frac{1}{2}}}{b} - 2\right\}$$

In view of our approximations, only a slight additional error will be made by taking $[a(a - b)]^{\frac{1}{2}} = a$, allowing us to combine Φ_{outside} and Φ_{inside} to obtain a simple formula for the self-inductance of a circular loop:

$$L = \mu_0 a \left[\ln \left(\frac{8a}{b}\right) - \frac{7}{4}\right] \tag{7.11-8}$$

We assumed in the calculation of the inductance of two parallel wires that the current density was uniform over the cross section of each wire. However, we arrived at an expression for the flux enclosed that varied from filament to filament and had to be averaged.   Our original assumption is only justified therefore if the variation of the electric field $\mathbf{E} = -\partial\mathbf{A}/\partial t$ over the wire is small enough that the resulting current density variations are negligible.   This variation of $\mathbf{E}$ can be estimated from eq. 7.11-6, by differentiating i with respect to t to get the emf per unit length for one wire only and then finding the derivative with respect to r.   The calculation is not strictly accurate because eq. 7.11-6 assumes a uniform $\mathbf{J}$.

The greatest effect on the current density will occur when the contribution of the static part of $\mathbf{E}$ to the total is negligible.   The effect will clearly be small if di/dt is small, so that uniform $\mathbf{J}$ occurs in the limit of zero rate of change of current.   If, on the other hand, di/dt is very large, as in high-frequency circuits, there will be a very large effect.   As seen by eq. 7.11-6, the emf will be largest at the center, and since the emf is directed against the build-up of current, the current will be largest near the edge.   As a result of concentrating the current in the outer parts of the wire, the effective resistance of the latter is increased.   This phenomenon is called the "skin effect."   For calculations and graphs of the

skin effect in wires, the reader is referred to other sources.[33]   A calculation
of a different sort is given in section 10.6.

Problem 7.11a.   A pair of concentric cylindrical shells is used in a circuit,
with equal and opposite currents along the two shells.   Assume the currents
to lie on the outside of the inner shell (radius R_1) and on the inside of the outer
shell (radius R_2).   Show that the inductance per unit length of this arrangement
is

$$L_l = \frac{\mu_0}{2\pi} \ln \frac{R_2}{R_1} \tag{7.11-9}$$

Problem 7.11b.   Find the mutual inductance of two coaxial circular coils
of the same radius a, separated by a distance z much less than a, by use of the
same type of expansion and the same integration, as used in the text to derive
eq. 7.11-8.   Calculate the force between the coils when they each carry current,
and show that the same result could be obtained by using eq. 7.5-3.

Problem 7.11c.   Find the self-inductance of a length l of an infinitely long
solenoid, with n_l turns per meter and radius a.

Problem 7.11d.   A circular loop of radius 2 cm is made of #18 copper wire
(consult a handbook for wire sizes).   Find its inductance and the flux linking it
when it carries 20 amp.   What rate of change of current is required to produce
a self-induced emf of 1.0 microvolt?

Problem 7.11e.   A transmission line consists of two parallel wires, of #18
copper, which are 2 in. apart.   What is the inductance of a section of length
10 ft of this line?

Problem 7.11f.   A toroidal coil of square cross section of side a has a mean
radius equal to b, and N turns.   Calculate its inductance.

Problem 7.11g.   An inductance of 250 millihenrys and resistance of 5?
ohms is connected by a switch to a battery of 10 v and internal resistance 1.0 ohm.
How long does it take after the switch is closed for the current to rise to one-half
its final value?   What is the value of the induced emf at this time?

7.12   Energy in Systems of Current-Bearing Circuits

In this section, we wish to consider briefly the magnetic-energy relations
involved in the establishment of currents and in the relative motion of
circuits.   Let us consider first a simple circuit with a cell of emf $\mathscr{E}$ volts,
a resistance of r ohms, and an inductance of L henries and R ohms, as
in Fig. 7.12a.   The extra switch K' is used to short-circuit the inductance
before opening the main switch K, so that the decrease of current can be
calculated in a more definite way than when K is opened first.   The resistor
r will protect the cell during this short-circuiting process.

[33] A simple calculation is given by J. H. Morecroft, *Principles of Radio Communication*
3rd ed., John Wiley, New York, 1933, p. 170 ff (out of print). See also F. E. Terman, *Electronic and Radio Engineering*, 4th ed., McGraw-Hill, New York, 1955, pp. 21–24; A. Hund,
Phenomena in High-Frequency Systems, McGraw-Hill, New York, 1936, pp. 335–338,

When K is closed, with K' open, the current i obeys the equation

$$\mathscr{E} = i(R + r) + L\frac{di}{dt}$$

During a short time dt, a charge $dq = i\,dt$ passes through the circuit, and work is done by the cell of amount

$$dW = \mathscr{E}i\,dt = i^2(R + r)\,dt + Li\frac{di}{dt}\,dt$$

If we integrate this expression from time $t = 0$ when $i = 0$ to an arbitrary time t_1, we have

$$W = \int_0^{t_1}\mathscr{E}i\,dt = \int_0^{t_1}i^2(R + r)\,dt + L\int_0^{t_1} i\frac{di}{dt}\,dt$$

The integral of $i^2(R + r)$ is just the heat dissipation in the wires and of

Fig. 7.12a. Illustrating energy storage in an inductance.

course increases as time goes on. The other integral on the right-hand side, however, can be written

$$L\int_{i_0}^{i_1} i\,di = \tfrac{1}{2}L(i_1^2 - i_0^2) = \tfrac{1}{2}Li_1^2$$

where i_0 refers to the current when $t = 0$, which is here taken to be zero, and i_1 refers to the current at $t = t_1$. As time goes on, i_1 approaches the limit $\mathscr{E}/(R + r)$ as we have seen. Thus a certain portion of the chemical energy expended in the cell has not gone into heat but is associated with the inductance. Dropping the subscript, we write the magnetic energy of the coil as

$$U = \tfrac{1}{2}Li^2 \qquad\qquad (7.12\text{--}1)$$

To see that we may treat this energy as stored in the coil and available for transformation into other forms of energy, let us short-circuit the coil by closing K'. Since a jump in the value of i would make an infinite back emf in the coil, we must assume that just after the instant of closing K', the current in L is still i_1. If the distributed capacitances of K' and the connecting wires are small enough, a current i will be established throughout the closed circuit made by K', R, and L, in a very short time. Treating the emf in L as an emf and not as a potential drop, we write for our circuit

$$\mathscr{E} = -L\frac{di}{dt} = Ri \qquad (7.12\text{-}2)$$

an equation which is just like eq. 5.3–1 for a discharging condenser. Its solution is therefore like eq. 5.3–2, namely

$$i = i_1 e^{-Rt/L} \qquad (7.12\text{-}3)$$

where $t = 0$ now refers to the time of the closing of K'.

Let us find the amount of heat developed in R. It will be $\int_0^\infty Ri^2\,dt$, a finite integral since the current falls off exponentially. From eq. 7.12–2, we find

$$\int_0^\infty Ri^2\,dt = -L\int_0^\infty i\frac{di}{dt}\,dt = -\tfrac{1}{2}Li^2\Big|_{t=0}^{t=\infty} = \tfrac{1}{2}Li_1^2$$

which is just the extra amount of energy originally provided by the cell. Thus it is quite legitimate to consider the quantity $U = \tfrac{1}{2}Li^2$ as energy stored in the inductance. It may be written $U = \tfrac{1}{2}i\Phi$, where Φ is the flux linking the circuit as a result of i.

Now consider a general system of rigid fixed circuits, which we shall number $1, 2, \cdots n$. Each will be assumed to contain an emf $\mathscr{E}'_j$ ($j = 1, 2 \cdots n$), which may be a chemical emf or an isolated generator whose magnetic field we shall not include in our discussion. These $\mathscr{E}$'s do not have to be constant. We denote the total resistances in each circuit by $R_1, R_2, \cdots R_n$, the self-inductances by $L_1, L_2, \cdots L_n$, and the various mutual inductances by $M_{12}, M_{13}, M_{23}, \cdots M_{jk} \cdots$. Each loop must of course have its own positive direction assigned. Let us imagine that in all circuits, the emf's are turned on simultaneously, with all currents initially zero. We can write for all the circuits

$$\mathscr{E}'_1 - L_1\frac{di_1}{dt} - M_{12}\frac{di_2}{dt} - M_{13}\frac{di_3}{dt} - \cdots - M_{1n}\frac{di_n}{dt} = i_1 R_1$$

$$\mathscr{E}'_2 - L_2\frac{di_2}{dt} - M_{21}\frac{di_1}{dt} - M_{23}\frac{di_3}{dt} - \cdots - M_{2n}\frac{di_n}{dt} = i_2 R_2$$

$$\;\;\cdot \qquad\quad \cdot \qquad\quad \cdot \qquad\quad \cdot \qquad\qquad \cdot \qquad\quad \cdot$$
$$\;\;\cdot \qquad\quad \cdot \qquad\quad \cdot \qquad\quad \cdot \qquad\qquad \cdot \qquad\quad \cdot$$
$$\;\;\cdot \qquad\quad \cdot \qquad\quad \cdot \qquad\quad \cdot \qquad\qquad \cdot \qquad\quad \cdot$$

$$\mathscr{E}'_n - L_n\frac{di_n}{dt} - M_{n1}\frac{di_1}{dt} - M_{n2}\frac{di_2}{dt} - \cdots - M_{nn-1}\frac{di_{n-1}}{dt} = i_n R_n$$

$$(7.12\text{-}4)$$

Let us put all the induced emf's on the right-hand side and simultaneously multiply each equation by its own $i_k \, dt$ for the charge that passes around the corresponding circuit in time dt. Making also the calculus transformation $(di_j/dt) \, dt = di_j$, we have

$$\mathscr{E}'_1 i_1 \, dt = L_1 i_1 \, di_1 + M_{12} i_1 \, di_2 + M_{13} i_1 \, di_3 + \cdots + M_{1n} i_1 \, di_n \quad + i_1^2 R_1$$

$$\mathscr{E}'_2 i_2 \, dt = L_2 i_2 \, di_2 + M_{21} i_2 \, di_1 + M_{23} i_2 \, di_3 + \cdots + M_{2n} i_2 \, di_n \quad + i_2^2 R_2$$

$$\mathscr{E}'_n i_n \, dt = L_n i_n \, di_n + M_{n1} i_n \, di_n + M_{n2} \, di_2 + \cdots + M_{nn-1} i_n \, di_{n-1} + i_n^2 R_n$$

The sum of the left-hand sides is the entire work done by all the external emf's in time dt. If we add all the right sides together and integrate from $t = 0$ to some upper limit which we can now call t, we will have the total heat developed plus a magnetic energy term U. We shall write down an expression for U by itself. Notice that for each self-inductance we will have a term of the form $\frac{1}{2} L i^2$. For the mutual-inductance terms, note that each mutual inductance comes in twice, once with respect to each of the two currents it links. We have, for instance,

$$M_{12} i_1 \, di_2 + M_{21} i_2 \, di_1 = M_{12}(i_1 \, di_2 + i_2 \, di_1) = M_{12} \, d(i_1 i_2)$$

by the usual calculus rule for the differential of a product. When we integrate, we have simply $M_{12} i_1 i_2$, evaluated at the time t. Thus we can write

$$U = \tfrac{1}{2} L_1 i_1^2 + \tfrac{1}{2} L_2 i_2^2 + \cdots + M_{12} i_1 i_2 + M_{13} i_1 i_3 + \cdots + M_{n-1n} i_{n-1} i_n$$

$$(7.12\text{--}5)$$

for the magnetic energy of a system of conductors. In this expression, each pair of currents is written once only.

Our function $U' = i\Phi$ of eqs. 7.7–6 and 7.10–13 is seen to be related to U. The necessity of keeping the currents constant was not stated in section 7.7, because induced emf's had not yet been considered. However, it is now clear that associated with the motion of circuits there will be induced emf's that will change the currents unless some control is provided to maintain them.

Before making a specific calculation of this effect, let us consider that peculiarity of the magnetic forces which is reflected in the sign discrepancy between U and U'. We saw in dealing with electrostatics that the motion of charges under the influence of the field is always in such a direction that the field is reduced as the charges get to new positions. The opposite is true for magnetic forces. Consider two equal wire loops, near and parallel to each other, carrying equal but opposite currents.   If they are sufficiently near, the forces will approximate those of parallel straight wires, for which case *opposite* currents *repel*.   Thus the loops will repel. While they are near, the resultant of their magnetic inductions at any point will be very small, but as they move apart it will *increase*.

Similarly, the coils of a loosely wound solenoid will all attract each other and, if they come closer together, L will increase, as will also $\frac{1}{2}Li^2$.

The paradox of work being done by magnetic forces while the field strength increases is resolved by calculating the work done by the energy sources in each circuit as the circuits are allowed to move.   Let circuit 1 be fixed, and let circuit 2 be displaced as a whole by a distance $\Delta\xi$ in some chosen direction, changing the mutual inductance by an amount ΔM_{12}. The work done by the magnetic forces will then be $F_\xi\,\Delta\xi = i_1 i_2\,\Delta M_{12}$. The flux produced by circuit 2 in circuit 1 will change by an amount $\Delta\Phi_1 = i_2\,\Delta M_{12}$ and that in circuit 2 by $\Delta\Phi_2 = i_1\,\Delta M_{12}$.   If the change takes a time Δt, there will be a back emf in circuit 1 of amount $-\Delta\Phi_1/\Delta t$, and extra work will be done by the external source of power in that circuit of amount $(+\Delta\Phi_1/\Delta t)(i_1\,\Delta t) = i_1 i_2\,\Delta M_{12}$, unless the current i is allowed to change, which case we shall exclude.   The same calculation made for circuit 2 shows that work $i_1 i_2\,\Delta M_{12}$ is *also* performed there. We see that, considering both circuits together, *twice as much work is done by the batteries as goes into mechanical work*, so that the magnetic energy of the system of currents increases by just the amount of the work done. This is why $U = -U'$.

It will be seen that this establishment of the law of conservation of energy would not have been possible if Lenz's law had had the opposite sign, for then the batteries would be charged up rather than perform work as circuits move under the action of magnetic forces.   We have also verified the statement at the end of section 1.7 concerning the difference between a system of charges at rest and a system of currents with respect to energy conservation.

If the currents are not kept constant, there must be a reduction of the self-energy $\frac{1}{2}L_1 i_1{}^2 + \frac{1}{2}L_2 i_2{}^2 + \cdots$ to compensate for the increase in the mutual-energy terms.   The forces for a given set of currents are dependent only on the actual values of those currents at the instant under considera-tion and do not depend on whether or not an arrangement has been made to keep them constant as the circuits move.

In the case of atoms with electrons circulating in orbits, we have currents with zero resistance and no emf's to maintain them.   Consequently, any motion of an atom into an external magnetic field in such a direction as to add to the mutual energy of the atom and the external field source will cause the atomic currents themselves to lose magnetic self-energy, an effect known as diamagnetism.   It is found in all substances, although in many materials it is masked by paramagnetism or ferromagnetism.

Both paramagnetism and ferromagnetism involve the turning of atomic-current circuits under the action of an applied field.   From the considerations above, we see that the turning of a circuit in response to a magnetic torque applied to it will increase the mutual energy, and so add to the field.   The strength of the atomic current may tend to decrease by the above-mentioned diamagnetic effect, but if sufficient turning occurs, the paramagnetic effect may overcome it.

We can write two other expressions for U.   Let us first divide up the terms of eq. 7.12–5 in a symmetrical way among all the circuits.   We can write

$$U = \tfrac{1}{2}L_1{i_1}^2 + \tfrac{1}{2}M_{12}i_1i_2 + \tfrac{1}{2}M_{13}i_1i_3 + \cdots + \tfrac{1}{2}M_{1n}i_1i_n +$$

$$\tfrac{1}{2}L_2{i_2}^2 + \tfrac{1}{2}M_{21}i_2i_1 + \tfrac{1}{2}M_{23}i_2i_3 + \cdots + \tfrac{1}{2}M_{2n}i_2i_n + \cdots \text{ etc.}$$

so that, on factoring out the appropriate current from each line, we have

$$U = \tfrac{1}{2}(i_1\Phi_1 + i_2\Phi_2 + \cdots + i_n\Phi_n) \qquad (7.12\text{–}6)$$

where Φ_1 is the total flux $L_1i_1 + M_{12}i_2 + \cdots + M_{1n}i_n$ through circuit 1, and so forth.   This expression might be compared with the electrostatic energy $U = \tfrac{1}{2}(Q_1V_1 + Q_2V_2 + \cdots + Q_nV_n)$ of eq. 4.7–2.

Now, Φ through any closed circuit can be written in terms of the vector potential produced by all the currents, $\Phi = \oint \mathbf{A} \cdot \mathbf{dl}$.   However, we had to calculate the self-inductance by an averaging process, integrating over the cross section of a wire in order to avoid infinities.   We can write, then, for the expression $\tfrac{1}{2}i_1\Phi_1 + \cdots + \tfrac{1}{2}i_n\Phi_n$ the integral

$$U = \tfrac{1}{2}\int_{\substack{\text{cross section}\\ \text{of each wire}}} J\Phi \, dS = \tfrac{1}{2}\int_{\substack{\text{cross section}\\ \text{of wires}}} J \, dS \oint_{\text{filament}} \mathbf{A} \cdot \mathbf{dl} = \tfrac{1}{2}\int_{\substack{\text{vol. of}\\ \text{wire}}} \mathbf{J} \cdot \mathbf{A} \, d\tau$$

$$\text{MKS} \quad (7.12\text{–}7)$$

In the first expression, Φ represents the flux linking the current filament that passes through the elemental area dS, and the integration over dS can be made at any point along each wire.   In the second expression, we have replaced Φ by $\oint A \cdot dl$ taken along the given filament.   Since $J \, dS$ is constant along a "tube of current," it may be multiplied into the l integration and be taken as applying to all of each wire.   For the third expression, we write $J \, \mathbf{dl} = \mathbf{J} \, dl$, since $\mathbf{dl}$ was taken along a current filament, and then $dl \, dS = d\tau$, a volume element.

Now we can replace **J** by its value for steady currents given by eq. 7.8–1

$$\mathbf{J} = \frac{1}{\mu_0} \operatorname{curl} \mathbf{B}$$

The integrand will then contain

$$(\operatorname{curl} \mathbf{B}) \cdot \mathbf{A} = \mathbf{A} \cdot (\nabla \times \mathbf{B})$$

which can be related to $\nabla \cdot (\mathbf{B} \times \mathbf{A})$.   In fact, in the latter expression ∇ operates on both **A** and **B**, and the rules for rearrangement of the triple scalar product can be used to give formula 5 of Table A.2B:

$$\nabla \cdot (\mathbf{B} \times \mathbf{A}) = \mathbf{A} \cdot (\nabla \times \mathbf{B}) - \mathbf{B} \cdot (\nabla \times \mathbf{A})$$

We recognize $\nabla \times \mathbf{A}$ as **B** so we can write

$$U = \tfrac{1}{2} \int_{\substack{\text{vol. of} \\ \text{wires}}} \mathbf{J} \cdot \mathbf{A}\, d\tau = \frac{1}{2\mu_0} \int [\mathbf{B} \cdot (\nabla \times \mathbf{A}) + \nabla \cdot (\mathbf{B} \times \mathbf{A})]\, d\tau$$

$$= \frac{1}{2\mu_0} \int B^2\, d\tau + \frac{1}{2\mu_0} \int \nabla \cdot (\mathbf{B} \times \mathbf{A})\, d\tau$$

Note now that **J** is zero outside the wires, so that the integral on the left could equally well be written over any larger volume containing the wires. However, **B** does not in general vanish outside the wires, so that extending the region of integration will amount to reshuffling the contributions of the two integrals on the right without changing their sum.   Since the first integral is positive, it will increase as the volume used increases.

The second integral $\int \nabla \cdot (\mathbf{B} \times \mathbf{A})\, d\tau$ can be transformed by the divergence theorem A.2–22 into a surface integral $\int_S (\mathbf{B} \times \mathbf{A}) \cdot d\mathbf{S}$ taken over the surface of whatever region we use.   It will become zero if we integrate over all space, since there will be no **B** or **A** at infinity.   Strictly, we should prove this by showing that the integral approaches zero as the surface expands.   The magnitude of **A** will fall off at least as fast as $1/r$, once the surface is far from the currents, and B will decrease at least as rapidly as $1/r^2$.   Hence the integrand will fall off at least as fast as $1/r^3$.   On the other hand, if the surface S is a large sphere its area will be $4\pi r^2$ and will not increase fast enough to prevent the $1/r^3$ behavior of the integrand from giving a smaller and smaller result.

We can finally write

$$U = \frac{1}{2\mu_0} \int_{\text{all space}} B^2\, d\tau \qquad\qquad \text{MKS} \quad (7.12\text{–}8)$$

and interpret the result by assigning an energy $B^2/2\mu_0$ joules/m^3 to each unit volume of a magnetic field, although of course we cannot really locate energy in this fashion. This result is to be compared with eq. 4.7–6 for the energy in a set of charged conductors, both formulas presenting energy entirely in terms of fields.

Problem 7.12a. A coil of one henry inductance carries a current of one ampere. How many volts would have to be established between the plates of a 1.0 μf capacitor to store as many joules as are stored in the coil?

Problem 7.12b. Find the energy contained in a length l of an infinitely long solenoid, by use of eq. 7.12–8 and by use of eq. 7.12–1 together with the answer to problem 7.11c.

Problem 7.12c. Calculate the rate at which energy is being stored at time t after closing a switch in a circuit containing inductance L and resistance R.

8

Magnetic Materials

8.1 Introduction

In this chapter, we shall discuss magnetic materials and measurements of their properties, by combining the material of Chapter 7 with the modern atomic theory of circulating sub-atomic currents. We shall introduce the pole concept and find a close analogy to exist between magnetizable materials and dielectrics; we shall thereby be able to borrow numerous mathematical results from Chapter 3 and obtain relations easily verifiable in the macroscopic realm. Our presentation will be governed largely by a desire to present an orderly arrangement of the material, suitable for clarity and ease in remembering, so that the historical development of the subject will not be followed and only brief consideration will be given to the experimental basis for our assertions about the atomic nature of magnetism. The applicability of our theory to the atomic realm is of course an assumption that is to be justified by its results.

8.2   Magnetic Dipoles

All atoms are known to contain circulating currents that are sources of magnetic field. These currents are of two types. The circulation of electrons around nuclei (orbital motion) is an obvious source, such circulation when averaged over sufficiently long times being equivalent to steady currents. The other type is involved in the intrinsic magnetic properties of separate electrons, protons, and neutrons. These properties are associated with the particles' intrinsic angular momentum, or spin. The particles act as if they "contained" circulating currents within themselves. No adequate theory of elementary particles now exists (1958), and we do not know whether or not to consider the magnetic properties of "elementary" particles as describable in terms of actual currents. However, the effects are the same as if there were such currents, and we need not pursue the theoretical question in this book.

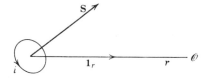

Fig. 8.2a.   The solid angle subtended by $\mathbf{S}$ at $\mathcal{O}$ is $\mathbf{S} \cdot \mathbf{1}_r / r^2$.

What we do require is a formation of the field produced by a small circulating current, as well as a formulation of the force and torque exerted on such a current by an external field. Both formulas are easy to derive from Chapter 7.

The field produced by a small loop can be found from Ampère's law in the solid-angle form, eq. 7.4–1, or its equivalent, eqs. 7.6–1 and 7.6–2. (A formulation in terms of the vector potential is suggested in problem 8.2d.) By small we mean that the largest dimension of the loop is small compared to the distance from it to a point of observation, a condition very well fulfilled when we wish to calculate the large-scale effects of atomic magnetism, and one that seems to be valid at all distances for the magnetic effects associated with spin.

The solid angle Ω subtended by a small plane loop at a distance r from a point $\mathcal{O}$ is $\Omega = \mathbf{S} \cdot \mathbf{1}_r / r^2$, where $\mathbf{S}$ is the vector area of the loop, and $\mathbf{1}_r$ is directed from the loop toward $\mathcal{O}$ (Fig. 8.2a). If a current i circulates around the loop in the positive direction, the magnetic scalar potential by eq. 7.6–2 will be

$$V_m = \frac{i\mathbf{S} \cdot \mathbf{1}_r}{4\pi r^2} \qquad \text{MKS}$$

V_m is actually multiple valued as discussed in section 7.6. However, the expression given here satisfies the conditions for the integral definition given in eq. 7.6–3 and remains single valued as long as points within or near the loop are excluded from consideration. The formula just given resembles that for the electrostatic potential of an electric dipole, eq. 3.1–4. The analogy can be made close by defining the quantity $i\mathbf{S}$ (with a factor $1/c$ for Gaussian units) as the electromagnetic moment (or just magnetic moment) $\mathbf{m}$ of the current loop,[1] and writing

$$V_m = \mathbf{m} \cdot \mathbf{1}_r/4\pi r^2 \qquad\qquad \text{MKS} \quad (8.2\text{–}1a)$$

$$V_m = \mathbf{m} \cdot \mathbf{1}_r/r^2 \qquad\qquad \text{Gaussian} \quad (8.2\text{–}1b)$$

with

$$\mathbf{m} = i\mathbf{S} \qquad\qquad \text{MKS} \quad (8.2\text{–}2a)$$

$$\mathbf{m} = i\mathbf{S}/c \qquad\qquad \text{Gaussian} \quad (8.2\text{–}2b)$$

The MKS unit of magnetic moment is thus the meter^2-ampere; the Gaussian unit (also the electromagnetic unit) is the abampere-centimeter^2.

The force and torque on a small current loop are to be calculated from derivatives of the energy function (cf. eq. 7.7–6)

$$U' = -i\Phi = -i\mathbf{S} \cdot \mathbf{B} = -\mathbf{m} \cdot \mathbf{B} \qquad\qquad (8.2\text{–}3)$$

where the last expression holds in either system of units. Smallness of $\mathbf{S}$ means here that $\mathbf{B}$ is to be taken as constant over the loop. We have then for the force

$$\mathbf{F} = \nabla(\mathbf{m} \cdot \mathbf{B}) \qquad\qquad (8.2\text{–}4)$$

and for the torque, by the result of problem 7.7c

$$\mathscr{L} = \mathbf{m} \times \mathbf{B} \qquad\qquad (8.2\text{–}5)$$

From these formulas it can be seen that alternative expressions for the units of magnetic moment are joule-meter^2/weber for MKS units and erg/gauss for Gaussian units.

Introduction of the Pole Fiction.   Formulas 8.2–1, 8.2–4, and 8.2–5 are mathematically similar to those for an electric dipole. To make the analogy complete and to arrive at formulas that were originally developed using the pole concept and which are still used now that the pole fiction is

---

[1] The letter $\mathbf{m}$ is not universally used for magnetic moment, but has appeared in a number of recent works (e.g., Peck, Harnwell, Whitmer, Stratton, Slater and Frank). In works on atomic physics, the symbol μ is commonly used, but the traditional use of μ_0 and μ for permeability precludes this choice for this textbook. We also use $\mathbf{p}_m = \mu_0\mathbf{m}$ for the sake of close analogy with the electric case. (The letter p is sometimes used for magnetic pole strength, as also is m.) It will not be difficult to distinguish $\mathbf{m}$ from the symbol for mass in what follows, as the latter is not frequently used in this text.

not taken as a fundamental starting point, we shall write these three results using $\mathbf{B}/\mu_0$ as the field quantity and $\mu_0\mathbf{m} = \mathbf{p}_m$ as the magnetic moment in weber-meters. To distinguish $\mathbf{p}_m$ from $\mathbf{m}$, we shall call the former the magnetic dipole moment. Except in the interior of magnetized materials, $\mathbf{B}/\mu_0$ is given the symbol $\mathbf{H}$ (in Gaussian units we write $\mathbf{B} = \mathbf{H}$ in vacuo, and continue to use $\mathbf{m}$).[2] Then we have, using eq. 7.6–1:

$$V_m = \frac{\mathbf{p}_m \cdot \mathbf{1}_r}{4\pi\mu_0 r^2} = \frac{\mathbf{m} \cdot \mathbf{1}_r}{4\pi r^2} \qquad\qquad \text{MKS} \quad (8.2\text{–}6a)$$

$$\mathbf{H} = -\nabla V_m \qquad\qquad\qquad\qquad\qquad (8.2\text{–}6b)$$

$$U' = -\mathbf{p}_m \cdot \mathbf{H} = -\mu_0 \mathbf{m} \cdot \mathbf{H} \qquad \text{MKS} \quad (8.2\text{–}6c)$$

$$\mathbf{F} = \nabla(\mathbf{p}_m \cdot \mathbf{H}) = \mu_0 \nabla(\mathbf{m} \cdot \mathbf{H}) \qquad \text{MKS} \quad (8.2\text{–}6d)$$

$$\mathscr{L} = \mathbf{p}_m \times \mathbf{H} = \mu_0 \mathbf{m} \times \mathbf{H} \qquad \text{MKS} \quad (8.2\text{–}6e)$$

In the last three formulas, μ_0 is to be set equal to one for Gaussian units; in the first formula the 4π is also removed for the latter units.

These formulas are exactly the same as the corresponding equations for electric dipoles, eqs. 3.1–4, 1.9–3, 3.2–5, 3.2–4, and 3.2–1, if only we replace $\mathbf{H}$ by $\mathbf{E}$, $\mathbf{p}_m$ by $\mathbf{p}$, μ_0 by ϵ_0, V_m by V, and U' by U. We can also make on eqs. 8.2–4 and 8.2–6e the reverse of the transformation that we made in going from $F = (\mathbf{p} \cdot \nabla)\mathbf{E}$ to $F = \nabla(\mathbf{p} \cdot \mathbf{E})$ in section 3.2, provided that $\mathbf{curl\ B} = 0$ at every point along the current loop (e.g., no current density $\mathbf{J}$ coincident with the loop), and write for the force

$$\mathbf{F} = (\mathbf{m} \cdot \nabla)\mathbf{B} = (\mathbf{p}_m \cdot \nabla)\mathbf{H} \qquad\qquad (8.2\text{–}7)$$

The eqs. 8.2–6 and 8.2–7 could be derived if we assumed the existence of magnetic "charges" or poles that have the correct properties in analogy to electric charge. The symbol q_m will be used for magnetic pole strength. We would need three equations; first

$$\mathbf{H} = \frac{q_m \mathbf{1}_r}{4\pi\mu_0 r^2} \qquad\qquad \text{MKS} \quad (8.2\text{–}8a)$$

$$\mathbf{H} = \frac{q_m \mathbf{1}_r}{r^2} \qquad\qquad \text{Gaussian} \quad (8.2\text{–}8b)$$

---

[2] It would be simpler if we only used $\mathbf{p}_m = \mu_0\mathbf{m} = \mu_0 i\mathbf{S}$ as the definition of magnetic moment, as is done in some texts. The practice we follow is that recommended by the Commission on Symbols, Units, and Nomenclature of the International Union of Pure and Applied Physics [SUN commission, see *Physics Today*, **9**, 23–27 (1956) and **10**, 30–34 (1957)], except for our use of the letter $\mathbf{m}$.

for the field produced by a single pole (Coulomb's law for poles), with of course the usual rules for attractions and repulsions; second

$$\mathbf{F} = q_m \mathbf{H} \qquad (8.2\text{-}8c)$$

for the force on a pole of strength q_m; and third

$$\mu_0 \mathbf{m} = \mathbf{p}_m = q_m \, \boldsymbol{\delta}\mathbf{l} \qquad \text{MKS} \quad (8.2\text{-}8d)$$

$$\mathbf{m} = \mathbf{p}_m = q_m \, \boldsymbol{\delta}\mathbf{l} \qquad \text{Gaussian} \quad (8.2\text{-}8e)$$

for the dipole moment, where $\boldsymbol{\delta}\mathbf{l}$ is a small but fixed separation of two equal and opposite imaginary poles.

Although we might *define* magnetic pole strength by an analogy of this kind, we shall be able to define it more directly and satisfactorily in the next section, when we shall justify eqs. 8.2–8. In the meantime, we may take the analogy as a working hypothesis. It is not difficult to show that in MKS units, **H** is measured in amperes/meter. In Gaussian units, **H** like **B** is measured in gauss, and for historical reasons connected with the ascribing of properties to empty space, its unit is also called the oersted.[3] The MKS unit of q_m is the weber, and the Gaussian unit is usually called the electromagnetic unit of pole strength, or emu (problem 8.2c).

The quantity **H** has traditionally been called the "magnetic field intensity" and where there is no confusion with the more fundamental quantity **B** this terminology will be used. An alternative name for **H** which is sometimes used and avoids any confusion is "magnetizing force."[4]

Before deriving the pole concept for the case of bulk matter, let us consider the case of a large current loop. We have already given five different expressions involving the magnetic field of a closed current, namely, the solid-angle rule, eq. 7.4–1, the integrated Laplace rule, eq. 7.4–4; the circuital rule, eq. 7.4–6; the vector-potential rule, eq. 7.6–5; and the differential equation 7.8–1. We can now derive a sixth one. Let us calculate Ω for a large circuit by taking an arbitrary surface S whose boundary is the circuit in question, and dividing it into differential

---

[3] The International Union of Pure and Applied Physics decided in 1934 to accept the point of view that **B** and **H** in free space are fundamentally different even if their ratio μ_0 is taken as unity, and hence the oersted was adopted at that time as the unit for **H**. Inasmuch as we do not wish in this book to ascribe properties to free space, but rather to deal with experimentally verifiable laws of physics, we can consider that "gausses" and "oersteds" are equal and interchangeable. This point of view, applied to MKS units, implies that μ_0 is dimensionless (see p. 270). For further details, and a full discussion, see article by R. T. Birge, *Am. Physics Teacher*, **3**, 171 (1931).

[4] A. Sommerfeld has suggested calling it the "magnetic excitation." See his *Electrodynamics* (*Lectures on Theoretical Physics*, Vol. III), E. G. Ramberg, trans., Academic Press, New York, 1952.

elements of area, of the sort used for integration.   The solid angle at 0 (Fig. 8.2b) may be written as a surface integral

$$\Omega = \int_S \frac{d\mathbf{S} \cdot \mathbf{1}_r}{r^2}$$

and the magnetic scalar potential

$$V_m = \frac{i}{4\pi} \int_S \frac{d\mathbf{S} \cdot \mathbf{1}_r}{r^2} = \int_S \frac{d\mathbf{p}_m \cdot \mathbf{1}_r}{4\pi \mu_0 r^2} \qquad \text{MKS} \quad (8.2\text{–}9a)$$

$$= \int_S \frac{d\mathbf{m} \cdot \mathbf{1}_r}{r^2} \qquad \text{Gaussian} \quad (8.2\text{–}9b)$$

where we have written $\mu_0 i\, d\mathbf{S} = d\mathbf{p}_m$, a differential element of magnetic dipole moment.   Thus the scalar potential produced by the current is the

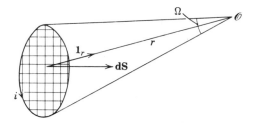

Fig. 8.2b.   Illustrating the dipole form of Ampère's Law.

same as if we substituted for it a physical surface coinciding with S, containing a positive distribution of magnetic poles on its front surface and a negative one on its back surface, separated by a very small distance δl (measured in the direction of the positive normal to S).   If we denote the quantity of magnetic pole per unit area by σ_m, we must have

$$d\mathbf{p}_m = \mu_0 i\, d\mathbf{S} = \sigma_m\, dS\, \delta l = \sigma_m\, \delta l\, d\mathbf{S}$$

We call such a surface a "magnetic shell" and define its strength or magnetic dipole moment per unit area as

$$P_{mS} = \mu_0 M_S = \sigma_m\, \delta l = \mu_0 i \qquad \text{MKS} \quad (8.2\text{–}10a)$$

$$= \frac{i}{c} \qquad \text{Gaussian} \quad (8.2\text{–}10b)$$

The shell is said to be *equivalent* to the current loop.

We can equally well derive this result by considering that the current loop is equivalent to the superposition of a large number of loops, namely, the loops formed by the boundaries of all the elements dS.   If each loop carries a current i, there will be a cancellation of the contribution from each portion of one loop that abuts on another, for there will be on such portions equal currents in opposite directions.   Only on the boundaries of the original loop will there be an uncanceled result.   But each separate loop acts like a dipole, and so the sum acts like a magnetic shell.   Note the complete analogy to the disk electret, section 3.6.

Thus any current circuit whatsoever produces a field that could be imagined to have arisen from a collection of magnetic poles.   Our derivation requires us to restrict the analogy to calculation of V_m at points far from the alleged dipoles.   Hence the equivalent shell must not be passed through any point where we wish to find the field.   The shell can, in fact, be taken on either side of the point $\mathcal{O}$, as in Fig. 8.2c.   The field calculated

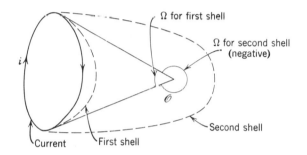

Fig. 8.2c.   Two locations for the shell equivalent to a current when the field is desired at point $\mathcal{O}$.

from the gradient of Ω will be the same in either case, but V_m will differ by $\pm i$, illustrating again its essential multiple valuedness.   (The sign of Ω must be determined in accordance with the rules stated in section 7.4.)

The relation between current loops and magnetic shells is exemplified by the agreement of eq. 3.6–9 for the outside value of **D** at the center of an electret disk and eq. 7.5–7b for the value of **B** at the center of a circular current.

Problem 8.2a.   Calculate the flux produced by a magnetic dipole through an arbitrary circle of radius R coaxial with dipole, whose center is a distance z from the dipole, and use the result to check eq. 7.10–7.

Problem 8.2b.   Find the flux produced by a circular current of arbitrary radius R through a small loop of radius a coaxial with the first loop and at a distance z from it.   If the currents in the two loops are i_1 and i_2, find the force on the small loop.

Problem 8.2c.   Show that the MKS unit of q_m is the weber and that of **H** is the ampere/meter.   Show that the emu of pole strength has the dimensions of gauss-centimeter^2, of abampere-centimeter, and of erg/gauss-centimeter.

Problem 8.2d.   By applying the theorem of eq. A.2–41 to the scalar $u = 1/r$, show that the vector potential of an arbitrary current loop can be written as the following integral over any surface bounded by the loop:

$$A = \frac{\mu_0 i}{4\pi} \int_S d\mathbf{S} \times \nabla \left(\frac{1}{r}\right) \qquad \text{MKS} \quad (8.2\text{–}11)$$

and that the vector potential of a magnetic dipole **m** is given by

$$A = \frac{\mu_0 \mathbf{m} \times \mathbf{1}_r}{4\pi r^2} \qquad \text{MKS} \quad (8.2\text{–}12)$$

Problem 8.2e.   Derive **B** from eq. 8.2–12 and show that the result is equivalent to eq. 8.2–6b.

Problem 8.2f.   Ten turns of wire are wrapped around the edge of a 5-cm square of plywood, that is hinged so as to fold along a line bisecting two opposite edges.   The coil carries a current of 0.40 amp.   Find the magnetic moment of the coil when the angle between the two parts of the square is (a) 180°, (b) 120°, (c) 90°, (d) 45°.   Describe the direction of **m** in each case.

Problem 8.2g.   Find **A** at a point in the plane of one half of the folding square of the previous problem, 10 m away from the hinge line on the perpendicular bisector of the hinge, for each angle given.

Problem 8.2h.   Find **B** at a point $\mathscr{P}$ 5 m from a circular coil of 3 cm diameter, with 30 turns of wire carrying 150 milliamps.   The line from $\mathscr{P}$ to the center of the coil makes an angle of 40° with the axis of the coil.

Problem 8.2i.   How is the field produced by a wire loop arranged in the form of a figure 8 to be described, at points far from it in comparison to its dimensions?

Problem 8.2j.   If the small loop in problem 8.2b moves away from the larger one along their common axis with speed v, find the emf induced in it and the emf it induces in the large loop.

Problem 8.2k.   Two small loops are a large distance r apart, the second one being on a line making an angle of 30° with the axis of the first one.   How is the second one to be oriented so the pair will have zero mutual inductance?

8.3   Magnetized Materials

Since a single atomic-current loop acts like a dipole, a collection of atoms will act like a piece of dielectric material.   We can borrow the results of sections 3.4 to 3.6, if we are careful in using the pole analysis to calculate fields far from individual atoms, which means *outside* the material (or in a cavity).

If there are several current loops in an atom, their resultant field at a great distance can be found by adding their magnetic dipole moments. If these moments add to zero, there may be a higher order contribution of a magnetic quadrupole or higher multipole nature, in exact analogy to the electric multipoles.   Also, a more accurate approximation to the field near a loop could be obtained by considering it to be composed of smaller loops and calculating the resultant dipole, quadrupole, and higher moments.   We shall be concerned here only with magnetic dipole moments.

The analysis which was given in the first part of section 3.4 was originally given by Poisson[5] for magnetic materials.   We take a group of atomic magnetic dipoles, large enough to be considered as an element of a continuous medium and to average out the variations of **m** from atom to atom (in many magnetic materials, **m** fluctuates considerably in direction from po'nt to point), but small enough to be an element of integration. If $d\tau$ is i s volume, we can write the sum of the dipole moments just as in q. 3.4–1

$$\sum_i \mathbf{m}_i = \mathbf{M}\, d\tau \qquad (8.3\text{--}1a)$$

or, multiplying by μ_0

$$\sum_i \mathbf{P}_m = \mu_0 \mathbf{M}\, d\tau = \mathbf{P}_m\, d\tau \qquad (8.3\text{--}1b)$$

where **M** is a vector which we shall call the magnetization, or magnetic moment per unit volume and the analog of the electric polarization, $\mathbf{P}_m$, may be called the magnetic polarization.   The field produced by a piece of magnetic material can then be found, in terms of the scalar potential V_m, by substituting eq. 8.3–1 in eq. 8.2–1 and integrating, making the same transformations as in section 3.4.   The result is the analogy of eq. 3.4–3:

$$V_m = \int_S \frac{\mathbf{P}_m \cdot \mathbf{dS}}{4\pi\mu_0 r} - \int_\tau \frac{\mathbf{\nabla} \cdot \mathbf{P}_m\, d\tau}{4\pi\mu_0 r} \qquad \text{MKS} \quad (8.3\text{--}2a)$$

$$= \int_S \frac{\mathbf{M} \cdot \mathbf{dS}}{r} - \int_\tau \frac{\mathbf{\nabla} \cdot \mathbf{M}\, d\tau}{r} \qquad \text{Gaussian} \quad (8.3\text{--}2b)$$

which we could equally well describe by saying that (a) the material contains on its surface S a "fictitious" or "effective" magnetic pole strength distribution of magnitude

$$\sigma_m = \mu_0 M_n = P_{mn} \qquad \text{MKS} \quad (8.3\text{--}3a)$$

$$\sigma_m = M_n \qquad \text{Gaussian} \quad (8.3\text{--}3b)$$

where M_n and P_{mn} are the components of **M** and $\mathbf{P}_m$ normal to the surface; and (b) the material contains within its volume τ a distribution

$$\rho_m = -\mu_0 \mathbf{\nabla} \cdot \mathbf{M} = -\mathbf{\nabla} \cdot \mathbf{P}_m \qquad \text{MKS} \quad (8.3\text{--}4a)$$

$$\rho_m = -\mathbf{\nabla} \cdot \mathbf{M} \qquad \text{Gaussian} \quad (8.3\text{--}4b)$$

---

[5] See, for instance, Sir. E. T. Whittaker, *A History of Theories of Aether and Electricity*, Thomas Nelson, London, 1951, Vol. I, pp. 63–65.

A positive magnetic pole is called "north" or "north-seeking," and a negative one "south" or "south-seeking." Equations 8.3–3 and 8.3–4 can be said to constitute a definition of magnetic pole strength.

To find the force exerted by external fields on a magnetized piece of material, we can use the calculation at the end of section 3.6. Starting with the use of eq. 8.2–7 for a volume element $d\tau$,

$$\mathbf{dF} = \sum_i (\mathbf{m}_i \cdot \mathbf{\nabla})\mathbf{B} = (\mathbf{M} \cdot \mathbf{\nabla})\mathbf{B} \, d\tau \qquad (8.3\text{–}5)$$

we end with the resultant force

$$\mathbf{F} = \int_S \mathbf{B}(\mathbf{M} \cdot \mathbf{dS}) - \int_\tau \mathbf{B}(\mathbf{\nabla} \cdot \mathbf{M}) \, d\tau \qquad (8.3\text{–}6)$$

$$= \int_S \mathbf{H}(\mathbf{P}_m \cdot \mathbf{dS}) - \int_\tau \mathbf{H}(\mathbf{\nabla} \cdot \mathbf{P}_m) \, d\tau$$

showing that we can find the forces on magnetic materials by use of the pole strengths σ_m and ρ_m. The vector $\mathbf{H} = \mathbf{B}/\mu_0$ of course is the externally produced field.

The torque on a piece of magnetized material is the sum of the torques on each separate dipole, by eq. 8.2–5, plus the torque $\mathbf{r} \times \mathbf{dF}$ associated with the force on each dipole in accordance with the mechanical relation A.2–37. We have then

$$\mathbf{d\mathscr{L}} = [\mathbf{M} \times \mathbf{B} + \mathbf{r} \times (\mathbf{M} \cdot \mathbf{\nabla})\mathbf{B}] \, d\tau \qquad (8.3\text{–}7)$$

which is to be integrated over the volume of the piece of material. The operator $(\mathbf{M} \cdot \mathbf{\nabla})$ is a scalar which can be factored out of the vector product if care is taken to indicate that $\mathbf{\nabla}$ operates only on $\mathbf{B}$. If we allow $\mathbf{\nabla}$ to operate on both $\mathbf{r}$ and $\mathbf{B}$, we can easily prove the vector relation (item 9 in Table A.2B)

$$(\mathbf{M} \cdot \overline{\mathbf{\nabla})(\mathbf{r} \times \mathbf{B}}] = [(\mathbf{M} \cdot \overline{\mathbf{\nabla})\mathbf{r}}] \times \mathbf{B} + \mathbf{r} \times (\mathbf{M} \cdot \mathbf{\nabla})\mathbf{B}$$

This relation together with the general relation for any vector $\mathbf{M}$ that $(\mathbf{M} \cdot \mathbf{\nabla})\mathbf{r} = \mathbf{M}$ (problem A.2r) allows us to rewrite eq. 8.3–7 as

$$\mathbf{d\mathscr{L}} = (\mathbf{M} \cdot \mathbf{\nabla})(\mathbf{r} \times \mathbf{B}) \, d\tau \qquad (8.3\text{–}8)$$

The same transformation can be made on the integral of this torque element as was made for the force element $\mathbf{dF} = (\mathbf{M} \cdot \mathbf{\nabla})\mathbf{B} \, d\tau$ with the result that the total torque is the sum of the integrals over the volume and surface pole densities multiplied by $\mathbf{r} \times \mathbf{H}$. That is, the torque can be found correctly from the pole strengths and the external field $\mathbf{H}$:

$$\mathscr{L} = \int_s (\mathbf{r} \times \mathbf{B})(\mathbf{M} \cdot \mathbf{dS}) - \int_\tau (\mathbf{r} \times \mathbf{B})(\nabla \cdot \mathbf{M}) \, d\tau \qquad (8.3\text{–}9a)$$

$$= \int (\mathbf{r} \times \mathbf{H})(\mathbf{P}_m \cdot \mathbf{dS}) - \int_\tau (\mathbf{r} \times \mathbf{H})(\nabla \cdot \mathbf{P}_m) \, d\tau \quad \text{MKS} \quad (8.3\text{–}9b)$$

In the case of a uniform field, a direct calculation is easy, for we need consider no torques to arise from $\mathbf{F} = (\mathbf{m} \cdot \nabla)\mathbf{B}$ (the derivatives in this expression are all zero), and can merely add the torques on each individual dipole. That is $\mathscr{L} = \sum_i \mathbf{m}_i \times \mathbf{B} = \tau \mathbf{M} \times \mathbf{B}$ for a uniform magnet, where τ is the volume.

We conclude that both for calculating fields outside magnetic materials and for finding external forces on them, we can use the concept of magnetic pole, taking eqs. 8.3–3 and 8.3–4 as definitions of pole strength and making calculations by analogy with electrostatics, using eqs. 8.3–2 and 8.3–6. In particular, we can use the results of section 3.6 to get the external fields produced by permanent magnets.

Thus a circular-cylindrical bar of uniform magnetization $\mathbf{M}$ directed parallel to the axis of the bar will have a pole-strength distribution $\sigma_m = \pm(\mu_0 M)$ on each end, and a field on the axis analogous to that of eq. 3.6–1. If the bar is also sufficiently slender, the total pole strengths $q_m = \sigma_m S$ on the two ends can be treated as point poles, their fields calculated by Coulomb's law, and forces on them found from $\mathbf{F} = q_m\mathbf{H}$. Actual bar magnets are rarely uniform in magnetization near the ends, and in fact $\nabla \cdot \mathbf{M}$ is generally not zero, with the result that there is a volume distribution ρ_m in these regions. For points not too near the magnet, each region can to a good approximation be replaced by a point pole. The field at great distances from any uniform or nearly uniform magnet will be a dipole field, namely that of a dipole located at the center of the magnet of moment given by the integral of $\mathbf{M}$ over the volume:

$$\mathbf{m} = \int_\tau \mathbf{M} \, d\tau \qquad (8.3\text{–}10)$$

For a uniform magnet, $\mathbf{m} = \mathbf{M}\tau$. The torque on it in a uniform field is

$$\mathscr{L} = \tau(\mathbf{M} \times \mathbf{B}) = \mathbf{m} \times \mathbf{B} = \mathbf{p}_m \times \mathbf{H} \qquad (8.3\text{–}11)$$

A uniformly magnetized sphere will have an external field even at points near its surface corresponding to that of a dipole of moment

$$\mathbf{m} = \tfrac{4}{3}\pi R^3 \mathbf{M} \qquad (8.3\text{–}12)$$

located at its center, in accordance with section 3.6.

The magnetic shell which is the equivalent of the disk electret has already been treated.   Let us make use of it to compare a solenoid to a bar magnet.   If the helical winding of a long uniformly wound solenoid can be replaced without sensible error by a set of closed circular loops, we can then replace each loop by a magnetic disk.   The resultant set of disks taken together form a cylindrical bar magnet.   If there are n_l turns per meter in the original solenoid, the strength of the shell formed by the discs in a length dx will be $dM_S = n_l i\, dx$.   The magnetic moment per

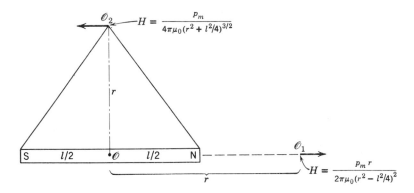

Fig. 8.3a.   Calculating H outside a bar magnet.

unit volume will then be $dM_S/dx = n_l i$.   Thus, the solenoid is equivalent to a uniform magnet whose magnetization is given by

$$M = n_l i \qquad (8.3\text{--}13)$$

We can confirm this statement by finding **H** outside the solenoid, on its axis, both from the direct calculation, eq. 7.5–10 and by analogy from eq. 3.6–3.   By either method we find

$$H = \frac{M}{2}(\cos\theta_1 + \cos\theta_2) = \frac{n_l i}{2}(\cos\theta_1 + \cos\theta_2) \qquad (8.3\text{--}14)$$

where the angles θ_1 and θ_2 are to be found in Figs. 3.6a and 7.5i.

For a slender magnet or solenoid, the angles of eq. 8.3–14 can be approximated in terms of the radius a of the bar and the distances $r + l/2$ and $r - l/2$ from the point where H is wanted ($\mathcal{O}_1$ in Fig. 8.3a) to the centers of the two end faces (r is the distance to the center of the bar, and l is its length).   Alternatively, the field can be found by use of the pole strengths $q_m = \pm\mu_0 M\pi a^2$.   The calculation is left to the reader (problems 8.3a and b), the result being

$$H = p_m r/[2\pi\mu_0(r^2 - l^2/4)^2] \qquad (8.3\text{--}15)$$

where $p_m = q_m l = \mu_0 M \pi a^2 l$, the magnetic moment of the entire magnet or solenoid. If the pole strength is distributed over small regions near the ends, l represents the distance between the approximate centers of these distributions.

Another simple and useful calculation is that for the field at a distance r from the center of the bar on a line perpendicular to the axis. The pole method is the simplest for this case. We find (problem 8.3b)

$$H = p_m/[4\pi\mu_0(r^2 + l^2/4)^{\frac{3}{2}}] \tag{8.3-16}$$

The similarity of eq. 8.3–15 and 8.3–16 to the expressions for the dipole

Fig. 8.3b. Resultant currents in a bar magnet.

fields at these points is evident. A dipole at $\mathcal{O}$ directed along SN would have a field at $\mathcal{O}_1$ given by the equivalent of eq. 3.1–7a

$$H = p_m/2\pi\mu_0 r^3 \tag{8.3-17}$$

and a field at $\mathcal{O}_2$ given by the equivalent of eq. 3.1–7b:

$$H = p_m/4\pi\mu_0 r^3 \tag{8.3-18}$$

We see that the dipole moment of the bar is the main factor in determining the field. The length l is of lesser importance at distances r that are by any appreciable amount larger than l. It is not always easy to locate the proper centers of the pole strengths so as to measure l; $\mathbf{p}_m$ can always be found with greater accuracy. The best way to find q_m is by the formula $q_m = \mathbf{p}_m/l$.[6]

The Current Analysis. Another way of calculating the combined effects of all the elementary dipoles in a magnet is to generalize the similarity between a solenoid and a uniform magnet (shown in Fig. 8.3b). The current loops in an arbitrary magnetic medium can be added so as to

[6] For the application of these formulas to magnetometer measurements, see almost any laboratory manual; also F. K. Harris, *Electrical Measurements*, John Wiley, New York, 1952, pp 356–360.

give a net volume current density $\mathbf{J}_m$, with a surface current of surface density J_{Sm} running around the sides of the piece of material.   This surface current will give rise to a discontinuity in the component of **B** parallel to the surface, just as occurs for the solenoid.   If the magnetization is uniform all the currents will cancel each other in the interior and only the surface current will be left.   The greatest surface density of current will occur

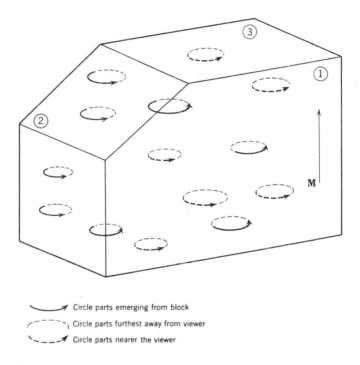

Circle parts emerging from block

Circle parts furthest away from viewer

Circle parts nearer the viewer

Fig. 8.3c.   A fragment of magnetized material with a few exaggerated atomic currents. Shown are surfaces: (1) parallel to **M**, (2) at an angle with **M**, (3) normal to **M**.

for surfaces parallel to **M**, for then the largest uncanceled currents can appear on the surface.   (Cf. Fig. 8.3c.)   A surface perpendicular to **M** will have no surface currents running in one direction along it, but could be thought of as having a current circulating around it, or a distribution of such currents.   The discontinuity in the tangential component of **B** for an arbitrarily oriented surface can be found by calculating the surface current density J_S produced by the uncanceled atomic currents, and using the result of problem 7.5h, namely, that $B_{t1} - B_{t2} = \mu_0 J_S$.

The net uncanceled current density $\mathbf{J}_m$ in the interior of a piece of magnetized material may be calculated as follows.   An arbitrarily oriented elementary current is equivalent in its magnetic effect to a sum of three current loops in the three coordinate planes, since the area vector **S** of the loop can be resolved into components (see the discussion on area vectors in Appendix A.2). The current $J_x \, \Delta y \, \Delta z$ through a small area normal to the x-direction (Fig. 8.3d) then comes only from the components of the current loops that are normal to this area. Any loop that both enters and leaves the area contributes no net current; it is only those that circulate about the boundary that count.

Along a side parallel to the z-axis, only currents whose normals are along z will count. Every loop whose center lies within a cylinder of

Fig. 8.3d. Only currents that go around the boundary of the area contribute to the current through it.

length Δz and area S_z, where S_z is the average area of the z-component of an atomic current loop, will surround the side in question. If n is the number of atoms per unit volume and i is the current in each, the total current contributed by this side will be

$$inS_z \, \Delta z = nm_z \, \Delta z = M_z \, \Delta z = \mathbf{M} \cdot \mathbf{\Delta l}$$

Thus the total current will be the circulation of **M**, $\oint \mathbf{M} \cdot \mathbf{dl}$ around the area, and the current density will be the z-component of the circulation density or curl of **M**.

The same will hold for the other components, so we can write for the magnetization current density $\mathbf{J}_m$ the equation

$$\mathbf{J}_m = \mathbf{\nabla} \times \mathbf{M} \qquad\qquad (8.3\text{--}19)$$

At a boundary, we can calculate the circulation of **M** around a path as shown in Fig. 8.3e, drawn in the plane of **M** and the normal to the boundary, $\mathbf{1}_n$. Then the circulation is just $M_t \, \Delta x$, plus terms dependent on Δy. If the surface current density is J_{Sm}—it must be normal to the plane of the figure, by eq. 8.3–19—the current surrounded by the path is $J_{Sm}\,\Delta x$. Thus letting $\Delta y \to 0$ we have the result for J_{Sm}

$$J_{Sm} = M_t \qquad\qquad (8.3\text{--}20a)$$

which confirms the qualitative statements made above about variously oriented boundaries.   A vector form for J_{Sm} can be obtained by using the vector product and the unit vector $\mathbf{1}_n$ normal to the surface.   We have

$$\mathbf{J}_{Sm} = \mathbf{M} \times \mathbf{1}_n \qquad\qquad (8.3\text{--}20b)$$

(Compare with problem 7.5h.)

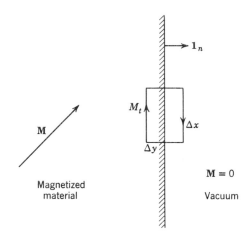

Fig. 8.3e.   Calculation of $\mathbf{J}_{Sm}$.

The current analysis given above can be used, together with $\mathbf{f}_r = \mathbf{J} \times \mathbf{B}$ (problem 7.2c), to calculate the force on a piece of magnetized material, but we shall content ourselves with the pole-analysis method.[7]

Problem 8.3a.   Approximate $\cos\,\theta_1$ and $\cos\,(\pi - \theta_2) = -\cos\theta_2$ in eq. 8.3–14 for the case of a slender bar of radius $a \ll l$, by using $\tan\theta_1 \simeq \theta_1$ etc, and derive eq. 8.3–15.

✓ **Problem 8.3b.**   Derive eqs. 8.3–15 and 8.3–16 by use of the pole concept.

Problem 8.3c.   A very small compass is used to plot the lines of force about a horizontal bar magnet, lying approximately east and west on a large sheet of paper.   Show about where a point of zero field should occur, taking the earth's field into account, and how the value of H_e together with the location of this neutral point can provide a value for the magnetic moment of the magnet. Under what conditions would no neutral point be found?

[7] The current-analysis method is worked out in E. R. Peck, *Electricity and Magnetism* McGraw-Hill, New York, 1953, sections 9.14–9.16.

Problem 8.3d.   For what current would a needle in the center of a pair of Helmholtz coils (problem 7.5f) arranged with their axis in the magnetic east-west direction be deflected 20° from the north direction, if there are 10 turns in each coil, and the radius is 15 cm? The horizontal component of the earth's field is 0.18 × 10⁻⁴ weber/m².

Problem 8.3e.   Two magnets of moments m_1 and m_2 are separated by a distance r large enough that each may be treated as a simple dipole. Find the force on each produced by the other if they lie (a) with their axes parallel and along **r**; (b) if one lies with its axis along **r** and one with its axis perpendicular to **r** and (c) if they are parallel but both axes are perpendicular to **r**. (Cf. problem 3.2b.)

Problem 8.3f.   Find the torques on each magnet in the circumstances of problem 8.3e.

Problem 8.3g.   Explain why in certain cases in problem 8.3f, the torques are not equal and opposite.

Problem 8.3h.   A cylindrical bar of length 8.0 cm and radius 0.5 cm has a magnetization **M** that is everywhere parallel to its axis, but whose value depends symmetrically on the distance x from the plane perpendicular to the axis and through its center, as follows: For $-0.030 < x < 0.030$ m, $P_m = 2.5 \times 10^{-2}$ weber/m²; for $0.030 < x < 0.040$ m, $P_m = 2.5 \times 10^{-2}[1 - 0.5 \times 10^4(x - 0.03)^2]$; and P_m has a similar variation for $-0.040 < x < -0.030$ m. Find the pole strength on the ends of the magnet and the volume density at distance x from the central plane. Find the total amount of positive pole. Find the dipole moment of the bar and hence the distance l to be used if the total pole strength of each sign is to be considered as concentrated at a point.

Problem 8.3i.   A bar magnet whose length is 8.0 cm has effectively point poles on its ends of strengths ±200 emu. Find the magnetic field at points 14 cm from the center of the bar (a) on the axis of the bar; (b) on a perpendicular to the axis; (c) on a line that makes an angle of 30° with the axis.

Problem 8.3j.   How far away from the magnet in problem 8.3i does the dipole formula for H fit the more accurate formula within 1% (a) along the axis and (b) along a perpendicular to the axis?

Problem 8.3k.   Show that, if the exponent of $1/r$ in eq. 8.2–8 is n instead of 2, the ratio of the expressions in eqs. 8.3–17 and 8.3–18 is similarly modified. (This fact is used in Gauss' method of verifying Coulomb's law for poles.)

Problem 8.3l.   A compass needle 3 cm long, 2 mm wide, and 1 mm thick has a uniform magnetization parallel to its length of $M = 0.32 \times 10^6$ amp/m. It is located midway between two parallel wires 10 cm apart, each carrying 50 amp but in opposite directions. Find the torque on the needle when it is parallel to the wires.

Problem 8.3m.   Find the force on a thin uniform bar magnet produced by a point pole a distance h from its near end, along the axis, by direct integration of eq. 8.3–5 and by use of the poles on the bar.

Problem 8.3n.   The magnet of problem 8.3i is held on the axis of a circular coil bearing 300 amp-turns (powered by a constant-current generator) whose radius is 10 cm.   The magnet and the coil are oriented with their north poles towards each other.   Find the force on the magnet in terms of the distance z between centers of coil and magnet.   Find the work done in bringing the magnet to the center of the coil from infinity.   How much work is then done by the generator?

8.4   B and H Inside Magnetic Material

The pole method breaks down when we try to calculate the magnetic induction **B** inside magnetic material, for we can no longer deal with points that are far from all sources of field.   Furthermore, a field calculated everywhere by the pole theory would have lines with beginnings and endings, which is a property not possessed by **B**.   Although we have defined **B** in terms of the Lorentz force on a moving charge, this definition is a rather theoretical one inside matter, for any ordinary measurement of the force $q(\mathbf{v} \times \mathbf{B})$ would involve making a cavity of some sort.   The situation is closely analogous to the problem of defining **E** in a dielectric medium by the equation $\mathbf{F} = q\mathbf{E}$.   However, there are certain differences.   High-speed charged particles can be allowed to pass through a piece of magnetized iron.   Their resultant displacement can be measured, leading to a certain average value of **B** over the path taken by the particle.   Neutrons, which are electrically neutral although each possesses a magnetic moment $\mathbf{m}_n$, can also be deflected within a piece of magnetic material, and a measure of an average of $(\mathbf{m}_n \cdot \nabla)\mathbf{B}$ thus obtained.

More importantly, the induced emf in a coil of wire around a piece of magnetic material can be readily measured, so that $d\Phi/dt$ can be found, where Φ is given by values of **A** outside the medium but can also be calculated by an integral $\int_S \mathbf{B} \cdot \mathbf{dS}$ over a surface which passes through the medium.

We can say, therefore, that to a limited extent we *can* measure **B** in the medium.   We can certainly define it as an average over all points in a region of suitable size of the induction produced by all sources.   We are chiefly interested, however, in expressing **B** in the medium in terms of the field in suitable cavities.   We can maintain a similarity to the electrostatic case by defining **H** as an auxiliary field vector that is calculated from the pole strengths introduced in the last section, as well as from currents in circuits that we do not choose to treat in terms of poles.   We shall see that this auxiliary field is, like **D** in the dielectric case, of considerable use even if it does not give a force on a unit of any existing physical entity.

If we consider a slot or coin-shaped cavity oriented in any direction, we see that the component of **B** normal to the slot surfaces is the same in the slot as in the medium, but the tangential component differs by $\mu_0 J_{Sm}$

in accordance with the result of problem 7.5h. In fact, we can write boundary conditions in general

$$B_{n1} = B_{n2} \tag{8.4-1}$$

$$B_{t1} - B_{t2} = \mu_0 J_{Sm} = \mu_0 M_t = \mu_0 \left| \mathbf{M} \times \mathbf{1}_n \right| \tag{8.4-2}$$

where in the second equation we have used eq. 8.3–20 (cf. problem 3.5a concerning $D_{t1} - D_{t2}$).

If we have a slot cut perpendicular to $\mathbf{M}$, M_t will be zero, and $\mathbf{B}$ itself will be the same in the slot as in the medium.   Thus the flux through a coil wound around a magnetic core can be calculated by imagining a thin slot to be cut through the core and finding the flux through a surface lying in the slot.   Or, we may simply imagine a Gaussian surface passed through the core that does not cut any atoms, as being equivalent to one in a slot.

We can, of course, calculate $\mathbf{B}$ in a slot by the pole method, since points in the slot are removed from the neighborhood of any atom.   But by a calculation identical with that for eq. 3.4–6, the field $\mathbf{B}/\mu_0 = \mathbf{H}_{cav}$ can be written

$$\frac{\mathbf{B}_{cav}}{\mu_0} = \mathbf{H}_{cav} = \mathbf{H}' + \frac{(\mu_0 \mathbf{M})}{\mu_0} = \mathbf{H}' + \mathbf{M}$$

$$\text{(Slot perpendicular to } \mathbf{M}\text{)} \quad (8.4\text{--}3)$$

where $\mathbf{H}'$ is the field calculated from all the pole strength on the material except that on the cavity walls and from all other sources of magnetic field outside the piece of material in question.   The term $\mathbf{M}$ in eq. 8.4–3 gives the contribution from the pole strength $\sigma_m = \pm \mu_0 M_n$ on the surfaces of the cavity.

In a needle-like drill-hole cavity parallel to $\mathbf{M}$, there will be no contribution to $\mathbf{B}$ from local equivalent pole strength.   Therefore we have

$$\frac{\mathbf{B}_{cav}}{\mu_0} = \mathbf{H}_{cav} = \mathbf{H}' \quad \text{(Drill hole parallel to } \mathbf{M}\text{)} \tag{8.4-4}$$

The induction will be reduced from that in the medium, because (using the current analysis rather than the pole analysis) the surface current $J_S = M_t = M$ on the side of the drill hole runs in a direction to produce a field within the cavity in the opposite direction to $\mathbf{M}$.   Another way of seeing this result is to consider that such a hole does not pass through any elementary current, whereas most of the flux will pass through these currents.   The average flux taken across a small drill hole will not be a proper average, for it will overweight the spaces between the atomic currents against their interiors.   Furthermore, just as in the dielectric case, the component of $\mathbf{B}/\mu_0$ parallel to the axis of an arbitrarily directed drill hole is seen on the pole analysis to be the component of $\mathbf{H}'$ in that direction.

Finally, consider the average induction **B** that acts on a piece of magnetic material.   For the dielectric case, we showed in section 3.9 that for spherical symmetry the average field acting on a piece of material is **E** + **P**/$3\epsilon_0$.   Therefore, by the identical calculation we must have the average **H** acting on a spherical piece of magnetic material equal to **H**′ + **P**$_m$/$3\mu_0$.[8]   We should expect the properties of the medium to be expressible in terms of a relation between the average moment **m** of an atom or molecule and this effective **H**.   Such a relation, can, however, be directly transformed into a relation between **H**′ and **M**.   Thus we see that **H**′ not only appears in the formulas for the cavity fields, but also can be used in a similar way to **E** for dielectrics in describing experimental results on magnetizability.

Therefore we shall define **H** to be a vector field calculated *everywhere*, inside a medium and out, from poles on magnetic media and from laboratory or macroscopic currents.   The symbol **H**′ will henceforth be replaced by **H**.

From eq. 8.4–3, we see that an exactly equivalent definition can be written as

$$\mathbf{H} = \frac{\mathbf{B}}{\mu_0} - \mathbf{M} \qquad (8.4\text{-}5a)$$

which can be written like the electrostatic formula **D** = ϵ_0**E** + **P**:

$$\mathbf{B} = \mu_0(\mathbf{H} + \mathbf{M}) = \mu_0\mathbf{H} + \mathbf{P}_m \qquad \text{MKS} \qquad (8.4\text{-}5b)$$

$$\mathbf{B} = \mathbf{H} + 4\pi\mathbf{M} \qquad\qquad \text{Gaussian} \qquad (8.4\text{-}5c)$$

Our analogy to electrostatics is now complete.   The vectors **E** and **H** can be calculated in the same way for dielectrics and for magnetizable material, and **D** and **B** can be found from them in the same way.   However, we should reiterate that the two fundamental vectors are **E** and **B** and that **D** and **H** are auxiliary vectors that are useful but do not represent forces on physical entities.   Finally, of course, **E** has contributions from free charges, whereas **H** has contributions from ordinary conduction currents, and also from displacement currents.

Let us, in fact, calculate the curl of **H**.   By eq. 7.8–3, applied to a path lying in a needle-like tunnel through the medium, $\oint \mathbf{H} \cdot \mathbf{dl} = \oint \mathbf{B} \cdot \mathbf{dl}/\mu_0$ is equal to all the current surrounded.   But such a tunnel surrounds *no*

---

[8] If spherical symmetry does not hold, the factor 1/3 will be changed.   Spherical symmetry may obtain in some cases for regions containing large numbers of elementary crystals, but for smaller regions in iron and similar materials it certainly fails (see section 8.6).

atomic currents, so that we can write the circuital form of Ampère's law as

$$\mathcal{H} = \oint \mathbf{H} \cdot \mathbf{dl} = \sum_k i_k + \frac{d\Phi_D}{dt} \qquad \text{MKS} \quad (8.4\text{-}6a)$$

$$\mathcal{H} = \oint \mathbf{H} \cdot \mathbf{dl} = \frac{4\pi}{c} \sum_k i_k + \frac{1}{c}\frac{d\Phi_D}{dt} \qquad \text{Gaussian} \quad (8.4\text{-}6b)$$

where the currents i_k refer to macroscopic currents only, and the displacement current is included for completeness. The quantity $\mathcal{H}$ is called the "magnetomotive force" or mmf, in analogy with induced emf. Its unit in the MKS system is the ampere, more commonly called the ampere-turn because the sum in eq. 8.4–6a becomes ni for a coil of n turns carrying a current i. The Gaussian unit of mmf is called the gilbert.

Similarly, we can write the Maxwell form of Ampère's law so as to include macroscopic current densities only:

$$\nabla \times \mathbf{H} = \mathbf{J} + \frac{\partial \mathbf{D}}{\partial t} \qquad \text{MKS} \quad (8.4\text{-}7a)$$

$$\nabla \times \mathbf{H} = \frac{4\pi\mathbf{J}}{c} + \frac{1}{c}\frac{\partial \mathbf{D}}{\partial t} \qquad \text{Gaussian} \quad (8.4\text{-}7b)$$

These current densities might include conduction currents in the magnetic medium itself (since such currents would not be counted in computing $\mathbf{M}$). Equations 8.4–7 and 8.4–5 are consistent with eq. 8.3 19 for $\mathbf{J}_m$, for we have

$$\nabla \times \mathbf{B} = \mu_0\nabla \times \mathbf{H} + \mu_0\nabla \times \mathbf{M} = \mu_0\mathbf{J} + \mu_0\frac{\partial \mathbf{D}}{\partial t} + \mu_0\mathbf{J}_m \quad (8.4\text{-}8)$$

which is eq. 7.8–2 with the total current density $\mathbf{J}$ divided into macroscopic and magnetization parts.

The boundary conditions for $\mathbf{B}$ and $\mathbf{H}$ are similar to those for $\mathbf{D}$ and $\mathbf{E}$. The tangential component of $\mathbf{H}$ is the same on both sides of a boundary provided no large-scale currents run along the boundary surface:

$$H_{t1} = H_{t2} \text{ (at a magnetic boundary that is free of}$$
$$\text{macroscopic currents)} \quad (8.4\text{-}9)$$

The normal components of $\mathbf{H}$ differ by the difference in $\mathbf{M}_n$'s (cf. problem 3.5a):

$$H_{n1} - H_{n2} = M_{n2} - M_{n1} \qquad \text{MKS} \quad (8.4\text{-}10)$$

Another feature of electrostatics whose analogue has not yet been given is Gauss' law for $\mathbf{E}$. (Gauss' law for $\mathbf{D}$ has the analogue $\int_{\text{closed } S} \mathbf{B} \cdot d\mathbf{S} = 0$ or div $\mathbf{B} = 0$.) We can clearly derive a result for $\mathbf{H}$ that

$$\int_{\text{closed } S} \mathbf{H} \cdot d\mathbf{S} = \frac{1}{\mu_0} \sum_k q_{m,k} \qquad (8.4\text{--}11)$$

where the sum can be replaced by surface and volume integrals wherever appropriate. The corresponding differential relationship is

$$\nabla \cdot \mathbf{H} = \frac{\rho_m}{\mu_0} \qquad (8.4\text{--}12)$$

which also follows directly from div $\mathbf{B} = 0$ and div $\mathbf{P}_m = -\rho_m$.

The $\mathbf{H}$ field inside a magnet can be found by comparison with the electret case. In particular, the $\mathbf{H}$ inside a uniformly magnetized cylindrical bar lies in the opposite direction to $\mathbf{B}$ and is given in some detail by the formulas for $\mathbf{E}$ in section 3.6. The strong reverse field just inside the ends of the bar provides a negative effective field acting on any given atom, of magnitude $\mathbf{H}_{\text{eff}} = -\mathbf{P}_m/2\mu_0 + \mathbf{P}_m/3\mu_0 = -\mathbf{P}_m/6\mu_0$.[9] This field is called the "demagnetizing field" and accounts for the tendency of permanent magnets to lose their magnetization. The same thing of course holds true for electrets. The demagnetizing field will be discussed further in section 8.6.

Lines of $\mathbf{H}$ evidently may either end on poles or continuously circulate, only coming back on themselves in ideally symmetric cases. In this respect they resemble lines of $\mathbf{E}$ that may have both electrostatic and electromagnetic origin.

Problem 8.4a.   Prove eqs. 8.4–9 and 8.4–10.

Problem 8.4b.   A uniform cylindrical bar magnet, 20 cm long and 5 cm in diameter, has a total magnetic moment p_m equal to 10^{-8} weber-meter. Find the field that acts on a small sphere of material (*a*) at the center of the bar, and (*b*) just inside one end.   Also find $\mathbf{B}$ and $\mathbf{H}$ at each of these positions.

Problem 8.4c.   Show by means of the electrostatic analogy that **curl H** can have no contribution from any magnetized material that does not carry any macroscopic currents.

Problem 8.4d.   Prove the formula $\mu_0(\mathbf{H} + \mathbf{M})$ for the induction $\mathbf{B}$ inside a piece of magnetized material by considering first the field due to the material outside a sphere of suitable size, as in section 3.4, and second the field produced by the sphere itself at its center.   For the latter, show that an integral $\int \mathbf{B}\, d\tau$ over the field of a magnetic dipole at the center of a sphere is required, and reduce this integral by use of eqs. A.2–26 and 8.2–12.

---

[9] The $\frac{1}{3}$ and $\frac{1}{6}$ will be different for cases without spherical symmetry.

Problem 8.4e.   Using eq. 8.2–12 for the vector potential of the dipole moment $\mathbf{M}\,d\tau$, the vector identity $\nabla \times (u\mathbf{M}) = u\nabla \times \mathbf{M} - \mathbf{M} \times \nabla u$, and eq. A.2–26, prove the following formula for the vector potential produced by an arbitrary magnet (cf. eq. 7.6–8):

$$\mathbf{A} = \frac{\mu_0}{4\pi} \int_\tau \frac{\mathbf{J}_m\,d\tau}{r} + \frac{\mu_0}{4\pi} \int_S \frac{\mathbf{J}_{Sm}\,dS}{r} \qquad (8.4\text{–}13)$$

✓ **Problem 8.4f.**   Find **B** and **H** in the interior and also outside an iron sphere uniformly magnetized parallel to a certain direction.

✓ **Problem 8.4g.**   Find **B** and **H** inside a uniformly magnetized circular disk, with **M** normal to its plane.   (Neglect edge effects.)

Problem 8.4h.   A spherical shell of internal radius a and external radius b is magnetized along the radius, with $\mathbf{M} = k\mathbf{r}$, where k is a constant.   Find ρ_m, σ_m, **B** and **H** wherever they do not vanish.

✓ **Problem 8.4i.**   A cylindrical rod of magnetic material whose radius is a and length is l is magnetized so that the lines of **M** are circles coaxial with the cylinder, with $M = Kr$, where K is a constant.   Calculate ρ_m, σ_m, $\mathbf{J}_m$ and $\mathbf{J}_{Sm}$ wherever they do not vanish, and find **B** and **H** inside the cylinder.

8.5   Properties of Magnetic Materials

We have seen that the value of **H** within a medium is a suitable quantity to which we can relate the production and variation of **M**.   However, it is usually more convenient to relate **B** and **H** than **M** and **H**, just as we use **D** and **E** in place of **P** and **E** for dielectrics.

Let us consider how we can measure **B**, **M**, and **H** for a given piece of material whose properties are to be studied.   Now **H** is the field produced by poles and laboratory currents; in order to make meaningful measurements, the effects of poles on the sample in question must be eliminated, because knowledge of them depends on knowledge of the properties being measured.   The use of poles on other objects as in permanent magnets or iron cores of electromagnets is often unsatisfactory since the presence of the sample may alter these other pole strengths.

The simplest way of eliminating poles in the sample is to make the material in question in the form of a ring and magnetize it so that **M** is (at least approximately) directed parallel to its surface, making $M_n = 0$.   If the ring is homogeneously magnetized, $\nabla \cdot \mathbf{M}$ will also vanish, so that there will be no pole strength.   Then **H** can be found from the current in a coil wrapped uniformly around the ring, by the methods of Chapter 7.

A way of reducing the effect of the poles, while not eliminating them, is to use a piece of material in the form of a very slender rod, so that the pole field over most of the specimen is very small compared with the external field.   In this case, it is important either to measure the magnetization M in the center of the rod or to measure an average of M throughout, say by measuring the total moment **m** of the specimen.

If the magnetization is very weak, it may be possible to disregard the pole field altogether, so that weakly magnetic materials can be studied in any shapes.   In this case, **H** may be a field of any sort—e.g., a field between the poles of a strong magnet.

The measurement of **B** is made by use of the emf generated in a suitable coil wound around a specimen.   The quantity actually detected is of course $d\Phi/dt$, where Φ is the entire flux through the test coil.   Thus we do not study **B** itself but the rate of change of its average over an appropriate surface in the material.   If the material is sufficiently homogeneous, the average will have a good physical meaning, with respect to a study of the intrinsic magnetic properties of the material.

The coil in such a case is usually connected to some type of galvanometer (see section 8.8).   The galvanometer will have a certain resistance and also an inductance.   Furthermore, the coil itself will have inductance that is not related to the flux we are measuring.   Indeed, if the current that flows in the measuring circuit is not sufficiently small, the measurement will be interfered with.   Let us then assume that the current is small, and let L and R be the *total* inductance and resistance in the measuring circuit.   The equation for the circuit is then (treating $d\Phi/dt$ as a positive emf)

$$\frac{d\Phi}{dt} = L\frac{di}{dt} + iR \tag{8.5-1}$$

Let us multiply both sides of the equation by dt and integrate over an arbitrary time interval (writing $i = dQ/dt$)

$$\int d\Phi = L\int di + R\int dQ$$

$$\Delta\Phi = L\,\Delta i + RQ \tag{8.5-2}$$

where $\Delta\Phi$, Δi, and Q are respectively the change in flux, the change in current, and the charge that passed around the circuit, in the arbitrary time interval.   We see by eq. 8.5-2 that it is the change of flux that can be measured and that, if we measure this change from a time when i is zero to another time when i also is zero (so that $\Delta i = 0$), we can reduce the problem of flux measurement to measurement of Q and knowledge of R.   The inductance, which even for small currents depends on the specimen being studied, does not appear in the final result.   The result is

$$Q = \frac{\Delta\Phi}{R} \tag{8.5-3}$$

for the charge Q passing any point of the circuit while Φ changes by $\Delta\Phi$. Methods of measuring Q will be treated in section 8.8.

Since only changes in flux are measured, there is a constant Φ_0 which is not directly known. This constant is usually made equal to zero by the process of treating the sample symmetrically with respect to two opposite directions by continued reversals of **H**.

The value of **M** for a sample in the form of a slender rod can be measured directly by finding the field produced by its total moment **m** at a distant magnetometer.[10]   The field **H** of the magnetizing coil needs to be balanced out by use of another similar coil on the other side of the magnetometer needle. If the sample is weakly magnetized and sufficiently small, we can measure the force on it when it is placed in an inhomogeneous field, and relate the moment **m** calculated from $\mathbf{F} = (\mathbf{m} \cdot \nabla)\mathbf{H}$ to the value of **H** at its center or to an average of **H** taken over its volume (cf. problem 8.5a).

Diamagnetic and Paramagnetic Materials. Measurements of the last-mentioned type show that nearly all substances can be classified into two general groups as regards their magnetic properties. One group, comprising the diamagnetic and paramagnetic materials, is very weakly magnetic and is linear and isotropic in behavior, so that **M**, **H**, and **B** are all proportional. The other group, consisting of the ferromagnetic substances, is very strongly magnetic, and its representatives are all decidedly non-linear. The exceptions consist of some very strongly paramagnetic salts and various substances exhibiting antiferromagnetism and ferrimagnetism (see the end of section 8.6).

For the linear materials, we can write

$$\mathbf{B} = \mu \mathbf{H} \qquad \text{MKS and Gaussian} \qquad (8.5\text{--}4)$$

and by analogy with $\kappa = \epsilon/\epsilon_0$, set

$$\mu_r = \mu/\mu_0 \qquad\qquad \text{MKS} \quad (8.5\text{--}5)$$

Furthermore, we shall set, for the proportionality of **M** and **H** in both systems of units,

$$\mathbf{M} = \chi_m \mathbf{H} \qquad\qquad\qquad (8.5\text{--}6)$$

from which (with $\mathbf{B} = \mu_0(\mathbf{H} + \mathbf{M})$ or $\mathbf{B} = \mathbf{H} + 4\pi\mathbf{M}$) we deduce readily that

$$\chi_m = \mu_r - 1 \qquad\qquad \text{MKS} \quad (8.5\text{--}7a)$$

$$\chi_m = \frac{\mu - 1}{4\pi} \qquad\qquad \text{Gaussian} \quad (8.5\text{--}7b)$$

The quantity μ is called the permeability of the medium, μ_r the relative permeability ($\mu_r = \mu$ in the Gaussian system), and χ_m the magnetic susceptibility.

[10] Cf. references in footnote 6, p. 345.

Diamagnetic substances are those for which $\mu_r < 1$ or χ_m is negative. As indicated in section 7.12, these substances are those whose atoms or molecules have no appreciable permanent magnetic moments that can line themselves up with an applied field, so that the diamagnetic effect of induced emf's in all the circulating currents prevails. Paramagnetic substances have small positive values of χ_m. Their molecules have permanent magnetic moments, which tend to rotate toward the direction of an applied field (more strictly, they precess in gyroscopic fashion, but nevertheless add to the field).

Tables 8.5*A* and 8.5*B* list the diamagnetic and paramagnetic susceptibilities for a number of common substances. It will be seen that the latter

Table 8.5A
Relative Permeabilities of Diamagnetic Materials

	μ_r
Antimony	$1 - 7.0 \times 10^{-5}$
Bismuth	$1 - 1.7 \times 10^{-4}$
Copper	$1 - 0.94 \times 10^{-5}$
Lead	$1 - 1.7 \times 10^{-5}$
Mercury	$1 - 3.2 \times 10^{-5}$
Quartz	$1 - 1.5 \times 10^{-5}$
Silver	$1 - 2.6 \times 10^{-5}$
Water	$1 - 0.88 \times 10^{-5}$
Argon (NTP)	$1 - 0.95 \times 10^{-8}$
Hydrogen (NTP)	$1 - 0.21 \times 10^{-8}$

NTP = Normal temperature (0°C) and pressure (1 atm)

Table 8.5B
Relative Permeabilities of Paramagnetic Materials

	μ_r
Aluminum	$1 + 0.21 \times 10^{-4}$
Neodymium	$1 + 3.0 \times 10^{-3}$
Oxygen (liquid at $-182°$C) .	$1 + 4.0 \times 10^{-3}$
Palladium	$1 + 8.2 \times 10^{-4}$
Platinum	$1 + 2.9 \times 10^{-4}$
Air (NTP)	$1 + 3.6 \times 10^{-7}$
Oxygen (NTP)	$1 + 17.9 \times 10^{-7}$

are numerically larger than the former but nevertheless always very small compared to 1.

A small paramagnetic object placed in an inhomogeneous magnetic field will be attracted toward the strongest part of the field, in similar fashion to the small dielectric object considered in section 3.8, where the force as given by eq. 3.8–7 is proportional to the susceptibility χ. A diamagnetic object, on the other hand, will experience a force toward the weaker part of the field, since χ_m is then negative. It is not easy to measure

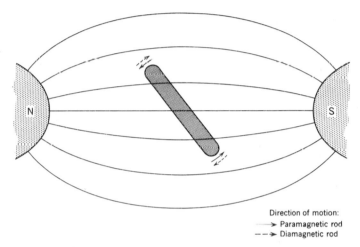

Direction of motion:
→ Paramagnetic rod
– – → Diamagnetic rod

Fig. 8.5a. An inhomogeneous field weaker in its center. [Adapted from A. R. Laufer, *Am. Journ. Phys.* 19, 275 (1951).]

the small forces involved, but, if a small rod of material is suspended on a light thread attached to its center of gravity, the torque on the rod can be observed.   When the non-uniformity of the field is of the sort produced by two fairly small poles widely separated and the rod is suspended midway between, it is easy to see that a paramagnetic rod will line up along the field and a diamagnetic one will set itself across the field.   (Fig. 8.5a).

On the other hand, a field of the opposite type of inhomogeneity will produce the opposite results for the two types of substances (Fig. 8.5b). It is therefore quite easy to test for the sign of χ_m for a given material by delicately suspending a rod made of it in a suitably shaped field of a strong magnet.

The effect on paramagnetic and diamagnetic rods in a uniform field is much weaker.   As shown in problem 3.8c, a dielectric rod will tend to line itself along the lines of a uniform electric field.   However, the magnetization is proportional in the magnetic case to χ_m, and the angle between

the resulting magnetization and the external field is nearly proportional
to χ_m. Hence, as in problem 3.8d, the torque is proportional to χ_m^2 and is
in the same sense for both types of materials. The small values of χ_m
for most materials make this second-order effect hard to observe.

The case of a paramagnetic fluid (e.g., gaseous or liquid oxygen)
surrounding a group of permanent magnets is even more difficult to handle
than the case of free charges immersed in a dielectric medium, both because
the magnetic case is inherently more complicated than the electric and

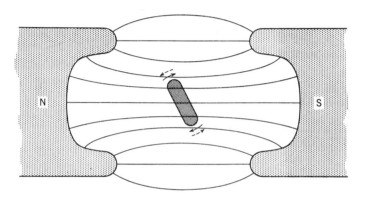

Fig. 8.5b.   An inhomogeneous field stronger in its center.
(Adapted from Laufer, *loc. cit.*)

because isolated poles can only be approximately realized by means of
very long thin magnets. Therefore the use of Coulomb's law for poles
with μ in place of μ_0 is even less meaningful, aside from the fact that
relative paramagnetic and diamagnetic permeabilities in most cases differ
so little from 1. Therefore we shall not treat the case of paramagnetic
fluids in the presence of permanent magnets.

However, the case of a magnetic material which behaves at least approximately like an ideal paramagnetic medium and which fills all the field-
occupied space near non-magnetic wires carrying currents is quite easy
to handle, for in this case **B** is simply μ_r times the **B** that would be produced
in empty space, or $\mathbf{B} = \mu\mathbf{H}$. Thus self-inductance and mutual-inductance
formulas can all have μ_0 replaced by μ. It should be clear from the
discussion in section 3.8 that this substitution will only be correct if there
are no boundaries present that carry poles.

Ferromagnetic materials. These materials are not only non-linear,
but also their magnetization depends on their previous history. Even if
the material is prepared in an isotropic way by making it suitably random
with respect to crystal structure—relieving strains produced in rolling and

cutting by appropriate heat treatments—any magnetization previous to the time that the material is set up for study will be partially retained and so give it a preferred direction.   Actually, most such materials are not isotropic and are studied with respect to magnetization in one or more directions of interest.

Let us describe the properties of such substances, therefore, by considering first a ring made of an unmagnetized, homogeneous, isotropic piece of iron, cobalt, or nickel or a related alloy.   (Some alloys of iron are

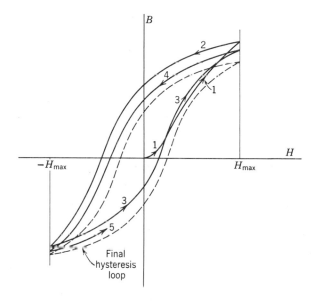

Fig. 8.5c.   The development of a regular hysteresis loop.

strongly paramagnetic but *not* ferromagnetic—e.g., certain stainless steels.) Since ferromagnetism always disappears above a certain temperature characteristic of the material in question, it is not hard to obtain such an unmagnetized sample by suitable heat treatment.[11]   Let us apply a field **H** to the ring by means of a current in the coil and increase it steadily to some maximum value H_{max}.   By measuring $\Delta\Phi$ and taking Φ_0 to be zero, we can plot B versus H.   (Because of the isotropic behavior of the material, **B** will be parallel to **H**.)   We get an initial magnetization curve somewhat like that labeled 1 in Fig. 8.5c.   If now we reduce H to zero and increase it negatively to $-H_{max}$, we get curve 2, showing that B does

---

[11] Some alloys are permanently changed by such heating and must be demagnetized by the methods described later in this section.

not go to zero when H does.   The material "remembers" its magnetization.   Another reversal will yield curve 3, which shows some memory of
the negative B.   Continued repetition leads ultimately to a symmetrical
loop, shown dashed in the figure, which is known as a "hysteresis loop."
In practice, 20 or 30 reversals may be necessary to erase any "memory" of
previous magnetizations.

   The hysteresis loop is the most reproducible indication of the properties
of any given magnetic material, so we shall restrict ourselves to descriptions

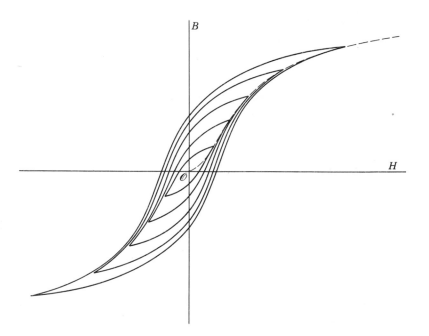

Fig. 8.5d.   A set of hysteresis loops of differing values of H_{max}, and a
normal magnetization curve (dashed).

of magnetic properties based on such loops.   There is a different loop for
each value of H_{max};   a series of such loops for varying values of H_{max} will
describe the behavior of the material in fairly general terms (Fig. 8.5d
shows such a series).   The curve drawn through the tips of the loops is
called a "normal magnetization curve."   It is not identical with curve 1
in Fig. 8.5c but differs from it only slightly.   In fact, the material cannot
be made to follow a normal magnetization curve directly, but it provides a
very useful approximate account of the behavior of the material.

   For any particular loop, there are two points that are of particular interest. The value of $|B|$ for $H = 0$ is called the "residual induction,"[12]B_r. The value of $|H|$ for $B = 0$ is called the coercive force H_c, representing the reverse external field needed to reduce B to zero (cf. Fig. 8.5e).

As loops are taken for larger and larger values of H_{max}, their upper ends approach a straight line of the form $B = \mu_0(H + M_{sat})$ where M_{sat} is a constant and must evidently represent a maximum possible value of M for the material in question. The quantity M_{sat} is called the saturation magnetization. The shape of a hysteresis loop except for its tips remains unchanged for values of H_{max} above that for which $\mu_0 M = B - \mu_0 H = \mu_0 M_{sat}$. The terms "residual induction" and "coercive force" are commonly taken in the literature to refer to maximum values obtained from any loop involving saturation. Substances with large H_c are said to be magnetically "hard," whereas those with small coercive force are called "soft."

More complete information can sometimes be given in graphs of B_r and H_c against H_{max} or B_{max}. For many materials, H_{max}/B_r and H_{max}/H_c are linear functions of H_{max} except for small values of the latter.[13]

The portion of a saturation hysteresis loop for which B is positive but H is negative is called a *demagnetization curve* and is important in the study and design of permanent magnets (cf. section 8.7).

For purposes of ferromagnetic theory, hysteresis loops are often constructed by plotting M vs H. (In gaussian units, the quantity $B - H = 4\pi M$, called the "ferric induction" is often used in place of $M = (B - H)/4\pi$.) However, for most materials, μ is of the order of several hundreds, up to 10^6, and the difference between B and $\mu_0 M$ is negligible, especially in comparison to the variations among samples with composition, heat treatments, and age. Although the shapes of hysteresis loops differ widely from one substance to another, the upper ends of most curves have a hyperbolic shape. The demagnetization curves can also be fitted closely by hyperbolas.

Various kinds of permeability may be defined from a hysteresis loop (see Fig. 8.5e). One may define the *ordinary* or *normal permeability* μ to be B/H for the tip of the loop—that is, for a point on the normal magnetization curve (μ is not used for other points on the loop). Graphs of μ as a function of H_{max} or B_{max} are frequently given in the literature (see Fig. 8.5j). The *differential permeability* is the slope dB/dH of the magnetization curve. Its value for $H = B = 0$ is called the *initial permeability*. If a steady value of H is applied to a specimen and then a small alternating H is superimposed, a minor hysteresis loop will be followed

---

[12] Also called "retentivity," "remanent induction," or "remanence."
[13] H. C. Roters, *Electromagnetic Devices*, John Wiley, New York, 1941, pp. 25–26.

that has its center near the original point on the *B–H* graph to which the specimen was taken (approximately but usually not exactly on the normal curve). The slope of the line connecting the tips of this minor loop is the *incremental permeability*. This quantity is useful for describing the effect of an alternating current in an iron-core coil when a large steady current is also present. A careful measurement of the slope $\Delta B/\Delta H$ of the line obtained by taking the material to a certain point on a hysteresis loop and then reversing the field by a slight amount $-\Delta H$ yields the *reversible permeability* μ_{rev}. It is slightly less than the incremental permeability.

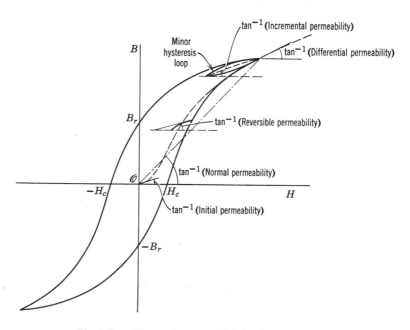

Fig. 8.5e. Illustrating several kinds of permeability.

The reversible susceptibility $\chi_m = (\mu_{\mathrm{rev}}/\mu_0) - 1$ is a quantity important in the development of thermodynamic magnetic theory. The *effective alternating-current permeability* is a suitable average ratio of B/H for the entire loop. One may estimate it by drawing some suitable straight line through the origin and roughly parallel to the sides of the loop, or one may calculate an appropriate analytical average, depending on the experimental circuit arrangement for defining and measuring this permeability.

Finally, the area of a hysteresis loop is significant, as it represents the energy used up in carrying a unit volume of material around the loop. To see this, let us magnetize the sample in a coil and calculate the power expended against the back emf produced by the induction B.   The work done will be

$$W = -\oint_{\text{one cycle}} \mathscr{E}i\, dt = \oint_{\text{cycle}} dt \cdot i \cdot \frac{d\Phi}{dt} = \oint_{\text{cycle}} i\, d\Phi$$

Let us divide all the flux in the material and surrounding space into tubes, each carrying a small amount Φ_1, $\Phi_2 \cdots$.   Let the kth tube link the coil n_k times.   Then

$$W = \oint_{\text{cycle}} i\, d\left[\sum_k n_k \Phi_k\right] = \oint_{\text{cycle}} \sum_k n_k i\, d\Phi_k$$

We can replace $n_k i$ by the mmf $\oint_{\text{tube}} \mathbf{H}_k \cdot \mathbf{dl}_k$, taken along the tube of force. We can also write $\Phi_k = B_k\, \Delta S_k$, where ΔS_k is the cross-sectional area of the kth tube at any point along it, and B_k is the induction at that point. If we assume $\mathbf{B}$ to be parallel to $\mathbf{H}$, we set $\mathbf{H}_k \cdot \mathbf{dl}_k = H_k\, dl_k$ and can finally write

$$W = \oint_{\text{cycle}} \sum_k \oint_{\text{tube}} H_k\, dl_k\, d(B_k\, \Delta S_k) = \sum_k \oint_{\text{tube}} d\tau \oint_{\text{cycle}} H_k\, dB_k$$

$$= \int_\tau d\tau \oint_{\text{cycle}} H\, dB \qquad (8.5\text{–}8)$$

assuming further that we can take the area of the tubes as constant in time.   We have written $dl_k\, \Delta S_k = d\tau$, and by summing over k obtained an integral over the volume τ of the specimen.   But, as shown in Fig. 8.5f, the integral $\oint H\, dB$ is the area of the loop, all areas outside it canceling in the calculation.   This energy goes of course into heating the material.

Thus if a continually alternating current is used to produce H, the energy lost per cycle can be found from the area, and a graph of areas against H or B is another useful representation of the properties of a magnetic substance.   The situation is complicated by the fact that induced currents in the material of the core ("eddy currents") will tend to produce an opposite H in the sample and require a larger applied one for the same B, so that a loop measured with alternating currents will be fatter along the H-axis than one measured by the methods of this chapter, by an amount that depends on the resistivity and structure of the magnetic material and on the frequency.

Figures 8.5g, h, i, and j, show hysteresis loops, magnetization curves, and permeability curves for a selected group of magnetic materials.   Tables 8.5C and 8.5D list relevant properties of these materials.[14]

[14] A more complete description of a variety of steels and alloys is given in S. S. Attwood, *Electric and Magnetic Fields*, 3rd ed., John Wiley, New York, 1949, Chapters 13 and 14.   A good summary of the various magnetic properties of use in magnets of all sorts is given in H. C. Roters, *op. cit.*, Chapter II.

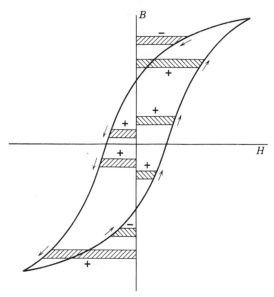

Fig. 8.5f. A hysteresis loop, showing various positions of elements of area $H dB$ for the integral $\int H \, dB$. The direction of integration and the signs of the resulting contributions are indicated.

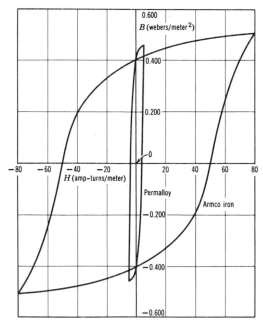

Fig. 8.5g. Hysteresis curves for permalloy and Armco iron. [Adapted from H. D. Arnold and G. W. Elmen, *Journ. Frank. Inst.*, **195**, 630 (1923).]

Table 8.5C

Properties of Typical Ferromagnetic Materials

Material	Initial Relative Permeability μ_{ri}	Maximum Relative Permeability μ_{rm}	Saturation Magnetization M_{sat}	Hysteresis Loss at Saturation W_∞	Residual Induction B_r	Coercive Force H_c	Curie Temperature T_c
			$\dfrac{\text{webers}}{\text{meter}^2}$	$\dfrac{\text{joules}}{\text{meter}^3}$	$\dfrac{\text{webers}}{\text{meter}^2}$	$\dfrac{\text{amperes}}{\text{meter}}$	°C
Cast iron	...	600	...	2000	0.53	366	
4 Si-Iron (Transformer)	400	6,700	2.0	350	1.2	40	690
Hipernik	3,000	70,000	1.65	22	0.73	3.2	500
Permendur	800	5,000	2.4	1200	1.4	159	1000
45–25 Perminvar	365	1,800	1.55	400	0.33	111	715
Supermalloy	100,000	1,050,000	0.8	...	...	0.32	400

Note: Values for μ_{ri}, μ_{rm}, W_∞, B_r, and H_c are subject to considerable variation, depending on purity of materials, composition, type of heat treatment, and final condition of mechanical stress.

Adapted from V. E. Legg, "Survey of Magnetic Materials and Applications in the Telephone System," *Bell System Technical Journal*, **18**, 438 (July 1939).

See also S. S. Attwood, *Electric and Magnetic Fields*, 3rd ed., John Wiley, New York, 1949, p. 376.

The proper method for demagnetizing a piece of iron is to establish it in a hysteresis loop large enough to erase the memory of previous magnetizations (including any in other directions) and then to continue a great many reversals of H while slowly reducing $H_{\max}$ to a low value—that is, to a value small compared to subsequent values of H that will be applied. A convenient method for performing this operation is to place the specimen in the field of a strong electromagnet operated on 60-cycle alternating current, and then to remove the specimen slowly from the electromagnet. Sometimes a repetition of this operation will help in reducing more completely the "memory" of magnetizations in various directions.

The saturable reactor, whose operation is based on the hysteresis properties of iron, is worth mentioning here. This is an iron core equipped with two coils, one of which is designed for a fairly large direct current and the other of which is used as a reactance element in an a-c circuit. The amount of steady current

Table 8.5D
Properties of Typical Permanent Magnet Materials

Name	Coercive Force (H_c) $\dfrac{\text{amperes}}{\text{meter}}$	Residual Induction (B_r) $\dfrac{\text{webers}}{\text{meter}^2}$	Energy Product, $(BH)_{\max}$ joules
1% carbon steel	4,000	0.82	1,600
18% tungsten, 15% cobalt steel	12,000	1.15	5,600
Copper-nickel-iron alloy (60% Cu, 20% Ni, 20% Fe) cold rolled	36,800	0.528	8,560
Nipermag (32% Ni, 12% Al + Ti)	52,000	0.53	10,000
Alnico I (20% Ni, 12% Al, 5% Co)	36,400	0.72	11,200
Platinum-cobalt alloy, cast (76.7% Pt, 23.3% Co)	122,400	0.64	28,400
Alnico V	44,000	1.25	36,000

From Attwood, *op. cit.*, p. 389.

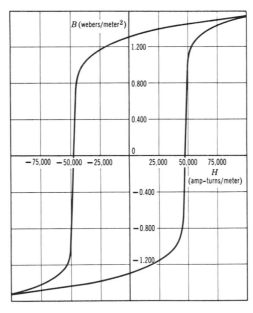

Fig. 8.5h.   A hysteresis curve for Alnico V. [Adapted from P. P. Cioffi, *Rev. Sci. Inst.* **21,** 624 (1950).]

Fig. 8.5i.   Magnetization curves for several magnetic materials. (Taken from S. S. Attwood, *Electric and Magnetic Fields*, 3rd ed. John Wiley, New York, 1949, Fig. 13.9.)

in the first coil determines the degree of saturation of the iron; the a-c reactance depends on the degree of saturation, for the incremental permeability which is the determining quantity will decrease as saturation is approached.   Magnetic amplifiers are devices based on saturable reactors as elements.

Problem 8.5a.   A small permanently magnetized sphere is placed in a strong inhomogeneous magnetic field.   Show how measurements of the force on the

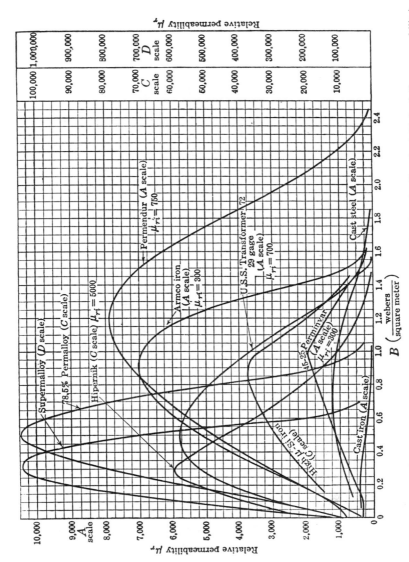

Fig. 8.5j. Normal permeability curves for several magnetic materials (μ_{ri} signifies the initial relative permeability). (Taken from Attwood, *op. cit.*, Fig. 13.12.)

small sphere can lead to a determination of the permanent moment m_1, as well as to any induced moment m_2 on the assumption that hysteresis is negligible.

Problem 8.5b.   A torus whose cross section has a radius of 1.00 cm and whose over-all diameter is 15.0 cm is made of Armco iron and is wound uniformly with 350 turns of wire.   When 1.5 amp is passed through the winding, what are the values of B and M that would be present if the material followed the normal magnetization curve for this iron in Fig. 8.5i?

✓ **Problem 8.5c.**   Using the Armco-iron hysteresis curve in Fig. 8.5g for the torus of problem 8.5b and assuming a secondary winding on the torus of 50 turns, find the charge in coulombs that passes through the secondary if its circuit resistance is 2.0 ohms and the primary current is changed from $+0.75$ amp to -0.040 amp on the downward portion of the loop. How much charge would flow in the secondary for the same current change if the iron were replaced by a vacuum?

✓ **Problem 8.5d.**   Find M and H inside a piece of bismuth when it is subjected to an external magnetic induction of 1.20 webers/m^2.   (See Table 8.5A.)

Problem 8.5e.   Find the ratio of $\mu_0 M$ to B for permendur, as shown in Fig. 8.5i, when $H = 200$ amp/m.

8.6   Theories of Magnetism

The explanation of the properties of magnetic materials is a complicated subject, involving atomic physics, physics of the solid state, physical chemistry, and some nuclear physics.   In a textbook on electricity and magnetism we can only consider certain limited aspects of this complicated problem.

In the first place, all matter should have diamagnetic properties.   Atoms or molecules whose atomic currents have zero resultant magnetic-dipole moments will not show any paramagnetic or ferromagnetic effects that mask their diamagnetism.

It is a relatively-easy matter to calculate the diamagnetic susceptibility for an atom using the semi-classical Bohr theory of atomic structure.[15] The result gives the susceptibility as proportional to the average moment of inertia of the electrons in the atom or molecule.   The modern quantum theory gives the same formula, but the calculation of moments of inertia is difficult; the experimental results are generally in good, although approximate, agreement with the calculations.   One important result of the theory is that diamagnetism is not associated with thermal agitation and is thus not temperature dependent.   This is experimentally verified for

[15] See, for instance, G. P. Harnwell, *Principles of Electricity and Electromagnetism*, 2nd ed., McGraw-Hill, New York, 1949, p. 393; Attwood, *op. cit.*, pp. 252–255.   A rather complete account of the experimental facts and a summary of the theory is given by R. M. Bozorth, "Magnetism," *Encycl. Britannica*, Chicago, 1954, Vol. 14, pp. 636–667, reprinted in *Revs. Mod. Phys.*, **19**, 62–65 (1947); see also the more extensive account in R. M. Bozorth, *Ferromagnetism*, D. Van Nostrand, Princeton, 1951.

most substances. There is a temperature dependence in certain exceptional cases that may be due to a temperature effect on the electron orbits
or to a variation in a minor paramagnetic contribution to the susceptibility.

Paramagnetism occurs not only for substances whose atoms or molecules each have a resultant magnetic moment, but also for conductors,
since the spins of the conduction electrons can also be rotated by an
external field. Resultant magnetic moments of molecules may arise
because the orbital motions or the spins of the outer electrons are not
completely arranged in equal and opposite pairs.

The complete inner shells of atoms always have a vanishing resultant
magnetic moment. It is only incomplete shells that can contribute to
paramagnetism. The chief examples are some of the so-called transition
elements and rare-earth elements which have inner shells with more than
the rare-gas complement of 8 but less than their full quota of 18 or 32
electrons. (Outer shell electrons generally get paired off in chemical
combination.)

The simplest theory of paramagnetism assumes that each atom with a
resultant moment will tend to turn (in a precessional fashion) toward the
direction of an applied field and that thermal agitation will tend to oppose
this lining-up tendency. The result is that to a good approximation the
susceptibility should be similar to the temperature dependent part of the
electric susceptibility (cf. eq. 3.10–1), namely that

$$\chi_m = \frac{nm^2 \mu_0}{3kT} \qquad\qquad \text{MKS} \quad (8.6\text{--}1a)$$

$$= \frac{nm^2}{3kT} \qquad\qquad \text{Gaussian} \quad (8.6\text{--}1b)$$

where n is the number of atoms or molecules per unit volume and m is the
permanent magnetic moment of each atom or molecule.[16]

The paramagnetism of the conduction electrons of metals is temperature
independent, because of the location of most electrons in the filled levels
of the conduction bands that are unaffected by temperature. The quantum
theory yields a simple expression if the electrons are assumed to be free
and a more complicated one if the actual "binding" in the metal is taken
into account. Diamagnetism is also present and reduces the paramagnetic
result by about one-third. The resulting susceptibility is a good deal
weaker than the paramagnetism resulting from permanent atomic or
molecular moments; the calculations agree with experiment to within
10% for sodium and with larger errors for other materials.

[16] Cf. Bozorth, "Magnetism," *Revs. Mod. Phys., op. cit.,* pp. 65–70.

This theory of paramagnetism that fits the experiments fairly well assumes that each dipole is acted on by an external field **H** but not to any great extent by the fields of neighboring dipoles.   Since χ_m is so small, the difference between **H** and **H** + **M**/3 (cf. section 8.4) will be insignificant. Let us try to see why we should expect the local interaction to be weak.

Let us first calculate an expression for the potential energy of a pair of dipoles situated at a distance **r** from each other.   By eq. 8.2–3 we have $U' = -\mathbf{m} \cdot \mathbf{B}$ for the energy of a dipole of moment **m** in an external field **B**, from which we find forces by $-\nabla U'$ in analogy with eq. 3.2–5 for the electric case.   However, from section 7.12, we see that the magnetic energy of a dipole is really $+\mathbf{m} \cdot \mathbf{B}$ and that the difference $2\mathbf{m} \cdot \mathbf{B}$ between the two expressions must be made up by energy changes in the elementary current circuits.   These latter energy changes are matters to be calculated by use of atomic quantum theory and will not concern us here.   Hence we can calculate dipole interactions by use of $U' = -\mathbf{m} \cdot \mathbf{B}$.   If we denote the two electromagnetic moments under consideration by $\mathbf{m}_1$ and $\mathbf{m}_2$, the field of $\mathbf{m}_2$ is given by

$$\mathbf{B}_2 = -\mu_0 \nabla \left(\frac{\mathbf{m}_2 \cdot \mathbf{1}_r}{4\pi r^2} \right) \tag{8.6-2}$$

which can be readily transformed into

$$\mathbf{B}_2 = \mu_0 \left[\frac{-\mathbf{m}_2 + 3(\mathbf{m}_2 \cdot \mathbf{1}_r)\mathbf{1}_r}{4\pi r^3} \right] \qquad \text{MKS} \quad (8.6-3)$$

(cf. problem 8.6d).   Thus we have for the potential energy

$$U' = -\mathbf{m}_1 \cdot \mathbf{B}_2 = \mu_0 \frac{\mathbf{m}_1 \cdot \mathbf{m}_2 - 3(\mathbf{m}_1 \cdot \mathbf{1}_r)(\mathbf{m}_2 \cdot \mathbf{1}_r)}{4\pi r^3} \quad \text{MKS} \quad (8.6-4a)$$

$$U' = \frac{\mathbf{m}_1 \cdot \mathbf{m}_2 - 3(\mathbf{m}_1 \cdot \mathbf{1}_r)(\mathbf{m}_2 \cdot \mathbf{1}_r)}{r^3} \qquad \text{Gaussian} \quad (8.6-4b)$$

This expression is symmetrical in $\mathbf{m}_1$ and $\mathbf{m}_2$ and so is also equal to $-\mathbf{m}_2 \cdot \mathbf{B}_1$. Furthermore, $\mathbf{1}_r$ may be reversed in sign without any change in U'.   Since it does not matter for the potential energy whether $\mathbf{m}_1$ is brought up from infinity toward $\mathbf{m}_2$ in such a way as to be always perpendicular to $\mathbf{B}_2$ and then is rotated into place or $\mathbf{m}_2$ is brought to $\mathbf{m}_1$, we can conclude that U' is the *joint* potential energy of the dipole system.   It is commonly called the *dipole-dipole interaction potential.*

A similar expression must hold for the mutual energy of two electric dipoles—we merely replace $\mu_0 \mathbf{m}_1$ and $\mu_0 \mathbf{m}_2$ by $\mathbf{p}_1$ and $\mathbf{p}_2$, and μ_0 by ϵ_0 for MKS units; $\mathbf{m}_1$ by $\mathbf{p}_1$ and $\mathbf{m}_2$ by $\mathbf{p}_2$ for Gaussian units.   Let us compare the magnitudes of the electric and magnetic dipole-dipole interactions, using the latter units.   If the two dipoles are parallel and each perpendicular to $\mathbf{1}_r$, $U' = m_1 m_2 / r^3$.   If they are parallel to each other and also to

1_r, $U' = -2m_1m_2/r^3$. In any case, it is the magnitude m_1m_2/r^3 that is to be compared with p_1p_2/r^3.

The electromagnetic moment of a single circulating electron can be found by comparing it with the angular momentum of the same electron. If the electron has a circular orbit of radius a over which it travels at speed v, its period of revolution is $2\pi a/v$. The average current is the charge divided by the period, so $i = ev/2\pi a$. Thus for its electromagnetic moment we have

$$m = iS = \frac{ev\pi a^2}{2\pi a} = \tfrac{1}{2}eva \qquad \text{MKS} \quad (8.6\text{--}5a)$$

$$m = \frac{iS}{c} = \frac{eva}{2c} \qquad \text{Gaussian} \quad (8.6\text{--}5b)$$

The angular momentum of the electron is m_0va, denoting the electron mass by m_0. The ratio of the magnetic moment of an atomic system to its angular momentum is called the "gyromagnetic ratio" G. For an electron in a circular orbit,

$$G_{\text{orb}} = \frac{m}{m_0va} = \frac{e}{2m_0} \qquad \text{MKS} \quad (8.6\text{--}6a)$$

$$G_{\text{orb}} = \frac{e}{2m_0c} \qquad \text{Gaussian} \quad (8.6\text{--}6b)$$

This ratio is found to hold for non-circular orbital motions as well and is unchanged by the introduction of the wave properties of electrons. The relation between the directions of the magnetic moment and angular momentum will be that appropriate to a negative charge.

One of the fundamental principles or theorems of quantum mechanics is that the angular momentum of a circulating electron can only have a magnitude equal to a whole number times $h/2\pi$, where h is Planck's constant, $[h = (6.6252 \pm 0.0002) \times 10^{-34}$ joule-sec]. Associated with one such unit of angular momentum we have therefore an electromagnetic moment

$$m_B = G_{\text{orb}} \frac{h}{2\pi} = \frac{eh}{4\pi m_0} \qquad \text{MKS} \quad (8.6\text{--}7a)$$

$$m_B = \frac{eh}{4\pi m_0 c} \qquad \text{Gaussian} \quad (8.6\text{--}7b)$$

This number is called the Bohr magneton. Its value is $(0.92712 \pm 0.00002) \times 10^{-23}$ joule-m^2/weber $= 0.92712 \times 10^{-20}$ erg/gauss.

The spin of the electron has a magnetic moment associated with it whose value is approximately one Bohr magneton (it is actually 1.00115961 larger). However, it only has half a unit of angular momentum (i.e., $h/4\pi$). Hence the gyromagnetic ratio for electron spin is twice that for orbital motion:

$$G_{\text{spin}} = \frac{e}{m_0} \qquad \text{MKS} \quad (8.6\text{-}8a)$$

$$= \frac{e}{m_0 c} \qquad \text{Gaussian} \quad (8.6\text{-}8b)$$

For any given collection of atoms or molecules, the gyromagnetic ratio can be written

$$G = g \frac{e}{2m_0} \qquad \text{MKS} \quad (8.6\text{-}9a)$$

$$= g \frac{e}{2m_0 c} \qquad \text{Gaussian} \quad (8.6\text{-}9b)$$

where g is a pure number which for atomic systems may be expected to be between 1 and 2, depending on the proportion of orbital and spin magnetic moments.   For nuclei it may have other values.

We can now compare the electric and magnetic dipole-dipole interactions. For the same inter-atomic distance we need only compare the moments. The electric dipole moments of permanently polarized molecules are, as indicated in section 3.10, of the order of magnitude of the electronic charge e times 10^{-9} cm.   Magnetic moments come in units m_B equal to e times the distance $h/4\pi m_0 c$, which is 1.93×10^{-11} cm.   Thus atomic magnetic moments are about 1/100 of atomic electric moments, and the interaction potential energies differ by a factor of 10^4.   Paramagnetic interactions are very weak indeed, and the term $M/3$ (or $4\pi M/3$ in Gaussian units) referred to above must indeed make a very small contribution.

This result makes a good introduction to the problem of ferromagnetism, for the very large values of M in ferromagnetic materials would seem to imply a very *large* interaction.   In fact, when a substance is approximately saturated, nearly all the magnetic moments are lined up, and they tend to remain lined up when H is removed.   We can easily show that at saturation, each atom contributes on the average about one whole Bohr magneton to the magnetization.   Inspection of Fig. 8.5i shows that saturation values of B range approximately from 1.0 to 2.0 webers/m^2 or 10,000 to 20,000 gauss.   Therefore in Gaussian units, M is about $10^4/4\pi$.   The number of atoms per cubic centimeter of iron is about $(6.02 \times 10^{23}) \times (7.9 \text{ g/cm}^3)/(56 \text{ g/mole}) \simeq 0.85 \times 10^{23}$, so that the average m per atom is $10^4/(4\pi \times 0.8 \times 10^{23}) \simeq 1.0 \times 10^{-20} \simeq m_B$.

If we assume that for some reason peculiar to ferromagnetic materials, there is a very strong local interaction (different from the one we have just calculated) we might describe it by replacing the term $M/3$ by a larger expression γM, with γ to be determined. The paramagnetic susceptibility given in eq. 8.6–1 is equivalent (since $M = \chi_m H$) to

$$M = \frac{nm^2 \mu_0 H}{3kT} \qquad \text{MKS} \quad (8.6\text{–}10)$$

but was derived on the assumption of weak local interaction. For strong interaction, H must be replaced by H_{eff}:

$$M = \frac{nm^2 \mu_0 (H + \gamma M)}{3kT} \qquad \text{MKS} \quad (8.6\text{–}11)$$

If we solve this equation for M, we find

$$M = \frac{nm^2 \mu_0 H}{3k(T - \theta)} \qquad \text{MKS} \quad (8.6\text{–}12)$$

where

$$\theta = \frac{nm^2 \mu_0 \gamma}{3k} \qquad \text{MKS} \quad (8.6\text{–}13a)$$

$$\theta = \frac{4\pi nm^2 \gamma}{3k} \qquad \text{Gaussian} \quad (8.6\text{–}13b)$$

We notice that, if T is considerably greater than the constant θ, the susceptibility behaves in the usual paramagnetic way, with γ playing no important role. On the other hand, if T is just above the value θ, there will be a large value of M even for a small H, and for temperatures equal to or less than θ, the formula gives physically meaningless results, indicating that the interaction has become so strong that M can sustain itself without an applied H, and the assumptions underlying eq. 8.6–1 are no longer valid.

It is in fact true that many substances are paramagnetic above a certain temperature, and follow eq. 8.6–12 fairly well. Below the temperature θ, called the Curie temperature,[17] these substances become ferromagnetic. The theory we have just given is the Weiss theory of ferromagnetism, first announced in 1907.[18] Curie temperatures of iron alloys are of the order of 700 or 800°. (See Table 8.5C.) Let us calculate γ for $\theta = 800°$, and $m = m_B$. In Gaussian units, $\gamma = 3k\theta/4\pi nm^2$. The calculation given above for saturation shows that the product nm_B is about $10^4/4\pi$ gauss. Using Boltzmann's constant $k = 1.38 \times 10^{-16}$ erg/degree and $m_B = 10^{-20}$ erg/gauss, we find that $\gamma = 4.1\, \theta$ when θ is in Kelvin degrees. Thus

[17] Named for Pierre Curie, who first found experimentally (1895) the relation between paramagnetic susceptibility and temperature given in eq. 8.6–1.

[18] P. Weiss, *J. de Phys.*, **6**, 667 (1907) For a brief account, see Bozorth, "Magnetism," *Revs. Mod. Phys., op. cit.*, pp. 73–74.

for 800°, γ is about 3300, showing the enormous interaction strengths we must assume to explain ferromagnetism.

Now we must inquire into the relative role of electron spins and electronic orbital motions. This question has a direct experimental answer, provided by experiments first performed by Barnett in 1914 and by Einstein and de Haas in 1915. The gyromagnetic ratio for a single atom can also be applied to a whole specimen. If magnetization consists in turning elementary dipoles toward a particular direction, there must be an increase of total angular momentum about an axis in that direction. If the angular momentum of the specimen is originally zero, the amount gained by the atomic systems must be compensated by an equal and opposite gain by the specimen as a whole. That is, a delicately mounted specimen should start to rotate when it is magnetized. Einstein and de Haas found this to be so and in fact measured G. So did Barnett, by the converse effect of producing magnetization by rotating the specimen.[19] The result is that g of eq. 8.6–9 is nearly equal to 2, but not quite (about 1.93 for iron). Thus we can conclude that the electron spin is mainly responsible for ferromagnetism.

Ferromagnetism can be explained in terms of quantum theory, but the explanation is still in a more or less qualitative stage. It is possible to understand why the phenomenon exists and, to a certain extent, the reason that certain particular substances show the effect. It is not yet possible (1958) to calculate the various measurable magnetic properties with any degree of accuracy.

We shall state here certain aspects of quantum theory that help to show why ferromagnetism exists. In the first place, electrons in any given atomic or molecular system arrange themselves into the types of allowable motions of lowest energy. In the second place, because of the Pauli exclusion principle, complete shells in atoms always contain even numbers of electrons with their spins and orbits so paired as to have no resultant magnetic moment.

Third, any pair of electrons that can interact will have their spins either parallel or antiparallel (having the same or opposite signs with respect to the direction in space to which they are both parallel). This property is intimately related to their wave nature and is *not* connected with or dependent on the dipole-dipole interaction. The types of motion that are possible for the electrons are different in the two cases, a fact which is a consequence of the exclusion principle. *It is this feature that provides the strong interaction involved in ferromagnetism.*

[19] For details of the experiments, the reader is referred to a review article by S. J. Barnett, *Revs. Mod. Phys.*, **7**, 129 (1935). Harnwell, *op. cit.*, has a brief account, pp. 377–381.

As an example, consider a pair of electrons that form a covalent bond between two atoms. Various types of motion[20] are possible, including cases in which one electron moves around each positive ion, cases in which both move around the same ion, and cases in which each moves around both ions. For each type of motion, the spins may be either parallel or antiparallel. It turns out that the situation in which each electron moves around both ions gives the two states of lowest energy. Detailed calculation of the energies in the parallel and antiparallel arrangements shows that the one with opposite spins has the actual lowest energy and provides for an attraction between the ions. (The motion is such that the electrons spend a good deal of time between the atoms and their attraction for each positive ion leads to a net over-all attraction.)

There are certain cases, however, in which a pair of electrons may have a motion of lowest energy with their spins parallel. This happens in the next-to-outermost electron shells of what chemists call the transition elements and leads to paramagnetism. It also may happen with a pair of electrons that each come from a separate paramagnetic atom, when the two atoms are neither too close nor too far apart.

Ferromagnetic materials are always solids and usually conductors. The problem here is the motion of whole groups of electrons in the resulting energy bands. It seems to be clear from the calculations of several investigators that certain of the conduction and next-to-outer-shell electrons in ferromagnetic materials can have collective motions involving spins all parallel to one given direction. These motions are undoubtedly a combination of the over-all motions of the electrical-conduction sort, and the partially localized ones in which electrons may spend a good deal of time moving around a pair of adjacent atoms.[21] The question of the circumstances under which such motions involve less energy than those with the spins all paired oppositely is a difficult question to answer, for the theory cannot be calculated with sufficient accuracy. However, the two energies are certainly close for the iron group of elements and far apart in most other cases, so that the ferromagnetism is at least not surprising in those cases in which it appears.

It is also not hard to show that a Curie temperature should exist, above which a formula like eq. 8.6–12 will hold for **M**.

There is, however, a serious difficulty with what we have said so far.

---

[20] "Motion" is only an approximate description of what actually happens but quite a good one for our purposes.

[21] The reader with some knowledge of quantum mechanics will find illuminating summaries of recent theory in a group of articles by C. Zener and R. R. Heikes, J. C. Slater, E. P. Wohlfarth, J. H. Van Vleck, and R. Smoluchowski in *Revs. Mod. Phys.*, **25**, 191–228 (1953). The last named author gives a summary of the results of the others.

Why would not any piece of iron spontaneously become magnetized to saturation? How could we demagnetize a ferromagnetic substance?

The answer is provided by the introduction of the concept of magnetic domains. Suppose that there are many very small regions in a piece of iron within which the spins all cooperate and line up in some particular direction. These directions are likely to have special relations to the crystal axes; they are called the "directions of easy magnetization." Each domain may have several such easy directions. Then demagnetization means that the domains are all magnetized in randomly varying directions.

The boundary between two domains may be the edge of a small crystallite or a region of strain or fracture. However, it is also possible (and has in fact been found experimentally) that a single crystal can have several domains, with boundaries that are simply regions separating two groups of atoms with different spin directions. The latter sort of boundary can very well migrate, as one domain obtains "converts" from the next one, turning the electron spins from one direction to another.

Two kinds of evidence have been found for these domains. One is that, if the coil used in a hysteresis experiment to determine **B** is connected to a sensitive a-c amplifier and **H** is slowly increased, many small sudden emf's will be detected, showing that Φ increases by discontinuous jumps. This is just what would be expected if the domains suddenly switched their directions from one at a considerable angle to **H** to another more nearly parallel to **H**. This effect is called the "Barkhausen effect."

The other evidence is found by sprinkling some very fine magnetizable powder on the surface of a smooth specimen and observing the powder patterns formed as the magnetization is changed. Such patterns seem to show that there are sharply defined regions of different magnetization. However, it may be that the actual domain sizes are much smaller than the powder-pattern spacings.[22]

It is now possible to describe a hysteresis loop and initial magnetization curves in terms of the domain changes that occur on various parts of them. At the beginning of a magnetization process, those domains which have positive components of **M** parallel to **H** will grow at the expense of their neighbors—the boundaries move. The lower bend in the curve represents reversible boundary motion, and the higher portions represent irreversible

---

[22] For a discussion of some of the unanswered problems of the domain theory, see W. F. Brown, Jr., *Revs. Mod. Phys.*, **17**, 15 (1945); for pictures of powder patterns, see F. Bitter, *Introduction to Ferromagnetism*, McGraw-Hill, New York, 1937, pp. 59–66; W. C. Elmore, *Phys. Rev.*, **62**, 486 (1942); R. M. Bozorth, *Ferromagnetism*, *op. cit.*, pp. 534–538; and K. H. Stewart, *Ferromagnetic Domains*, Cambridge University Press, Cambridge, 1954.

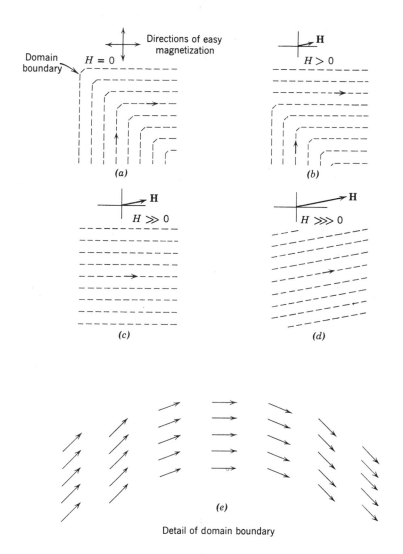

Fig. 8.6a. Schematic diagram of changes in domains at various stages of magnetization. (Adapted from R. M. Bozorth.)

motion.   Finally, for very strong **H**, the spins in each domain rotate together toward the **H**, so that at saturation, all the spins are parallel. Figures 8.6a and b illustrate these concepts.

There are a number of materials that show interesting modifications of ferromagnetic behavior.   These materials are characterized by containing two interlocking sets of atoms or atom groupings each of which has the spin-lining-up character of ordinary ferromagnetic substances.   In some of these materials, the two sub-lattices, as they are called, tend to magnetize in the same direction, and to behave a good deal like ferromagnetic substances.   In others, the two sub-lattices tend to magnetize oppositely. If in these substances the sub-lattices have identical magnetic moments per atom or atomic grouping, there will be a cancellation of the total magnetization to a high order of accuracy, but there will still be a Curie temperature and strong paramagnetic behavior above it.   These substances are said to be "antiferromagnetic."

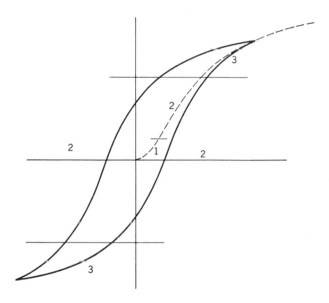

Fig. 8.6b. A hysteresis loop and an initial magnetization curve, showing regions in which different types of domain changes occur. Region 1—reversible motion of domain walls. Region 2—irreversible motion of domain walls. Region 3—rotation of domain magnetizations toward **H**.

If the two sub-lattices are not identical, there will be a net effect similar to ferromagnetism but considerably weaker.   The name for this phenomenon is ferrimagnetism (for emphasis, the second syllable is sometimes pronounced to rhyme with "eye") and substances possessing it are called ferrites.   Ferrites are often poor electrical conductors and have very low eddy-current and hysteresis losses at very high frequencies, so they can be used for cores in radio-frequency transformers, and for many other applications.

Problem 8.6a. Show that, if an atomic system has an angular momentum $kh/2\pi$ where k is a quantum number (integer or half-odd-integer), the magnetic moment can be written $m = gkm_B$. Assume a charge of one electronic unit to be involved.

Problem 8.6b. What is the least value of the dipole-dipole interaction energy for two Bohr magnetons 10^{-8} cm apart?

Problem 8.6c. Two magnetic dipoles m_1 and m_2 are held a fixed distance r apart and are arranged to rotate while keeping a fixed angle between them. Sketch graphs showing the variation of U' with the angle between $\mathbf{m}_1$ and $\mathbf{1}_r$ if (a) $\mathbf{m}_1$ and $\mathbf{m}_2$ are perpendicular; (b) $\mathbf{m}_1$ and $\mathbf{m}_2$ are parallel; (c) $\mathbf{m}_1$ and $\mathbf{m}_2$ are antiparallel.

Problem 8.6d. Transform eq. 8.6–2 into eq. 8.6–3.

Problem 8.5e. Show that eqs. 8.6–1a and 8.6–1b are consistent with each other.

8.7 The Magnetic Circuit

Most applications of ferromagnetic materials involve current-bearing coils containing iron cores which do not lie along the lines of the flux produced by the coils. Permanent magnets are also frequently used with associated pieces of soft iron whose dimensions do not fit the flux patterns produced by the magnets. In either case, the presence of the iron modifies the flux pattern and the concept of the magnetic circuit is extremely useful in the discussion of these modifications. We shall proceed to develop this concept in the present section.

Consider a coil of wire as shown in Fig. 8.7a, with an inserted bar of soft iron. Although B/H is not a constant for the iron, we can take a rough average of μ_r—e.g., 5,000 for Armco iron—as adequate for our purposes. The field produced by the coil without iron is shown in dotted lines in the figure.

Now, if the iron should become magnetized along the lines of the original **H**, north and south poles will appear on the edges of the iron as shown. The **H** produced inside the iron by these poles will be approximately normal to the surface and directed away from it. Thus the resultant **H** will be altered inside the bar, and **M** will change as a consequence. Because of the large value of μ_r, it will take only a weak additional **H** to make a substantial readjustment of **M**. The direction of the adjusted **M** will be more nearly parallel to the surface of the iron. In other words, the demagnetizing effect of the poles will be to produce a strong tendency for the magnetic flux to run parallel to the edges of the bar.

The flux must leave the bar near its ends, and there will also be a strong demagnetizing field there. However, the pole strength at the ends cannot disappear the way the pole strength can at the sides, for a small change at the sides will result in a large displacement of the poles, and a small field change at the end can make only a small pole displacement. Consequently, there will be a final state of equilibrium, in which the pole density near the ends is a complicated function of the shape of the bar, but depends very little on the pattern of the flux produced by the coil alone.

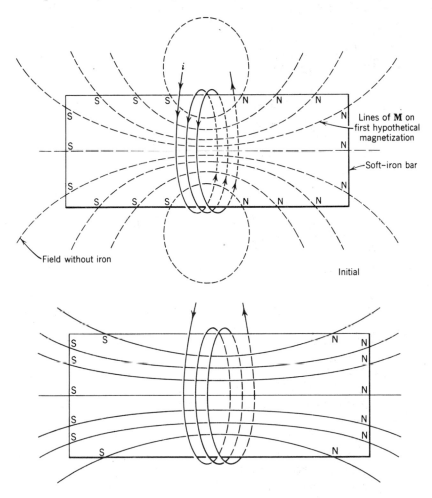

Fig. 8.7a. Initial state (hypothetical) (upper diagram). Equilibrium state of magnetization (lower diagram).

In actual practice, the final equilibrium state will be reached almost immediately as the current is turned on or the bar inserted. The process we have imagined is thus rather hypothetical in nature.

Let us now imagine that a closed iron path for the flux is made by adding a U-shaped piece of soft iron to the bar, as shown in Fig. 8.7b.   Induced pole strengths on the parts of the U that are adjacent to the ends of the bar will reduce the demagnetizing field materially and make the lines of force in the bar become more nearly parallel to its axis even near its ends. Poles will also appear on the far side of the U but they will also be displaced in the same fashion.   They will in fact be displaced toward the main body of the U, because any displacement away from it will call into play a further demagnetizing field.   The flux will finally be contained within the

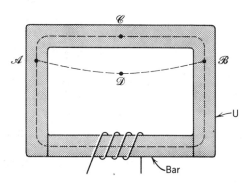

Fig. 8.7b.   A closed magnetic circuit.

iron, in almost the same way that a current is contained in an electrical conductor.   We call the path followed by the flux in the iron a magnetic circuit.

In close analogy to the case of the **E** in a conducting wire, the field **H** inside the iron is made to be nearly parallel to its edges by small residual amounts of q_m on the various surfaces of the magnetic circuit.   At points far from the coil, **H** may be modified considerably.   However, the pole part of **H** contributes nothing to $\oint \mathbf{H} \cdot \mathbf{dl}$, so that the mmf $\mathscr{H} = \oint \mathbf{H} \cdot \mathbf{dl} = ni$ produced by the coil is unchanged.   Let us consider a tube of flux that lies everywhere within the iron.   Along this tube, $\Phi = BS$ if B is sufficiently uniform (S is the cross-sectional area of the tube, which is usually taken to be approximately the area of the specimen itself.   It is expected to vary from point to point along the tube.)   Now, if we treat μ as a constant at any one point in the iron, although it may vary from place to place, we can derive a practical formula from the mmf equation.   We calculate $\oint \mathbf{H} \cdot \mathbf{dl}$ along a line of force, and write

$$ni = \mathscr{H} = \oint \frac{B \, dl}{\mu} = \oint \frac{\Phi \, dl}{\mu S} = \Phi \oint \frac{dl}{\mu S} = \Phi \mathscr{R} \qquad (8.7\text{–}1)$$

where the constancy of Φ around the circuit is of course fundamental.

(The fact that lines of B do not actually close on themselves does not prevent the flux from forming an essentially closed figure.)

Equation 8.7–1 is the equation of the magnetic circuit.   It is analogous to the equation of the simple electric circuit if we compare Φ with i, $\mathcal{H}$ with $\mathcal{E}$, and the quantity $\mathcal{R} = \oint dl/\mu S$ with R.   The quantity $\mathcal{R}$ is called the "reluctance," and its reciprocal is called the "permeance." It is principally a function of the dimensions and material of the magnetic circuit, but also depends on the previous history of magnetization.

Fig. 8.7c.   A parallel magnetic circuit.

Fig. 8.7d.   A three-loop magnetic circuit.

One can pursue this analogy.   To each portion of the circuit one can assign a part of the mmf, just as the emf of a cell is divided up into potential drops around a circuit.   One can, in fact, use the concept of magnetic potential drop, and write

$$V_m = \Phi \mathcal{R} \tag{8.7–2}$$

for any portion of a magnetic circuit.   It is usual to use the term mmf for V_m and to consider it as positive in the rising rather than the dropping sense.   One can use series-parallel treatments, since reluctance and mmf add when in series, and flux can divide and rejoin, as in Fig. 8.7c.   More complicated cases (Fig. 8.7*d*) require a Kirchhoff's law type of treatment, with junction equations for the flux and loop equations for the mmf, and they can be handled in exactly the same way as in the electric case.

One important distinction between the magnetic and electric circuits is that the former always involves some leakage flux, whereas the latter commonly involves no leakage current.   Consider two points $\mathscr{A}$ and $\mathscr{B}$ in the circuit of Fig. 8.7*b*.   The magnetic potential difference $-\int_{\mathscr{A}}^{\mathscr{B}} \mathbf{H} \cdot \mathbf{dl}$ between the two points may be calculated either along a path in the iron, $\mathscr{A}\mathscr{C}\mathscr{B}$, or through the air, $\mathscr{A}\mathscr{D}\mathscr{B}$.   The results must be the same, because there is no current passing between the two paths.   Therefore there must be a field $\mathbf{H}$ in the space outside the iron and a flux of $\mathbf{B}$ accompanying it.   The electric case always involves an external $\mathbf{E}$, by the analogous argument, but there is in general no current accompanying $\mathbf{E}$.   If μ_r is large, however, the flux leakage will be small.   One could describe this result by saying that the air (or vacuum) surrounding a magnetic circuit provides a parallel path of high but not infinite reluctance. It is like immersing a coil of wire in a liquid of low, but not zero, conductivity.

This leakage flux is one source of inaccuracy in the magnetic-circuit equation.   The other reason for its being approximate lies in the expression for the reluctance.   The permeability μ is admittedly only an approximate constant.   Furthermore, S is the area of a tube of flux.   If the tube is chosen to fill out the iron, it will fit well in the straight sections, but poorly at the corners.   Thus the integral $\oint dl/\mu S$ is not accurate if S is taken as the cross-sectional area of the entire piece of iron.

However, the reluctance can be defined exactly as the ratio between $\mathscr{H}$ and the flux Φ across the area of a chosen particular part of the circuit, for a particular value of Φ.   Reluctance can thus be measured for a whole circuit and indeed also for a part (see below).   In fact, permeability measurements are actually reluctance measurements.[23]   The problem of the variability of μ can be handled for many engineering problems by arranging to have S constant for each part of a given type of material, so that the constancy of Φ insures that $\mathbf{B}$ is constant and the material in different portions of the circuit is operated on the same portion of the magnetization curve (or on the same hysteresis loop in the a-c case).   In fact, if S is too small in one portion of the circuit, there may not be enough atomic currents to pass the flux through the circuit and the leakage will be considerable—the effective μ will be small and $\mathscr{R}$ will be large.

The magnetic-circuit equation indicates that the flux depends on the

[23] For details on magnetic measurements, see the *National Bureau of Standards Circular* C456, "Magnetic Testing," by Raymond L. Sanford, Washington, 1946.

number of ampere-turns of the coil, but not on its location.   Actually, moving the coil must change the surface pole strengths, but this of course is a small effect (except near saturation, when coil locations become very important) and will change the reluctance only slightly through alterations of S.

Magnetic shielding of sensitive apparatus is accomplished by surrounding the apparatus with a suitably thick layer of high-permeability soft iron.

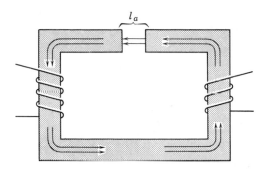

Fig. 8.7e.   A magnetic circuit with an air gap.

The functioning of such a shield may readily be described in terms of low-reluctance magnetic circuits that "conduct" external flux around rather than through the objects to be shielded.

Let us consider now the case of an air gap in a magnetic circuit.   Figure 8.7e shows the magnetic circuit of an electromagnet.   The reluctance of the gap, of length l_a and area S is $\mathcal{R}_a = l_a/\mu_0 S$.   Let us assume that the iron has a constant cross section also equal to S, a constant value of μ, and an effective length of l_i, so its reluctance is $\mathcal{R}_i = l_i/\mu S$.   Then we have

$$\Phi = \frac{\mathcal{H}}{\mathcal{R}_i + \mathcal{R}_a} = \frac{\mathcal{H}}{\dfrac{l_i}{\mu S} + \dfrac{l_a}{\mu_0 S}} \tag{8.7-3}$$

Now, if μ/μ_0 is much greater than l_i/l_a, the reluctance of the iron will be small, and the air gap will be the controlling element in the determination of Φ.   The flux will be very much less than if the air gap were not there, and most of the mmf will appear across the gap.   We might describe this situation by saying that the field produced by the poles points in the positive direction in the gap and is strong because of the narrowness of the gap.   The pole-produced **H** is in a reversed direction in the rest of the circuit, and, although the field produced by the poles at the gap will not of itself conform in shape to the magnetic circuit, it will be made to do so by the presence of additional induced poles on the surface of the iron. Thus **H** and the flux in the iron will be weakened by the presence of the air gap.

It is possible to use normal magnetization curves rather than averages of μ for more precision in the design of magnets. For instance, suppose that certain materials and dimensions have been chosen for an electromagnet, which is to provide a predetermined flux Φ in a given gap. Then

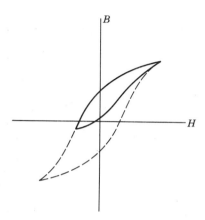

Fig. 8.7f. An unsymmetrical hysteresis loop for a d-c electromagnet.

S is known for each portion of the circuit, and the value of **B** can be calculated. If this **B** is either to be produced in previously demagnetized materials or represents the maximum to be reached in each cycle of an alternating emf, the **H** needed can be found from the appropriate curve. Therefore the mmf needed for each portion of the magnetic circuit can be separately calculated, and the sum found, so that the ampere-turns needed in the coil are established. If such calculations are made for several values of Φ, a graph of flux against magnetomotive force can be made for the particular magnet in question, giving considerable information on the behavior of the magnet.

If an electromagnet is used for one direction of magnetization only, the result of several turnings on and off will be to make the material follow an unsymmetrical loop that is approximately the same as a combination of the normal magnetization curve and the downward part of a hysteresis loop to such a point that a reversal of **H** will bring **B** back through zero. (Cf. Fig. 8.7f.) The reason for the appearance of negative values of H is that residual pole strength is left when the current is turned off.

Demagnetization curves and complete loops of the sort just mentioned can be constructed for the Φ and $\mathscr{H}$ in a particular magnetic circuit. Let us consider a case in which a permanent magnet is made by applying an mmf to a circuit containing a piece of hard magnet steel and a removable piece of soft iron (Fig. 8.7g).   For each piece (1 and 2) we can construct

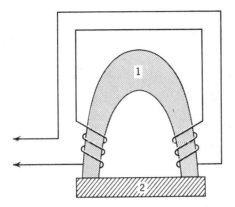

Fig. 8.7g.   Making a permanent magnet.   Piece 1—hard magnet steel; Piece 2—soft iron.

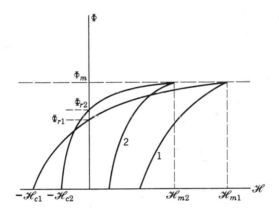

Fig. 8.7h.   Showing Φ–$\mathscr{H}$ curves for pieces 1 and 2 in Fig. 8.7g.

a curve, as in Fig. 8.7h.[24]   We have indicated in the figure that the maximum Φ is the same in both pieces (leakage is considered negligible) and that the $\mathscr{H}_{max}$ needed for piece 2 is smaller than that for piece 1, because of smaller reluctance.

[24] It may take considerable effort to calculate the reluctance of a piece shaped like piece 2, because of uncertainties in the flux pattern.   Cf. H. C. Roters, *op. cit.*, Chapters IV and V.

For the combined magnetic circuit, we can add the mmf's on the downward portions of the two curves for the same values of Φ, getting something like Fig. 8.7*i*.   When the current is turned off, the total mmf reduces to zero, and flux Φ'_r remains.   It is perhaps easier to picture what happens

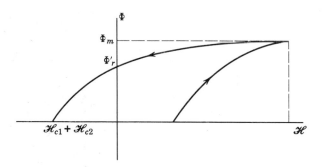

Fig. 8.7*i*. $\mathcal{H}$ added for same values of Φ, from Fig. 8.7*h*.

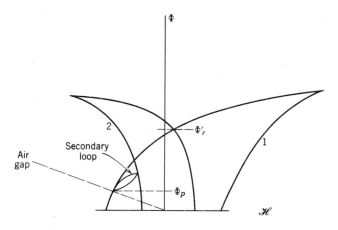

Fig. 8.7*j*.   Showing the soft-iron loop of Fig. 8.7*h* plotted in reverse.

if the mmf of piece 2 is plotted with reversed sign (as if it were a potential drop), as in Fig. 8.7*j*.   At the point where the two downward curves cross the total mmf will equal zero.   Therefore the value Φ'_r will be the residual flux left in the magnet in this act of magnetization.

If the soft iron is removed, we then have an air gap with a much larger reluctance; its negative Φ–$\mathcal{H}$ curve will be a straight line and will lie a good deal under the curve for the soft iron piece.   Hence the magnet will demagnetize to the point Φ_p in Fig. 8.7*j*.   If the soft iron is demagnetized and then is replaced, the flux will rise again, for the induced poles in the soft iron will counteract the poles on the hard steel, but the rise will be along a minor hysteresis loop, to the rising part of the magnetization curve of piece 2. (Small loop in Fig. 8.7*j*.)

In this way, a fairly complete prediction can be made of permanent-magnet properties. To obtain a strong magnet, we should use a material with large coercive force and arrange the gap to have as small a reluctance as is practical. The long-time permanence of a magnet is assisted by closing the circuit while not in use, with a soft-iron bar or another magnet. A bar used in this way is called a "keeper." Without a keeper, thermal and mechanical shocks may assist the demagnetizing field of the poles in disaligning the elementary domains.

An example that is easily calculable is the case in which the cross-sectional area S is constant throughout the iron and the gap has two parallel faces close enough that the flux occupies essentially the same area S in the gap. Then the field H_a in the gap will be uniform, so that the mmf of the gap will be $H_a l_a$ where l_a is its length. Unless the length l_i of the flux path in the iron is very long, H_i in the iron will be essentially uniform, because even for hard steels there cannot be a large amount of leakage flux without surface poles appearing that provide local fields in excess of H_i. Thus poles will arise to straighten out **B** and **H** inside the iron. We shall have, when the current is turned off, $H_i l_i = H_a l_a$. Since $H_a = B_a/\mu_0 = \Phi/\mu_0 S = B_i/\mu_0$ we can write

$$ H_i = \frac{B_i l_a}{\mu_0 l_i} \qquad (8.7\text{--}4) $$

and the condition the magnet is left in will be found by plotting $H_i = -B_i l_a/\mu_0 l_i$ on the demagnetization curve and finding the intersection (note the minus sign for plotting because of the relative directions of H_i and B_i).

Two desirable properties of permanent magnets are large values of the flux Φ in the usable portion of the gap and of the mmf $\mathscr{H}_a$ across this gap. The product of these two is often considered to be a useful single criterion for the "quality" of a magnet. This product is equal to twice the energy stored in the field of the gap, since (taking an integral along a flux line)

$$ \mathscr{H}_a \Phi = \int_{\text{gap}} \mathbf{H} \cdot \mathbf{dl} \Phi = \int_{\text{gap}} \mathbf{H} \cdot \mathbf{B}\, dl\, dS = \int_{\text{gap}} \mathbf{H} \cdot \mathbf{B}\, d\tau \qquad (8.7\text{--}5) $$

which according to eq. 7.12–8 is twice the magnetic energy to be assigned to the field in the gap.

For the simple case of the magnet with uniform area and uniform fields, $\mathscr{H}_a \Phi = H_a l_a B_a S = B_i H_i l_i S = B_i H_i \tau_i$, so that for a given value of $\mathscr{H}_a \Phi$, the least volume of iron required can be obtained if the largest value of the product $B_i H_i$ is used.   Consequently, curves are frequently given for the product of B and $|H|$ taken along the demagnetization curve.[25]   However, it may or may not actually be practical in particular cases to design for the maximum BH product, although the maximum BH is an indication of the general value of a given substance for permanent magnets.[26]   Certain aluminum-nickel-cobalt-iron alloys, prepared by a special type of heat treatment, have unusually large BH values and have allowed the construction of powerful magnets of very small size.   Alnico V is an outstanding example.

The force between two parts of a magnetic circuit that can move relative to one another, as in relays and traction magnets, is a rather complicated function of the flux and the variation of reluctance with displacement. Derivations of the appropriate formulas may be made by considering the energy changes for various portions of the relevant hysteresis loops.[27]   The case of two parallel faces with an essentially uniform field and high relative permeability is quite easy to calculate, and we shall restrict ourselves to this case.

If μ_r is very large, H will be negligibly small inside the iron.   Since we can calculate the force on a magnet by the pole fiction, we find an analogy with the force on the surface of a conductor, because $E = 0$ inside the conductor.   In eq. 2.3-2, we found the force per unit area to be $\sigma^2/2\epsilon_0$, so that here we should have $\sigma_m^2/2\mu_0$.   But $\sigma_m = \mu_0 M_n$, which in the iron is nearly equal to B.   Thus for an area S, the force on either surface will be

$$F = \frac{B^2 S}{2\mu_0} = \frac{\Phi^2}{2\mu_0 S} \tag{8.7-6}$$

The force will vary with the gap separation, because Φ depends on the reluctance, which is strongly dependent on the separation (cf. problem 8.7a).

One other example of magnetic forces should be mentioned here. Consider the attraction of a permanent magnet for a distant, unmagnetized object.   The field of the magnet will be a dipole field at great distances, with B proportional to r^{-3}.   The induced magnetic moment will be roughly proportional to B.

The force on the magnet, $(\mathbf{m} \cdot \boldsymbol{\nabla})\mathbf{B}$, involves the product of the magnetic moment and the gradient of $\mathbf{B}$, and so it varies like $r^{-3} \times (d/dr)(r^{-3}) \sim r^{-7}$. The inverse seventh-power law that results explains why magnetic attractions are appreciable over only very short distances.   Exact formulas are called for in problem 8.7b.

[25] Attwood, *op. cit.*, pp. 382–386.
[26] The product $B_r H_c$ is also a useful although rough indication of value.
[27] See Roters, *op. cit.*, Chapter VIII.

Problem 8.7a.   The magnetic circuit of a certain relay contains a hinge, so that the air-gap length l_a is variable, but the effective path length l_i in the iron is constant.   Assuming the cross-sectional area S to be a constant for the entire circuit, find how the force between the poles varies with l_a.   Sketch a graph of this force for l_a varying from zero to $10\mu_0 l_i/\mu$, where μ is the average permeability of the iron.

Problem 8.7b.   Find the force of attraction on a small paramagnetic sphere a distance $r \gg l$ from a uniform bar magnet of length l and moment $\mathbf{m}$, when the sphere is (a) on the axis of the magnet and (b) on its perpendicular bisector.

Problem 8.7c.   Write an approximate formula for the self-inductance L of an iron-cored coil of n turns with reluctance $\mathscr{R}$.

Problem 8.7d.   Find the reluctance of the magnetic circuit shown in Fig. 8.7c, using the value of μ for Armco iron corresponding to an induction on the normal magnetization curve of 8000 gauss.   The open rectangles are each 4 cm × 7 cm, and the iron cross section in the straight portions is 1 cm in the plane of the figure by 3 cm in the perpendicular direction.   Use center lines for calculating the l's.

Problem 8.7e.   It is observed that the force of attraction between two opposite poles of a pair of similar bar magnets, when the poles are in contact, is considerably larger than the force of repulsion when two like poles are forced into contact. Explain.

8.8   Galvanometers

Current-indicating devices can be made with moving magnets, with wires that change their lengths when heated by the passage of current, and by other means, but by far the most common type of instrument is that with a coil that rotates in a fixed magnetic field.   This type was invented by Sturgeon in 1836, improved by Thomson in 1867 by use of a fixed soft-iron core within the coil, and brought into essentially its modern form by D'Arsonval[28] in 1882, by the addition of pole pieces to the magnet. Figure 8.8a gives schematic diagrams of side and axial views of two such galvanometers, showing the rectangular coils that can rotate through 90° or so, a pair of coil springs and a wire suspension that exert torques tending to keep the coils in a rest position, and the shaped pole pieces which together with the central iron core make magnetic fields that are accurately radial over the range of motion of the sides of the coils.   Current enters and leaves the coil in such an instrument by the suspension springs or wires, and the deflection resulting from the torque of the field on the coil is indicated by either a pointer and scale or a spot of light reflected from the mirror to a distant scale.

We will not concern ourselves here with constructional details[29] but with the principles underlying the motion of the coil.   The torque on the

[28] A. D'Arsonval, *Comptes Rendus*, **94**, 1347 (1882).
[29] See, for instance, F. K. Harris, *loc. cit.*, Chapter 4.

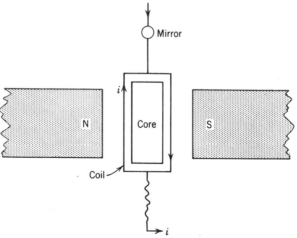

Fig. 8.8a.   D'Arsonval galvanometers.

coil may be found from eq. 8.2–5 or the result of problem 7.7c.   If the
coil has n turns, width w, length l, and area $S = wl$, we have

$$\mathcal{L}_m = nBSi = \tau i \qquad (8.8\text{–}1)$$

where $\tau = nBS$ is called the torque constant for the coil.

The mechanical suspension produces a restoring torque that is opposite
in sense to the angular deflection θ and generally obeys Hooke's law rather
closely.   We denote the restoring torque by $\mathcal{L}_r$, and write

$$\mathcal{L}_r = -k\theta \qquad (8.8\text{–}2)$$

where k is the torque constant of the suspension.   The angle θ is measured
in radians, although when static deflections are considered it is often given
in equivalent scale divisions.

The coil can only remain stationary if $\mathcal{L}_m + \mathcal{L}_r = 0$ or $k\theta = \tau i$.   The
value of θ for which equilibrium holds we will call θ_F, or the final deflection, since we will study at some length the approach of a galvanometer
coil to equilibrium.   Thus we have the equation

$$k\theta_F = \tau i \qquad (8.8\text{–}3)$$

which of course is only meaningful if i is a constant.

Now, we have pointed out in section 7.3 that the motor effect is always
accompanied by the generator effect.   Let us calculate the induced emf
$\mathcal{E}_b$ accompanying motion of the coil.   If θ is the deflection, then $d\theta/dt$ is
the angular velocity and $(w/2)\, d\theta/dt$ is the linear velocity of the wires
parallel to the axis.   Thus by the formula $\mathcal{E} - vBl$, eq. 7.3–9, we have for
one wire the emf $\frac{1}{2}Blw\, d\theta/dt$ and for the n turns on the two sides, we have
$nBlw\, d\theta/dt = nBS\, d\theta/dt$.   Using the appropriate minus sign, the back emf
$\mathcal{E}_b$ is given by

$$\mathcal{E}_b = -\tau\, d\theta/dt \qquad (8.8\text{–}4)$$

Another property of the system that we must consider is friction.   A
coil with an axle that is supported in jewels will have a certain constant
amount of frictional torque that changes its direction each time the pointer
motion reverses and tends to disappear when the pointer comes to rest.
In all well-made galvanometers this torque is small, and its effects are in
any case not important to calculate (they are also quite difficult to calculate with accuracy).   Hence we shall neglect them.   On the other hand,
air resistance is always present and may have a considerable frictional
effect known as "damping," which is often a quite desirable effect (see
below).   The torque of air friction is to a good approximation proportional to the angular velocity of the coil, so we write

$$\mathcal{L}_a = -b_a\, d\theta/dt \qquad (8.8\text{–}5)$$

where the minus sign indicates that the torque always opposes the motion. The constant b_a is called the "frictional damping constant."

Now suppose that a constant external emf $\mathscr{E}$ is applied to the coil and that the coil resistance together with any series resistance in the circuit is R. The current that results will depend on the angular velocity of the coil, because of the back emf, so that we have

$$\mathscr{E} - \tau \frac{d\theta}{dt} = iR. \tag{8.8-6}$$

The motion of the coil is determined by Newton's second law in rotational form:

$$\mathscr{L} = I \frac{d^2\theta}{dt^2}$$

where $\mathscr{L}$ is the total torque acting, I is the moment of inertia of the coil and $d^2\theta/dt^2$ represents of course the angular acceleration. There are three torques that act on the coil, $\mathscr{L}_m$, $\mathscr{L}_r$, and $\mathscr{L}_a$, so that the equation of motion reads

$$\mathscr{L}_m + \mathscr{L}_r + \mathscr{L}_a = \tau i - k\theta - b_a \, d\theta/dt = I \, d^2\theta/dt^2 \tag{8.8-7}$$

Using eq. 8.8-6 to eliminate i, and rearranging, we have a differential equation for θ:

$$I \frac{d^2\theta}{dt^2} + \left(b_a + \frac{\tau^2}{R} \right) \frac{d\theta}{dt} + k\theta = \frac{\tau\mathscr{E}}{R} \tag{8.8-8a}$$

The term $(\tau^2/R) \, d\theta/dt$ acts just like $b_a \, d\theta/dt$ in producing a frictional effect. We will call it the "electromagnetic damping" and write for the combined damping a coefficient b, given by

$$b = b_a + \tau^2/R \tag{8.8-8b}$$

Before studying eq. 8.8-8 in the general case, let us consider two special cases. In the first place, if the coil is at rest with no current in it, and $\mathscr{E}$ is then switched on, it is clear that because of friction, θ will stop changing after sufficient time has elapsed, and its derivatives will become zero. The current will also become a constant, equal to $\mathscr{E}/R$. Setting the derivative terms equal to zero leaves $k\theta = \tau\mathscr{E}/R$, and so after a long time we will have $\theta = \theta_F$ as given by eq. 8.8-3.

The current sensitivity of a galvanometer S_i is defined as the ratio of the final deflection to the final steady current and is thus seen to be given by $S_i = \tau/k$. It is usually measured in scale divisions per ampere or microampere. For mirror instruments, the scale divisions are commonly taken to be millimeters for a scale at a standard lamp-to-scale distance of

1 m. It is also common to quote sensitivity in reciprocal terms—i.e., microamperes per scale divisions, etc. The voltage sensitivity S_v is the ratio $\theta_F/\mathscr{E} = \tau/kR$ and is measured in corresponding units.

As our second special case, imagine the damping coefficient b to be zero and the external emf $\mathscr{E}$ to have been removed after the coil started moving. The equation of motion reduces to

$$I\frac{d^2\theta}{dt^2} + k\theta = 0 \qquad (8.8\text{–}9)$$

which is the equation of simple harmonic motion. Any simple harmonic function $\theta(t)$ that satisfies eq. 8.8–9 will be of the form

$$\theta = \theta_{\text{max}} \sin\left[t\left(\frac{k}{I}\right)^{\frac{1}{2}} + \phi\right] \qquad (8.8\text{–}10)$$

where θ_{max} and ϕ can have arbitrary values. The period of the motion, which we shall call T_0, the "undamped period," is given by the relation $T_0(k/I)^{\frac{1}{2}} = 2\pi$, or

$$T_0 = 2\pi\left(\frac{I}{k}\right)^{\frac{1}{2}} \qquad (8.8\text{–}11a)$$

and the angular frequency ω_0 of the motion is related to the frequency f_0 and the period T_0 by

$$\omega_0 = 2\pi f_0 = \frac{2\pi}{T_0} = \left(\frac{k}{I}\right)^{\frac{1}{2}} \qquad (8.8\text{–}11b)$$

Thus, if there were no damping and no external force, the coil once set in motion would continue to oscillate indefinitely with period T_0.

The reader familiar with simple harmonic motion will recognize that eq. 8.8–10 includes, for suitable values of θ_{max} and ϕ, all possible motions that satisfy eq. 8.8–9—that is, that have the period T_0. It is a general property of second-order differential equations that any function that satisfies such an equation for arbitrary values of two independently adjustable constants, is the general solution of the equation, meaning that all possible solutions can be found by suitably adjusting these constants (see Appendix A.3). The two constants for the undamped case are θ_{max} and ϕ.

Let us now turn to the general, damped case and seek a solution of eq. 8.8–8 with two adjustable constants, which we will proceed to adjust so as to fit appropriate physical situations. Since the right-hand side of eq. 8.8–8a is equal to $k\theta_F$, we can write the equation in the form

$$I\frac{d^2\theta}{dt^2} + b\frac{d\theta}{dt} + k(\theta - \theta_F) = 0 \qquad (8.8\text{–}12a)$$

Furthermore, since θ_F is a constant, we can use the reduced angle $\theta_r = \theta - \theta_F$ as a variable, obtaining a so-called homogeneous equation (all terms containing the unknown to the first degree)

$$I\frac{d^2\theta_r}{dt^2} + b\frac{d\theta_r}{dt} + k\theta_r = 0 \qquad (8.8\text{–}12b)$$

To find a solution with arbitrary constants in it, we observe that one way for a constant to enter is by multiplication of θ_r. If a particular θ_r satisfies eq. 8.8–12b, so will $c\theta_r$ where c is any number. Furthermore, if θ_{r1} and θ_{r2} are two different solutions, their sum is also one, by the rules for differentiating a sum. Hence we will try to find two simple solutions and then add them after multiplying them by adjustable constants.

A function whose derivatives are proportional to itself would be a good one to try. Such a function is $e^{\lambda t}$ where λ is a constant. If we try $\theta_r = e^{\lambda t}$, we have on substitution

$$I\lambda^2 e^{\lambda t} + b\lambda e^{\lambda t} + ke^{\lambda t} = 0$$

and since $e^{\lambda t}$ cannot be zero, we have

$$I\lambda^2 + b\lambda + k = 0 \qquad (8.8\text{–}13)$$

The roots of this equation are

$$\lambda = -\frac{b}{2I} \pm \frac{1}{2I}(b^2 - 4kI)^{\frac{1}{2}}$$

which we shall write in the form

$$\lambda_1 = -\alpha + \beta \qquad (8.8\text{–}14a)$$

$$\lambda_2 = -\alpha - \beta \qquad (8.8\text{–}14b)$$

with

$$\alpha = \frac{b}{2I} = \left(\frac{k}{I}\right)^{\frac{1}{2}} \cdot \frac{b}{2(kI)^{\frac{1}{2}}} = \omega_0\gamma \qquad (8.8\text{–}15a)$$

$$\beta = \frac{1}{2I}(b^2 - 4kI)^{\frac{1}{2}} = \left(\frac{k}{I}\right)^{\frac{1}{2}}\left(\frac{b^2}{4kI} - 1\right)^{\frac{1}{2}} = \omega_0(\gamma^2 - 1)^{\frac{1}{2}} \qquad (8.8\text{–}15b)$$

and

$$\gamma = \frac{b}{2(kI)^{\frac{1}{2}}} = \frac{1}{2(kI)^{\frac{1}{2}}}\left(b_a + \frac{\tau^2}{R}\right) \qquad (8.8\text{–}16)$$

γ is called the "relative damping" for reasons to be seen later. Note that β if real is less than α, and that $\alpha^2 - \beta^2 = \omega_0^2$. We observe that $e^{\lambda_1 t}$ and $e^{\lambda_2 t}$ are each solutions of the differential equation for any values of I, b, and k, although β will be real only if γ is greater than 1. We shall assume for the time being that this is so. Let us then add our two solutions, each multiplied by an arbitrary constant, yielding a general solution

$$\theta_r = c_1 e^{\lambda_1 t} + c_2 e^{\lambda_2 t} \qquad (8.8\text{–}17a)$$

or

$$\theta = \theta_F + c_1 e^{\lambda_1 t} + c_2 e^{\lambda_2 t} \qquad (8.8\text{–}17b)$$

Now we must ask how c_1 and c_2 are to be specified. There are two simple physical situations that govern most of the cases with which we are concerned. In the first, referred to already, the system starts at $t = 0$ with $\theta = 0$ or $\theta_r = -\theta_F$ and with no initial velocity, and so $d\theta_r/dt = 0$. In the second, we will have $\theta = \theta_r = 0$ at the start and $d\theta/dt$ a certain initial value. This latter case is that of the "ballistic" use of the galvanometer (so called because "ballistics" involves objects—balls, projectiles, etc.—that are given initial velocities and are then subject to Newton's laws of motion) and will be taken up shortly. These two sets of conditions are both referred to as "initial conditions."

Once the dependence of θ on t is determined, the variation of i with t can be found from eq. 8.8–6 (see problem 8.8g).

The Approach to a Steady Deflection. For the case of a steady impressed emf, we have

$$\theta_r = -\theta_F; \qquad d\theta_r/dt = 0 \qquad \text{at } t = 0 \qquad (8.8\text{–}18)$$

which yields two equations for c_1 and c_2:

$$\theta_F = c_1 + c_2 \qquad (8.8\text{–}19)$$

$$0 = \lambda_1 c_1 + \lambda_2 c_2$$

whose solutions are

$$c_1 = \frac{\theta_F \lambda_2}{\lambda_1 - \lambda_2}$$

$$\qquad (8.8\text{–}20)$$

$$c_2 = \frac{-\theta_F \lambda_1}{\lambda_1 - \lambda_2}$$

as can be easily verified. Using eqs. 8.8–14 and 8.8–17, we have

$$\theta = \theta_F \left[1 - \frac{\alpha + \beta}{2\beta} e^{-(\alpha - \beta)t} + \frac{\alpha - \beta}{2\beta} e^{-(\alpha + \beta)t} \right] \qquad (8.8\text{–}21)$$

Now, $\alpha - \beta$ and $\alpha + \beta$ are both positive real numbers when $\gamma > 1$, so that the three terms in the brackets represent respectively a constant and two decreasing exponential terms. Thus θ approaches θ_F in exponential fashion, although in a more complicated way than in the cases of the charges and currents of sections 5.3 and 7.11. If γ is fairly large, α and β will be nearly equal, and the term with $e^{-(\alpha+\beta)t}$ will decrease much more rapidly than $e^{-(\alpha-\beta)t}$ so that after a short time only the latter will be important.

In particular, we can find the time taken for θ to approach within, say, 1% of θ_F. If $\alpha \simeq \beta$, $(\alpha + \beta)/2\beta$ is nearly 1, so that we need only set $e^{-(\alpha-\beta)t} = 0.01$, or $t \simeq 4.6/(\alpha - \beta)$.

Now let us consider what happens if, keeping the initial conditions fixed, the constant b is decreased to the point where $\gamma = 1$. By eq. 8.8–15, $\beta = 0$, and $\alpha = \omega_0 = 2\pi/T_0$. This situation is often dealt with by an independent solution of the equation, but the results are readily obtained by taking a limit in eq. 8.8–21. The two exponential terms can be written as follows

$$-\frac{\alpha e^{-\alpha t}}{2\beta}(e^{\beta t} - e^{-\beta t}) - \frac{e^{-\alpha t}}{2}(e^{\beta t} + e^{-\beta t}) \qquad (8.8\text{–}22)$$

When β goes to zero, the second term becomes just $-e^{-\alpha t}$. The first term has the form $0/0$ and can be evaluated either by de l'Hôpital's rule (differentiate numerator and denominator with respect to β and then take limits) or by using the Maclaurin series for e^x:

$$e^x = 1 + x + \frac{x^2}{2!} + \cdots$$

The first terms for the two exponentials will cancel; the second terms yield together $2\beta t$, which on dividing by 2β yields the constant t; and the rest of the terms go to zero as $\beta \to 0$. Thus we end up with

$$-\alpha t e^{-\alpha t} - e^{-\alpha t}$$

so that

$$\theta = \theta_F[1 - e^{-\alpha t}(\alpha t + 1)]$$
$$= \theta_F[1 - e^{-\omega_0 t}(\omega_0 t + 1)] \qquad (8.8\text{–}23)$$

Again we have an exponential approach of θ to θ_F, but of a different character because of the factor $(\alpha t + 1)$. The reader can verify that if $\alpha t \simeq 6.65$ or $t \simeq 1.06 T_0$, θ is about 1% less than θ_F (problem 8.8*l*). This case is called that of "critical damping." It will be noted that $2(kI)^{\frac{1}{2}} = b$ for critical damping which explains why γ is in general called the "relative damping."

Now let us suppose that γ is less than 1. We could also in this case start the solution process over—we might, correctly, guess that the solution had a combined exponential and sinusoidal character, because when $\gamma \to 0$ it must approach the simple harmonic solution, eq. 8.8–10. However, we can again use our original solution with the same boundary conditions, by making use of complex numbers. A considerable use of complex numbers will be required in the next chapter, and many of their properties are taken up in Appendix A.5.   Here we need only to quote the relations (see Appendix A.5–11):

$$\sin x = \frac{e^{jx} - e^{-jx}}{2j} \quad \text{and} \quad \cos x = \frac{e^{jx} + e^{-jx}}{2} \qquad (8.8\text{–}24)$$

where we use j for the quantity $\sqrt{-1}$ in accord with current practice in the physics of electromagnetism and in engineering.

When γ is less than one, we shall write

$$\beta = \omega_0(\gamma^2 - 1)^{\frac{1}{2}} = \omega_0(-1)^{\frac{1}{2}}(1 - \gamma^2)^{\frac{1}{2}} = j\omega_0(1 - \gamma^2)^{\frac{1}{2}} = j\omega$$

so that what we shall call the damped angular frequency ω is given by

$$\omega = \omega_0(1 - \gamma^2)^{\frac{1}{2}} \qquad (8.8\text{–}25)$$

(Note that $\alpha^2 + \omega^2 = \gamma^2\omega_0^2 + \omega^2 = \omega_0^2$.)   We can easily rewrite eq. 8.8–21 with ω instead of β:

$$\theta = \theta_F\left[1 - \frac{\alpha e^{-\alpha t}}{2j\omega}(e^{j\omega t} - e^{-j\omega t}) - \frac{e^{-\alpha t}}{2}(e^{j\omega t} + e^{-j\omega t})\right]$$

making use of eq. 8.8–22.   The relations 8.8–24 now yield

$$\theta = \theta_F\left[1 - e^{-\alpha t}\left(\frac{\alpha}{\omega}\sin \omega t + \cos \omega t\right)\right] \qquad (8.8\text{–}26)$$

which is the solution of eq. 8.8–12a that satisfies the initial conditions of eq. 8.8–18 and holds for $\gamma < 1$ or $b < 2(kI)^{\frac{1}{2}}$.

The variable θ now approaches θ_F in an oscillatory fashion, with a steadily decreasing amplitude of oscillation about θ_F, proportional to $e^{-\alpha t}$.   Figure 8.8b shows the relation between θ and t for particular examples of the three cases we have considered.

The frequency of the oscillating part of eq. 8.8–26 is $\omega/2\pi$ (the sum of two simple harmonic motions of frequency ω is equal to a simple one of the same frequency) and is less than ω_0.   The damping has the effect of slowing down the oscillations from the frequency they would have with $\gamma = 0$.   When $\gamma \to 1, \omega \to 0$; the oscillations disappear as critical damping is approached.

Let us calculate the position of the maxima and minima of the expression 8.8–26.   Differentiating with respect to t and canceling two terms, we find

$$\frac{d\theta}{dt} = \theta_F\left(\frac{\alpha^2}{\omega} + \omega\right)e^{-\alpha t}\sin \omega t$$

which is zero when $\sin \omega t$ is 0, or $\omega t = n\pi$ with $n = 1, 2, 3 \cdots$, yielding for t_n, the time of the nth extreme value

$$t_n = \frac{n\pi}{\omega} = \frac{n\pi}{\omega_0(1 - \gamma^2)^{\frac{1}{2}}} = \frac{nT_0}{2(1 - \gamma^2)^{\frac{1}{2}}} \tag{8.8-27}$$

The values of $\theta = \theta_n$ at the maxima and minima are easily found from eq. 8.8–26. We have $\sin \omega t = 0$ and $\cos \omega t = \cos n\pi = (-1)^n$. Further-

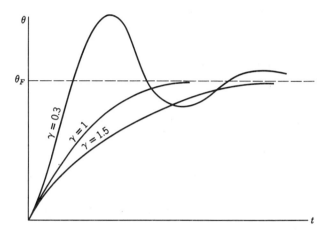

Fig. 8.8b.   The approach to equilibrium of a damped galvanometer for three different values of the relative damping γ.

more, we can write $\alpha T_0/2$ as $\pi\gamma$ from eq. 8.8–15a. Therefore, θ_n for the nth extreme value is

$$\theta_n = \theta_F[1 - (-1)^n e^{-\gamma\pi n/(1 - \gamma^2)^{\frac{1}{2}}}] \tag{8.8-28}$$

The ratio of successive (opposite) maximum deviations from the final value θ_F reduces to a simple expression:

$$\frac{\theta_n - \theta_F}{\theta_F - \theta_{n-1}} = e^{-\gamma\pi/(1 - \gamma^2)^{\frac{1}{2}}} \tag{8.8-29}$$

The negative logarithm of this ratio is called the "logarithmic decrement" δ:

$$\delta = -\ln \frac{\theta_n - \theta_F}{\theta_F - \theta_{n-1}} = \frac{\gamma\pi}{(1 - \gamma^2)^{\frac{1}{2}}} \tag{8.8-30}$$

In the case of low damping or considerable oscillation, the logarithmic decrement is easy to obtain experimentally. Note that the last two equations hold for any integer n, including the value 1 if we set $\theta_0 = 0$ (their validity in this case follows directly from eq. 8.8–28 by setting $n = 1$).

It is left to the reader to show (problem 8.8*b*) that, if after the galvano-meter has attained a steady deflection $\theta = \theta_F$ the circuit is suddenly opened, the deflection θ obeys the equation we have set up for θ_r, with $b = b_a$. The galvanometer oscillates in a damped fashion about $\theta = 0$, or, if more than critically damped by its own friction, it returns to zero exponentially.

The Ballistic Use of a Galvanometer. The ballistic operation of a galvanometer involves giving to the coil an angular impulse during a very short period of time, the subsequent swing occurring without the action of any external emf. In other words, the motion after the initial impulse will be governed by eq. 8.8–8 with $\mathscr{E} = 0$, which is the same as eq. 8.8–12*b* for $\theta_r = 0$. The general solution for θ can be written from eq. 8.8–17*a* as

$$\theta = c'_1 e^{\lambda_1 t} + c'_2 e^{\lambda_2 t} \tag{8.8–31}$$

where c'_1 and c'_2 are new constants. To find them, we must examine the initial conditions. The ideal case is one in which the initial impulse occurs during a time so short compared to the period T_0 that the deflection during this period is smaller than the errors of measurement. There will, however, be angular velocity $d\theta/dt$ acquired during this time. Let us take the equation of motion in its initial form eq. 8.8–7, multiply it by dt and integrate over the time Δt of the initial impulse:

$$\tau \int_0^{\Delta t} i \, dt - k \int_0^{\Delta t} \theta \, dt - b_a \int_0^{\Delta t} \frac{d\theta}{dt} \, dt = I \int_0^{\Delta t} \frac{d^2\theta}{dt^2} \, dt$$

Assuming that all quantities are zero at $t = 0$, and that θ is zero throughout the initial time interval, two of the integrals vanish and we have

$$\tau Q = I \left(\frac{d\theta}{dt} \right)_{t=\Delta t}$$

where Q is the total charge passed through the coil. Hence the angular velocity $\hat{\omega}$ acquired with the initial impulse is given by

$$\hat{\omega} = \left(\frac{d\theta}{dt} \right)_{t=\Delta t} = \frac{\tau}{I} Q \tag{8.8–32}$$

(The reader may recognize that τQ represents the angular impulse $\int \mathscr{L} \, dt$ delivered to the coil, and $I\hat{\omega}$ represents the angular momentum acquired.)

Now if Δt is small enough, we can consider that $d\theta/dt = \tau Q/I = \hat{\omega}$ when $t = 0$. Thus we have for the initial conditions for the ballistic galvanometer

$$\theta = 0, \qquad d\theta/dt = \hat{\omega} \qquad \text{when } t = 0 \tag{8.8–33}$$

allowing us to determine c'_1 and c'_2 in eq. 8.8–31. The result for θ is

(as may be readily verified)

$$\theta = \hat{\omega} \frac{e^{\lambda_1 t} - e^{\lambda_2 t}}{\lambda_1 - \lambda_2} = \frac{\hat{\omega} e^{-\alpha t}}{2\beta} (e^{\beta t} - e^{-\beta t}) \tag{8.8–34}$$

which is the appropriate form of the solution when $\gamma > 1$ and β is real (overdamped case). Letting $\beta \to 0$ as before we find for the critically damped case

$$\theta = \hat{\omega} t e^{-\alpha t} = \hat{\omega} t e^{-\omega_0 t} \tag{8.8–35}$$

whereas if $\gamma < 1$ and $\beta = j\omega$, we immediately have for the underdamped case

$$\theta = \frac{\hat{\omega}}{\omega} e^{-\alpha t} \sin \omega t \tag{8.8–36}$$

Figure 8.8c shows the variation of θ with t for various values of γ. It will be noted that the coil finally comes to rest in the shortest time when $\gamma = 1$.

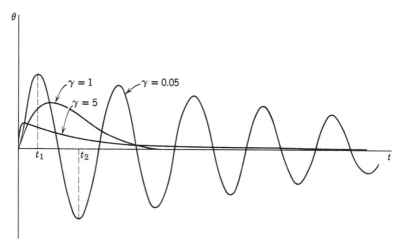

Fig. 8.8c. The deflection of a ballistic galvanometer as a function of time for different amounts of relative damping.

The usual method of making observations is to observe the value of θ at the first maximum, and so we require formulas for this value, θ_1, and for the time t_1 at which it occurs. The completely undamped case, $\gamma = 0$, gives the equation

$$\theta = \frac{\hat{\omega}}{\omega_0} \sin \omega_0 t$$

with the values

$$\theta_1 = \frac{\hat{\omega}}{\omega_0} \quad \text{and} \quad t_1 = \frac{\pi}{2\omega_0} = \frac{T_0}{4}; \quad \gamma = 0 \tag{8.8–37}$$

When $0 < \gamma < 1$ we set the derivative of eq. 8.8–36 equal to zero and obtain for any extreme value t_n,

$$\tan \omega t_n = \omega/\alpha \qquad (8.8\text{–}38)$$

The smallest time for which this equation is satisfied is given by the angle

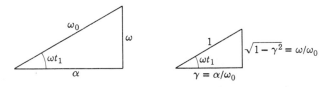

Fig. 8.8d. Illustrating $\tan \omega t_1 = \omega/\alpha$.

ωt_1, shown in Fig. 8.8d, from which we see immediately that $\sin \omega t_1 = \omega/(\omega^2 + \alpha^2)^{\frac{1}{2}} = \omega/\omega_0$. We have as a result

$$\theta_1 = \frac{\hat{\omega}}{\omega_0}\, e^{-\alpha t_1} = \frac{\hat{\omega}}{\omega_0}\, e^{-\frac{\alpha}{\omega}\sin^{-1}\frac{\omega}{\omega_0}} = \frac{\hat{\omega}}{\omega_0}\, \exp\left[\frac{-\gamma}{(1-\gamma^2)^{\frac{1}{2}}}\sin^{-1}(1-\gamma^2)^{\frac{1}{2}}\right]$$

$$(8.8\text{–}39a)$$

and

$$t_1 = \frac{1}{\omega}\sin^{-1}\frac{\omega}{\omega_0} = \frac{\sin^{-1}(1-\gamma^2)^{\frac{1}{2}}}{\omega_0(1-\gamma^2)^{\frac{1}{2}}}$$

$$= \frac{T_0}{4}\cdot\frac{2}{\pi(1-\gamma^2)^{\frac{1}{2}}}\sin^{-1}(1-\gamma^2)^{\frac{1}{2}}; \quad 0 < \gamma < 1 \qquad (8.8\text{–}39b)$$

When γ is very small, the angle ωt_1 is nearly $\pi/2$, in fact, $\sin(\pi/2 - \omega_1 t) = \gamma$, $\frac{\pi}{2} - \omega t_1 \simeq \gamma$, and $\omega \simeq \omega_0$. Then θ_1 is approximately $(\hat{\omega}/\omega_0)\,e^{-\pi\gamma/2}$. Expanding the exponential to the first-power term, we can write

$$\theta_1 \simeq \frac{\hat{\omega}}{\omega_0}\left(1 - \frac{\pi\gamma}{2}\right) \quad \text{and} \quad t_1 \simeq \frac{T_0}{4}\left(1 - \frac{2\gamma}{\pi}\right); \quad \gamma \ll 1 \qquad (8.8\text{–}40)$$

When $\gamma \to 1$, $(1-\gamma^2)^{\frac{1}{2}}$ becomes small, $\sin^{-1}(1-\gamma^2)^{\frac{1}{2}} \simeq (1-\gamma^2)^{\frac{1}{2}}$, and $t_1 = 1/\omega_0$, so that we have a result which can also be obtained from eq. 8.8–35:

$$\theta_1 = \frac{\hat{\omega}}{\omega_0 e} \quad \text{and} \quad t_1 = \frac{1}{\omega_0} = \frac{T_0}{4}\cdot\frac{2}{\pi}; \quad \gamma = 1 \qquad (8.8\text{–}41)$$

For the overdamped case, we differentiate eq. 8.8–34, getting

$$(-\alpha + \beta)e^{-(\alpha-\beta)t_1} + (\alpha + \beta)e^{-(\alpha+\beta)t_1} = 0,$$

which yields

$$e^{2\beta t_1} = \frac{\alpha + \beta}{\alpha - \beta} = \frac{(\alpha + \beta)^2}{\omega_0^2} = \frac{\omega_0^2}{(\alpha - \beta)^2},$$

the last two forms being obtained from $\alpha^2 - \beta^2 = \omega_0^2$. Thus we have

$$e^{\beta t_1} = \frac{\alpha + \beta}{\omega_0} = \frac{\omega_0}{\alpha - \beta}$$

Furthermore, using $e^{-\beta t_1} = (\alpha - \beta)/\omega_0$,

$$\theta_1 = \frac{\hat{\omega}}{2\beta} e^{-\alpha t_1} \left(\frac{\alpha + \beta}{\omega_0} - \frac{\alpha - \beta}{\omega_0} \right) = \frac{\hat{\omega}}{\omega_0} e^{-\alpha t_1}$$

so we have

$$\theta_1 = \frac{\hat{\omega}}{\omega_0} \exp\left[-\frac{\alpha}{\beta} \ln \frac{\alpha + \beta}{\omega_0} \right] = \frac{\hat{\omega}}{\omega_0} \exp\left\{ -\frac{\gamma}{(\gamma^2 - 1)^{\frac{1}{2}}} \ln [\gamma + (\gamma^2 - 1)^{\frac{1}{2}}] \right\}$$

$$t_1 = \frac{1}{\beta} \ln \left(\frac{\alpha + \beta}{\omega_0} \right) = \frac{1}{\omega_0(\gamma^2 - 1)^{\frac{1}{2}}} \ln [\gamma + (\gamma^2 - 1)^{\frac{1}{2}}]; \quad \gamma > 1 \qquad (8.8\text{-}42)$$

Finally, when γ is very large, $(\gamma^2 - 1)^{\frac{1}{2}} \simeq \gamma$, and we have

$$\theta_1 \simeq \frac{\hat{\omega}}{\omega_0} e^{-\ln 2\gamma} = \frac{\hat{\omega}}{2\gamma\omega_0}$$

$$t_1 \simeq \frac{\ln 2\gamma}{\omega_0 \gamma}; \quad \gamma \gg 1 \qquad (8.8\text{-}43)$$

It will be seen from these various formulas as well as from Fig. 8.8c that as γ increases, θ_1 and t_1 both decrease. The question of the proper choice of γ depends on various factors involving the use of the galvanometer.

One use of a ballistic galvanometer is for comparison of capacitances by direct measurement of the charges on two condensers produced by the same charging potential V. However modern bridge methods have largely superseded this method for measuring capacitance. The deflection θ_1 given by eq. 8.8-39a is a measure of Q, since $\hat{\omega} = \tau Q/I$. We can in fact define the coulomb sensitivity S_Q of the galvanometer as the ratio

$$S_Q = \theta_1/Q = (\tau/\omega_0 I) e^{-\alpha t_1}. \qquad (8.8\text{-}44)$$

The coulomb sensitivity is largest when γ is as small as possible.

The most important use of the ballistic galvanometer is for flux measurements. As shown in section 8.5, the charge Q that passes around a circuit when a change in flux linkage $\Delta\Phi$ is made in it is given by $Q = \Delta\Phi/R$. Hence if a search coil or test winding is connected in series with a ballistic galvanometer and a flux change produced by motion or by change of the magnetic field, a ballistic deflection will occur given by

$$\theta_1 = \frac{\tau \Delta\Phi}{\omega_0 IR} e^{-\alpha t_1} \qquad (8.8\text{-}45)$$

(a formula valid for any γ) and comparison methods can be used to measure unknown flux changes in terms of known ones. One can also proceed from measurements of R, γ, γ_0, S_i, and T_0 to make absolute measurements. Third, one can use a standard condenser and known voltage V to measure the coulomb sensitivity S_Q, which together with the value of R gives the flux-linkage sensitivity

$$S_\Phi = \frac{\theta_1}{\Delta\Phi} = \frac{S_Q}{R} \qquad (8.8\text{–}46)$$

The optimum value of γ for flux measurements—that is, the best value of R—is now not determined by having S_Q large and $\gamma \simeq 0$, but by having γ large (problem 8.8k).   When a galvanometer is used for this purpose with a small resistance R and consequent large damping, a rapid return to zero after a deflection is read is best accomplished by arranging a series key to be opened to start an undamped swing toward 0, which can be arrested by closing the key at 0.

We have assumed in the above an ideal case in which the initial impulse is instantaneous.   A careful analysis of the case of a prolonged impulse, which we shall omit here,[30] shows that the error resulting from the finite length of an actual impulse is least for large damping and, as to be expected, for the largest practical period T_0.   Hence a ballistic galvanometer for flux-measuring purposes should have both a large relative damping and a long period.   Since $\gamma = b/2(kI)^{\frac{1}{2}}$ and $T_0 = 2\pi(I/k)^{\frac{1}{2}}$, the attainment of large T_0 and large γ is aided by the reduction of k, so that a weak suspension is of use for increased sensitivity; so also, by the result of problem 8.8k, is a low value of the torque constant $\tau = nBS$.   Some galvanometers are in fact provided with magnetic shunts for reducing B in the coil gap when extra sensitivity is desired.

The Fluxmeter.   This is a galvanometer especially arranged for flux measurements with nearly zero restoring torque, and can be used with slow flux changes as well as fast ones.   Let us analyze the system from the original equations in order to appreciate its action.   If an emf $d\Phi/dt$ acts in the fluxmeter circuit, we have the circuit equation

$$\frac{d\Phi}{dt} = Ri + L\frac{di}{dt} + \tau\frac{d\theta}{dt}$$

The mechanical equation becomes, with $k = 0$,

$$\tau i = I\frac{d^2\theta}{dt^2} + b_a\frac{d\theta}{dt}$$

Using the latter equation to eliminate i from the former, we have an equation which on integration gives the desired result directly:

$$\frac{d\Phi}{dt} = L\frac{di}{dt} + \frac{RI}{\tau}\frac{d^2\theta}{dt^2} + \left(\frac{b_a R}{\tau} + \tau\right)\frac{d\theta}{dt} \qquad (8.8\text{–}47)$$

[30] Harris, *op. cit.*, pp. 321–329.

We now integrate this equation with respect to dt over a time interval such that both current and coil motion vanish at the ends of the interval. We then obtain, using Δ's for the changes in the quantities over the interval,

$$\Delta\Phi = L\,\Delta i + \frac{RI}{\tau}\,\Delta\left(\frac{d\theta}{dt}\right) + \left(\frac{b_a R}{\tau} + \tau\right)\Delta\theta$$

which because of the conditions just stated becomes

$$\Delta\Phi = \left(\frac{b_a R}{\tau} + \tau\right)\Delta\theta \qquad\qquad (8.8\text{--}48)$$

The angular deflection is a direct measure of $\Delta\Phi$ regardless of how fast or slow is the change in Φ. (In practice, changes generally have to be made within five seconds or so to avoid errors due to drifting.) In order to get sensitivity, b_a is made as small as possible, and τ may be reduced by means of magnetic shunts.

It will be noted that the deflection is not measured from zero but may occur at any part of the scale. Arrangements are usually made to provide controllable flux changes in an auxiliary coil to bring the pointer or light spot to a convenient place before making a measurement. The restoring torque of the suspension is sometimes reduced to a very small value by means of an opposing magnetic torque, but it is not usually possible to reduce it altogether to zero; some drift of the coil back to a rest position will generally occur on long standing.

Problem 8.8a.   Show that eq. 8.8–23 satisfies eq. 8.8–12 when $\gamma = 1$.

Problem 8.8b.   Discuss the motion of a galvanometer subject to a steady deflection $\theta = \theta_F$, when the circuit is suddenly opened so that i and $\mathscr{E}$ are zero.

Problem 8.8c.   If ΔT represents the increase in period over the undamped value T_0 when γ is small, derive an approximate expression for ΔT, showing that it is proportional to b^2.

Problem 8.8d.   Find the time in units of T_0 at which the deflection of a galvanometer with $\gamma = 0.825$ first gets to within 1% of θ_F. Show that this value of γ gives the shortest time for the galvanometer to come and remain within 1% of θ_F.

Problem 8.8e.   Write a formula for the external critical damping resistance (abbreviation: CDRX) of a galvanometer in terms of τ, k, I, γ_0, and the resistance R_g of the galvanometer itself.

Problem 8.8f.   Derive eq. 8.8–41 from eq. 8.8–35.

Problem 8.8g.   By use of eq. 8.8–6, write formulas and sketch graphs for the variation of current with time for a galvanometer with a constant impressed emf and values of γ respectively less than, equal to, and greater than 1.

Problem 8.8h.   Find θ_1 and t_1 in terms of $\hat{\omega}/\omega_0$ and $T_0/4$ for a ballistic galvanometer with $\gamma = 0.2, 0.707, 2,$ and 10.

Problem 8.8i.   Show how to find the galvanometer design constants b_a, I, k, and τ from the readily measurable quantities R, γ, γ_0, ω_0, and S_i, where γ_0 is the open-circuit relative damping $b_a/2(kI)^{\frac{1}{2}}$.

Problem 8.8j.   Discuss the influence of a shunt across a galvanometer on its use for the measurement of capacitance.

Problem 8.8k.   Show that S_Φ increases steadily with γ as γ ranges from 0 to ∞, with a limiting value $1/\tau$.

Fig. 8.8e.   A circuit for an Ayrton shunt.

Problem 8.8l.   Verify the statement following eq. 8.8–23.

Problem 8.8m.   Figure 8.8e gives the circuit of an Ayrton shunt for a galvanometer.   If the current i is independent of the switch position (for instance if the line resistance $R_L \gg R_0$), show that i_g is proportional to the fraction x, no matter what constant value of R_g is used.

Problem 8.8n.   A long flexible non-magnetic coil in the form of a ribbon-shaped solenoid has a double layer of windings, wound so that their fields add. The two leads come out at one end and are carefully twisted so as not to enclose appreciable area.   Show that, if such a coil is connected to a fluxmeter and moved into an arbitrary position in a magnetic field, the deflection resulting will be a measure of $\int \mathbf{H} \cdot \mathbf{dl}$ along the final position of the coil.

9

Alternating Currents

9.1 Introduction

Alternating-current theory deals with the currents and voltages produced in circuits containing resistances, inductances, capacitances, transformers, rotating machines, and other devices, when alternating emf's are applied. The emf's are usually taken to vary sinusoidally, and we shall write for a typical emf the general formula

$$\mathscr{E} = \mathscr{E}_m \cos{(\omega t + \varphi_V)} \qquad (9.1\text{-}1)$$

where $\mathscr{E}_m$, ω, and φ_V are constants and t is the time. The quantity ω is called the angular frequency; the period T of one complete cycle of oscillation is given by $\omega T = 2\pi$, or $T = 2\pi/\omega$. The frequency f in cycles per second is therefore $\omega/2\pi$, and $\mathscr{E}_m$ is called the amplitude of the alternating emf.

Other types of variation are also treated in this theory, but we shall emphasize the case of sinusoidal variations and later deal briefly with other cases (harmonic analysis and pulse theory, sections 9.7 and 9.8).

We shall also restrict ourselves for the time being to the case in which emf's of the type of eq. 9.1–1 have been established for a long enough time that the transient effects due to their establishment have died out. It seems obvious that if the emf's are sinusoidal, the currents will be too, with the same angular frequency ω; we shall show that a solution of the relevant differential equation of this form does in fact exist.   The transient treatment in section 9.8 will provide the proof that it is the *unique* solution and in fact show how rapidly it becomes established.

The main part of our analysis will deal with circuits containing only resistances, capacitances, and inductances, and we shall assume these quantities to be lumped, as in sections 5.3 (for condensers) and 7.11 (for self-inductances).   Our treatment with lumped quantities will lay the foundation for introductory work with distributed quantities in section 10.2.   The fact that all capacitance of any importance in our circuits appears explicitly in the indicated condensers means that no charging up or discharging occurs at any other place, so that all currents are the same throughout any branch at any given instant, and Kirchhoff's junction law remains valid.   Similarly, the lumping of inductance elements means that all the electromagnetically induced emf's are explicitly introduced at the designated inductance coils and can be written as potential drops as in section 7.11, so that Kirchhoff's loop rule for emf's also remains valid at any instant.

The final restriction to be kept in mind is that we take R's, L's, M's, and C's to be constants, thus assuming ideal linear behavior of each of these elements.   In particular, we shall not consider such high frequencies that the skin effect discussed at the end of section 7.11 is important. Some reference to non-ideal behavior will be made later.

9.2 Series Circuits

We begin our alternating-current (a-c) theory with a discussion of the circuit of Fig. 9.2a, containing a resistance R, a self-inductance L, and a capacitance C in series, with an applied alternating emf $\mathscr{E}$ (often called by the redundant expression an "a-c voltage").   By treating the emf $-L(di/dt)$ as a PD, we can write the generalization of eqs. 5.3–5 and 7.11–3:

$$\mathscr{E} = L\frac{di}{dt} + Ri + \frac{q}{C} \qquad (9.2\text{–}1)$$

where the current i and charge q are related by

$$i = \frac{dq}{dt} \qquad (9.2\text{–}2)$$

As stated above, we shall use eq. 9.1–1 and assume that i also varies in a sinusoidal way, so that (introducing new constants i_m and φ_i),

$$i = i_m \cos (\omega t + \varphi_i) \tag{9.2–3}$$

from which we have

$$L\frac{di}{dt} = -L\omega i_m \sin (\omega t + \varphi_i) \tag{9.2–4}$$

and

$$\frac{q}{C} = \frac{1}{C}\int i\, dt = \frac{i_m}{\omega C} \sin (\omega t + \varphi_i) \tag{9.2–5}$$

The constant of integration arising from the indefinite integral for q must be zero if eq. 9.2–1 is to be satisfied.   To see this, we integrate both sides

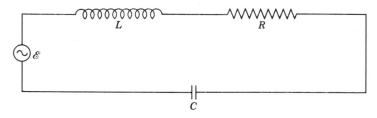

Fig. 9.2a.   A series circuit with R, L, and C.

of the equation over a period T.   The sine and cosine terms will integrate to zero because they are periodic.   Thus any constant term in q/C must be zero.

It is a straightforward matter to substitute eqs. 9.2–3, 9.2–4, and 9.2–5 into eq. 9.2–1 and evaluate the constants i_m and φ_i, by means of suitable trigonometric relations, but we shall leave this method of calculation to the reader in problem 9.2a.   A method more instructive for our purposes is to represent alternating currents and voltages graphically as projections of rotating vectors.

If a vector of length i_m, as in Fig. 9.2b, makes an angle θ with a given line and θ increases steadily with the time in accordance with the formula $\theta = \omega t + \varphi_i$, the projection $\mathcal{O}\mathcal{M}$ obeys eq. 9.2–3.   The reader will observe that the point $\mathcal{M}$ executes simple harmonic motion (SHM) about $\mathcal{O}$.   The line $\mathcal{O}\mathcal{P}$ is called the current vector representing i.   Similarly any sinusoidal voltage can be represented as the projection of a voltage vector.

Now, each term on the right in eq. 9.2–1 is an alternating voltage and can be represented as the projection of an appropriate voltage vector. The sum indicated is thus a sum of projections of appropriate vectors, and we shall express it as the projection of the sum of these vectors.   It is the linear property of the circuit elements that makes this addition possible. (Voltage proportional to i, di/dt, or $\int i\,dt$.)

The quantity Ri is simply R times $\mathcal{OM}$, or the projection of the current vector times R.   The term $L(di/dt)$ is equal to $-L\omega i_m \sin(\omega t + \varphi_i) = -L\omega i_m \sin\theta$ and is indicated in Fig. 9.2c as the projection of a vector of length $L\omega i_m$, 90° from $\mathcal{OP}$ in the positive sense.   Since $\cos(\theta + \pi/2)$ is always equal to $-\sin\theta$, this relation is valid for all values of θ.   The term representing q/C, according to eq. 9.2–5, is $(i_m/\omega C)\sin\theta$, and is shown in Fig. 9.2c as the projection of a vector opposite to that for $L(di/dt)$.   We say that the vector for the inductive voltage is ahead of the resistive vector and that the capacitive-voltage vector is behind.

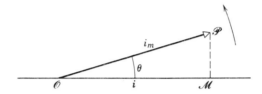

Fig. 9.2b.   A graphical representation of an alternating current as the projection of a vector.

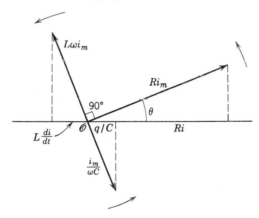

Fig. 9.2c.   Voltages in a series circuit as projections.

The sum of the three projections is the emf $\mathcal{E}$, so we can construct a vector representation for $\mathcal{E}$ by adding the three vectors already found, as in Fig. 9.2d.

We have, for convenience, performed the vector addition by adding the two oppositely directed vectors first, and combining this result with the Ri_m vector.   From Fig. 9.2d we can immediately find the constants $\mathcal{E}_m$

and φ_V of eq. 9.1–1.   We see that $\mathscr{E}_m$ is the hypotenuse of a right triangle and is given by

$$\mathscr{E}_m = \left[(Ri_m)^2 + \left(L\omega i_m - \frac{i_m}{\omega C} \right)^2 \right]^{\frac{1}{2}}$$

$$= i_m \left[R^2 + \left(L\omega - \frac{1}{\omega C} \right)^2 \right]^{\frac{1}{2}} \qquad (9.2\text{–}6)$$

The angles $\omega t + \varphi_V$ and $\omega t + \varphi_i$ are indicated in Fig. 9.2d, so that their difference, the angle $\varphi = \varphi_V - \varphi_i$, is seen to be given by the relation

$$\tan (\varphi_V - \varphi_i) = \tan \varphi = \frac{L\omega - \dfrac{1}{\omega C}}{R} \qquad (9.2\text{–}7)$$

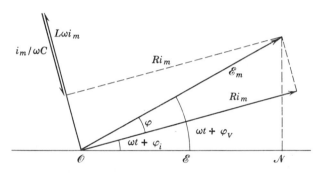

Fig. 9.2d.   The emf $\mathscr{E}$ is the projection $\mathcal{ON}$ of a vector found by adding the three vectors of Fig. 9.2c.   Note that the phase angle $\varphi = \varphi_V - \varphi_L$.

It will be noted that these equations could be derived by drawing the vectors of Fig. 9.2d as stationary, with $\omega t + \varphi_i = 0$.   It is possible to analyze a-c circuits of considerable complexity by using stationary-vector diagrams.   The complex-number type of analysis, to be treated in section 9.4, is an algebraic extension of the vector method.

The angle φ is sometimes called the phase angle of the emf with respect to the current.   The angle θ is sometimes called the phase, but as it is not a constant it is not often referred to.   In this case, the voltage vector leads the current vector.   In the case $L\omega < 1/\omega C$, the diagram will be reversed, and the current vector will lead the voltage vector; the angle $\varphi_V - \varphi_i$ will become negative.   We can also say that in the first case, the current lags behind the voltage, and vice versa for the second case.   Either φ_V or φ_i can be taken as zero without loss of generality, since t can be measured from any arbitrary zero of time.

The square root in eq. 9.2–6 is a quantity of first importance. It is equal to the ratio $\mathscr{E}_m/i_m$ and is called the impedance,[1] Z. The quantity $L\omega$ is called the inductive reactance X_L; $1/\omega C$ is called the capacitive reactance X_C; and the difference $X_L - X_C$ or $X_C - X_L$ is called the reactance X. (It is not necessary to give a definite sign to X since it appears squared; it may be denoted as principally capacitive or principally inductive depending on which of X_C or X_L is the larger. We shall find it convenient, however, to define X algebraically as $X_L - X_C$.)

To summarize

$$X_L = L\omega \tag{9.2–8}$$

$$X_C = 1/\omega C \tag{9.2–9}$$

$$X = X_L - X_C \tag{9.2–10}$$

$$Z = (R^2 + X^2)^{\frac{1}{2}} \tag{9.2–11}$$

$$\varphi_V - \varphi_i = \varphi = \tan^{-1}\frac{X}{R} = \sin^{-1}\frac{X}{Z} = \cos^{-1}\frac{R}{Z} \tag{9.2–12}$$

The different expressions for φ in the last line are derived from the right triangle formed by $i_m R$, $i_m X$, and $i_m Z$. Reactance and impedance are, like resistance, measured in ohms.

Although we have made the calculation assuming that an emf is directly applied to the circuit under consideration, the results also give the relation between voltage drop and current in the circuit when it is a branch of a more complex circuit.

For a circuit containing only resistance and capacitance, we can set $L = 0$ and obtain

$$i_m = \mathscr{E}_m/(R^2 + 1/\omega^2 C^2)^{\frac{1}{2}} \tag{9.2–13}$$

from which we see that the current decreases with increasing R, as expected, and increases with increasing C and ω. At very high frequencies or for large capacitance values, the impedance reduces essentially to the resistance R. For zero frequency, Z is infinite and i is zero. No direct current will pass through a condenser.

The phase relation between current and voltage may be represented by a time graph, produced by measuring the current and voltage vertically (i.e., choosing a vertical line for projection) and the time horizontally and to the right. Then it is easy to see that the quantity whose vector leads the other in Fig. 9.2d will arrive at a maximum or a minimum somewhat

---

[1] "Impedance" and "reactance" are sometimes used to designate *objects* that possess the quantities referred to

before the other (to the left in the time graph) as in Fig. 9.2e.[2]   The amount by which one curve is ahead of the other can be measured in seconds, or radians, but is usually measured in degrees.   The phase angle in a capacitive circuit has the maximum value of 90° when $R = 0$.

The case of a circuit with resistance and inductance is to be treated by

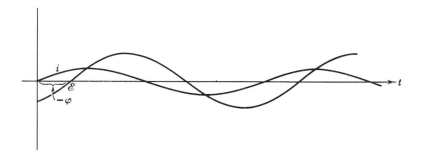

Fig. 9.2e.   Phase relations in a capacitive circuit.

Fig. 9.2f.   Phase relations in an inductive circuit.

letting $C \to \infty$ so that q/C and $1/\omega C$ are zero.   Then we have, of course,

$$i_m = \frac{\mathscr{E}_m}{(R^2 + L^2\omega^2)^{\frac{1}{2}}} \tag{9.2-14}$$

and we see that in this case the largest current occurs for zero ω and L. For very high frequencies, i_m is approximately $\mathscr{E}_m/\omega L$ and gets very small.

[2] The order of the current and voltage graphs in Figs. 9.2e and f can be remembered from the fact that in a condenser, charge and voltage cannot be acquired until after a current has been established for a period of time, whereas in an inductance, the current tends to stay constant and so lags behind the emf that tries to change it.   The reader should remember that in graphs like these, a point representing a time t is to be thought of as moving to the right as time goes on, with the graph stationary.   If it is desired to keep the time point fixed and think of the graph as a moving wave, it must be made to move to the left.

The phase relation is shown in Fig. 9.2*f*. Since no actual coil can have zero resistance, the angle by which $\mathscr{E}$ leads i is always less than 90°.

When both C and L are present, the reactance is large and capacitive for low frequencies and large and inductive for high frequencies. There is a value ω_0 of ω for which $X = 0$ and hence Z has its minimum value R. A series circuit for which X is zero is said to be resonant. The angle φ must also be zero; we say that the current and voltage are in phase with one another.

To find ω_0 we set

$$X = L\omega_0 - \frac{1}{\omega_0 C} = 0$$

which gives $\omega_0{}^2 LC = 1$ or

$$\omega_0 = \frac{1}{(LC)^{\frac{1}{2}}} \tag{9.2-15}$$

For the resonance frequency, we then have

$$f_0 = \frac{\omega_0}{2\pi} = \frac{1}{2\pi(LC)^{\frac{1}{2}}} \tag{9.2-16}$$

Figure 9.2*g* shows the ratio of R to Z as a function of ω/ω_0 for three values of the parameter $\omega_0 L/R$, since the ratio can be written (using $\omega_0 CL = 1/\omega_0$)

$$\frac{R}{Z} = \frac{R}{\left[R^2 + \omega_0{}^2 L^2 \left(\dfrac{\omega}{\omega_0} - \dfrac{1}{\omega\omega_0 CL}\right)^2\right]^{\frac{1}{2}}}$$

$$= \frac{1}{\left[1 + \dfrac{\omega_0{}^2 L^2}{R^2}\left(\dfrac{\omega}{\omega_0} - \dfrac{\omega_0}{\omega}\right)^2\right]^{\frac{1}{2}}} \tag{9.2-17}$$

The quantity $\omega_0 L/R$ is commonly denoted by Q_0 and is sometimes called the "figure of merit" or "quality ratio" but is most often referred to simply as "Q" (not to be confused with charge!). It is here seen as a property of a series circuit and may be defined in general for any resonant type of circuit. In many cases the resistance is that of the coil winding, and for these cases, Q_0 is a property of the coil (and of course is frequency-dependent). For an arbitrary frequency ω it is written simply $Q = \omega L/R$. It is evident from Fig. 9.2*g* that Q_0 determines the sharpness of the maximum of $i_m = \mathscr{E}_m/Z = (\mathscr{E}_m/R)(R/Z)$ obtained when the frequency is varied.

A method of describing the sharpness is to find the two values of ω for which R/Z is $1/\sqrt{2}$ times its maximum value (the so-called half-power points—see problem 9.3f and Fig. 9.2g) and to record their difference. The value of Z will be $\sqrt{2}R$ when $X^2 = R^2$ or $X = \pm R$.   Hence we can write for these two values, which we call ω_1 and ω_2

$$\left.\begin{array}{c} \omega_1 L - \dfrac{1}{\omega_1 C} = R \\[3mm] \dfrac{1}{\omega_2 C} - \omega_2 L = R \end{array}\right\} \qquad (9.2\text{--}18)$$

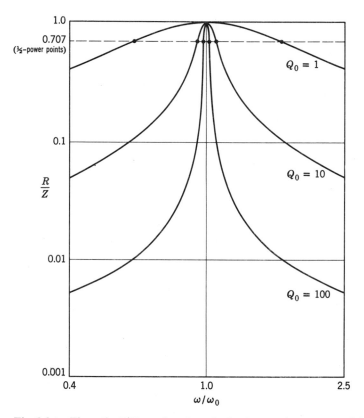

Fig. 9.2g.   The ratio R/Z as a function of ω/ω_0 for a series resonant circuit.
$$Q_0 = \omega_0 L/R.$$

Setting these two expressions equal, we readily obtain

$$(\omega_1 + \omega_2)L = \frac{\omega_1 + \omega_2}{\omega_1 \omega_2 C}$$

so that

$$\omega_1 \omega_2 = \frac{1}{LC} = \omega_0^2 \qquad (9.2\text{--}19)$$

Adding the two eqs. 9.2–18 yields

$$(\omega_1 - \omega_2)L + \frac{\omega_1 - \omega_2}{\omega_1 \omega_2 C} = 2R$$

which with eq. 9.2–19 gives

$$\omega_1 - \omega_2 = \frac{R}{L} \qquad (9.2\text{--}20)$$

and the relative difference in comparison to ω_0 is

$$\frac{\omega_1 - \omega_2}{\omega_0} = \frac{R}{\omega_0 L} = \frac{1}{Q_0} \qquad (9.2\text{--}21a)$$

The difference $f_1 - f_2$ between the two half-power frequencies is frequently called the "bandwidth" BW of the resonant curve. We see that BW is given by the formula

$$f_1 - f_2 = BW = \frac{f_0}{Q_0} = \frac{R}{2\pi L} \qquad (9.2\text{--}21b)$$

Resonant circuits form the basis of oscillators, radio receivers, etc., and for all such that demand sharp resonance curves (sharp "tuning"), a large Q_0 is desirable.

The phase angle φ can be expressed readily in terms of Q_0 and ω/ω_0:

$$\varphi = \tan^{-1}\left(\frac{\omega L - \dfrac{1}{\omega C}}{R}\right) = \tan^{-1} Q_0\left(\frac{\omega}{\omega_0} - \frac{\omega_0}{\omega}\right) \qquad (9.2\text{--}22)$$

Figure 9.2h shows this function for three values of Q_0.

Besides the effect of resonance in producing a minimum impedance at a certain frequency, there is also the effect of producing voltage amplitudes on the inductance and capacitor that are considerably larger than the amplitude of the applied emf. It will be noted from Fig. 9.2d that at resonance the inductive and capacitive voltage vector exactly cancel each other, and so each of them can readily be quite large. In fact, for the capacitor voltage amplitude, we have

$$V_m = i_m/\omega C = \frac{\mathscr{E}_m}{\omega C Z}$$

which at resonance is

$$V_{mC} = \frac{\mathscr{E}_m}{\omega_0 C R} = \mathscr{E}_m \frac{\omega_0 L}{R} = Q_0 \mathscr{E}_m \qquad (9.2\text{--}23)$$

and so can be very much larger than $\mathscr{E}_m$. The voltage on the inductance itself has of course the same resonance value. The voltage amplitude at resonance on the inductance coil, including the resistance, is related to the current by eq. 9.2–14, so we have

$$V_{mL} = i_m(R^2 + L^2\omega_0^2)^{\frac{1}{2}} = \frac{\mathscr{E}_m}{R}(R^2 + L^2\omega_0^2)^{\frac{1}{2}} = \mathscr{E}_m(1 + Q_0^2)^{\frac{1}{2}} \quad (9.2\text{–}24)$$

These voltages V_{mL} and V_{mC} can be large enough to be dangerous to human beings and to apparatus even when $\mathscr{E}_m$ is quite safely low.

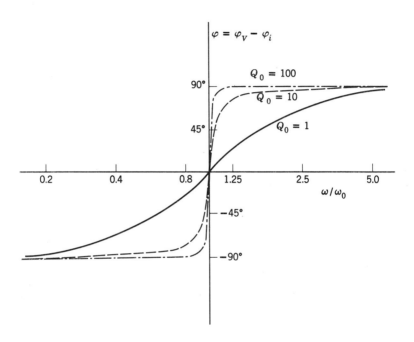

Fig. 9.2h. The variation of phase angle with frequency in a series circuit.

It might be thought that the Q of a coil could be made arbitrarily large at high frequencies, but this is not the case. The time constant L/R can be made as large as 1 sec by the use of magnetic core materials, but then as the frequency increases, the effective permeability decreases. Also, at high frequencies the skin effect increases R, and the effects of distributed capacitance between the windings make the coil act like a smaller effective inductance. As a result, Q is often a rough constant over a considerable range of frequencies. Values in the range 50 to 300 are practical and common. For further details of coil construction, the reader is referred elsewhere.[3]

An interesting case of variable Q concerns the use of proton magnetic resonance for the measurement of magnetic fields. Protons, like electrons, have spins and magnetic moments. Each proton has an angular momentum of $h/4\pi$, like that of an electron; its electromagnetic moment, however, is not so simply related to its mass as is true for an electron. The proton magnetic moment m_p has been measured and found to be (2.79275 ± 0.00003) times the nuclear magneton $eh/4\pi M_p c$ (5.0505×10^{-24} erg/gauss), where M_p is the proton mass. A proton in a magnetic field can line up with the field or against it, with thus two possible energy values $m_p B$ and $-m_p B$. At any given temperature in a steady field there will be a slightly greater proportion of protons with the lower energy value—the difference in numbers being about 1 part in 10^5 at room temperature.

Now, according to the quantum theory, energy changes can be induced by alternating electric and magnetic fields whose frequency f is related to the energy change U by $U = hf$. So if some proton-bearing material, water for instance, is inserted in a coil, and the combination is placed in a field of strength B, energy jumps can occur when an alternating current of frequency $f = U/h = m_p B/h$ is passed through the coil. Since there are more protons in the lower energy state, there will result from many random changes a small but finite absorption of energy. The result is just the same as if the resistance of the coil were increased or the Q decreased.

Thus, if a fixed frequency is applied to a coil and B is varied, there will be a change of Q when $B = hf/m_p$, and the alternating PD on the coil will change, although by a very small amount. If a sensitive arrangement, usually an a-c bridge, is made for detecting this change, B can be measured in terms of frequency and m_p. Since frequency can be measured to a part in 10^6, and m_p is known (by use of a calibrated magnet at the National Bureau of Standards) to 1 part in 50,000, very high accuracy in magnetic-field measurements can be attained. Accuracy is especially high in relative determinations of one field with respect to another.

The circuit relations we have calculated in this section can readily be applied to a more complicated series circuit. For instance, if elements R_1, L_1, C_1, and R_2, L_2, C_2 are all connected in series, as indicated in Fig. 9.2i, the current amplitude will be

$$i_m = \frac{\mathscr{E}_m}{[(R_1 + R_2)^2 + (X_1 + X_2)^2]^{\frac{1}{2}}} = \frac{\mathscr{E}_m}{Z}$$

with $\mathscr{E}$ ahead of i by the angle

$$\varphi = \tan^{-1} \frac{X_1 + X_2}{R_1 + R_2}$$

[3] G. P. Harnwell, *Principles of Electricity and Electromagnetism*, 2nd ed., McGraw-Hill, New York, 1949, pp. 469–473; F. E. Terman, *Radio Engineer's Handbook*, McGraw-Hill, New York, 1943, pp. 74ff.

The amplitude of the voltage V_2 on the impedance Z_2 will then be

$$V_{2,m} = i_m(R_2{}^2 + X_2{}^2)^{\frac{1}{2}} = i_m Z_2 = \frac{\mathscr{E}_m Z_2}{Z}$$

and the angle of lead of V_2 ahead of i will be

$$\varphi_2 = \tan^{-1}\frac{X_2}{R_2}$$

so that the angle by which $\mathscr{E}$ leads V_2 is

$$\varphi' = \tan^{-1}\frac{X_1 + X_2}{R_1 + R_2} - \tan^{-1}\frac{X_2}{R_2}$$

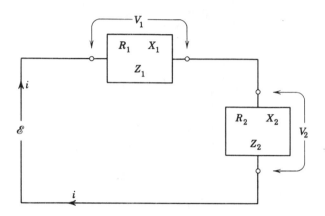

Fig. 9.2i.   Two impedances in series.

Similarly, the relative magnitudes and phase angles of the voltages V_1 and V_2 can be readily calculated.

We have been dealing with resistors, capacitors and inductors as ideal or "pure" elements.   Actually, any resistor has capacitance between its various parts, which can be approximately represented as a small capacitance between its ends and a small series inductance (extremely small if a non-inductive winding is used).   An inductance coil is similar but has a large Q rather than a small one.   A capacitor will in general have a small leakage conductance, representable by a large resistance in parallel, and dielectric losses, which are associated with the same current that charges the condenser, but which introduce a lag in the phase of the current, so that the effect of these losses can be represented by a small series resistor.   Figure 9.2j shows the equivalent circuits.

Problem 9.2a.   Set $\varphi_V = 0$ and substitute for $\mathscr{E}$ and i in eq. 9.2–1.   Equate coefficients of sin ωt and cos ωt, and find i_m and φ.   Check with the calculation in the text.

Problem 9.2b.   Discuss the variation of the ratio $\mathscr{E}/i$ with time and tell why it is not a useful quantity for describing a-c circuits.

Problem 9.2c.   In what mathematical way does the current approach zero with ω in a circuit with resistance and capacitance?

Problem 9.2d.   Show that the maximum voltage amplitude on the inductance L in a series circuit occurs for a frequency somewhat different from the resonance value, and find a formula for this maximum.

Problem 9.2e.   Express the ratio of the voltage amplitude on the condenser in a series circuit to $\mathscr{E}_m$ as a function of Q_0 and ω/ω_0, and sketch graphs of this ratio against ω/ω_0 for $Q_0 = 1$ and $Q_0 = 10$.

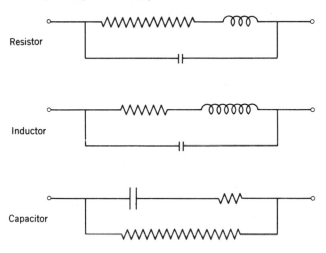

Fig. 9.2j.   Circuit representations of actual elements.   The drawings are made so as to give some indication of relative magnitudes.

Problem 9.2f.   Solve problem 9.2e for the voltage on the inductance coil (L and R together).

Problem 9.2g.   Find the capacitances that would resonate with a 10-henry inductance at 60 cycles and at 1000 cycles.   What should the resistance be in each case for a Q_0 of 10?

Problem 9.2h.   A series circuit is often tuned to resonance by varying the capacitance, with ω fixed.   Find the values C_1 and C_2 for which the impedance is $\sqrt{2}R$, and express $(C_1 - C_2)/C_0$ in terms of Q, where C_0 is the resonant capacitance.   Show how to find C_0 in terms of C_1 and C_2.   (These are easier to determine with precision.)   Express L and R in terms of C_1, C_2, and ω.

Problem 9.2i.   Write R/Z for a simple series circuit as a function of the relative deviation δ of the frequency from resonance, where $\delta = (\omega - \omega_0)/\omega_0$.   Make a simple approximation of this expression for small δ.   (This expression is easier to evaluate numerically than eqs. 9.2-6 or 9.2-17, as it eliminates the subtraction of two nearly equal quantities.)

Problem 9.2j.   Two impedances Z_1 and Z_2 are connected in series to a 400-cycle emf of $\mathscr{E}_m = 20$ v. Z_1 consists of a resistance of 50 ohms, and an inductance of 20 mh. Z_2 consists of a 20 ohm resistance, a 70-mh inductance, and a 20-μf condenser. Find the voltage amplitudes on Z_1 and Z_2 and the phase angle between them.

Problem 9.2k. Show that a plot of $\mathscr{E}$ vs i, as given by eliminating t from eqs. 9.1–1 and 9.2–3, is an ellipse. In particular, show that in terms of the variables $x = \mathscr{E}/\mathscr{E}_m$ and $y = i/i_m$, the ellipse has its principal axes at 45° to the x and y axes. Set $\varphi_V = 0$ and show that the shape of the ellipse depends on φ_i.

9.3   Power Relations

The instantaneous rate at which the emf $\mathscr{E}$ of section 9.2 furnishes energy for the circuit of that section is given by

$$P = \mathscr{E}i = \mathscr{E}_m i_m \cos{(\omega t + \varphi_V)} \cos{(\omega t + \varphi_i)} \qquad (9.3\text{–}1)$$

which by eqs. 9.2–1, 9.2–3, 9.2–4, and 9.2–5 can be written, setting $\varphi_i = 0$ and $\varphi_V = \varphi$ for convenience,

$$P = -L\omega i_m^2 \sin{\omega t} \cos{\omega t} + R i_m^2 \cos^2{\omega t} + \frac{i_m^2}{\omega C} \sin{\omega t} \cos{\omega t} \qquad (9.3\text{–}2a)$$

By the rules of trigonometry, we can rewrite this as

$$P = -\tfrac{1}{2}L\omega i_m^2 \sin{2\omega t} + \tfrac{1}{2}R i_m^2 (1 + \cos{2\omega t}) + \frac{i_m^2}{2\omega C} \sin{2\omega t} \qquad (9.3\text{–}2b)$$

By combining terms in eq. 9.3–2, using $X = Z \sin{\varphi}$ and $R = Z \cos{\varphi}$, or by transforming eq. 9.3–1 directly, we can write finally

$$P = \tfrac{1}{2}i_m^2 Z[\cos{(2\omega t + \varphi)} + \cos{\varphi}] \qquad (9.3\text{–}3)$$

Figure 9.3a shows time graphs of the separate terms of eq. 9.3–2 which are of course the powers for the three circuit elements, and the total as calculated from eq. 9.3–3.

It will be noted that energy alternately enters and leaves the inductance and capacitance, in symmetrical fashion with regard to positive and negative power consumption. The power expended in the resistor is always positive, and the total is positive more often than negative (problem 9.3a).

The energy stored in the inductance is, according to section 7.12, $U_L = \tfrac{1}{2}Li^2$. That in the condenser, by problem 2.7c or section 4.7, is $U_C = \tfrac{1}{2}q^2/C$. Utilizing eqs. 9.2–3 and 9.2–5, we can graph these quantities as shown in Fig. 9.3b. It will be noted that energy flows in and out of these elements but never builds up. We see from both figures that the average power expended in the two reactive elements is zero; this is also clear from eq. 9.3–2, since the average value of a sine or cosine is zero.

On the other hand, the average power in the resistor is $\frac{1}{2}Ri_m{}^2$, which is therefore the entire average power and can in fact be found from eq. 9.3-3.

The situation bears a striking resemblance to that of forced vibratory SHM of constant amplitude, for instance of a mass m on a spring of force constant k,

Fig. 9.3a.   The power consumption in R, L, C, and the entire series circuit.

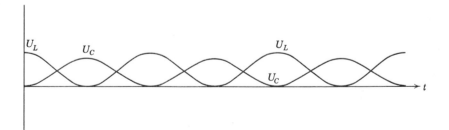

Fig. 9.3b.   The energy stored in the inductance and capacitance
of a series circuit.

with displacement x and a frictional force proportional to $v = dx/dt$.   In this case, the power expended by the external force all goes into friction; the potential energy $\frac{1}{2}kx^2$ of the spring and the kinetic energy $\frac{1}{2}mv^2$ continually interchange with each other and with the external power source.   To show that the analogy is in fact exact, we replace, in eq. 9.2–1, q by x, i by v, $1/C$ by k, L by m, R by a frictional constant b, and $\mathscr{E}$ by an external force F_{ext}.   Then the equation can be rearranged to give

$$F_{ext} - kx - bv = m\frac{dv}{dt} = m\frac{d^2x}{dt^2}$$

which is Newton's law $F = ma$ written for an external force plus a restoring spring force $-kx$ and an opposing friction force $-bv$.   The galvanometer equation of section 8.8 is another example.   In fact, any complicated mechanical system with linear elastic behavior and friction forces can be represented by a corresponding a-c network, which in many cases can be studied experimentally so as to solve otherwise difficult mechanical or acoustical problems.

Because of this analogy, the reciprocal of capacitance is sometimes called "elastance."

Because the average power in any circuit is $\frac{1}{2}Ri_m^2$, it is convenient to choose, as a measure for the current, not the amplitude i_m but $i_e = i_m/\sqrt{2}$, which is called the root mean square (rms) or effective current.   In fact $\frac{1}{2}Ri_m^2 = Ri_e^2$ is the average of Ri^2 as can be seen from eq. 9.3–2 (problem 9.3c), so the mean square current is $\frac{1}{2}i_m^2$, and i_e is its square root.   By making a-c ammeters read the rms current value, the calculation of power in resistors becomes the same for alternating current as for direct current. It then becomes necessary to use $\mathscr{E}_e = \mathscr{E}_m/\sqrt{2}$ and $V_e = V_m/\sqrt{2}$ as measures of emf and voltage in order that the impedance will remain equal to the voltage-to-current ratio.

The power expended in a circuit can now be written

$$P_{av} = Ri_e^2 = i_e^2 Z \cos \varphi$$

so that

$$P_{av} = \mathscr{E}_e i_e \cos \varphi \tag{9.3–4}$$

This differs from the expression $\mathscr{E}_e i_e$ that would correspond to the d-c case by the factor $\cos \varphi$, which is for this reason called the power factor.   For a given emf $\mathscr{E}_e$ and power consumption P_{av}, the required current is the larger the smaller $\cos \varphi$.   To reduce heating losses in power transmission lines, it is desirable to have $\cos \varphi$ as near to unity as practicable.

We see that for a purely resistive circuit, the power formulas of d-c analysis are applicable:

$$P_{av} = i_e^2 R = \mathscr{E}_e i_e = \mathscr{E}_e^2/R \tag{9.3–5}$$

When no ambiguity is involved in what follows, the subscript e will be dropped, and the symbols $\mathscr{E}$, V, and i will be used for rms values instead of for instantaneous values.   Likewise P will be used in place of P_{av}.

We have referred here only to power in a simple series circuit, and we shall, in the next two sections, take up several more complex circuits. However, in any two-terminal passive network to which an alternating emf $\mathscr{E}$ is applied, there will result a current i with some angle of lag φ. Equations 9.3–1 and 9.3–3 will apply to this more general case, and eq. 9.3–4 follows directly.   Power is measured in watts or kilowatts, and the product Ei is referred to as volt-amperes (va) or kilovolt-amperes (kva).

A pure reactance, like an ideal condenser, takes no power, since $\cos \varphi$ is 0.   It is sometimes useful to refer to the product of volts and amperes for a condenser as volt-amperes-reactive (var).   In general, the number of var is given by $\mathscr{E}i \sin \varphi$.

A real condenser in which power is used up in alternating the polarization of the dielectric must clearly have a phase angle less than 90° and a power factor that is different from zero.   The effect can be described as a phase-shifting hysteresis.

Problem 9.3a.   For what values of t will P as given by eq. 9.3–3 be negative?

Problem 9.3b.   Sketch a graph showing the total energy U delivered to a resistor as a function of the time, when an alternating emf is applied, letting $U = 0$ when $t = 0$.

Problem 9.3c.   Prove that the average square of a sinusoidal current or voltage is one-half the square of the amplitude by direct use of the integral calculus; e.g., by $(i^2)_{\mathrm{av}} = (1/T) \int_0^T i^2\, dt$.

Problem 9.3d.   If a certain piece of apparatus acts like a series circuit with power factor 0.80, and the line has a resistance of 0.02 ohm, calculate the line loss when 10 kw are being supplied at 125 v (rms) and the reduction in this loss that could be achieved if the power factor were changed to 1.00.

Problem 9.3e.   A 60-cycle alternating emf of 120 v supplies current to a 120-volt, 200-watt lamp.   Assuming the lamp resistance to be constant, find the current required to operate it at 200 watts and at 100 watts.   If the current is to be reduced by a series resistor, find the value of this resistor and the power expended in it.   If the current is to be reduced by the introduction of a series choke coil, which is an inductance of high Q, find (a) the necessary inductance value taking $Q = 100$, (b) the power expended in the coil, and (c) the power drawn from the line.   (*Suggestion:* Disregard the coil resistance when calculating the impedance of the *combination* of coil and lamp.)

Problem 9.3f.   Find the three relations corresponding to eq. 9.3–5 for circuits whose reactance is *not* zero.   Justify the reference in section 9.2 to "half-power" points on the curve of R/Z versus ω/ω_0.

Problem 9.3g.   An emf $\mathscr{E}$ feeds two impedances Z_1 and Z_2 in series.   Find an expression for the power expended in Z_2.

Problem 9.3h.   Show that, if an emf $\mathscr{E}$ supplies power P at a power factor $\cos \varphi$, the resistance of the circuit must be $(\mathscr{E}^2 \cos^2 \varphi)/P$.

9.4   The Complex Number Method for A-C Analysis

The complex-number method for analyzing a-c circuits combines the graphic features of the vector method introduced in section 9.2 with the simplicity of algebraic calculations. Let us first examine some of the features of the vector method. In general, any voltage or current can be represented by two quantities—by a magnitude and a direction or phase angle with respect to some reference, or equivalently by two "components" at right angles. Not only can we add a-c voltage vectors to get the vector that represents a sum of PD's in series, but we can add a-c current vectors to represent the sum of currents at a junction. Vector products have no meaning for these vectors, and the only scalar product that appears is the power, $\mathscr{E}i \cos\varphi$. However, current and voltage vectors are related by impedances and phase angles, in a multiplicative sort of way.

Now, it is remarkable that the complex numbers used in algebra have properties exactly like all those mentioned, with the minor exception that scalar products are not readily representable. As we show in what follows, if we represent our vectors as complex numbers,[4] we can make all our calculations with ordinary algebra.

The elements of complex-number algebra that we need for electrical quantities are given in Appendix A.5. We shall assume first that the stationary vectors referred to just above are to be written as complex numbers. Then, to represent rotating vectors, we need only multiply by $e^{j\omega t}$, since multiplication with a complex number of unit magnitude rotates a vector through the appropriate angle and since in this case the angle is ωt. The actual sinusoidal currents and voltages are to be the projections on the x-axis or axis of reals—i.e., they are the *real parts* of the rotating vectors. The imaginary parts could equally well be used. (The important results, namely, relative amplitudes and phases, will be the same in either case.) Finally, impedances will be represented by constant complex numbers.

Instead of using the results of section 9.2 to derive the complex number that represents an impedance, it is more useful to start directly from the differential equation 9.2–1 for a series circuit. This equation is linear in $\mathscr{E}$ and i, so that the sum of two solutions is also a solution (see Appendix A.3). Conversely, if we find a solution in terms of complex rotating vectors, the real and imaginary parts must separately be solutions. (See problem 9.4g.) Thus we shall write $\mathscr{E} = \mathscr{E}_m e^{j\omega t}$ and $i = i_m e^{j\omega t}$, and substitute into eq. 9.2–1, using eq. 9.2–5:

$$\mathscr{E}_m e^{j\omega t} = L i_m j\omega e^{j\omega t} + R i_m e^{j\omega t} + \frac{1}{j\omega C} i_m e^{j\omega t}$$

so that, dividing out $e^{j\omega t}$ and collecting terms (note that $j = -1/j$), we have

$$\mathscr{E}_m = \left[R + j\left(\omega L - \frac{1}{\omega C}\right) \right] i_m \qquad (9.4\text{–}1)$$

[4] A-c vectors represented by complex numbers are sometimes called "phasors."

We can immediately write this equation in terms of a complex impedance Z (dropping the subscripts so that either amplitudes or rms values can be understood):

$$\mathcal{E} = \mathsf{Z}\mathsf{i} \qquad\qquad (9.4\text{--}2a)$$

$$\mathsf{Z} = R + j\left(\omega L - \frac{1}{\omega C}\right) = R + jX \qquad\qquad (9.4\text{--}2b)$$

which in exponential form is

$$\mathsf{Z} = (R^2 + X^2)^{\frac{1}{2}} e^{j\,\tan^{-1}(X/R)} \qquad\qquad (9.4\text{--}2c)$$

Thus the impedance Z when multiplied into i multiplies the current magnitude by $Z = (R^2 + X^2)^{\frac{1}{2}}$ and advances its angle on a vector diagram by $\varphi = \tan^{-1}(X/R)$ exactly as in section 9.2.   We see that the real part of the complex impedance is the resistance and the imaginary part is the reactance.

For complicated circuits, we can formulate Kirchhoff's laws in complex terms (since the relations must hold for the real parts of the rotating vectors and by symmetrical reasoning for the imaginary parts):

1. The sum of the complex currents entering any junction of any three or more circuit elements equals the sum of the complex currents leaving that junction.

2. The sum of the complex emf's around any closed loop in a circuit, taken with due regard to signs (phases), equals the sum of the complex potential drops around the loop.   Emf's due to self and mutual inductances are to be included with the potential-drop terms.

Therefore, we can use the d-c analysis of sections 5.4 and 5.5 directly. Series impedances add:

$$\mathsf{Z} = \mathsf{Z}_1 + \mathsf{Z}_2 + \cdots \qquad\qquad (9.4\text{--}3)$$

and parallel impedances are combined by the reciprocal rule:

$$\frac{1}{\mathsf{Z}} = \frac{1}{\mathsf{Z}_1} + \frac{1}{\mathsf{Z}_2} + \cdots \qquad\qquad (9.4\text{--}4)$$

The impedance for two elements in parallel can thus be written

$$\mathsf{Z} = \mathsf{Z}_1\mathsf{Z}_2/(\mathsf{Z}_1 + \mathsf{Z}_2)$$

The reciprocal of an impedance is called an "admittance" and is written Y.   Its real and imaginary parts can be found by use of eq. A.5–10:

$$\mathsf{Y} = \frac{1}{\mathsf{Z}} = \frac{1}{R + jX} = \frac{R - jX}{R^2 + X^2} = \frac{R}{R^2 + X^2} - j\frac{X}{R^2 + X^2}$$

or

$$Y = G + jB \tag{9.4-5}$$

where the real part, called the conductance, is

$$G = \frac{R}{R^2 + X^2} \tag{9.4-6}$$

and the imaginary part, called the susceptance, is

$$B = -\frac{X}{R^2 + X^2} \tag{9.4-7}$$

Since $Y = 1/Z$, we can write

$$i = Y\mathcal{E} \tag{9.4-8}$$

Let us as a first example treat the parallel circuit of Fig. 9.4a. The admittances of the two branches can be written down immediately and

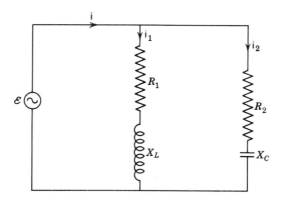

Fig. 9.4a.   A parallel circuit.

added (remembering that $X_L = +\omega L$ and $X_C = -1/\omega C$):

$$Y = Y_1 + Y_2 = \frac{R_1}{R_1{}^2 + \omega^2 L^2} - \frac{j\omega L}{R_1{}^2 + \omega^2 L^2} + \frac{R_2}{R_2{}^2 + \left(\dfrac{1}{\omega C}\right)^2} + \frac{j\left(\dfrac{1}{\omega C}\right)}{R_2{}^2 + \left(\dfrac{1}{\omega C}\right)^2} \tag{9.4-9}$$

$$= \frac{R_1}{R_1{}^2 + \omega^2 L^2} + \frac{R_2 \omega^2 C^2}{R_2{}^2 \omega^2 C^2 + 1} + j\left[\frac{\omega C}{R_2{}^2 \omega^2 C^2 + 1} - \frac{\omega L}{R_1{}^2 + \omega^2 L^2}\right]$$

The condition that i and $\mathcal{E}$ are in phase is that Y be a real number.

This condition is called "antiresonance" or "parallel resonance."   Setting
the imaginary part of Y equal to zero yields immediately

$$\frac{\omega L}{R_1^2 + \omega^2 L^2} = \frac{\omega C}{R_2^2 \omega^2 C^2 + 1} \tag{9.4-10}$$

Using $Q_1 = \omega L/R_1$ and $Q_2 = 1/R_2\omega C$, inverting each side and factoring,
we can write

$$\omega L\left(\frac{1}{Q_1^2} + 1\right) = \frac{1}{\omega C}\left(\frac{1}{Q_2^2} + 1\right)$$

or

$$\omega^2 = \frac{1}{LC} \cdot \frac{\dfrac{1}{Q_2^2} + 1}{\dfrac{1}{Q_1^2} + 1} \tag{9.4-11}$$

so that, if the Q of each element is large, the parallel resonant frequency
is nearly the same as the series resonant frequency for the same two
elements.

At parallel resonance, the current, being in phase with $\mathcal{E}$, is given by

$$i = \frac{\mathcal{E} R_1}{R_1^2 + \omega^2 L^2} + \frac{\mathcal{E} R_2 \omega^2 C^2}{R_2^2 \omega^2 C^2 + 1} \tag{9.4-12}$$

It is evident from eq. 9.4–12 that i is small if R_1 and R_2 are.   This apparently
strange phenomenon can be understood if it is realized that the oppositely
phased (i.e., inductive and capacitive) currents in the two branches at
resonance are in the same phase with respect to currents circulating
around the loop—i.e., when the loop is considered a series circuit.   Thus,
large currents alternate back and forth around the loop, and only their
small difference enters and leaves at the junctions.   If R_1 and R_2 could be
both zero, an alternating current of any magnitude could circulate around
the loop without any outside contributions, the latter being only necessary
to offset the power losses in the resistors.

In particular, if a condenser with negligible resistance is placed in parallel
with an inductive circuit, it will make the power factor in the transmission
line supplying the inductive circuit more nearly 1, thus serving to cut
down line losses.

The use of algebraic symbols, as in eq. 9.4–9, yields complicated
formulae for a-c impedances and admittances; in contrast to most calculations in physics, it is convenient in solving a-c problems to substitute
numerical values right at the start.   We shall illustrate by giving the

results of a slide-rule calculation[5] for the circuit of Fig. 9.4b. We find

$$Z_1 = 100 + (250 - 300)j = 100 - 50j \text{ ohms}$$
$$= 112e^{-26.6°j} \text{ ohms}$$
$$Z_2 = 150 + 200j = 250e^{53.1°j} \text{ ohms}$$
$$Z_3 = -125j = 125e^{-90°j} \text{ ohms}$$

so that for the parallel branch

$$Y_{23} = \frac{1}{Z_2} + \frac{1}{Z_3} = \frac{1}{150 + 200j} - \frac{1}{125j} = \frac{150 - 200j}{150^2 + 200^2} + \frac{j}{125}$$
$$= 0.00240 - 0.00320j + 0.00800j$$
$$= 0.00240 + 0.00480j \text{ mhos,}$$

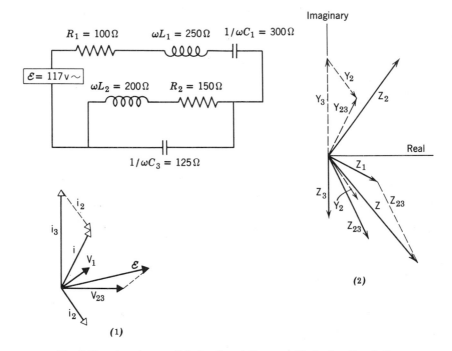

Fig. 9.4b. A series-parallel circuit and diagrams illustrating its solution: (1) voltage-current diagram, (2) impedance diagram.

[5] The principal slide-rule operation needed beyond elementary multiplication and division is that of calculating $(a^2 + b^2)^{\frac{1}{2}}$ with the simultaneous finding of $\tan^{-1}(b/a)$. See any slide-rule manual.

The symbol j is generally written before algebraic symbols but after arabic numerals. The angles in the exponents are most conveniently written in degrees, although radian measure is more commonly used in mathematical analysis.

and

$$Z_{23} = \frac{1}{Y_{23}} = \frac{0.00240 - 0.00480j}{0.00240^2 + 0.00480^2} = 83.3 - 167j \text{ ohms}$$
$$= 186e^{-63.4^\circ j} \text{ ohms}$$

The total impedance is

$$Z = Z_1 + Z_{23} = 183.3 - 217j = 284e^{-49.8^\circ j} \text{ ohms}$$

If we take $\mathcal{E}$ to be $117e^{0.0^\circ j}$ v (rms) the current i will be

$$i = \mathcal{E}/Z = (117/284)e^{49.8^\circ j} = 0.412e^{49.8^\circ j} \text{ amp}$$

The current leads the voltage by 49.8° and the power factor is 0.645. The power drawn is then $117 \times 0.412 \times 0.645 = 31.1$ watts (note that the power cannot be found by multiplication of complex numbers).

The analysis can be carried further. For example, the voltage drop on the parallel circuit is

$$V_{23} = Z_{23}i = 186e^{-63.4^\circ j} \times 0.412e^{49.8^\circ j} = 76.6e^{-13.6^\circ j} \text{ v}$$

lagging behind $\mathcal{E}$ by 13.6°. The currents through branches 2 and 3 are $i_2 = V_{23}/Z_2 = 0.307e^{-66.7^\circ j}$ and $i_3 = 0.613e^{76.4^\circ j}$. The voltage V_{C1} on C_1 is $i(-300j) = 124e^{-40.2j}$ v; that on the combination of L_1 and R_1 is $i(100 + 250j) = 111e^{118.0^\circ j}$. These various values are illustrated graphically in Fig. 9.4b. The reader is advised to locate on the voltage-current diagram the appropriate impedance angles.

No mention was made of frequency, since for simplicity the reactance values were given directly in ohms. For a frequency of 60 cycles ($\omega = 377$) it is an easy matter to find what values L_1, C_1, L_2, and C_3 must have in this example. For a different frequency with the same L and C values, the results would be quite different, and the calculation must be gone through again completely from the beginning. It is quite clear that a-c circuit calculations are complicated and lengthy. Although engineering texts give a number of rules for assistance in computation, the only one of use in a physics text is this: in nearly every case, reflection and ingenuity will produce a shorter or easier method of calculation than that which may appear suitable at first glance.

Let us illustrate the simple results that can sometimes be obtained by an approximate calculation. We shall consider a one-stage filter circuit, used for removing alternating components of the current delivered by a rectifier tube. Figure 9.4c shows an inductance and a condenser in a single "L-section" filter, feeding a load resistor.

The aim of the filter is to provide for d-c a low series resistance (in L) and a very high shunt resistance (in C) so that the steady part of the current is little affected by the filter, and to have for alternating current a high series impedance (in L) and a high parallel admittance in C. We shall make an approximate calculation of the ratio of voltage input (voltage output from rectifier) to voltage output (input to load). For 60 cycles, $\omega = 377$ and in the circuit of the figure, $\omega L = 3770$ ohms and $1/\omega C = 332$ ohms. Consequently, the parallel impedance of C and R together is very close to that of the condenser alone, namely $-j/\omega C = -332j$ ohms. The impedance of the inductance coil is, approximately, just its reactance

Fig. 9.4c.   A simple filter for a rectifier circuit.

$j\omega L = 3770j$ ohms.   The ratio of voltages we seek is the ratio of condenser impedance to the total, which is

$$\frac{-j/\omega C}{j\omega L - j/\omega C} = -\frac{1}{\omega^2 LC - 1} = \frac{-332j}{(3770 - 332)j}$$

$$= \frac{-332}{3438} = -0.097 \qquad (9.4\text{--}13)$$

The minus sign indicates that the phase of the voltage on the load is just opposite to that on the entire circuit, a fact which is easily understood by considering that the current in the entire circuit is very largely inductive, lagging the applied voltage by 90° and that the voltage on the condenser lags the current also by nearly 90°, producing an over-all 180° phase change.

If now two similar L-section filters are put in tandem, as in Fig. 9.4d, the second section will act on the first in a similar way to the high resistance load, namely, to have an almost negligible effect on the admittance of the first condenser.   Its own action will duplicate that of the first, and we have just twice the effect of one filter, i.e., the reduction in voltage is the square of eq. 9.4–13, that is,

$$(\omega^2 LC - 1)^{-2} = (0.097)^2 = 0.0094 \simeq 1\%$$

If, as is frequently the case, the frequency of the most important alternating voltage produced by the source is 120 cycles, the voltage ratio will be about one-fourth that given for a single section and one-sixteenth for two sections, as can be seen from the ω^2 in the denominator of eq. 9.4–13.

Problem 9.4a. A certain motor acts like an inductance in drawing 800 watts of power with a power factor of 0.76 from a 220-volt line. Find the apparent impedance and resistance of the motor, and the reactance of that capacitor which when put in parallel with the motor will just bring the power factor to 1.00. Find the ratio of the current drawn by the motor to the total current. Line drops are to be neglected.

Problem 9.4b. Show that for a parallel resonant circuit the circulating current is approximately $Q_1 Q_2/(Q_1 + Q_2)$ times the net current, for large Q values.

Fig. 9.4d. A two-stage filter.

Problem 9.4c. Repeat the calculation in the text for the circuit of Fig. 9.4b for the case in which the frequency is doubled.

Problem 9.4d. For the circuit of Fig. 9.4e, find the currents and also the voltage on the inductance coil.

Problem 9.4e. The Anderson bridge for comparing a capacitance C and an inductance L is shown in Fig. 9.4f. Write equations from which the current in the detector can be determined by Kirchhoff's laws. Do not solve them, but assume that this current is zero and find two equations that relate C, L, and the resistances and that do not contain the emf $\mathcal{E}$ or the currents.

Fig. 9.4e. Problem 9.4d.

Problem 9.4f. An alternating emf $\mathcal{E}$ of 0.100 v is applied to the amplifier network shown in Fig. 9.4g. Find to slide-rule accuracy the voltage between the open-circuited points $\mathcal{A}$ and $\mathcal{B}$ when the frequency is (a) 20 cycles, (b) 600 cycles, and (c) 20,000 cycles.

Problem 9.4g. Show that if $\mathcal{E} = \mathcal{E}_0 e^{j(\omega t + \varphi_V)}$ and i satisfy eq. 9.2–1, the real parts give the solution corresponding to $\mathscr{E} = \mathscr{E}_0 \cos(\omega t + \varphi_V)$ and the imaginary parts give the solution corresponding to $\mathscr{E} = \mathscr{E}_0 \sin(\omega t + \varphi_V)$.

Problem 9.4h. Write and simplify an algebraic formula for the complex impedance Z of two parallel branches, one with $Z_1 = R + jX$ and the other with $Z_2 = -jX'$. What does Z become when $X = X'$?

Problem 9.4i. Solve the circuits of Fig. 9.4c and Fig. 9.4d exactly, for the voltage ratio (output/input).

Problem 9.4j. A resistor R and condenser C are in series with a parallel combination of an equal pair of R and C. Find how the voltage on the parallel combination varies in phase and magnitude as the frequency is varied and the over-all emf is fixed in magnitude (*Hint:* Calculate the ratio $Z_{total}/Z_{parallel}$ first).

Problem 9.4k. Prove that the power expended by an emf $\mathcal{E}$ in any circuit is correctly given by $P = \frac{1}{2}(\mathcal{E}\bar{\imath} + \bar{\mathcal{E}}i)$, if i is the current delivered by $\mathcal{E}$.

Fig. 9.4f. The circuit of an Anderson bridge.

Fig. 9.4g. An R–C coupled amplifier network.

Problem 9.4l. An emf $\mathcal{E}_1 + \mathcal{E}_0 \sin \omega t$ is applied to a circuit consisting of a 2000-Ω resistance and a 10-μf condenser in parallel. Find the currents in each when $\mathcal{E}_1 = 3.0$ v, $\mathcal{E}_0 = 1.0$ v, and $\omega/2\pi = $ (a) 10 cycles; (b) 100 cycles; (c) 1000 cycles.

9.5   Circuits with Mutual Inductance

Any two circuits in proximity to each other will have mutual inductance, since there will be magnetic flux about all the wires and some interlinking will surely occur.   However, it is convenient here as earlier to divide the effects into those big enough to be treated as lumped or localized, and those small enough to neglect.   (At very high frequencies, this division is inadequate, for distributed effects become very important.)   Let us apply our complex-number analysis to certain types of circuits with specific mutual inductances.

The coupled circuits of Fig. 9.5a are linked only by the mutual inductance indicated by M.   The two coils may actually be wound more or less closely

Fig. 9.5a.   A circuit coupled only through a mutual inductance (transformer).   The resistances of the coils are included in Z_A and Z_B.

together, but are drawn apart for clarity.   A current i_1 in circuit 1 will produce flux $\Phi_{11} = L_1 i_1$ in coil 1 and $\Phi_{21} = M i_1$ in coil 2, where L_1 is the self-inductance of coil 1 and M is the mutual inductance of the pair. Similarly, a current i_2 in circuit 2 will make flux $\Phi_{22} = L_2 i_2$ in coil 2 and $\Phi_{12} = M i_2$ in coil 1.   It is necessary to specify positive directions for the currents in the two circuits and is convenient to draw the circuit (or choose the definitions) so that, if two adjacent ends of the two coils were connected, one current flows toward the junction and one away, as in Fig. 9.5a. The directions of the coil windings can either be so arranged that, when i_1 and i_2 are both positive, Φ_{11} and Φ_{12} are opposite in sign, or so that they are of the same sign.   Let us call M positive when Φ_{11} and Φ_{12} are of the same sign.   It will then also be true that (for positive currents) Φ_{22} and Φ_{21} are of the same polarity (problem 9.5h).

Now, if i_1 and i_2 can be written as complex currents $i_1 e^{j\omega t}$ and $i_2 e^{j\omega t}$, the fluxes can be written as $\phi_{11} e^{j\omega t}$, etc.   The emf induced in coil 1 will be

$$\mathcal{E}_1 = -\frac{d}{dt}[\phi_{11} e^{j\omega t} + \phi_{12} e^{j\omega t}]$$

$$= -j\omega[\phi_{11} e^{j\omega t} + \phi_{12} e^{j\omega t}]$$

$$= -j\omega[L_1 i_1 e^{j\omega t} + M i_2 e^{j\omega t}]$$

and the voltage drop across coil 1 will be the same but with a positive sign. The second coil will have a similar emf in it, which we may write either as an emf or as a potential drop, there being no other emf in the circuit.

The equations for the two circuits can thus be written (omitting $e^{j\omega t}$ as usual)

$$\mathcal{E} = Z_A i_1 + j\omega L_1 i_1 + j\omega M i_2 \tag{9.5-1a}$$

$$0 = Z_B i_2 + j\omega L_2 i_2 + j\omega M i_1 \tag{9.5-1b}$$

Fig. 9.5b. A series-parallel circuit that behaves like the coupled circuit in Fig. 9.5a, if $Z_M = -j\omega M$.

which can be solved for i_1 and i_2, giving the relations

$$\frac{\mathcal{E}}{i_1} = Z_A + \frac{j\omega L_1 Z_B + \omega^2(M^2 - L_1 L_2)}{Z_B + j\omega L_2} \tag{9.5-2}$$

$$\frac{\mathcal{E}}{i_2} = -\frac{(Z_A + j\omega L_1)}{j\omega M}\left[Z_B + \frac{j\omega L_2 Z_A + \omega^2(M^2 - L_1 L_2)}{Z_A + j\omega L_1}\right] \tag{9.5-3}$$

Equations 9.5–1 are easily related to the material of section 9.4, if we consider the circuit of Fig. 9.5b. Let us write the loop equations for the loops indicated in the figure:

$$\mathcal{E} = Z_A i_1 + j\omega L'_1 i_1 + Z_M(i_1 - i_2) \tag{9.5-4a}$$

$$0 = Z_B i_2 + j\omega L'_2 i_2 + Z_M(i_2 - i_1) \tag{9.5-4b}$$

which are identical with eq. 9.5–1 if we take $Z_M = -j\omega M$, $L'_1 = L_1 + M$, and $L'_2 = L_2 + M$. Thus a pair of impedances coupled by a mutual inductance behave (at least at a particular frequency) like a single series-parallel combination with an inductance or a capacitance in parallel, depending on whether M is negative or positive. A more complicated circuit like that of Fig. 9.5c can be treated in the same way. (Problem 9.5a.)

If two inductances in series have mutual flux linkage, we can include this effect in a simple series-circuit calculation. We must have, in fact, for the voltage drop on the series combination

$$V = L_1 \frac{di}{dt} + L_2 \frac{di}{dt} \pm 2M \frac{di}{dt} \qquad (9.5\text{-}5)$$

where the factor 2 enters because each coil has an emf induced in it by the other one. For a current of angular frequency ω, we have

$$V = (j\omega L_1 + j\omega L_2 \pm 2j\omega M)i \qquad (9.5\text{-}6)$$

The two coils thus act like a single one. If the effective self-inductance of the combination can be measured with the coils first arranged to produce

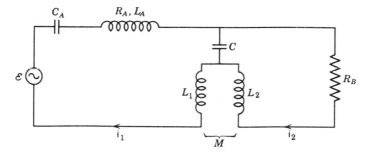

Fig. 9.5c. A coupled circuit of moderate complexity.

flux in the same direction (positive coupling) and then in the same position but with opposite coupling, we can write

$$L_+ = L_1 + L_2 + 2M \qquad (9.5\text{-}7a)$$

$$L_- = L_1 + L_2 - 2M \qquad (9.5\text{-}7b)$$

from which we can find

$$M = \tfrac{1}{4}(L_+ - L_-) \qquad (9.5\text{-}8)$$

If the coils are arranged to rotate with respect to one another, so that M varies continuously from a positive value M_0 to a negative value $-M_0$, the resultant value of L will vary from L_+ to L_-. It is in this way that convenient variable inductors are made.[6]

Since by Lenz's law self-inductance is always a positive quantity, we see by eq. 9.5-7b that for any two coils whatever, their mutual inductance M is restricted to values less than $\tfrac{1}{2}(L_1 + L_2)$:

$$M < \tfrac{1}{2}(L_1 + L_2) \qquad (9.5\text{-}9)$$

[6] See F. K. Harris, *Electrical Measurements*, John Wiley, New York, 1952, p. 667.

A further and more useful restriction on M is that M is less than the geometric mean of L_1 and L_2:

$$M^2 \leqslant L_1 L_2 \tag{9.5–10}$$

which condition we can write

$$M = k(L_1 L_2)^{\frac{1}{2}} \tag{9.5–11}$$

where k is called the coefficient of coupling and is a number between -1 and $+1$.

$$-1 \leqslant k \leqslant +1 \tag{9.5–12}$$

This result is actually a property of Neumann's integral, eq. 7.7–10, for mutual and self-inductance, but it is not easy to prove directly. One method of verifying it is to consider a rather ideal coupled circuit, namely one like that of Fig. 9.5a in which Z_B is almost exactly zero. A practical case is one with the secondary circuit inside a piece of metal in the super-conducting state, near the absolute zero of temperature. In accordance with eq. 9.5–1, we will have $j\omega L_2 i_2 + j\omega M i_1 = 0$, which means of course that the flux produced by i_1 in the metal is exactly canceled by that produced in the metal by i_2. (It is indeed a fact that magnetic fields cannot be set up inside superconducting material.) Equation 9.5–2 now becomes

$$\mathcal{E} = Z_A i_1 + j\omega \left(L_1 - \frac{M^2}{L_2} \right) i_1 \tag{9.5–13}$$

showing that the circuit has an effective inductance $L = L_1 - M^2/L_2$. This quantity must be positive, which leads immediately to eq. 9.5–10. The reference to superconducting material cannot actually be of importance for the proof, since the properties of Neumann's formula have nothing to do with any external resistance or impedance in the circuit.

Equation 9.5–10 can also be proved from the formula, eq. 7.12–5, for the magnetic energy of a set of coils (problem 9.5c). It is more instructive, however, to turn to an approximate proof based on coil structure. Suppose the two coils have, respectively, N_1 turns and N_2 turns. Suppose that when i_1 flows in coil 1, the average flux through each turn of the coil is $b_1 i_1$. Then the flux linkage in coil 1 is $\Phi_{11} = N_1 b_1 i_1 = L_1 i_1$. Now, not all of the flux $b_1 i_1$ is likely to link each turn of coil 2. Thus the flux linking all the turns of coil 2 is less than $N_2 b_1 i_1$, so we write

$$\Phi_{21} = \pm k_1 N_2 b_1 i_1 = M i_1, \quad \text{where} \quad 0 \leqslant k_1 \leqslant 1$$

Similarly, when i_2 flows in coil 2, we can write $\Phi_{22} = L_2 i_2 = N_2 b_2 i_2$ and $\Phi_{12} = M i_2 = \pm k_2 N_1 b_2 i_2$, with $0 \leqslant k_2 \leqslant 1$.

From the equations with i_1, we can obtain the ratio $M/L_1 = \pm k_1 N_2/N_1$;

from the other equations $M/L_2 = \pm k_2 N_1/N_2$. The product of these ratios eliminates N_1 and N_2, giving the expected result

$$\frac{M^2}{L_1 L_2} = k_1 k_2 \leqslant 1$$

from which we also see that the coefficient of coupling k is $(k_1 k_2)^{\frac{1}{2}}$, the geometric mean of the two fractions that give the flux of one coil that links the other.

The coefficient of coupling will be 1 when $k_1 = 1$ and $k_2 = 1$, that is, when all of the flux produced by either coil links the other. It will be observed that if $k = 1$, the second term in eq. 9.5–13 vanishes, so that the vanishing of flux in coil 2 is accompanied by zero resultant flux in coil 1. This situation is clearly an ideal limit, which can never be perfectly achieved in practice. Nevertheless, a closely wound pair of coils can have a k very near unity.

Transformers. A transformer is a mutual inductance with k nearly 1 and with large values of L_1 and L_2, in comparison to the circuit components with which it will be used. An ordinary a-c transformer consists of two coils wound on an iron core that "conducts" nearly all its flux through both coils. Both L_1 and L_2 are large because of the iron and because of large numbers of turns on each coil.

The analysis given above with reference to numbers of turns is a good approximation here, so we can write $k_1 = 1$, $k_2 = 1$,

$$\frac{M}{L_1} = \frac{L_2}{M} = \frac{N_2}{N_1} \tag{9.5–14}$$

and

$$\frac{ML_2}{L_1 M} = \frac{L_2}{L_1} = \frac{N_2^2}{N_1^2} \tag{9.5–15}$$

Neglecting Z_B in the second equation of eqs. 9.5–1 gives

$$\frac{i_2}{i_1} = \frac{-M}{L_2} = \frac{-N_1}{N_2} \tag{9.5–16}$$

so that the currents have a constant ratio and are 180° out of phase. If we attempt to substitute eq. 9.5–16 into the first of eqs. 9.5–1, however, we get no inductive effect at all. When the inductive effect is reduced nearly to zero, Z_B will have an effect on i_1 and we must use a closer approximation. In eq. 9.5–2, we can neglect Z_B in the denominator where it is added to $j\omega L_2$, but not in the numerator, since $M^2 - L_1 L_2 \simeq 0$. Thus we have

$$\mathcal{E} = \left(Z_A + Z_B \frac{L_1}{L_2}\right) i_1 = \left(Z_A + Z_B \frac{N_1^2}{N_2^2}\right) i_1 \tag{9.5–17}$$

Assuming that Z_A is small compared to ωL_1, eq. 9.5–3 yields

$$-\mathscr{E}\,\frac{M}{L_1} = \left(Z_B + \frac{L_2}{L_1}Z_A\right)i_2$$

or

$$-\mathscr{E}\,\frac{N_2}{N_1} = \left(Z_B + \frac{N_2^2}{N_1^2}Z_A\right)i_2 \qquad (9.5\text{–}18)$$

Equation 9.5–17 shows us that viewed from the input end or primary side the transformer has the effect of replacing Z_B by $Z_B\,(N_1^2/N_2^2)$—the

Fig. 9.5d. Equivalent circuits for the input and output sides of an ideal transformer.

impedance is "transformed" by the square of the turns ratio. Equation 9.5–18 shows that on the output or secondary side, the input impedance Z_A is also transformed (by the inverse ratio, of course), and that the emf appears multiplied by the ratio N_2/N_1 (as well as being reversed in phase). The voltage drop on the primary side, $\mathscr{E} - Z_A i_1 = Z_B(N_1^2 i_1/N_2^2) = -Z_B(N_1 i_2/N_2)$, is just equal to $-(N_1/N_2)$ times the secondary voltage drop $Z_B i_2$. Finally, the currents are in the inverse ratio to the emf's, as shown by eq. 9.5–16.

In many practical cases, the above analysis in terms of an "ideal" transformer is quite adequate. One can write "equivalent" circuits for the input and output ends, in accordance with eqs. 9.5–17 and 9.5–18, as shown in Fig. 9.5d. It is to be noted that a "transformed" impedance appears larger when looked at from the side of the transformer with the larger number of terms; the same is true of the emf, and the reverse is true for the current. Also note that $\mathscr{E}i_1 = \mathscr{E}_2 i_2$ where $\mathscr{E}_2 = -\mathscr{E}N_2/N_1$, (the power factors are also the same) showing that the assumptions we have made imply no power loss in the transformer.

In any actual transformer, considered in closer approximation than that of ideality, there are several factors to consider. It is convenient to treat them as additions or corrections to an ideal transformer. In the first place, we should treat the resistances R_1 and R_2 of the windings as parts of the transformer rather than including them in Z_A and Z_B. Next, k will not be exactly 1. We can correct for this by describing the flux in the primary coil that does not link the secondary as leakage flux, attributing it to an independent series inductance L'_1; similarly there will be an L'_2 in the output circuit. Furthermore, there will not be a complete cancellation of the flux in the transformer core, since ωL_2 while large is not infinite in comparison to Z_B. We shall assume that the flux actually present (which

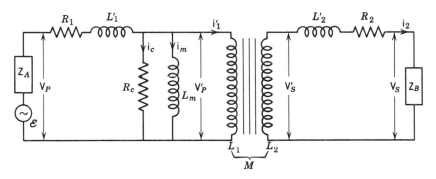

Fig. 9.5e. An actual transformer, drawn as an ideal transformer with modifications.

R_1 = primary resistance	i_c in R_c = core loss current
L'_1 = primary leakage inductance	R_2 = secondary resistance
i_m in L_m = magnetizing current	L_2 = secondary leakage inductance

of course provides the induced emf's that make the transformer operate) is produced by a small "magnetizing" current in the primary in addition to that which exactly balances the secondary current by eq. 9.5–16. This requires a shunt inductance L_m in the primary circuit for its representation. Finally, there will be energy losses in the core due to hysteresis and eddy currents, which can be represented by a primary current in phase with the primary voltage—i.e., in a shunt resistor R_c. (The ohmic losses in the windings increase with i_1 and i_2 and can be represented by series resistors. The core losses increase with the rate of change of flux—i.e., with the voltage across the windings, and so must be represented by one or two parallel resistors.)

As a result, we draw a diagram like Fig. 9.5e. V_P is the voltage drop on the primary of the actual transformer, and V'_P that at the primary of the ideal one, with a similar notation for V_S and V'_S. If we denote the turns ratio N_2/N_1 by n we write $V'_S = -nV'_P$ and $i_2 = i'_1/n$. (V'_S is the drop on the load plus that on the correction elements, i.e., it is the emf generated in the secondary coil.) We can then construct equivalent circuits like those in Fig. 9.5d (problems 9.5d and e).

It is instructive to draw a complex vector diagram for the circuit of Fig. 9.5e.   In so doing (see Fig. 9.5f) we can start with an assumed direction for i_2, draw $V_S = i_2 Z_B$ and add $i_2(R_2 + j\omega L'_2)$ to get V'_S.   The vectors V'_P and i'_1 can then be drawn in by use of the ratio n, in the respective opposite directions.   The magnetizing current i_m will be related to V'_P as in a pure inductance; since the drop in L_2 is $-V'_S$ the relation of i_m and V'_S will, of course, be of the opposite sort.   The core-loss current i_c will be

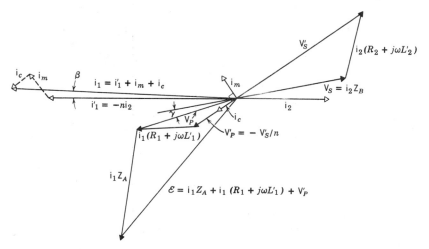

Fig. 9.5f.   A vector diagram for the transformer of Fig. 9.5e.

in phase with V'_P, and the three currents i_c, i_m and i'_1 can then be added to give i_1.   The final construction of $\mathcal{E}$ is then straightforward.

The angles β and $-\gamma$ between the reversed secondary current and voltage vectors and the corresponding (unreversed) primary vectors are called the transformer phase angles.   They are shown as respectively positive and negative according to standard convention.

It will be seen from the diagram that an actual transformer approximates ideal behavior if i_m, i_c, $\omega L'_1$, and $\omega L'_2$ are all small.   This requirement puts limitations on the frequency range for which the transformer is useful. At very low frequencies, the inductance L_m will have a very low impedance compared to R_1, so that nearly all of V_P will appear across R_1 (L_m acts like a "short circuit").   For very high frequencies $\omega L'_1$ (and also $\omega L'_2$) will be large, and again V'_P will be only a small part of V_P.   In addition, distributed capacitance effects will enter at high frequencies, providing a different type of "short circuit" across the primary.   The core-loss resistance R_c is frequency dependent; i_c will be large at high frequencies where eddy-current and hysteresis loss is large.   Commercial audio transformers have useful frequency ranges of the order of 20 to 10,000 or 20,000 cycles.

This frequency dependence explains what would otherwise be a paradox. If Z_B is a pure resistance, the transformed primary impedance Z_B/n^2 is also a pure resistance and is independent of frequency.   Yet if the frequency is zero (d-c), the transformer does not work at all—the effective resistance being then R_1 instead of $R_1 + Z_B/n^2$, which may be a great deal larger than R_1.

An extreme example of a non-ideal transformer is that of a self-inductance operating at high frequency with considerable eddy-current induction

Fig. 9.5g.   A coupled pair of tuned circuits.

in surrounding pieces of metal.   Without an iron core, L_m will be large. The transformer itself, consisting of flux linkage with the metal objects, will act like a resistor in parallel with L_m.   For this reason, it is a good approximation to treat an inductance at high frequency as having a resistance in parallel rather than in series.

Coupled Tuned Circuits.   Another important application of mutual inductance is that of partially coupled tuned circuits.   We shall give here only an approximate treatment and refer the reader elsewhere for more exact (and more complicated) discussions.[7]

Let us assume that Z_A in Fig. 9.5a consists of a small resistance and a condenser C_1 which is tuned with L_1 to a resonant frequency ω_0, that is $\omega_0^2 L_1 C_1 = 1$.   Let us similarly insert for Z_B another condenser and small resistance, tuned also to ω_0, $\omega_0^2 L_2 C_2 = 1$.   (See Fig. 9.5g.)   We shall take k to be less than 1.   For simplicity we shall define X_1 and X_2 by the equations

$$Z_A + j\omega L_1 = R_1 + j\left(\omega L_1 - \frac{1}{\omega C_1}\right) = R_1 + j\omega L_1\left(1 - \frac{\omega_0^2}{\omega^2}\right)$$

$$= R_1 + jX_1$$

$$Z_B + j\omega L_2 = R_2 + j\left(\omega L_2 - \frac{1}{\omega C_2}\right) = R_2 + j\omega L_2\left(1 - \frac{\omega_0^2}{\omega^2}\right)$$

$$= R_2 + jX_2$$

[7] See for instance, L. Page and N. I. Adams, *Principles of Electricity*, 3rd ed., D. Van Nostrand, Princeton, 1958, sections 125 127; F. E. Terman, *op. cit.*, pp. 148 169.

We can rewrite eqs. 9.5–2 and 9.5–3 in the forms

$$\frac{\mathcal{E}}{i_1} = Z_A + j\omega L_1 + \frac{\omega^2 M^2}{Z_B + j\omega L_2} = \frac{(R_1 + jX_1)(R_2 + jX_2) + \omega^2 M^2}{R_2 + jX_2}$$

$$= \frac{R_1 R_2 + j(X_1 R_2 + X_2 R_1) - X_1 X_2 + \omega^2 M^2}{R_2 + jX_2} \qquad (9.5\text{–}19)$$

and

$$\frac{\mathcal{E}}{i_2} = -\frac{R_1 R_2 + j(X_1 R_2 + X_2 R_1) - X_1 X_2 + \omega^2 M^2}{j\omega M} \qquad (9.5\text{–}20)$$

If the R's are much smaller than the reactances, the numerators in eqs. 9.5–19 and 9.5–20 will be almost equal to $\omega^2 M^2 - X_1 X_2$. At the angular frequency ω_0, when $X_1 = X_2 = 0$, $\omega^2 M^2$ will be large compared to $R_1 R_2$. The numerators will be small, implying large currents, when $X_1 X_2 = \omega^2 M^2$, or

$$\omega^2 L_1 L_2 \left(1 - \frac{\omega_0^2}{\omega^2}\right)^2 = \omega^2 M^2 = \omega^2 k^2 L_1 L_2$$

which, discounting the value $\omega = 0$, is true if

$$1 - \frac{\omega_0^2}{\omega^2} = \pm k$$

that is, for the two values

$$\omega_1 = \frac{\omega_0}{(1 + k)^{\frac{1}{2}}} \qquad (9.5\text{–}21a)$$

and

$$\omega_2 = \frac{\omega_0}{(1 - k)^{\frac{1}{2}}} \qquad (9.5\text{–}21b)$$

The frequencies for actual maxima of i_1 and i_2 will differ from these values, but only by a small amount. We see that in place of a single resonant frequency, there are two. The currents as functions of frequency are shown in Fig. 9.5h.

The sharpness of each peak is determined, as to be expected, by the Q's of each circuit, $Q_1 = \omega_0 L_1 / R_1$ and $Q_2 = \omega_0 L_2 / R_2$. However, the coupling factor k also enters, for when k is small, M is small, and the numerators of eqs. 9.5–19 and 9.5–20 are not especially large when $\omega = \omega_0$. Furthermore, the relative influence of the terms in R is greater as $X_1 X_2$ recedes from the (small) value of $\omega^2 M^2$. Thus reducing k can broaden the peaks and, as seen in eqs. 9.5–20, bring them closer together. It is possible so to choose k that the peaks for i_2 just coalesce, giving a flat-topped resonance maximum of a better shape for radio broadcast receivers than is attainable with ordinary series resonance.

If k is very small, there is essentially only one peak, of frequency ω_0. Thus a very loosely coupled secondary circuit can be used to measure the frequency of a current in a primary circuit by ordinary series tuning. Such a device, with a detecting instrument for indicating a current maximum, is called a wavemeter.

Problem 9.5a.   Set up and solve the current equations for the circuit of Fig. 9.5c.

Problem 9.5b.   What small but almost unavoidable error limits the accuracy of eq. 9.5–8?

Fig. 9.5h.   Primary and secondary currents in a tuned coupled circuit. (Adapted from F. E. Terman, *Radio Engineers Handbook*, McGraw-Hill, New York, 1943.)

Problem 9.5c.   Use eq. 7.12–5 for two coils to show that $L_1L_2 \geqslant M^2$ (*Hint:* The energy is always positive; calculate the minimum energy for i_1 fixed and i_2 variable, and set this minimum greater than zero).

Problem 9.5d.   Construct an equivalent primary circuit for the actual transformer of Fig. 9.5e.

Problem 9.5e.   Construct an equivalent secondary circuit for the actual transformer of Fig. 9.5e. Characterize the behavior of the transformer when the secondary is open-circuited and when it is short-circuited, as functions of frequency.

Problem 9.5f.   The following circuit (Fig. 9.5i) can be used for an inductor and capacitor in parallel at high frequencies. Set up a differential equation for

$V_{\parallel}$ in terms of $i_{\parallel}$, compare it with the series circuit eq. 9.2–1, and show that the two are mathematically equivalent if the correct pairs of quantities are transposed (*Hint:* $R_{\parallel}$ and $1/R$ are one pair), then compare $Z_{\parallel}$ and Z_{series}, and write formulas corresponding to eqs. 9.2–16, 9.2–17, 9.2–21, and 9.2–22.   Show that we should write $Q_{\parallel} = \dfrac{R_{\parallel}}{X_{\parallel}}$.

Problem 9.5g.   Check problem 9.5f by direct use of complex analysis.

Problem 9.5h.   Prove the statement in the text that if Φ_{11} and Φ_{12} are of the same sign for a given choice of directions for i_1 and i_2, Φ_{22} and Φ_{21} will also be of the same sign.

Fig. 9.5i.   (Problem 9.5f.)

Problem 9.5i.   A dynamic loudspeaker operates by means of a small coil that can vibrate in a permanent magnetic field.   Assuming the speaker cone and its attached coil to obey damped SHM with an external force due to the current in the coil, write a differential equation for the coil displacement x.   Assuming the coil circuit to contain an applied emf, a resistance, an inductance, and the induced emf produced by the velocity dx/dt of the coil, write a differential equation for the current i in the coil.   Show by considering a single angular frequency ω that dx/dt and i are related in the same way as the two currents in a pair of coupled circuits.

9.6   A-C Networks

The treatment of mutual inductance in the last section allows us to complete the statement in section 9.4 that Kirchhoff's laws can be applied to a-c circuits, for we see that mutual inductance can be treated just like other impedances common to two branches.   We can therefore take over in a quite general way the d-c theorems discussed in Chapter 5, namely, the superposition theorem,[8] the reciprocity theorem, the compensation theorem, and Thévenin's theorem.

Thévenin's theorem allows us to represent any two-terminal network by an emf and impedance.   Because of the variation of impedance values

[8] The superposition theorem can be applied to cases of emf's with different frequencies, using the complex method if the factors $e^{j\omega_1 t}$, $e^{j\omega_2 t}$, etc., for the different frequencies are left in the equations.   The special case in which some emf's have zero frequency (direct current) is of course included.

with frequency, both the equivalent emf and the equivalent impedance of an arbitrary network will vary with frequency. If for a fixed frequency, a variable impedance receives power from an arbitrary network, we can calculate the power transfer as we did in the d-c case and inquire into the conditions for it to be a maximum.

Let us represent a two-terminal network by an emf $\mathcal{E}$ and an impedance $z = r + jx$ and imagine it connected to a load impedance $R + jX$. The magnitude of the current will then be $i = \mathcal{E}/[(r + R)^2 + (x + X)^2]^{\frac{1}{2}}$ and the power expended in the load will be

$$P = \frac{\mathcal{E}^2 R}{(r + R)^2 + (x + X)^2} \qquad (9.6\text{–}1)$$

This expression will vary as both X and R are changed. Setting $X = -x$ will give a zero reactance term and the largest power for any fixed R (i.e., series resonance will occur). Then P is given by exactly the same expression as eq. 5.4–4 for the d-c case, so that the condition for maximum P when both R and X are varied is that

$$R = r \qquad \text{and} \qquad X = -x \qquad (9.6\text{–}2a)$$

which can be written with the complex conjugate notation

$$Z = \bar{z} \qquad (9.6\text{–}2b)$$

It is not always feasible to adjust both the angle and magnitude of Z. In fact, impedance matching is most important in communications work in which a wide range of frequencies is involved, and only approximate matching is possible over this range. One type of approximate matching occurs when the magnitude Z of Z but not its angle θ is subject to variation. We can then write

$$P = \frac{\mathcal{E}^2 Z \cos \theta}{[(r + Z \cos \theta)^2 + (x + Z \sin \theta)^2]} \qquad (9.6\text{–}3)$$

and find the maximum of P with respect to Z. It is left to the reader (problem 9.6a) to show that this maximum occurs for $Z = z = (r^2 + x^2)^{\frac{1}{2}}$ and that the resulting value of P is

$$P = \frac{\mathcal{E}^2 \cos \theta}{4z \cos^2 \frac{1}{2}(\theta - \theta_S)} \qquad (9.6\text{–}4)$$

if θ_S is the angle of the internal impedance z. As in the d-c case (problem 5.4b), it can be shown that the power transfer changes rather slowly as Z departs from its optimum value. (See problem 9.6b.)

An arbitrary two-terminal passive network can have either sign of equivalent reactance but only a positive resistance, since the network will consume power but not produce it.   However, vacuum-tube circuits that contain power sources can under some circumstances present equivalent input impedances with negative resistance.   Our general theory can be extended readily to cover these cases, but of course maximum power transfer is not then of importance.

Let us now consider four-terminal passive networks (or "passive quadrupoles").   Examples of these are matching networks, attenuators, filters, and phase-shifting networks.   One type of four-terminal network was

Fig. 9.6a.   A passive four-terminal network arranged to connect a source $\mathcal{E}, Z_s$, to a load Z_L, or alternatively a fictitious pure emf $\mathcal{E}_1$, to a fictitious pure emf $\mathcal{E}_2$.

considered in problem 5.6a, but before we consider the a-c analogue of this, let us consider certain general properties of linear four-terminal networks.   Figure 9.6a shows a four-terminal network which has an input emf $\mathcal{E}$ with impedance Z_S in the source and an output load Z_L. For purposes of calculation, it is convenient to replace each of these by pure emf's, as indicated by the dashed lines.

If we solve the network equations with $\mathcal{E}_1$ and $\mathcal{E}_2$ connected as shown, we can write for the two currents i_1 and i_2 (ignoring all other currents within the network):

$$i_1 = Y_1 \mathcal{E}_1 + Y_t \mathcal{E}_2 \qquad\qquad (9.6\text{--}5a)$$

$$i_2 = Y_t \mathcal{E}_1 + Y_2 \mathcal{E}_2 \qquad\qquad (9.6\text{--}5b)$$

where Y_1, Y_t, and Y_2 are constants determined by all the elements within the network.   Normally, a general homogeneous linear relation between two currents and two emf's would involve four arbitrary constants, but the reciprocity theorem tells us that the same constant must relate i_1 to $\mathcal{E}_2$ and i_2 to $\mathcal{E}_1$.

These constants have dimensions of mhos and may be called admittances.   Any linear four-terminal passive network is thus determined by three quantities, which depend on frequency but are otherwise constant.

We can of course choose other constants than Y_1, Y_t, and Y_2 to represent the network, and will shortly do so, but any other three can always be written as functions of these.   Networks that are symmetric with respect to input and output have $Y_1 = Y_2$ and are characterized by two constants only.

An interpretation of the constants Y_1, Y_t, and Y_2 is readily obtained, by considering first $\mathcal{E}_2 = 0$ and then $\mathcal{E}_1 = 0$.   The condition $\mathcal{E}_2 = 0$ corresponds to a short-circuit at the output or terminal-2 end of the network.   It is seen that Y_1 represents the input admittance when the output is short-circuited—it is called for brevity the short-circuit input admittance.   Similarly Y_2 is the short-circuit output admittance.   When $\mathcal{E}_2 = 0$, there will be a short-circuit current i_2 given by $i_2 = Y_t \mathcal{E}_1$, so we can call Y_t the short-circuit transfer admittance.

It is similarly possible to find the input admittance or impedance when $i_2 = 0$—i.e. when the output is an open circuit.   It is left to the reader (problem 9.6c) to find the three open-circuit quantities analogous to the three short-circuit ones.

Four-terminal networks are frequently used to provide a matching of impedance between source and load or are used as filters under conditions of impedance matching.[9]   That is, when Z_L and the source with $\mathcal{E}$ and Z_S are connected in Fig. 9.6a, the network has an impedance Z_S at terminals 1 and has an impedance Z_L at terminals 2.   These two values, Z_S and Z_L, give two conditions on the network parameters, and a third one may also be specified.   The usual one is the ratio between the output and input volt-ampere products.   Since we have removed the fictitious $\mathcal{E}_1$ and $\mathcal{E}_2$, we must replace them in eqs. 9.6–5 by V_1 and $-V_2$, as indicated by the signs in the figure.   The volt-ampere product ratio is generally expected to be less than one, so we write

$$\frac{V_2 i_2}{V_1 i_1} = \frac{V_2^2/Z_L}{V_1^2/Z_S} = e^{-2\alpha} \cdot e^{-2j\varphi}$$

where 2α is a real, positive number (except in cases of resonance, when it may be negative) and 2φ is the phase angle of the ratio.   The impedances Z_S and Z_L are in the present case properties of the network and are called the input and output image impedances, Z_{I1} and Z_{I2} respectively.   We can also define an image transfer constant Γ (capital Greek gamma) as

$$\Gamma = \alpha + j\varphi \tag{9.6–6}$$

[9] The most common case is that in which Z_S and Z_L are purely resistive, so that matching in the conjugate sense of eq. 9.6–2 is the same as ordinary matching; the more general case is easily handled.

so that the volt-ampere ratio is

$$\frac{V_2^2/Z_{I2}}{V_1^2/Z_{I1}} = e^{-2\Gamma} \qquad (9.6\text{-}7)$$

and the voltage ratio is

$$\frac{V_2}{V_1} = \left(\frac{Z_{I2}}{Z_{I1}}\right)^{\frac{1}{2}} e^{-\Gamma} \qquad (9.6\text{-}8)$$

In the case of filters, designed so as to pass certain frequencies and suppress others, it is common to have two or more networks connected in tandem

$$Z_1 = jX_1; \; Z_2 = jX_2$$

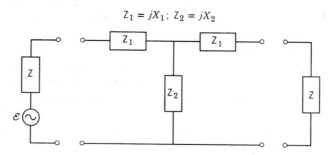

Fig. 9.6b.   A symmetrical a-c T-section network.

(cascade) under conditions of impedance matching. Then the voltage ratio at the final output to that at the first input is the product of several factors like eq. 9.6–8:

$$\frac{V_n}{V_1} = \frac{V_2}{V_1} \cdot \frac{V_3}{V_2} \cdots \frac{V_n}{V_{n-1}} = \left(\frac{Z_{I2}}{Z_{I1}}\right)^{\frac{1}{2}} \left(\frac{Z_{I3}}{Z_{I2}}\right)^{\frac{1}{2}} \cdots \left(\frac{Z_{In}}{Z_{In-1}}\right)^{\frac{1}{2}} e^{-\Gamma_1 - \Gamma_2 \cdots -\Gamma_n}$$

$$= \left(\frac{Z_{In}}{Z_{I1}}\right)^{\frac{1}{2}} e^{-(\Gamma_1 + \Gamma_2 + \cdots + \Gamma_n)} \qquad (9.6\text{-}9)$$

so that the image transfer constant is additive when networks are connected in cascade. The three image constants describing a single network are thus Z_{I1}, Z_{I2}, and Γ. It is possible, at least in principle, to match any two impedances to each other with any degree of attenuation and any phase shift. However, there are certain restrictive relations between actually attainable values of the constants that are too complicated to consider here.[10] It is generally possible to arrange for approximately zero attenuation ($\alpha = 0$) and a phase shift variable over a considerable range (nearly from 0° to 180° in case the image impedances are both purely resistive).

Let us now use the a-c analogue of the T-section attenuator of Fig. 5.6c to illustrate the above. We shall first consider strict matching and simply

[10] See, for instance, Terman, *op. cit.*, section 3, part 27.

write Z_1, Z_2, and Z in place of R_1, R_2, and R. (Fig. 9.6b.) Furthermore, we shall take the case in which the resistive parts of Z_1 and Z_2 are negligible, so that we can write, to a good approximation,

$$Z_1 = jX_1; \qquad Z_2 = jX_2 \qquad\qquad (9.6\text{--}10)$$

We can take over directly the formulas 5.6–8 and 5.6–9 of problem 5.6a, and shall replace x_a by $e^{-\Gamma}$ since the input and output image impedances are equal (cf. eq. 9.6–7). We have the matching condition

$$Z^2 = Z_1^2 + 2Z_1Z_2 \qquad\qquad (9.6\text{--}11)$$

the attenuation factor

$$e^{-\Gamma} = \frac{Z_2}{Z_2 + Z_1 + Z} \qquad\qquad (9.6\text{--}12)$$

and the equations for Z_1 and Z_2 (cf. eq. A.5–12 for hyperbolic functions)

$$Z_1 = \frac{1 - e^{-\Gamma}}{1 + e^{-\Gamma}} Z = Z \tanh \frac{\Gamma}{2} \qquad\qquad (9.6\text{--}13)$$

$$Z_2 = \frac{2e^{-\Gamma}}{1 - e^{-2\Gamma}} Z = \frac{Z}{\sinh \Gamma} \qquad\qquad (9.6\text{--}14)$$

Using eq. 9.6–10, eq. 9.6–11 becomes

$$Z^2 = -(X_1^2 + 2X_1X_2) = -X_1(X_1 + 2X_2) \qquad\qquad (9.6\text{--}15)$$

so that, if X_1 and $X_1 + 2X_2$ are both positive or both negative, Z is a pure imaginary number. We can then write $Z = jX$ and

$$X^2 = X_1^2 + 2X_1X_2 \qquad\qquad (9.6\text{--}16a)$$

$$e^{-\Gamma} = \frac{X_2}{X_2 + X_1 + X} \qquad\qquad (9.6\text{--}16b)$$

Equation 9.6–16 then shows that $e^{-\Gamma}$ is a real number, positive or negative, which means that either $\Gamma = \pm\alpha$ or $\Gamma = \pm\alpha \pm j\pi$ where α is positive. Let us consider the various possible cases. If we determine Z by eq. 9.6–15, either sign of square root may be taken, so that $Z = \pm j(X_1^2 + 2X_1X_2)^{\frac{1}{2}}$; i.e., Z can be a reactance of either sign. Since $(X_2 + X_1)^2 = X^2 + X_2^2$, we see that the magnitude of $X_2 + X_1$ is always greater than that of X. Hence if X_1 and X_2 are reactances of the same sign, this sign will also be the sign of the denominator of eq. 9.6–16 and the entire fraction will be positive, regardless of the sign of X. There will be no voltage phase shift. If X_1 and X_2 are of opposite sign, the magnitude of X_1 must be greater than that of $2X_2$ for Z^2 to be negative, so that the denominator will have the sign of X_1 and the fraction will be negative—the voltage V_2 will be 180° out of phase with V_1.

It is easy to see that when all X's are positive, $e^{-\Gamma}$ is less than 1 and attenuation occurs. It is left to the reader to show (problem 9.6e) that attenuation occurs when X and X_1 have the same sign, whereas voltage multiplication occurs when X and X_1 are of opposite sign (a type of resonance occurs).

Now suppose that $X_1^2 + 2X_1X_2$ is negative and Z is real, thus being equal to a (necessarily positive) resistance R. This will occur if $1 + 2X_2/X_1$ is negative, or $2X_2/X_1 < -1$. Then we can write eq. 9.6–12 as

$$e^{-\Gamma} = \frac{jX_2}{j(X_2 + X_1) + [-(X_1^2 + 2X_1X_2)]^{\frac{1}{2}}} = \frac{jX_2}{j(X_2 + X_1) + R} \qquad (9.6\text{–}17a)$$

For the magnitude of $e^{-\Gamma}$ we have

$$|e^{-\Gamma}| = e^{-\alpha} = \frac{X_2}{[(X_1 + X_2)^2 + (-X_1^2 - 2X_1X_2)]^{\frac{1}{2}}} = \frac{X_2}{X_2} = 1 \qquad (9.6\text{–}17b)$$

so $\alpha = 0$ and we have neither attenuation nor multiplication of voltage. The angle of $e^{\Gamma} = e^{j\varphi}$ is, on the other hand, given by

$$\tan \varphi = -\frac{R}{X_2 + X_1} \qquad (9.6\text{–}17c)$$

and φ can vary over a wide range.

Now suppose that a group of T-section networks are placed in cascade, and terminated by an impedance that is approximately resistive, but which has a reactive component of the same sign as X_1. As the frequency is varied, the end sections will not remain properly matched, but the intermediate ones almost will. For the range of frequencies that gives $(2X_2/X_1) < -1$ or $-1 < (X_1/2X_2) < 0$, there will be no attenuation; the set of networks is said to "pass" this set of frequencies, the range being called the "pass band." For other frequencies, there will be attenuation; the consequence of several sections in cascade will be to add the attenuation constants α; these frequencies are said to be "suppressed." It is in this way that practical filters are designed. Those designed to pass all frequencies below a certain limit are called low-pass filters (the rectifier filter in section 9.4 is a special example). Those designed to suppress all frequencies below a certain limit are called high-pass filters. If the range of passed frequencies is relatively narrow, we have a band-pass filter, and for the suppression of a narrow band we have band-elimination filters. The pass band can be found by plotting $2X_2$ and $-X_1$ as functions of the frequency and observing where $2X_2/(-X_1) > 1$.

Filters are usually designed to be matched to pure resistive loads. In order to provide suitable approximate matching at a variety of frequencies, L-networks (resembling halves of T-networks) are used between the T's and the source or load. The details are complicated, and the reader is referred elsewhere for them.[11]

As another example that shows some of the potentialities of alternating-current circuits, consider Fig. 9.6c, with a fixed frequency, fixed L and C,

Fig. 9.6c.   A circuit for constant-current or variable phase applications.

and variable R.   (The coil resistance is considered to be negligible.)   The impedance Z of the entire circuit is:

$$Z = j\omega L + \frac{R(-j/\omega C)}{R - j/\omega C} = \frac{j\omega L - \omega^2 LCR + R}{1 + j\omega CR} \qquad (9.6\text{–}18)$$

and the current in the resistance R is

$$i_R = i \frac{(-j/\omega C)}{R - j/\omega C} = \frac{\mathscr{E}}{Z} \cdot \frac{1}{1 + j\omega CR} = \frac{\mathscr{E}}{j\omega L - \omega^2 LCR + R} \qquad (9.6\text{–}19)$$

Now, if L and C are tuned to resonance, $\omega^2 LC = 1$ and $i_R = \mathscr{E}/j\omega L$, so i_R is independent of the value of R. This constitutes a constant-current circuit. The current will depend slightly on R if the Q of the coil is not extremely high, but for practical purposes this effect is unimportant.

On the other hand, if $\omega^2 LC = 1/2$, Z has interesting properties. We have

$$Z = \frac{j\omega L + \tfrac{1}{2}R}{1 + \dfrac{jR}{2\omega L}} = \omega L \frac{j\omega L + \tfrac{1}{2}R}{\omega L + \tfrac{1}{2}jR} \qquad (9.6\text{–}20)$$

so that the magnitude of Z is ωL and is independent of R. The angle of Z, on the other hand, is $\varphi = \tan^{-1}(2\omega L/R) - \tan^{-1}(R/2\omega L) = 2\tan^{-1}(2\omega L/R) - \pi/2$, which varies from $\pi/2$ to $-\pi/2$ when R varies from 0 to

[11] See Terman, *loc. cit.*; Page and Adams, *op. cit.*, section 129; Harnwell, *op. cit.*, section 14.4.   These authors use $\tfrac{1}{2}Z_1$ for our Z_1.

∞. Thus we have an impedance of constant magnitude and variable phase, of use in certain circuit applications.

Another type of four-terminal network is the bridge circuit, which is of such importance for electrical measurements. Using complex analysis, the balance condition for an a-c Wheatstone bridge is found to be directly analogous to that for the d-c bridge, namely

$$\frac{Z_1}{Z_2} = \frac{Z_3}{Z_4} \tag{9.6-21}$$

This relation is actually two equations, for the equality of the real and imaginary parts; balancing an a-c bridge involves two adjustments.[12]

Fig. 9.6d. The General Radio $Z-Y$ Bridge (by permission of the General Radio Co., Cambridge, Mass.).

Fig. 9.6d shows a so-called $Z-Y$ bridge[13] which is used for measuring either an arbitrary impedance Z introduced in series in arm 4 or an arbitrary admittance Y introduced in parallel in arm 1. We consider it in detail because of the variety of principles it illustrates.

It is convenient in this case to write the balance condition in terms of admittances for branches 1 and 3 and impedances for 2 and 4. We have,

[12] See Harris, *op. cit.*, Chapter 15 for a discussion of a-c bridges and their balancing, particularly the use of the complex-number plane to describe the approach to balance.

[13] I. G. Easton and H. W. Lamson, *General Radio Experimenter*, Vol. 30, No. 2, July 1955.

in fact, $Z_2Y_1 = Z_4Y_3$; the quantities $Z_2 = R_2$ and $Y_3 = j\omega C_3$ are considered to be fixed.   In general, $Y_1 = G_1 + jB_1$ and $Z_4 = R_4 + jX_4$, so we write for the real and imaginary parts of the balance equation

$$R_2G_1 = -\omega C_3 X_4 \tag{9.6-22}$$

and

$$R_2B_1 = \omega C_3 R_4 \tag{9.6-23}$$

The bridge is operated by the substitution method, which has the advantages of balancing out stray capacitances and inductances and the departures from ideal behavior of the fixed bridge elements.   The bridge is first balanced without the unknown in either the Z or Y position.   The magnitude of $G_1 = G_a$ is varied to satisfy eq. 9.6-22, and $R_4 = R_b$ is varied to satisfy eq. 9.6-23.

Now, if an unknown Z is added to branch 4, the resulting change ΔX_4 in X_4 is compensated by a change ΔG_a in the setting of G_a:

$$\Delta X_4 = -\frac{R_2}{\omega C_3} \Delta G_a$$

The additional resistance in branch 4 is compensated by reducing R_b to maintain R_4 fixed.   The unknown Z is thus found from the observed changes ΔG_a and ΔR_b.

On the other hand, if an unknown Y is added to branch 1, the additional conductance is compensated by reduction of G_a to keep G_1 fixed, and the added susceptance is measured by the change needed in the setting of R_b. From eq. 9.6-23 we have

$$\Delta B_1 - \frac{\omega C_3}{R_2} \Delta R_b$$

and Y is found from ΔR_b and ΔG_a.

It is a straightforward matter to choose the ratio $\omega C_3/R_2$ and the dial calibrations to make the bridge easy to read.   It can also be arranged so that if the bridge can handle values of Z up to, say, 1000 ohms, it can handle values of Y up to 0.001 mho—i.e., any element whatsoever will fall into the range of the bridge at either the Y or Z position (of course, the finite sensitivity of the bridge will eliminate very small Z's or Y's). The advantages of being able to make all adjustments with variable resistors, which are more readily produced and calibrated than variable inductors and capacitors, are considerable.

Problem 9.6a.   Show that the maximum of eq. 9.6-3 occurs when $Z = (r^2 + x^2)^{\frac{1}{2}}$, if θ is fixed.   Also show that for this value of Z, P in eq. 9.6-3 takes the value given by eq. 9.6-4.

Problem 9.6b. Show that the ratio of the maximum power transfer from a two-terminal network to the actual value is proportional to sec θ times the magnitude of the complex number $(Z + z)^2/Zz = [(Z/z)^{\frac{1}{2}} + (z/Z)^{\frac{1}{2}}]^2$. Show also that because R and r cannot be negative, the positive[14] square root of Z/z or

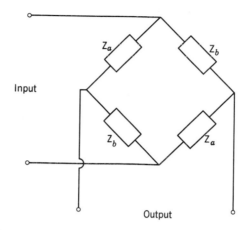

Fig. 9.6e.   A four-terminal symmetrical lattice.

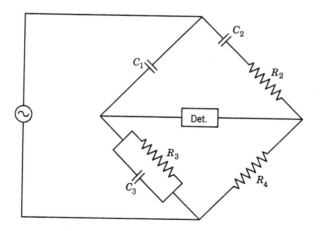

Fig. 9.6f.   The Schering bridge circuit.

z/Z has a positive real part.   Hence show that for any phase angles of Z and z, a power ratio substantially different from 1 is obtained only if the magnitudes of Z and z have a large ratio.

Problem 9.6c. Find the open-circuit input and output impedances for Fig. 9.6a in terms of Y_1, Y_t, and Y_2, and also the ratio between the input and output voltages when the output is open-circuited.

[14] The "positive" square root is the one which becomes $+1$ when $Z = z$.

Problem 9.6d.   Relate the quantity α in eq. 9.6–6 to the quantity α_{db} of problem 5.6c.

Problem 9.6e.   Consider all eight sign possibilities for X_1, X_2, and X in eq. 9.6–16, and verify the statements in the text, namely that the sign of $e^{-\Gamma}$ is the

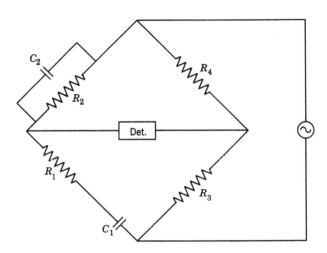

Fig. 9.6g.   The Wien bridge circuit.

Fig. 9.6h.   The Carey-Foster or Heydweiller mutual-inductance bridge.

same as that of X_2/X_1, and that $e^{-\Gamma}$ is greater than or less than 1 in magnitude according as X/X_1 is negative or positive. (*Hint:* a useful relation for this problem is obtained if we multiply numerator and denominator of 9.6–16b by $X_1 + X_2 - X$.)

Problem 9.6f. Consider the four-terminal symmetrical lattice, as in Fig. 9.6e. By use of the appropriate equations in section 5.5, show that the image impedance is $Z = (Z_a Z_b)^{\frac{1}{2}}$ and that tanh $\Gamma/2 = (Z_a/Z_b)^{\frac{1}{2}}$. (This arrangement allows Z and Γ to be chosen quite independently of one another.)

Problem 9.6g. If the resistance R_2 of the coil in Fig. 9.6c is not negligible, find a relation between time constants in the circuit that makes i_R nearly independent of R.

Problem 9.6h. Figure 9.6f shows the circuit of a Schering bridge, used for condenser measurements. Write the balance equations for finding C_2 and R_2. What happens to this result as $\omega \to 0$? For any reasonable frequency, show which elements should be made variable to give independent adjustments.

Problem 9.6i. The circuit of a Wien frequency-sensitive bridge is shown in Fig. 9.6g. Find the balance equations, show how ω can be determined, and show the relation of this bridge to the circuit of problem 9.4j. Show what the balance condition becomes in the usual case that C_1 and C_2 are fixed and equal, R_3 and $2R_4$ are likewise fixed and equal, and R_1 and R_2 are kept equal and varied.

Problem 9.6j. The Carey-Foster or Heydweiller mutual-inductance bridge has a circuit as shown in Fig. 9.6h. Analyze this bridge with Kirchhoff's laws, assuming M to have the appropriate sense.

9.7   Non-sinusoidal Alternating Currents

In this section, we wish to give a brief description of methods used for handling periodic variations of current and voltage that are not sinusoidal in nature. Figure 9.7a shows four simple examples of time variations that might apply to voltages or currents. They are all referred to as "waves" because of the appearance of the various time graphs. Square waves are used in certain pulse circuits and for testing purposes. Sawtooth waves are used for cathode-ray oscillograph sweep circuits. The full- and half-wave rectifier outputs are the two common varieties of unidirectional voltages applied to the inputs of rectifier filters such as that described at the end of section 9.4. All these waves are periodic with a period T, which as indicated can be measured from any part of the curve to the next corresponding part. In the rectifier graphs, the period T_0 of the original cosine wave is also indicated.

The general method of handling such non-sinusoidal variations is to make use of the celebrated Fourier expansion theorem, which states that any periodic function $f(t)$ can be represented as a (usually infinite) series of sine and cosine functions whose frequencies are multiples of the frequency of repetition of $f(t)$. Explicitly, if $f(t)$ has the period T and the angular frequency $\omega = 2\pi/T$, we can write

$$f(t) = \tfrac{1}{2}a_0 + a_1 \cos \omega t + a_2 \cos 2\omega t + \cdots + a_n \cos n\omega t + \cdots$$

$$+ \, b_1 \sin \omega t + b_2 \sin 2\omega t + \cdots + b_n \sin n\omega t + \cdots \quad (9.7\text{--}1)$$

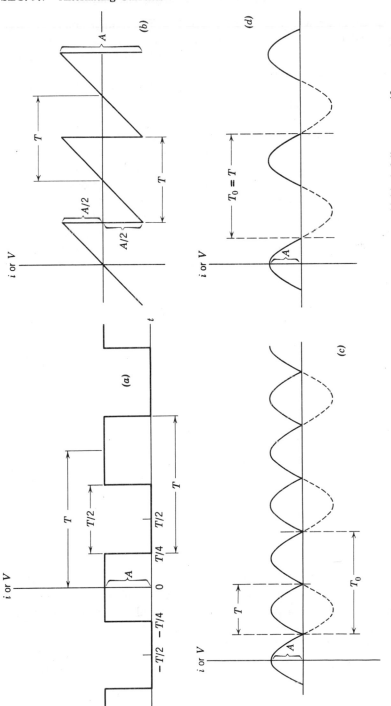

Fig. 9.7a.   Some non-sinusoidal periodic functions: (a) square wave, (b) sawtooth wave, (c) ideal full-wave rectifier output, (d) ideal half-wave rectifier output.

Such a sum is known as a "Fourier series." The term $\frac{1}{2}a_0$ represents the average value of $f(t)$, since all the other terms average to zero. The terms in $\cos \omega t$ and $\sin \omega t$ together constitute what is called the "fundamental" or the "first harmonic." The terms with $2\omega t$, $3\omega t \cdots$ are called the second harmonic, third harmonic, etc. This theorem is proved in detail in advanced mathematics books[15] and there shown to apply to any function of physical interest.

The use of the theorem consists first in obtaining the coefficients a_n and b_n for a given applied emf by a method to be given shortly, thus writing the emf as a sum of sinusoidal emf's. Then ordinary a-c analysis is applied to each term separately, yielding a series for the desired current or PD. This latter series can sometimes be summed analytically (chiefly by recognizing it as a known series) or by machine methods (on a so-called harmonic synthesizer). It is often, however, just as convenient to use the results in the series form, giving the amplitude and phase of the current or voltage for each multiple of the original frequency.

The coefficients can be found if $f(t)$ is known by use of the following integral relations, whose derivation is indicated by use of suitable trigonometric identities (note that the integration is over an integral number of periods for each trigonometric function).

$$\int_{-\pi/\omega}^{\pi/\omega} \sin n\omega t \cos m\omega t \, dt = \frac{1}{2}\int_{-\pi/\omega}^{\pi/\omega} [\sin (n+m)\omega t + \sin (n-m)\omega t] \, dt$$

$$= 0 \qquad \text{for all } n,m \tag{9.7-2a}$$

$$\int_{-\pi/\omega}^{\pi/\omega} \cos n\omega t \cos m\omega t = \frac{1}{2}\int_{-\pi/\omega}^{\pi/\omega} [\cos (n+m)\omega t + \cos (n-m)\omega t] \, dt$$

$$= \begin{cases} 0 & \text{if } n \neq m \\ \pi/\omega & \text{if } n = m \end{cases} \tag{9.7-2b}$$

$$\int_{-\pi/\omega}^{\pi/\omega} \sin n\omega t \sin m\omega t = \frac{1}{2}\int_{-\pi/\omega}^{\pi/\omega} [-\cos (n+m)\omega t + \cos (n-m)\omega t] \, dt$$

$$= \begin{cases} 0 & \text{if } n \neq m \\ \pi/\omega & \text{if } n = m \end{cases} \tag{9.7-2c}$$

The symbols m and n represent two integers, which may or may not be equal. If we choose a particular integer m, multiply both sides of eq. 9.7-1 by $\cos m\omega t$ and integrate over t from $-\pi/\omega$ to π/ω (i.e., $-T/2$ to $T/2$), every term on the right save that one with $\cos m\omega t$ will drop out

[15] See, e.g., R. V. Churchill, *Fourier Series and Boundary Value Problems*, McGraw-Hill, New York, 1941.

by eq. 9.7–2, and we obtain an equation for a_m.   Similarly we can obtain b_m by multiplying by sin $m\omega t$ and integrating.   The results are

$$a_m = \frac{\omega}{\pi} \int_{-\pi/\omega}^{\pi/\omega} f(t) \cos m\omega t \; dt \qquad m = 0,1,2 \cdots \qquad (9.7\text{-}3a)$$

$$b_m = \frac{\omega}{\pi} \int_{-\pi/\omega}^{\pi/\omega} f(t) \sin m\omega t \; dt \qquad m = 1,2,3 \cdots \qquad (9.7\text{-}3b)$$

The factor $\frac{1}{2}$ in front of a_0 in eq. 9.7–1 is introduced to allow eq. 9.7–3a to hold as written for the case $m = 0$.

To illustrate, let us consider first the square wave shown in Fig. 9.7a. The function $f(t)$ in the range $-T/2$ to $T/2$ is given by

$$f(t) = 0, \qquad -T/2 < t < -T/4$$
$$f(t) = A, \qquad -T/4 < t < T/4 \qquad\qquad (9.7\text{-}4)$$
$$f(t) = 0, \qquad T/4 < t < T/2$$

From eq. 9.7–3a we have for $m > 0$

$$a_m = \frac{\omega A}{\pi} \int_{-\pi/2\omega}^{\pi/2\omega} \cos m\omega t \; dt = \frac{A}{\pi m} \sin m\omega t \Big|_{-\pi/2\omega}^{\pi/2\omega}$$

$$= \frac{2A}{\pi m} \sin \frac{m\pi}{2} = \begin{cases} 0 & m = 2,4,6,8 \cdots \\ 2A/\pi m & m = 1,5,9 \cdots \\ -2A/\pi m & m = 3,7,11 \cdots \end{cases}$$

For $m = 0$, we have

$$a_0 = \frac{\omega A}{\pi} \Big|_{-\pi/2\omega}^{\pi/2\omega} dt = A$$

From eq. 9.7–3b, we find

$$b_m = \frac{-A}{\omega m} \cos m\omega t \Big|_{-\pi/2\omega}^{\pi/2\omega} = 0$$

We should, in fact, expect all the b's to be zero since $f(t)$ is an even function, $f(-t) = f(t)$, which property is satisfied by all the cosines and none of the sines.   The resulting Fourier series for a square wave is

$$f(t) = \tfrac{1}{2}A + \frac{2A}{\pi}\left\{ \cos \omega t - \frac{1}{3} \cos 3\omega t + \frac{1}{5} \cos 5\omega t - \frac{1}{7} \cos 7\omega t + \cdots \right\}$$

$$(9.7\text{-}5)$$

Figure 9.7*b* shows the effect of adding successively more terms of this series to approximate the infinite sum.

The sawtooth wave of Fig. 9.7*a* is an odd function, $f(-t) = -f(t)$. The function $f(t)$ in this case is given by

$$f(t) = \frac{At}{T} = \frac{\omega A}{2\pi} t, \qquad -T/2 < t < T/2 \qquad (9.7\text{-}6)$$

(1)

(2)

(3)

(4)

Fig. 9.7*b*.   The effect of adding successively more terms of eq. 9.7–5.   (1) two terms, (2) three terms, (3) four terms, (4) five terms.

The coefficients b_m are given by

$$b_m = \frac{\omega^2 A}{2\pi^2} \int_{-\pi/\omega}^{\pi/\omega} t \sin m\omega t \, dt = \frac{\omega^2 A}{2\pi^2} \left[\frac{-t \cos m\omega t}{m\omega} + \frac{\sin m\omega t}{m^2\omega^2} \right]_{-\pi/\omega}^{\pi/\omega}$$

$$= \frac{\omega^2 A}{2\pi^2} \cdot \frac{2\pi}{m\omega^2} (-1)^{m+1} = \frac{A}{\pi m} (-1)^{m+1}$$

so that the sawtooth wave series is

$$f(t) = \frac{A}{\pi} \left[\sin \omega t - \frac{1}{2} \sin 2\omega t + \frac{1}{3} \sin 3\omega t - + \cdots \right] \qquad (9.7\text{-}7)$$

In a similar way, the full-wave rectifier output may be analyzed.   In this case, $f(t)$ is given by

$$f(t) = A \cos \frac{\omega t}{2}, \qquad -T/2 < t < T/2 \qquad (9.7\text{-}8)$$

and the resulting series turns out to be (cf. problem 9.7*b*)

$$f(t) = \frac{2A}{\pi} \left[1 + \frac{2}{3} \cos \omega t - \frac{2}{15} \cos 2\omega t + \cdots + \frac{2(-1)^{n+1}}{4n^2 - 1} \cos n\omega t + \cdots \right]$$

$$(9.7\text{-}9)$$

It is to be especially noticed that the frequencies appearing in this series are all multiples of twice the frequency of the original cosine wave before rectification (dotted line in Fig. 9.7a).   The first harmonic of the rectified voltage is thus the second harmonic of the original alternating current.

The half-wave series can be gotten readily from the full-wave series by the addition of the cosine function $A \cos \omega t/2$, for all t (cf. problem 9.7c).

To illustrate the use of Fourier series, suppose that an ideal full-wave voltage like that of eq. 9.7–9 is applied to a simple L–C filter like that of Fig. 9.4c.   The nth term of the voltage series is (setting $A = V$)

$$V_n \cos n\omega t = \frac{4V(-1)^{n+1}}{\pi(4n^2 - 1)} \cos n\omega t$$

In accordance with eq. 9.4–13 the output voltage for this term will be, approximately

$$\frac{-V_n \cos n\omega t}{(n\omega)^2 LC - 1} = \frac{4V(-1)^n \cos n\omega t}{\pi(4n^2 - 1)(n^2\omega^2 LC - 1)}$$

except for $n = 0$, when the result is

$$\frac{V_0 R}{R + R'} = \frac{2VR}{\pi(R + R')}$$

so that the entire voltage is

$$\frac{2VR}{\pi(R + R')} - \frac{4V \cos \omega t}{3\pi(\omega^2 LC - 1)} + \frac{4V \cos 2\omega t}{15\pi(4\omega^2 LC - 1)}$$

$$- \cdots + \frac{(-1)^n \, 4V \cos n\omega t}{\pi(4n^2 - 1)(n^2\omega^2 LC - 1)} + \cdots \qquad (9.7\text{–}10)$$

The successive terms decrease very rapidly, since the denominator is approximately proportional to n^4, so that the sum of the first two or three makes a very good approximation.   The terms beyond the first constitute the "ripple."   The percentage of ripple can be defined as 100 times the ratio of the amplitude of the second term to the value of the first:

$$\text{per cent ripple} = 100 \cdot \frac{2}{3(\omega^2 LC - 1)} \cdot \frac{R + R'}{R}$$

It is readily seen that the effect of two filter sections in tandem is to reduce the first harmonic considerably and the higher harmonics very much indeed, since each factor $n^2\omega^2 LC - 1$ will then appear squared.

Non-sinusoidal voltages are produced by various means, in addition to the rectifiers and special circuits we have referred to.   For instance, a sinusoidal current in the primary of a transformer will produce a non-sinusoidal variation of flux, because of the non-linear shape of the hysteresis loop of the iron core. This fact can be seen quickly without detailed analysis by showing that if the hysteresis curve has, for instance, a depen- dence on H^2 and therefore on i^2, the flux will have a dependence on, say, $\cos^2 \omega t$. But $\cos^2 \omega t = \frac{1}{2}(1 + \cos 2\omega t)$, so we see that a second-degree term in the equation of the hysteresis loop introduces a second harmonic into the flux variation. Third-degree terms will introduce both third and second harmonics, and so forth. Consequently any complex curve like a hysteresis loop can be expected to introduce a whole series of harmonics, although, if only the relatively linear portion is used, the higher harmonics may all have small coefficients.

A tungsten lamp filament operated on a-c will have a slight alternating variation in temperature and hence a generally non-sinusoidal variation of resistance, so that the current $i = V/R$ produced by a sinusoidal V will always have some higher harmonics in its variation.

For many such effects, the coefficients a_n and b_n are not easy to compute, because $f(t)$ is known only by a graph or set of numerical data. There are a number of methods of graphical analysis and also a number of mechanical and electrical machines used to obtain these coefficients, but we do not have the space to describe them here.[16]

The most important sources of non-sinusoidal voltages and currents, from a practical point of view, are music and speech. Sustained musical tones and vowel sounds are complex periodic variations in air velocity and pressure. By the action of microphones they are connected into similar voltage and current variations. Amplifier circuits that are intended to give accurate reproduction of these sounds are conveniently analyzed in terms of their response to sinusoidal voltages of frequencies over the range of interest; the uniformity of this response gives a measure of the accuracy of the reproduction.

Staccato notes, percussion sounds, and most speech sounds are not sustained periodic vibrations but are better described as "pulses" or "transients." Some consideration will be given to these in the next section, but it should be stated here that a pulse can be analyzed into a continuous range of frequencies by the so-called Fourier integral theorem (which is closely related to the Laplace transform method) so that accurate reproduction of pulses also requires a circuit response that is suitably uniform over the relevant range of frequencies.

Problem 9.7a.   Prove that any even $f(t)$ is represented as a Fourier series by cosines alone and that any odd $f(t)$ is represented by sines alone.

Problem 9.7b.   Derive the series eq. 9.7–9 for the full-wave rectifier output.

[16] See, for instance, R. H. Frazier, *Elementary Electric-Circuit Theory*, McGraw-Hill, New York, 1945, pp. 279–286.

Problem 9.7c.   Derive a series for the half-wave rectifier output (a) by the formulas of the text and (b) by adding $A \cos \omega t/2$ to eq. 9.7–9 and dividing the sum by two.

Problem 9.7d.   If we represent the voltage in a given circuit element by $V = V_0 + V_{1c} \cos \omega t + V_{2c} \cos 2\omega t + \cdots + V_{1s} \sin \omega t + V_{2s} \sin 2\omega t + \cdots$ and the current in the same element by $i = i_0 + i_{1c} \cos \omega t + i_{2c} \cos 2\omega t + \cdots + i_{1s} \sin \omega t + i_{2s} \sin 2\omega t + \cdots$, show that the rms voltage is $(V_0^2 + \frac{1}{2}V_{1c}^2 + \frac{1}{2}V_{1s}^2 + \frac{1}{2}V_{2c}^2 + \frac{1}{2}V_{2s}^2 + \cdots)^{\frac{1}{2}}$, the rms current is $(i_0^2 + \frac{1}{2}i_{1c}^2 + \frac{1}{2}i_{1s}^2 + \frac{1}{2}i_{2c}^2 + \frac{1}{2}i_{2s}^2 + \cdots)^{\frac{1}{2}}$, the average power expended is $V_0 i_0 + \frac{1}{2}V_{1c}i_{1c} + \frac{1}{2}V_{1s}i_{1s} + \frac{1}{2}V_{2c}i_{2c} + \frac{1}{2}V_{2s}i_{2s} + \cdots$) and the nth term of this last equation can be written as the sum of the ordinary power terms for sinusoidal currents, $V_n i_n \cos \varphi_n$ where $\cos \varphi_n$ is the power factor for the nth harmonic.

9.8   Transients and Pulses

Transients are the variations in current or voltage that occur when a system is rapidly changed from one steady state to another, as when a steady or alternating emf is first turned on or a sudden change is made in the amplitude or phase of a steady sinusoidal alternating emf.   Pulses are variations that occur for a short time and then disappear.   In this section we shall give a brief introduction to methods of handling transients and pulses.

The simplest case to start with is the switching on of a steady emf $\mathscr{E}$ in a series circuit with R, L, and C.   We have already considered the special cases of R and C only (section 5.4) and R and L only (section 7.11).   The equation of a series circuit in its general form is

$$L\frac{di}{dt} + Ri + \frac{q}{C} = \mathscr{E}$$

Since $i = dq/dt$, we can write this as

$$L\frac{d^2q}{dt^2} + R\frac{dq}{dt} + \frac{q}{C} = \mathscr{E} \qquad (9.8\text{–}1)$$

For constant $\mathscr{E}$, this equation has the same mathematical form as eq. 8.8–8 or eq. 8.8–12a.   Furthermore, the boundary conditions are the same as for the d-c galvanometer, for if the condenser in the circuit is originally uncharged, we will have $q = 0$ and $i = dq/dt = 0$ at $t = 0$.   Consequently we can take over directly the results of section 8.8.   Comparing with eq. 8.8–12a, and using eqs. 8.8–15, 8.8–16, and 8.8–25 we can construct the equivalences in Table 9.8A and evaluate the constants α, β, ω, and γ.

Equation 8.8–21 for the solution with the given boundary conditions, when damping is more than critical, can be taken over with only a change in θ and θ_F:

$$q = \mathscr{E}C\left[1 - \frac{\alpha + \beta}{2\beta}e^{-(\alpha - \beta)t} + \frac{\alpha - \beta}{2\beta}e^{-(\alpha + \beta)t}\right] \qquad (9.8\text{–}2)$$

Table 9.8A

	Galvanometer	RLC Circuit
Variable quantity	θ	q
Inertia constant	I	L
Friction constant	b	R
"Restoring force" constant	k	$1/C$
Applied "force"	$k\theta_F$	$\mathscr{E}$
Undamped (natural) angular frequency	$\omega_0 = \left(\dfrac{k}{I}\right)^{\frac{1}{2}}$	$\omega_0 = \dfrac{1}{(LC)^{\frac{1}{2}}}$
Relative damping	$\gamma = b/2(kI)^{\frac{1}{2}}$	$\gamma = R(C/4L)^{\frac{1}{2}}$
Attenuation constant	$\alpha = \omega_0\gamma = b/2I$	$\alpha = R/2L$
Second attenuation constant	$\beta = \omega_0(\gamma^2 - 1)^{\frac{1}{2}} = \dfrac{1}{2I}(b^2 - 4kI)^{\frac{1}{2}}$	$\beta = \dfrac{1}{2L}\left(R^2 - \dfrac{4L}{C}\right)^{\frac{1}{2}}$
Damped angular frequency	$\omega = \omega_0(1 - \gamma^2)^{\frac{1}{2}} = \dfrac{1}{2I}(4kI - b^2)^{\frac{1}{2}}$	$\omega_d = \dfrac{1}{2L}\left(\dfrac{4L}{C} - R^2\right)^{\frac{1}{2}}$

from which we find the current to be

$$i = \frac{dq}{dt} = \frac{\mathscr{E}C(\alpha^2 - \beta^2)}{2\beta}\left[e^{-(\alpha-\beta)t} - e^{-(\alpha+\beta)t}\right] \tag{9.8–3}$$

It is to be noted that $\mathscr{E}C$ is the final charge on the condenser and could as well be written q_F. For the underdamped case, we get from eq. 8.8–26

$$q = \mathscr{E}C\left[1 - e^{-\alpha t}\left(\frac{\alpha}{\omega}\sin\omega t + \cos\omega t\right)\right] \tag{9.8–4}$$

and

$$i = \mathscr{E}C\left(\frac{\alpha^2}{\omega} + \omega\right)e^{-\alpha t}\sin\omega t \tag{9.8–5}$$

The critically damped case, from eq. 8.8–23, gives

$$q = \mathscr{E}C[1 - e^{-\alpha t}(\alpha t + 1)] \tag{9.8–6}$$

and

$$i = \mathscr{E}C\alpha^2 t e^{-\alpha t} \tag{9.8–7}$$

The variation of q with t and thus the variation of the condenser voltage q/C for various values of the relative damping $\gamma = R(C/4L)^{\frac{1}{2}}$ is of the same form as that for θ in Fig. 8.8b. The current will vary like the curves for θ in Fig. 8.8c.

The variations of q and i that occur when a charged condenser is discharged through an R–L–C circuit that initially had no current are obtained in the same way as is used to determine the return of a galvanometer to rest. The results are readily obtained from previous results by writing $q_2 = \mathscr{E}C - q_1$ where q_1 is the previous result and q_2 is the discharge result. The current will simply have its sign reversed.

A more complicated case is that of turning on a sinusoidal emf of arbitrary amplitude, frequency, and phase, in a series R–L–C circuit. Since we shall return to using the symbol ω for the angular frequency of an alternating emf, the damped angular frequency ω of section 8.8 can be called, for instance, ω_d. The equation for the charge on the condenser is now

$$L\frac{d^2q}{dt^2} + R\frac{dq}{dt} + \frac{q}{C} = \mathscr{E}_m \cos(\omega t + \varphi_V) \qquad (9.8\text{–}8)$$

subject to the initial conditions $q = 0$ and $i = 0$ when $t = 0$. Let us see how to construct the solution of eq. 9.8–8 from our previous results. By the complex-number method we know how to find the steady-state solution $q_s = q_{sm} \cos(\omega t + \varphi)$. It will not be necessary to specify here the values of q_{sm} and φ. If we write $q = q_t + q_s$, substitute in eq. 9.8–8, and use the fact that q_s itself satisfies the equation (which we know without calculating derivatives), we see that q_t satisfies the so-called "reduced equation" (see Appendix A.3):

$$L\frac{d^2q_t}{dt^2} + R\frac{dq_t}{dt} + \frac{q_t}{C} = 0 \qquad (9.8\text{–}9)$$

q_t is called the transient part of the solution. Since $q = 0$ and $i = 0$ when $t = 0$, q_t and i_t must have values which are the negatives of q_s and i_s at $t = 0$:

$$q_t(0) = -q_s(0); \qquad i_t(0) = -i_s(0) \qquad (9.8\text{–}10)$$

Now let us write $q_t = q_{t1} + q_{t2}$, specifying that q_{t1} satisfies eq. 9.8–9 with $q_{t1}(0) = q_t(0)$ and $i_{t1}(0) = 0$, whereas q_{t2} satisfies eq. 9.8–9 with $q_{t2}(0) = 0$ and $i_{t2}(0) = i_t(0)$. That is, q_t is broken up into a sum of a part with vanishing initial charge and one with a vanishing initial current. It should be evident to the reader that $q = q_s + q_{t1} + q_{t2}$ satisfies our original requirements and that the three parts can be found from, respectively, the steady-state solutions of sections 9.2 and 9.4, the d-c galvanometer eqs. 8.8–21, 8.8–23, and 8.8–26 that follow from eq. 8.8–18, and the ballistic galvanometer eqs. 8.8–34, 8.8–35, and 8.8–36 that follow from eq. 8.8–33. It is left to the reader to complete the solution. In the over-damped case, the current approaches its steady-state alternating value in an exponential way. In the under-damped case, transient oscillations of frequency ω_d are superimposed on those of frequency ω. The two frequencies, of course, need not be of the same order of magnitude.

In discussing transients, we are primarily concerned with the establishment of a steady state after a change in the applied emf has been made. Pulses, on the other hand, are variations of emf or current that start from zero and reduce again to zero after short periods of time, and whose effects we wish to study during such short periods. Suppose, for instance, that an emf $\mathscr{E}(t)$ which varies as shown in Fig. 9.8a is applied to the circuit of Fig. 9.8b, and the resulting PD on R is observed.

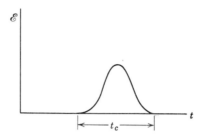

Fig. 9.8a. A simple pulsed emf.

Fig. 9.8b. An a-c circuit for pulse differentiation.

Let us suppose that the time constant RC of the circuit is small compared to the characteristic time t_c of the pulse, meaning the time during which most of the variation occurs. Then we know that the condenser will charge to a potential that is almost equal to $\mathscr{E}(t)$ during the pulse. We can write, therefore,

$$V = q/C \simeq \mathscr{E}(t)$$

and the current i will be given by

$$i = dq/dt \simeq C\frac{d\mathscr{E}}{dt} \tag{9.8–10}$$

so that the PD on R is a measure of the derivative of $\mathscr{E}$. Figure 9.8c shows the variation of V. The charging and discharging of the condenser during the pulse are clearly indicated. Such an R–C circuit is called a "differentiating circuit."

If on the other hand, RC is large compared to t_c, the condenser will

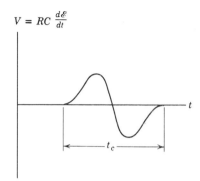

$$V = RC \frac{d\mathscr{E}}{dt}$$

Fig. 9.8c. The derivative of the pulse in Fig. 9.8a.

have almost no time to charge up, and Ri will be almost equal to $\mathscr{E}$, so that the condenser voltage represents the integral of $\mathscr{E}$:

$$Ri \sim \mathscr{E}(t)$$

$$V_C = \frac{q}{C} = \frac{1}{C} \int i \, dt = \frac{1}{RC} \int \mathscr{E}(t) \, dt \qquad (9.8\text{–}11)$$

Appropriate limits can be inserted for the integral in particular cases. If the circuit is not opened after $\mathscr{E}$ becomes zero, the condenser will slowly discharge with the time constant RC, if the impedance of the source is assumed to be small (see Fig. 9.8d). Problem 9.8b deals with similar uses of an inductance and a resistance.

We can make accurate calculations of circuit behavior when pulses are applied if the pulses are of simple form, such as the square or trapezoidal pulses of Fig. 9.8e, by using several steps of the transient analysis just given. The turning off of the square pulse is similar to the turning off of a long-established emf, except that i and q will not in general have reached their steady-state values after the turning on of the pulse. The formulas for the first transient must be used to find the initial conditions for the second. For the trapezoidal pulse, we have to solve the original differential equation for a linearly increasing $\mathscr{E}(t)$, such as $\mathscr{E} = a + bt$, and then use two additional calculations of initial conditions, for the flat part and the decreasing part of the emf, respectively.

The calculations are quite tedious and cumbersome.   For this reason, we introduce the reader in the next few paragraphs to a mathematical method which greatly reduces the labor of pulse analysis.

The Laplace Transform Method.[17]   We shall introduce the Laplace transform method of calculation from a relatively elementary point of

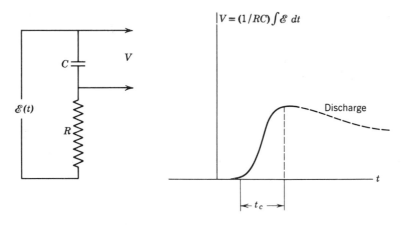

Fig. 9.8d.   An integrating circuit and the resulting voltage for $\mathcal{E}(t)$ of Fig. 9.8a.

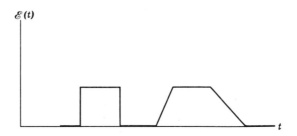

Fig. 9.8e.   A square pulse and a trapezoidal pulse.

view.   A more advanced study requires mathematics of a sort not used in this book.   For such study and further details, the reader is referred elsewhere.[18]   The essence of the method is to replace the calculation of any particular function of t, such as $\mathcal{E}(t)$, $i(t)$, $V(t)$, etc., by the calculation

    [17] The material of the remainder of this section is not referred to later and can be omitted.

    [18] See, for instance, R. V. Churchill, *Modern Operational Mathematics in Engineering*, McGraw-Hill, New York, 1944; H. S. Carslaw and J. C. Jaeger, *Conduction of Heat in Solids*, Clarendon Press, Oxford, 1947, Chapter XI; and W. C. Elmore, "Electronics for the Nuclear Physicist," *Nucleonics*, **2**, 4–17 (Feb. 1948).

of a new function derived from the given one by a certain integration formula.   To be exact, if $F(t)$ is the given function, we deal with a new function $f(p)$ defined by the integral relation

$$f(p) = \int_0^\infty e^{-pt} F(t)\, dt \tag{9.8–12}$$

The new function $f(p)$ is called the Laplace transform of $F(t)$.   The symbol p represents a number which may be real or complex, but must have a sufficiently positive real part that the integral is convergent.   It will be noted that for any value of p, $f(p)$ depends on *all* the values of $F(t)$. It can be proved quite generally that for all functions of physical interest, the relation 9.8–12 is essentially unique—that is, there is only one $F(t)$ that will yield any particular $f(p)$.   Because of the factor e^{-pt}, it is not hard to see that $f(p) \to 0$ as $p \to +\infty$.

The point of calculating $f(p)$ instead of $F(t)$ is, first, that a sufficiently simple differential equation for $F(t)$ turns into an algebraic one for $f(p)$ and, second, that the initial conditions on $F(t)$ appear explicitly in the equation for $f(p)$, so that the particular solution sought is automatically obtained.   The necessary information for using the method is a sufficiently large table of related pairs of functions $F(t)$ and $f(p)$ so that when an $f(p)$ has been found, the corresponding $F(t)$ can be recognized.

Let us consider some special properties of the Laplace transform.

1. The relation between $F(t)$ and $f(p)$ is linear.   That is, if $F(t) = aF_1(t) + bF_2(t)$, then $f(p) = af_1(p) + bf_2(p)$, where f_1 and f_2 are respectively the transforms of F_1 and F_2 and a and b are constants.   This property allows us to apply the transformation to an entire linear equation.

2. If we replace $F(t)$ by a derivative $F'(t) = dF/dt$, we obtain a formula for the transform of a derivative:

$$\int_0^\infty e^{-pt} \frac{dF}{dt}\, dt = F(t)\, e^{-pt} \Big|_0^\infty + p \int_0^\infty e^{-pt} F(t)\, dt$$

$$= -F(0) + pf(p) \tag{9.8–13}$$

A similar result involving $F(0)$ and $F'(0)$ can be calculated for the transform of d^2F/dt^2.

3. For the integral of F, i.e., $\int_0^t F(t')\, dt'$, we find by the usual rules for interchange of order of integration (Appendix A.1)

$$\int_0^\infty e^{-pt}\, dt \int_0^t F(t')\, dt' = \int_0^\infty dt'\, F(t') \int_{t'}^\infty e^{-pt}\, dt$$

$$= \int_0^\infty dt'\, F(t') \frac{e^{-pt'}}{p} = \frac{1}{p} f(p) \tag{9.8–14}$$

It is to be noted that $(1/p)f(p)$ is the transform of that integral of $F(t)$ which vanishes at $t = 0$.

4. If $F(t)$ represents a transient that is zero for $t < 0$, we have $F(t - t_1) = 0$ for $t < t_1$ and find, setting $t' = t - t_1$,

$$\int_0^\infty e^{-pt} F(t - t_1)\, dt = \int_0^\infty e^{-pt_1 - pt'} F(t')\, dt'$$
$$= e^{-pt_1} f(p) \tag{9.8-15}$$

so that $e^{-pt_1} f(p)$ is the transform of a function that vanishes for all t before the time $t = t_1$.

5. For certain particular functions $F(t)$, $f(p)$ is easy to find by straight-forward integration. Table 9.8B lists a number of these, which the reader

Table 9.8B

$F(t)$	$f(p) = \int_0^\infty e^{-pt} F(t)\, dt$
1	$1/p$
$\begin{cases} F(t) = 0 & \text{for } 0 < t < t_1 \\ F(t) = 1 & \text{for } t_1 < t < \infty \end{cases}$	$\dfrac{1}{p} e^{-pt_1}$
$\begin{cases} F(t) = 0 & \text{for } 0 < t < t_1 \\ & \text{and } t_2 < t < \infty \\ F(t) = 1 & \text{for } t_1 < t < t_2 \end{cases}$	$\dfrac{1}{p}(e^{-pt_1} - e^{-pt_2})$
$e^{-at} \quad (a > 0)$	$\dfrac{1}{p + a}$
t	$1/p^2$
$t^n \quad (n > -1)$	$n!/p^{n+1}$
$\sin bt$	$b/(p^2 + b^2)$
$\cos bt$	$p/(p^2 + b^2)$
$e^{-at} \sin bt$	$b/[(p + a)^2 + b^2]$
$e^{-at} \cos bt$	$(p + a)/[(p + a)^2 + b^2]$
$aF_1(t)$	$af_1(p)$
$\displaystyle\int_0^t F_1(t')\, dt'$	$f_1(p)/p$
$F'_1(t)$	$-F_1(0) + pf_1(p)$
$\begin{cases} F_1(t - t_1) & t > t_1 \\ 0 & t < t_1 \end{cases}$	$e^{-pt_1} f_1(p)$

should be able to verify directly or by means of a table of integrals.[19]

[19] Extensive Laplace transform tables are given in the references cited. A large table is available in A. Erdélyi, ed., *Tables of Integral Transforms*, McGraw-Hill, New York, 1954, Vol. I.

The square pulse is given in this table, but the trapezoidal pulse has been left as an exercise for the reader (problem 9.8c).

Let us now see how to apply the method by considering $F(t)$ to represent the current $i(t)$ in an R–L–C circuit to which a square pulse is applied. The equation of the circuit, as before, is

$$\mathscr{E}(t) = L\frac{di}{dt} + Ri + \frac{\int i\, dt}{C}$$

and we shall assume that $q = \int i\, dt$ is zero at $t = 0$, [otherwise the initial constant q_0/C should be subtracted from $\mathscr{E}(t)$]. Let us multiply both sides of this equation by $e^{-pt}\, dt$ and integrate. Let $g(p)$ be the Laplace transform of $\mathscr{E}(t)$, with $f(p)$ the transform of $i(t)$. We then have

$$g(p) = -Li(0) + Lpf(p) + Rf(p) + \frac{f(p)}{pC} \qquad (9.8\text{–}16)$$

which is easily soluble for $f(p)$. We shall assume here that $i(0) = 0$, but this is not necessary for use of the method. We have

$$f(p) = \frac{g(p)}{Lp + R + \dfrac{1}{pC}} \qquad (9.8\text{–}17)$$

which bears a close resemblance to eq. 9.4–2 for the complex current in the steady-state case. If we replace $\mathscr{E}$ by $g(p)$, i by $f(p)$, and $j\omega$ by p in eq. 9.4–2, we get eq. 9.8–17 exactly. From the derivation it is easy to see that this rule holds for any impedance calculation, so the method can be applied to find the current or PD at any point in any complex a-c circuit when a pulse or transient emf is applied whose Laplace transform can be calculated. Note that the transform of the PD on any element of the circuit can be found from $f(p)$—e.g., the voltage on the condenser corresponds to $f(p)/pC$.

Now, if $\mathscr{E}(t)$ is a square pulse of height $\mathscr{E}_0$, starting for simplicity at $t_1 = 0$, we have from the table

$$g(p) = \mathscr{E}_0\frac{1 - e^{-pt_2}}{p}$$

and hence

$$f(p) = \mathscr{E}_0\frac{1 - e^{-pt_2}}{Lp^2 + Rp + \dfrac{1}{C}}$$

the denominator of which can be rearranged to give

$$f(p) = \frac{\mathscr{E}_0}{L} \frac{1 - e^{-pt_2}}{\left(p + \dfrac{R}{2L}\right)^2 + \dfrac{1}{LC} - \dfrac{R^2}{4L^2}}$$

With use of the abbreviations in Table 9.8A, this can be written

$$f(p) = \frac{\mathscr{E}_0}{L} \left\{ \frac{1}{(p + \alpha)^2 + \omega^2} - \frac{e^{-pt_2}}{(p + \alpha)^2 + \omega^2} \right\}$$

Fig. 9.8f. A square wave applied to an R–L–C circuit.

Comparison of this formula with Table 9.8B now gives us $i(t)$:

$$i(t) = \frac{\mathscr{E}_0}{L} \frac{e^{-\alpha t} \sin \omega t}{\omega}; \qquad 0 < t < t_2 \tag{9.8–18}$$

$$= \frac{\mathscr{E}_0}{L} \left\{ e^{-\alpha t} \frac{\sin \omega t}{\omega} - e^{-\alpha(t - t_2)} \frac{\sin \omega(t - t_2)}{\omega} \right\}; \quad t_2 < t < \infty$$

In case ω is imaginary and β is real, this solution can be directly converted into the overdamped variety. On the other hand, we can treat the denominator by partial fractions as follows

$$\frac{1}{(p + \alpha)^2 - \beta^2} = \frac{1}{(p + \alpha - \beta)(p + \alpha + \beta)} = \frac{1}{2\beta} \left[\frac{1}{(p + \alpha - \beta)} - \frac{1}{(p + \alpha + \beta)} \right]$$

and each term is now a special case of $1/(p + a)$ in the table (problem 9.8d).

Figure 9.8f shows the current in an R–L–C circuit when a square voltage pulse is applied.

Problem 9.8a. Find the variation of q and i with time in a series R–L–C circuit when an emf $\mathscr{E} = \mathscr{E}_0 \sin \omega t$ is turned on at time $t = 0$, assuming q and i to be zero at that time.

Problem 9.8b.   Show how to use an inductance L and a resistance R as (a) a differentiating circuit and (b) an integrating circuit.

Problem 9.8c.   Find the Laplace transform of a trapezoidal pulse which starts at $t = 0$, rises linearly to 1 at $t = t_1$ [$F(t) = t/t_1$ during the rise], is equal to 1 from t_1 to t_2, and drops linearly to 0 at $t = t_3$ [$F(t) = (t_3 - t)/(t_3 - t_2)$ during the fall], being zero thereafter.

Problem 9.8d.   Find the solution corresponding to eq. 9.8–18 for the over-damped case.

Problem 9.8e.   Use the Laplace transform method to find the current in a series R–L–C circuit when a constant emf $\mathscr{E}_0$ is turned on at $t = 0$.

Fig. 9.8g.   (Problem 9.8g.)

Problem 9.8f.   Find the current in an inductance coil of L henrys and R ohms, in parallel with a capacitance of C farads, when the combination is connected at time $t = 0$ to an emf of constant value $\mathscr{E}_0$ volts and internal resistance R_2 ohms.

Problem 9.8g.   A square pulse of 10 v lasting for 1 millisec is applied to the circuit illustrated (Fig. 9.8g). Find the resulting voltage on the 10,000-ohm resistor as a function of time. Sketch a graph of this voltage.

Problem 9.8h.   Find the result of applying the trapezoidal pulse of problem 9.8c, multiplied by a constant $\mathscr{E}_0$, to the differentiating circuit of Fig. 9.8b.

10

Electromagnetic Radiation

10.1 Introduction

In this chapter we shall consider some of the properties of electric and magnetic fields that follow from the Maxwell equations which we derived in sections 1.5, 3.5, 7.7, 7.8, 7.9, and 8.4. We give them here for reference, along with the Lorentz force law, which defines **E** and **B**, and the equations relating **D** with **E** and **H** with **B**. We use ρ for the density of free charge only and assume that **J** is likewise a current of free charges only. We have, therefore, in MKS units:

$$\nabla \cdot \mathbf{D} = \rho \qquad\qquad \text{eqs. 1.5–1, 3.5–4} \quad (10.1\text{–}1a)$$

$$\nabla \cdot \mathbf{B} = 0 \qquad\qquad \text{eq. 7.7–1} \quad (10.1\text{–}2a)$$

$$\nabla \times \mathbf{H} = \mathbf{J} + \frac{\partial \mathbf{D}}{\partial t} \qquad\qquad \text{eqs. 7.8–2, 8.4–7} \quad (10.1\text{–}3a)$$

$$\nabla \times \mathbf{E} = -\frac{\partial \mathbf{B}}{\partial t} \qquad \text{eq. 7.9-2} \quad (10.1\text{-}4a)$$

$$\mathbf{F} = q(\mathbf{E} + \mathbf{v} \times \mathbf{B}) \qquad \text{eq. 7.2-3} \quad (10.1\text{-}5a)$$

$$\mathbf{D} = \epsilon_0 \mathbf{E} + \mathbf{P} \text{ (general)} \qquad \text{eq. 3.5-1}$$

$$\mathbf{D} = \epsilon_0 \mathbf{E} \text{ (free space)} \qquad\qquad\qquad (10.1\text{-}6a)$$

$$\mathbf{D} = \epsilon \mathbf{E} \text{ (isotropic linear dielectric)} \qquad \text{eq. 3.7-3}$$

$$\mathbf{B} = \mu_0(\mathbf{H} + \mathbf{M}) \text{ (general)} \qquad \text{eq. 8.4-5}$$

$$\mathbf{B} = \mu_0 \mathbf{H} \text{ (free space)} \qquad\qquad\qquad (10.1\text{-}7a)$$

$$\mathbf{B} = \mu \mathbf{H} \text{ (isotropic linear magnetic} \qquad \text{eq. 8.5-4}$$
$$\text{medium)}$$

and in Gaussian units:

$$\nabla \cdot \mathbf{D} = 4\pi\rho \qquad\qquad\qquad (10.1\text{-}1b)$$

$$\nabla \cdot \mathbf{B} = 0 \qquad\qquad\qquad (10.1\text{-}2b)$$

$$\nabla \times \mathbf{H} = \frac{4\pi}{c} \mathbf{J} + \frac{1}{c}\frac{\partial \mathbf{D}}{\partial t} \qquad\qquad (10.1\text{-}3b)$$

$$\nabla \times \mathbf{E} = -\frac{1}{c}\frac{\partial \mathbf{B}}{\partial t} \qquad\qquad (10.1\text{-}4b)$$

$$\mathbf{F} = q\left(\mathbf{E} + \frac{1}{c}\mathbf{v} \times \mathbf{B}\right) \qquad\qquad (10.1\text{-}5b)$$

$$\mathbf{D} = \mathbf{E} + 4\pi\mathbf{P} \text{ (general)}$$

$$\mathbf{D} = \mathbf{E} \text{ (free space)} \qquad\qquad\qquad (10.1\text{-}6b)$$

$$\mathbf{D} = \kappa\mathbf{E} \text{ (isotropic linear dielectric)}$$

$$\mathbf{B} = \mathbf{H} + 4\pi\mathbf{M} \text{ (general)}$$

$$\mathbf{B} = \mathbf{H} \text{ (free space)} \qquad\qquad\qquad (10.1\text{-}7b)$$

$$\mathbf{B} = \mu\mathbf{H} \text{ (isotropic linear magnetic medium)}$$

These equations, as we have pointed out before, relate the field quantities, the charge density, and the current density at one single point in space, through their time and space derivatives. They contain all the physical information we have obtained from Coulomb's, Ampère's, and Faraday's laws, and they have been modified by Maxwell's assumption so as to satisfy the law of continuity of charge.   Our procedure now is to assume them to be true and to seek solutions in the form of explicit formulas for **E** and **B** as functions of time and space coordinates.   Then we will try to understand the physical significance of these solutions and to see how their consequences are verified experimentally.   As the reader is undoubtedly aware, the result of greatest importance is the existence of electromagnetic radiation of a wavelike character.

That the assumption of the validity of Maxwell's equations for all types of time variations constitutes in itself a further physical hypothesis (in addition to the above-mentioned laws) was shown in the discussion of the term $-\nabla V$ in eq. 7.9–5 and will become especially evident in connection with the retarded potentials in section 10.3.

We shall begin with the study of the transmission of signals along cables and lines, because we can proceed in a rather elementary way and because we will wish later to contrast this type of transmission with that in wave guides.   Then we shall prove the general theorems about the propagation of effects with the velocity of light and the transmission of energy by electromagnetic fields.   This will allow us to describe radiation from simple antennas and will lead to descriptions of electromagnetic waves and their optical properties.   We shall follow this material with a study of wave guides and cavities.   We shall finally conclude with a brief introduction to the connection between electromagnetic theory and special relativity.

10.2   Cables and Lines

Coaxial cables are commonly used to transmit high-frequency alternating currents and fast pulses.   Parallel-wire transmission lines also have a number of uses, and both can be treated in the same way by the use of the concepts of distributed inductance and capacitance.   Their study forms a convenient bridge between the lumped-constant circuit theory of Chapter 9 and the radiation theory of the rest of this chapter.

Consider a coaxial line consisting of a pair of concentric conducting circular cylinders with inner cylinder of radius a and outer cylinder of inner radius b.   We shall assume that the rates of change of the fields are high enough so that the skin effect restricts the current to the surfaces of the conductors.

We saw in section 2.7 that such an arrangement has a capacitance per unit length C_l given by

$$C_l = \frac{2\pi\epsilon_0}{\ln (b/a)} \qquad \text{eq. 2.7–5} \quad (10.2\text{–!})$$

and in problem 7.11a that it has an inductance per unit length L_l given by

$$L_l = \frac{\mu_0}{2\pi} \ln (b/a) \qquad \text{eq. 7.11–9} \quad (10.2\text{–}2)$$

assuming the space between the cylinders to be essentially evacuated.   If it is filled with material of uniform linear dielectric and magnetic properties, we must replace ϵ_0 by ϵ and μ_0 by μ.   We shall need the product and ratio of L_l and C_l:

$$L_l C_l = \mu\epsilon = \frac{1}{v^2} > \frac{1}{c^2} \quad \text{uniform linear material} \qquad (10.2\text{–}3a)$$

$$L_l C_l = \mu_0 \epsilon_0 = \frac{1}{c^2} \approx \frac{1}{9 \times 10^{16} \text{ m}^2/\text{sec}^2} \quad \text{vacuum case} \qquad (10.2\text{–}3b)$$

$$\frac{L_l}{C_l} = \frac{\mu}{\epsilon} \left[\frac{\ln (b/a)}{2\pi} \right]^2 \qquad (10.2\text{–}3c)$$

The number c was discussed earlier and called the velocity of light.   We shall identify c and the new constant v as velocities on p. 483.

Let us suppose further that there is a total resistance per unit length R_l, including both conductors, and a leakage conductance per unit length G_l of the gas or other dielectric between the conductors.   We will assume that R_l is small enough that the current in the outer cylinder will automatically be equal and opposite to that in the inner cylinder because of the tendency of the magnetic field set up by the inner current to produce an outer current that cancels the field inside the material of the outer cylinder.   We shall in fact deal mostly with the case in which R_l and G_l can each be set equal to zero.

Now, if a potential difference between the two conductors is set up at one end of the cable, charge will start to flow.   The inductance, however, will oppose the flow of charge, and this effect coupled with the finite time required for the current to charge up the distributed capacitance will result in a time lag for the development of voltage across, and current in, the whole of the cable.   We might look at the cable as if it were a long series of inductances with interspersed parallel capacitors, forming a series of cascaded filters with considerable phase shift in each.   Let us find differential equations for the current i and the potential V_c of the central wire with respect to the outer one, as functions of the distance z along the wire and of the time t (Fig. 10.2a).

The current i and voltage V_c will vary with z in general, so that we can choose an element of length Δz and indicate their increments in Δz by Δi and ΔV_c.   There are four physical relations or quantities of importance: the relation between the average V_c and the charge on the central wire in

Δz, the emf associated with the rate of change of the average current in Δz, the iR drop in the conductors, and the leakage current between the conductors due to conductance of the intervening medium.

If we denote by q_l the charge per unit length of the wire (called λ in Chapter 1), we can write using superior bars to represent averages in Δz

$$\bar{V}_c = \bar{q}_l \, \Delta z / C_l \, \Delta z = \bar{q}_l / C_l$$

Since $\bar{q}_l$ arises from the current, we see that Δi represents the net rate of decrease of $\bar{q}_l \, \Delta z$, along with the average loss of current by leakage:

$$\Delta i = -\partial(\bar{q}_l \, \Delta z)/\partial t - \bar{V}_c G_l \, \Delta z$$

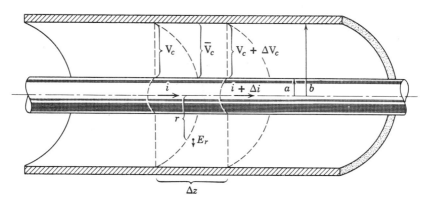

Fig. 10.2a. A portion of a coaxial cable.

On substituting, dividing by Δz and taking limits, we have

$$\frac{\partial i}{\partial z} = -C_l \frac{\partial V_c}{\partial t} - G_l V_c \tag{10.2–4}$$

The emf associated with L_l will be taken as a voltage drop as in our previous analysis, so that we have for the total drop in Δz (it does not matter how much we ascribe to the central wire and how much to the outer conductor)

$$-\Delta V_c = (L_l \, \Delta z)\frac{\partial i}{\partial t} + i R_l \, \Delta z$$

which yields our second differential equation

$$\frac{\partial V_c}{\partial z} = -L_l \frac{\partial i}{\partial t} - i R_l \tag{10.2–5}$$

These equations, as they stand, can be applied to a parallel-wire transmission line or in fact any form of line, provided the appropriate formulas for L_l and C_l are used.

Let us consider right away the simpler case in which R_l and G_l are negligible. Then we have

$$\frac{\partial i}{\partial z} = -C_l \frac{\partial V_c}{\partial t} \tag{10.2-6}$$

and

$$\frac{\partial V_c}{\partial z} = -L_l \frac{\partial i}{\partial t} \tag{10.2-7}$$

To solve these equations, let us differentiate the first with respect to t and the second with respect to z and then eliminate $\partial^2 i/\partial z\, \partial t$ from the results. We obtain

$$L_l C_l \frac{\partial^2 V_c}{\partial t^2} = \frac{\partial^2 V_c}{\partial z^2} \tag{10.2-8}$$

If we reverse the differentiations, we can eliminate $\partial^2 V_c/\partial z\, \partial t$ and obtain

$$L_l C_l \frac{\partial^2 i}{\partial t^2} = \frac{\partial^2 i}{\partial z^2} \tag{10.2-9}$$

Replacing $L_l C_l$ by $1/v^2$ ($1/c^2$ if no material substance is present between the conductors), we have for each quantity an equation which we shall write

$$\frac{1}{v^2} \frac{\partial^2 f}{\partial t^2} = \frac{\partial^2 f}{\partial z^2} \tag{10.2-10}$$

As can readily be checked by substitution, this equation has the solution

$$f(z, t) = f_1(t - z/v) + f_2(t + z/v) \tag{10.2-11}$$

where $f_1(t)$ and $f_2(t)$ are any arbitrary functions whatsoever (as long as they are properly differentiable). From the remarks in Appendix A.3, it is clear that eq. 10.2–11 represents a *general* solution of eq. 10.2–10.

Each of these functions represents a traveling wave, the first traveling in the direction of z, and the second in the direction $-z$. To see this, consider a particular value of $f_1(t)$, say $f_1(t')$ for argument t'. Then $f_1(t - z/v)$ has this value for all pairs of t and z for which $t - z/v = t'$. That is, if we consider successive values of t and z which increase together so as to satisfy this relation, we will find the value of f_1 remaining constant. This value thus appears to "travel" with a point whose coordinate z obeys the equation $z = v(t - t')$—i.e., when the point moves with the speed v in the forward direction. The function $f_1(t)$ might for instance represent a pulse or sine wave.

Similarly, $f_2(t + z/v)$ represents a wave traveling with speed $-v$. Figure 10.2b illustrates these remarks with space graphs for two different times. Thus we see that both V_c and i in general have arbitrary wave forms, moving with the speed v in either direction along the cable. It is important to note that, if one of these functions is determined as an arbitrary wave, the other is also determined. For instance, if $V_c = f_1(t - z/v)$, then $\partial V_c/\partial t = f'_1(t - z/v)$ and by eq. 10.2–6

$$\frac{\partial i}{\partial z} = -C_l f'_1(t - z/v)$$

Fig. 10.2b. Illustrating generalized waves.

so that on integration

$$i = vC_l f_1(t - z/v) + g(t) = vC_l V_c + g(t)$$

where $g(t)$ can be any function of t but is constant with respect to z. Substitution in eq. 10.2–7 shows, however, that $g(t)$ must be independent of t and since we are not considering steady currents, it must be set equal to zero. Thus i and V_c are proportional to each other. A similar result but with a minus sign in front of v holds for the wave traveling in the other direction.

These sign relations to which we have just referred have a simple physical interpretation. When the current in the central wire is positive at a place of maximum positive potential on the wire, charge is being transported in the positive direction so that the position of maximum V_c will shift in that direction, corresponding to positive wave velocity. Conversely, a negative current will carry a positive maximum of V_c in the negative direction.

The proportionality of i and V_c has the consequence that any section of the cable acts to the previous section as if it were a pure resistance of value $V_c/i = 1/vC_l = (L_l/C_l)^{\frac{1}{2}}$. This ratio is called the "characteristic impedance" of the cable Z_c:

$$Z_c = \left(\frac{L_l}{C_l}\right)^{\frac{1}{2}} = \frac{1}{2\pi}\left(\frac{\mu}{\epsilon}\right)^{\frac{1}{2}}\ln\frac{b}{a}; \quad \text{filled cable} \qquad (10.2\text{--}12a)$$

$$Z_c = \left(\frac{L_l}{C_l}\right)^{\frac{1}{2}} = \frac{1}{2\pi}\left(\frac{\mu_0}{\epsilon_0}\right)^{\frac{1}{2}}\ln\frac{b}{a}; \quad \text{empty cable} \qquad (10.2\text{--}12b)$$

Let us consider briefly what will happen if a forward-traveling pulse of voltage and current comes to the end of a cable. If the end is open-circuited or has a very high resistance connected between the cylinders, the current at the end when the voltage pulse arrives will be smaller than that which accompanied the pulse on the cable. The inductance of the portion near the end will make the charge tend to keep flowing toward the end and charge up the capacitance of the end portion. This capacitance will then discharge back into the line, and we will have a current of opposite sign to the voltage pulse. In other words, a pulse will start back along the cable in the negative direction. All portions of the voltage pulse will be thus reflected, so that the entire reflected pulse has the same time variation as the oncoming pulse.

On the other hand, if the end of the cable is short-circuited (i.e., through a very low resistance) the current at the end will be large and V_c will be small. The effect will be as if another voltage of opposite sign were superimposed on the arriving voltage pulse; this additional voltage and the original current form again a reflected pulse, this time of reversed voltage.

Finally, if the line is terminated with a resistance equal to Z_c, the current and voltage in this resistor will be in exactly the same ratio as if another section of cable were joined, and no reflection will occur. Thus when a coaxial cable is used to transmit pulses, it should be properly terminated to prevent reflections. When a cable is thus terminated in its characteristic impedance, it also presents the same impedance value at its input end. Typical values of Z_c for commercial cables are 52 ohms, 76 ohms, 93 ohms, etc.

Let us now consider a sinusoidal wave and investigate the fields between the cylinders, restricting ourselves for simplicity to the vacuum case. If V_c at any one point on the cable is to be alternating with an angular frequency ω, we must have $f_1(t)$ equal to $V_m \sin \omega t$, for instance. Then we can write

$$V_c = V_m \sin \omega\left(t - \frac{z}{c}\right) = V_m \sin\left(\omega t - \frac{z}{\lambda}\right) \qquad (10.2\text{--}13)$$

where $\lambdabar$ ("lambda-bar") $= c/\omega = c/2\pi f = \lambda/2\pi$ is called the reduced wave length. (λ is the distance by which z must increase to make the angle $\omega t - (z/\lambdabar)$ increase by 2π.)

We also have

$$i = \left(\frac{C_l}{L_l}\right)^{\frac{1}{2}} V_c = \frac{2\pi V_m}{\ln\,(b/a)} \left(\frac{\epsilon_0}{\mu_0}\right)^{\frac{1}{2}} \sin\left(\omega t - \frac{z}{\lambdabar}\right) \qquad (10.2\text{-}14)$$

These two quantities are readily seen to satisfy eq. 10.2–6 and eq. 10.2–7 if we substitute them, and use the relation

$$\lambdabar\omega = c = 1/(L_l C_l)^{\frac{1}{2}} \qquad (10.2\text{-}15)$$

The charge per unit length is then

$$q_l = C_l V_c = \frac{2\pi\epsilon_0 V_m}{\ln\,(b/a)} \sin\left(\omega t - \frac{z}{\lambdabar}\right) \qquad (10.2\text{-}16)$$

Let us tentatively assume that we can use eq. 1.7–14 to find the potential V at a distance r from the axis, at a distance z along the cable and at time t. Assuming that $V = 0$ when $r = b$ (outer conductor grounded) we have

$$V(r, z, t) = \frac{q_l}{2\pi\epsilon_0} \ln\,(b/r) = \frac{\ln\,(b/r)}{\ln\,(b/a)} V_m \sin\left(\omega t - \frac{z}{\lambdabar}\right) \qquad (10.2\text{-}17)$$

We can now find the components of the "electrostatic" field $\mathbf{E}_{\text{stat}} = -\boldsymbol{\nabla}V$. We find for the radial component the expected result (cf. eq. 1.3–5)

$$E_{r\,\text{stat}}(r, z, t) = -\frac{\partial V}{\partial r} = \frac{V_m}{r\,\ln\,(b/a)} \sin\,(\omega t - z/\lambdabar) \qquad (10.2\text{-}18)$$

and for the axial component (parallel to the axis)

$$E_{z\,\text{stat}}(r, z, t) = -\frac{\partial V}{\partial z} = \frac{V_m \ln\,(b/r)}{\lambdabar \ln\,(b/a)} \cos\,(\omega t - z/\lambdabar) \qquad (10.2\text{-}19)$$

This perhaps unexpected result for the axial field serves to show that we must use our earlier static formulas with care. Since we do not have a static case because of alternating magnetic fields, let us find $\mathbf{B}$ and $\mathbf{A}$ and see if there is an electric field of magnetic origin. The magnetic field at a given place along the cable can be found from eq. 7.5–1, which we might expect to hold in this case of variable current because it can be derived from the circuital form of Ampère's law even for changing currents. We have (since by symmetry $\mathbf{B}$ is tangent to a coaxial circle)

$$B_\phi(r, z, t) = \frac{\mu_0 i}{2\pi r} = \frac{(\mu_0\epsilon_0)^{\frac{1}{2}} V_m}{r\,\ln\,(b/a)} \sin\left(\omega t - \frac{z}{\lambdabar}\right) \qquad (10.2\text{-}20)$$

The flux per unit length of cable Φ_l lying between the radii r and b is found by multiplying B_ϕ by an element of area $dr\,dz$, integrating over r, and dividing out dz:

$$\Phi_l = \int_r^b B_\phi\,dr = \frac{(\mu_0\epsilon_0)^{\frac{1}{2}}\ln(b/r)}{\ln(b/a)} V_m \sin(\omega t - z/\lambda) \quad (10.2\text{-}21)$$

Finally, we come to the vector potential **A**.   In section 7.8, we saw that when the currents are not steady (but do not vary rapidly), we still have $\mathbf{A} \propto \int i\,\mathbf{dl}/r$, so that **A** here has the direction of all the **dl**'s, namely the z direction.   Now, we can if we wish assume A_z to be zero when $r = b$. To see this, let us recall the relation, eq. 7.8–5, between **A** and V that follows from the formula for **A** just quoted:

$$\mathbf{V} \cdot \mathbf{A} + \mu_0\epsilon_0 \frac{\partial V}{\partial t} = 0 \quad (10.2\text{-}22)$$

We have $\partial V/\partial t = 0$ when $r = b$ for all z, so $(\text{div } \mathbf{A})_{r=b} = (\partial A_z/\partial z)_{r=b} = 0$ and $(A_z)_{r=b}$ is a constant with respect to both t and z, so that we may set it equal to zero.

Now we can find A_z from Φ_l, since the flux in a length Δz is

$$\Phi_l\,\Delta z = \oint \mathbf{A} \cdot \mathbf{dl} = \Delta z A_z(r, t, z) - \Delta z A_z(b, t, z)$$

$$= \Delta z A_z(r, t, z)$$

so A_z is equal to Φ_l:

$$A_z = \Phi_l = \frac{(\mu_0\epsilon_0)^{\frac{1}{2}}\ln(b/r)V_m}{\ln(b/a)}\sin(\omega t - z/\lambda) \quad (10.2\text{-}23)$$

It is readily verified that A_z and V satisfy eq. 10.2 22.

Let us next calculate $\mathbf{E}_{\text{mag}} = \mathbf{1}_z E_{z\,\text{mag}} = -\mathbf{1}_z\,\partial A_z/\partial t$, using the relation $\omega(\mu_0\epsilon_0)^{\frac{1}{2}} = 1/\lambda$:

$$E_{z\,\text{mag}} = -\frac{V_m\ln(b/r)}{\lambda\ln(b/a)}\cos(\omega t - z/\lambda) \quad (10.2\text{-}24)$$

We see that $E_{z\,\text{mag}}$ is the exact negative of $E_{z\,\text{stat}}$, so that in fact the total z component of **E** is zero:

$$E_z = E_{z\,\text{stat}} + E_{z\,\text{mag}} = 0 \quad (10.2\text{-}25)$$

This is an expression of the fact that in a resistanceless conductor, the PD set up by charges on its surface exactly counteracts the induced emf, for otherwise with zero resistance there would be infinite current.

At this point, the reader may wonder if there are other components of **B** to consider.   How about the displacement current between the conductors? Does it contribute to **B**?   Let us answer all questions about possible further components of **B** and **E**, as well as doubts about the use of the steady-state formulas 10.2–17 and 10.2–20, by seeing if the fields we have established in eqs. 10.2–18, 10.2–20, and 10.2–25 satisfy Maxwell's equations. We see that since $\mathbf{E} = 1_r E_r$ has the radial dependence of the static case, by eq. 1.3–5, it must satisfy div $\mathbf{E} = 0$ in the space between the cylinders and the Gauss flux law with respect to the charge on the inner wire. Since B_ϕ similarly has the same radial dependence as in the steady current case, **B** satisfies div $\mathbf{B} = 0$. The equation with **curl E** must be satisfied, since it expresses the same induced emf law as is involved in eq. 10.2–24. But we shall check it directly. By symmetry we have $E_\phi = 0$ and all derivatives with respect to ϕ equal to zero. Hence, writing the components of **curl E** in cylindrical coördinates (Appendix A.2) we see that two vanish identically, so we have

$$\left. \begin{array}{l} -\dfrac{\partial B_r}{\partial t} = \text{curl}_r\,\mathbf{E} = \dfrac{1}{r}\dfrac{\partial E_z}{\partial \phi} - \dfrac{\partial E_\phi}{\partial z} = 0 \\[3mm] -\dfrac{\partial B_z}{\partial t} = \text{curl}_z\,\mathbf{E} = \dfrac{1}{r}\dfrac{\partial(rE_\phi)}{\partial r} - \dfrac{1}{r}\dfrac{\partial E_r}{\partial \phi} = 0 \\[3mm] -\dfrac{\partial B_\phi}{\partial t} = \text{curl}_\phi\,\mathbf{E} = \dfrac{\partial E_r}{\partial z} - \dfrac{\partial E_z}{\partial r} = \dfrac{\partial E_r}{\partial z} \end{array} \right\} \quad (10.2\text{–}26)$$

The last equation is readily seen to hold by differentiating eqs. 10.2–18 and 10.2–20.

We can analyze the **curl H** equation similarly. **J** is of course zero in the space between the cylinders. Thus we can write

$$\left. \begin{array}{l} \dfrac{\partial D_r}{\partial t} = \epsilon_0\dfrac{\partial E_r}{\partial t} = \text{curl}_r\mathbf{H} = \dfrac{1}{\mu_0}\left(\dfrac{1}{r}\dfrac{\partial B_z}{\partial \phi} - \dfrac{\partial B_\phi}{\partial z}\right) = -\dfrac{1}{\mu_0}\dfrac{\partial B_\phi}{\partial z} \\[3mm] \dfrac{\partial D_z}{\partial t} = \epsilon_0\dfrac{\partial E_z}{\partial t} = \text{curl}_z\mathbf{H} = \dfrac{1}{r\mu_0}\left(\dfrac{\partial(rB_\phi)}{\partial r} - \dfrac{\partial B_r}{\partial \phi}\right) = 0 \\[3mm] \dfrac{\partial D_\phi}{\partial t} = \epsilon_0\dfrac{\partial E_\phi}{\partial t} = \text{curl}_\phi\mathbf{H} = \dfrac{1}{\mu_0}\left(\dfrac{\partial B_r}{\partial z} - \dfrac{\partial B_z}{\partial r}\right) = 0 \end{array} \right\} \quad (10.2\text{–}27)$$

The first of these is satisfied because of eqs. 10.2–18 and 10.2–20; the second is satisfied because E_z is zero and rB_ϕ is independent of r; the third contains only vanishing components. Thus the four Maxwell equations for **E** and **B** are satisfied, and we have completed our investigation. There are no extra components of **B** arising from the displacement current—it is evident that the variation of B_ϕ with z accounts for the mmf that could be calculated from $\partial \mathbf{D}/\partial t$. We have here, incidentally, an illustration of the statement made in section 7.8 that the displacement current *or* the conduction current corresponding to a given filament can be used for calculation, but not both together.

We thus have found a situation in which electric and magnetic fields are propagated with the velocity of light. In the next section, we shall prove a general theorem on such propagation. In the section following the next we shall study the energy relations in propagated fields and find reasons for focusing more attention on the fields than on the accompanying currents and potential differences.

Attenuation. Let us now consider briefly the effects of non-vanishing values of R_l and G_l. We shall consider only the sinusoidal case but shall extend our treatment to consider arbitrary source and load impedances. The complex-number method is useful here. We write as in section 9.4 $V_c = V_m e^{j\omega t}$ and $i = i_m e^{j\omega t}$ where now V_m and i_m are functions of z. Substituting in eqs. 10.2–4 and 10.2–5 and dividing out $e^{j\omega t}$, we have:

$$\frac{di_m}{dz} = -(j\omega C_l + G_l)V_m$$

$$\frac{dV_m}{dz} = -(j\omega L_l + R_l)i_m \tag{10.2–28}$$

Differentiating the first equation and using the second, we have:

$$\frac{d^2 i_m}{dz^2} = (j\omega L_l + R_l)(j\omega C_l + G_l)i_m \tag{10.2–29}$$

An identical equation holds for V_m. This equation has two exponential-type solutions which we can readily obtain in terms of the complex number γ defined by:

$$\gamma^2 = (j\omega L_l + R_l)(j\omega C_l + G_l) = -\omega^2 L_l C_l \left(1 + \frac{R_l}{j\omega L_l}\right)\left(1 + \frac{G_l}{j\omega C_l}\right)$$

$$\tag{10.2–30}$$

It is evident that, if R_l and G_l are very small, γ^2 is nearly equal to $-\omega^2 L_l C_l = -\omega^2/c^2 = -1/\lambda^2$ and eq. 10.2–29 is a simple harmonic type which will yield the sinusoidal result discussed previously. The symbol γ itself is to be taken as that root of eq. 10.2–30 which is approximately $+j\omega/c$. We shall write in general

$$\gamma = \alpha + j\beta \tag{10.2–31}$$

and take as the general solution for i_m

$$i_m = K_1 e^{-\gamma z} + K_2 e^{\gamma z} \tag{10.2–32a}$$

where K_1 and K_2 are arbitrary complex constants which can be found from boundary or initial conditions.

The result for i is then

$$i = K_1 e^{-\alpha z + j(\omega t - \beta z)} + K_2 e^{\alpha z + j(\omega t + \beta z)} \qquad (10.2\text{-}32b)$$

and comparison with f_1 and f_2 as given in eq. 10.2–11 shows that the first term represents, except for the factor $e^{-\alpha z}$, a forward-traveling wave, and the second similarly a backward-traveling wave. It can also be seen that β represents $1/\lambda$ for these waves, and $\omega/\beta = \omega\lambda$ represents their velocity.

Just as earlier, the current and voltage are proportional. Substituting in the first of eqs. 10.2–28 and using eq. 10.2–30 gives

$$V_m = \left(\frac{j\omega L_l + R_l}{j\omega C_l + G_l}\right)^{\frac{1}{2}} (K_1 e^{-\gamma z} - K_2 e^{\gamma z}) \qquad (10.2\text{-}33)$$

The sign relations between V_c and i are the same as for the case of no R_l or G_l.

The square root in the last equation is the new characteristic impedance:

$$Z_c = \left(\frac{j\omega L_l + R_l}{j\omega C_l + G_l}\right)^{\frac{1}{2}} = \left(\frac{L_l - jR_l/\omega}{C_l - jG_l/\omega}\right)^{\frac{1}{2}} \qquad (10.2\text{-}34)$$

Let us consider now the ends of the cable. At the output end where $z = l$, let there be a load impedance Z_l, so that for a steady state, $V_m/i_m = Z_l$. We have

$$Z_l = Z_c(K_1 e^{-\gamma l} - K_2 e^{\gamma l})/(K_1 e^{-\gamma l} + K_2 e^{\gamma l})$$

from which it is easy to show that

$$K_2 = e^{-2\gamma l} K_1 (Z_c - Z_l)/(Z_c + Z_l) \qquad (10.2\text{-}35)$$

This equation relates the backward wave to the forward one and thus describes reflections. The ratio

$$\frac{Z_c - Z_l}{Z_c + Z_l} = \Gamma_l \qquad (10.2\text{-}36)$$

is called the output reflection coefficient. We see again that if $Z_l = Z_c$, there is no reflection.

Suppose now that the input end, where $z = 0$, is fed by an emf $\mathcal{E}$ with an internal impedance Z_0. We then have at $z = 0$

$$\mathcal{E} - Z_0 i_m = V_m$$

or, substituting,

$$\mathcal{E} = K_1(Z_0 + Z_c) + K_2(Z_0 - Z_c)$$

which with eqs. 10.2–35 and 10.2–36 gives

$$K_1 = \frac{\mathcal{E}}{Z_0 + Z_c}\left[\frac{1}{1 - \Gamma_l e^{-2\gamma l}(Z_c - Z_0)/(Z_c + Z_0)}\right] \qquad (10.2\text{-}37)$$

This expression contains a ratio called the input reflection coefficient Γ_0

$$\Gamma_0 = \frac{Z_c - Z_0}{Z_c + Z_0} \tag{10.2-38}$$

The meaning of Γ_0 is brought out if we expand the bracket in eq. 10.2–37 by the binomial theorem.

$$[1 - \Gamma_l\Gamma_0 e^{-2\gamma l}]^{-1} = 1 + \Gamma_l\Gamma_0 e^{-2\gamma l} + \Gamma_l^2\Gamma_0^2 e^{-4\gamma l} + \cdots \tag{10.2-39}$$

the successive terms of which are seen to represent an unreflected wave, a wave that has traveled down and back suffering one reflection at each end, a wave having had two reflections at each end, and so forth.

The equations given here are sufficient for finding V_m and i_m at any point on a cable and the input impedance for any output load, etc. They can of course be used for lines of any geometrical arrangement.

The term $e^{-2\alpha l}$ that appears when γ is replaced in these formulas by $\alpha + j\beta$ represents the attenuation associated with R_l and G_l. It is not easy nor useful to write explicit formulas for α and β in general, but if R_l and G_l are small, approximate results can readily be obtained. We have, in fact, by eq. 10.2–30

$$\begin{aligned}
\gamma &= j\omega(L_l C_l)^{\frac{1}{2}}\left(1 + \frac{R_l}{j\omega L_l}\right)^{\frac{1}{2}}\left(1 + \frac{G_l}{j\omega C_l}\right)^{\frac{1}{2}} \\
&= j\omega(L_l C_l)^{\frac{1}{2}}\left(1 + \frac{R_l}{2j\omega L_l} + \cdots\right)\left(1 + \frac{G_l}{2j\omega C_l} + \cdots\right) \\
&= j\omega(L_l C_l)^{\frac{1}{2}}\left(1 + \frac{R_l}{2j\omega L_l} + \frac{G_l}{2j\omega C_l} + \cdots\right) \\
&\simeq j\omega(L_l C_l)^{\frac{1}{2}} + \frac{1}{2}\left[R_l\left(\frac{C_l}{L_l}\right)^{\frac{1}{2}} + G_l\left(\frac{L_l}{C_l}\right)^{\frac{1}{2}}\right]
\end{aligned} \tag{10.2-40}$$

so that a nearly lossless line transmits waves with the same velocity as the ideal line considered earlier and has an attenuation constant α given by

$$\alpha = \frac{1}{2}\left(\frac{R_l}{Z_{c\,\text{ideal}}} + G_l Z_{c\,\text{ideal}}\right) \tag{10.2-41}$$

Actual cables can be made with low losses so that these formulas are reasonably accurate. We have of course been assuming the lines to be straight, but the usual bends and curves found in practice have very little influence.

Aside from the transmission of alternating currents and pulses of any frequency up to rather high limits, coaxial cables are useful for introducing short delays into pulse-measuring systems. Because of the high velocity of light, only very short delays, of the order of 10^{-8} sec, are practical to obtain in this way. We remarked, however, on the similarity between a cable and a series of $L-C$ filters in tandem. We can make a delay line that acts very much like a cable but allows for longer delays in a given distance by using an actual set of equal inductors in series and capacitors in parallel. Any one pair L and C can be approximately likened to the L_l and C_l for a unit length of the cable we have analyzed. The time delay of the cable, in seconds per meter, is of course $1/c = (L_l C_l)^{\frac{1}{2}}$. Hence the time delay of the series of filters is $(LC)^{\frac{1}{2}}$ per section and can be chosen almost at will. Lines of this sort of 10 or more sections are frequently used for over-all time delays up to 10^{-5} sec. It is also possible to use a continuously wound solenoid with metallic strips on its outside to make a continuous parallel capacitance to ground, with values of $(L_l C_l)^{\frac{1}{2}}$ considerably larger than $1/c$.

The reflecting properties of coaxial or other types of delay lines can be put to a number of uses. For instance, if a cable open at its far end is charged to a constant voltage V_0 and the input end is suddenly connected to a resistance equal to Z_c (for instance by firing a thyratron), the voltage will suddenly drop to $V_0/2$, and a negative step pulse of magnitude $V_0/2$ will travel down the line, reducing V_c all along the wire to $V_0/2$. At the far end, the pulse is reflected without change of sign, and as it passes back it reduces V_c to 0. The PD finally gets to zero at the original end at a time equal to twice the delay time for one passage down the cable, and a rather accurate "step" pulse of amplitude $V_0/2$ has been generated.

The far-reaching success of the theory of coaxial lines in accounting for the many quantitative experimental results that have been obtained is powerful evidence for the correctness of Maxwell's equations, including of course Maxwell's modification of Ampère's law by means of the displacement current. The success of the theory in dealing with waves in free space, with the optics of reflection, refraction, diffraction, etc, and with waves in pipes and cavities is even more impressive (see the rest of this chapter).

Problem 10.2a. Polyethylene has a dielectric constant $\kappa = 2.29$ and has $\mu_r = \mu/\mu_0 = 1$. Find a numerical formula for the characteristic impedance of lossless coaxial cables filled with polyethylene in terms of b/a. If $a = 0.250$ inches, find b so that $Z_c = 52$ ohms. Find C_l in micromicrofarads per foot for this cable.

Problem 10.2b. Use the formulas 7.11-7 and 4.5-5 to derive a formula for Z_c for a parallel-wire line. If the wires each have diameters of 0.100 in., how far apart must they be for Z_c to be 93 ohms?

Problem 10.2c. Write formulas for i_m and V_m on a cable with attenuation in terms of V_{m0} (for $z = 0$), γ, l, and Z_l.

Problem 10.2d.   Find an expression for the input impedance of an improperly terminated cable, with attenuation.

Problem 10.2e.   Given the parameters L_l, C_l, R_l, and G_l in microhenries/foot, micromicrofarads/foot, ohms/foot, and mhos/foot, write formulas with numerical constants for Z_c in ohms, α in decibels per foot, and $1/v$ in microseconds/foot.

10.3   Propagation of Electromagnetic Fields

Let us write the field equations for free space and show that the components of **E** and **B** satisfy a wave equation similar to that for V_c and i for the transmission line of the previous section.   Setting ρ, **J**, **P**, and **M** equal to zero, and $\epsilon = \epsilon_0$ and $\mu = \mu_0$, we have

$$\mathbf{\nabla} \cdot \mathbf{E} = 0 \tag{10.3-1a}$$

$$\mathbf{\nabla} \cdot \mathbf{B} = 0 \tag{10.3-1b}$$

$$\mathbf{\nabla} \times \mathbf{B} = \mu_0 \epsilon_0 \, \partial \mathbf{E}/\partial t \tag{10.3-1c}$$

$$\mathbf{\nabla} \times \mathbf{E} = -\partial \mathbf{B}/\partial t \tag{10.3-1d}$$

Let us eliminate **B** from the last two equations, by taking the curl of the last one:

curl curl $\mathbf{E} = \mathbf{\nabla} \times (\mathbf{\nabla} \times \mathbf{E}) = -\mathbf{curl}\,(\partial \mathbf{B}/\partial t) = -\partial(\mathbf{curl}\ \mathbf{B})/\partial t$

using the interchangeability of space and time derivatives.   By item 10, Table A.2B, the triple vector product can be simplified:

$$\mathbf{\nabla} \times (\mathbf{\nabla} \times \mathbf{E}) = \mathbf{\nabla}(\mathbf{\nabla} \cdot \mathbf{E}) - (\mathbf{\nabla} \cdot \mathbf{\nabla})\mathbf{E}$$

and using eqs. 10.3–1a and 10.3–1c, together with $\mu_0 \epsilon_0 = 1/c^2$ we have finally

$$\nabla^2 \mathbf{E} = \frac{1}{c^2} \frac{\partial^2 \mathbf{E}}{\partial t^2} \tag{10.3-2a}$$

which resembles eq. 10.2–10 except that it involves all three second derivatives in $\nabla^2 = (\partial^2/\partial x^2 + \partial^2/\partial y^2 + \partial^2/\partial z^2)$ and that it involves a vector **E** instead of a scalar f.   Each Cartesian component of **E**, in fact, obeys a three-dimensional wave equation.   Exactly the same operation can be carried out starting with eq. 10.3–1c, yielding the result for **B**:

$$\nabla^2 \mathbf{B} = \frac{1}{c^2} \frac{\partial^2 \mathbf{B}}{\partial t^2} \tag{10.3-2b}$$

There are three fairly simple types of solutions of these wave equations that show the character of electromagnetic waves.   In the first place, suppose that **E** and **B** are, within a certain region of space, functions of x only.   This means that all y and z derivatives must vanish.   The equation div $\mathbf{E} = 0$ becomes $\partial E_x/\partial x = 0$, which means that E_x is a constant in x. We set $E_x = 0$, therefore, since uniform fields are not of interest in this section. The other components E_y and E_z obey the one-dimensional wave equation. For E_y we have

$$\frac{\partial^2 E_y}{\partial x^2} = \frac{1}{c^2} \frac{\partial^2 E_y}{\partial t^2}$$

whose solution must be of the form

$$E_y = f_1\left(t - \frac{x}{c}\right) + f_2\left(t + \frac{x}{c}\right)$$

by comparison with eq. 10.2–11 in the last section. Similar results hold for E_z, B_y, and B_z. Just as for the coaxial line, these quantities are related to each other. Equations 10.3–1c and 10.3–1d reduce to the following in this case:

$$\text{curl}_y\, B = -\frac{\partial B_z}{\partial x} = \frac{1}{c^2}\frac{\partial E_y}{\partial t} \qquad (10.3\text{–}3a)$$

$$\text{curl}_z\, E = \frac{\partial E_y}{\partial x} = -\frac{\partial B_z}{\partial t} \qquad (10.3\text{–}3b)$$

$$\text{curl}_z\, B = \frac{\partial B_y}{\partial x} = \frac{1}{c^2}\frac{\partial E_z}{\partial t} \qquad (10.3\text{–}4a)$$

$$\text{curl}_y\, E = -\frac{\partial E_z}{\partial x} = -\frac{\partial B_y}{\partial t} \qquad (10.3\text{–}4b)$$

From eqs. 10.3–3 we get a result like that for V_c and i of section 10.2— namely, the pair of related solutions

$$E_y = f_1\left(t - \frac{x}{c}\right) + f_2\left(t + \frac{x}{c}\right)$$
$$B_z = \frac{1}{c} f_1\left(t - \frac{x}{c}\right) - \frac{1}{c} f_2\left(t + \frac{x}{c}\right) \qquad (10.3\text{–}5)$$

whereas from eqs. 10.3–4 we find another, independent pair of solutions

$$E_z = g_1\left(t - \frac{x}{c}\right) + g_2\left(t + \frac{x}{c}\right)$$
$$B_y = -\frac{1}{c} g_1\left(t - \frac{x}{c}\right) + \frac{1}{c} g_2\left(t + \frac{x}{c}\right) \qquad (10.3\text{–}6)$$

Thus we see that there exist plane wave solutions of Maxwell's equations (called "plane wave" because there is complete uniformity over the y–z

plane) that involve transverse fields, normal to the direction of travel, with the electric and magnetic vectors mutually perpendicular. The sign relations for f_1, f_2, g_1, and g_2 can all be summarized in a single rule, which says that the vector product $\mathbf{E} \times \mathbf{B}$, formed from the vectors corresponding to any one of these solutions, points in the direction of wave propagation. Specifically, for f_1, $\mathbf{E} \times \mathbf{B} = \mathbf{1}_x E_y B_z = \mathbf{1}_x f_1^2/c$ whereas for f_2, $\mathbf{E} \times \mathbf{B} = -\mathbf{1}_x f_2^2/c$. For g_1, $\mathbf{E} \times \mathbf{B} = -\mathbf{1}_x E_z B_y = \mathbf{1}_x g_1^2/c$, and for g_2, $\mathbf{E} \times \mathbf{B} = -\mathbf{1}_x g_2^2/c$.

Plane-wave solutions can of course be written for the other two planes. They can also be written for an arbitrary direction of propagation. Suppose that $\mathbf{1}_u$ represents an arbitrary unit vector, of components u_1, u_2, and u_3: $\mathbf{1}_u = \mathbf{1}_x u_1 + \mathbf{1}_y u_2 + \mathbf{1}_z u_3$. Then consider the expression, using E_y as an example,

$$E_y = F\left(t - \frac{\mathbf{r} \cdot \mathbf{1}_u}{c}\right) = F\left(t - \frac{xu_1 + yu_2 + zu_3}{c}\right) \qquad (10.3\text{--}7)$$

where $\mathbf{r} = \mathbf{1}_x x + \mathbf{1}_y y + \mathbf{1}_z z$. We have on differentiating

$$\frac{\partial E_y}{\partial t} = F'; \qquad \frac{\partial^2 E_y}{\partial t^2} = F''; \qquad \frac{\partial E_y}{\partial x} = -\frac{u_1}{c} F'; \qquad \frac{\partial^2 E_y}{\partial x^2} = \frac{u_1^2}{c^2} F''; \qquad \text{etc.,}$$

so that, since $u_1^2 + u_2^2 + u_3^2 = 1$,

$$\nabla^2 E_y = \frac{\partial^2 E_y}{\partial x^2} + \frac{\partial^2 E_y}{\partial y^2} + \frac{\partial^2 E_y}{\partial z^2} = \frac{u_1^2 + u_2^2 + u_3^2}{c^2} F'' = \frac{1}{c^2} F'' = \frac{1}{c^2} \frac{\partial^2 E_y}{\partial t^2}$$

and E_y satisfies the general wave equation. One can then find relations between solutions for the various field components so as to satisfy eqs. 10.3–1, but we shall not work them out here.

Note, however, that $\mathbf{r} \cdot \mathbf{1}_u$ has a simple interpretation. It is the projection of $\mathbf{r}$ in the direction of $\mathbf{1}_u$. If the latter were taken as a new x-axis, $\mathbf{r} \cdot \mathbf{1}_u$ would become simply x, and we would have plane waves moving in the x-direction, with their planes perpendicular to it. Thus eq. 10.3–7 represents plane waves traveling in the $\mathbf{1}_u$-direction.

A third type of solution is one that depends only on t and r, the distance from some particular origin. It is simplest for a scalar, and since we shall show that V obeys the wave equation, we shall use V as an example. We will get to our result most easily if we write

$$V = \frac{f(t, r)}{r}$$

and substitute in the wave equation, utilizing the relations $\partial r/\partial x = x/r$, $\partial r/\partial y = y/r$, and $\partial r/\partial z = z/r$. We have, in fact,

$$\frac{\partial V}{\partial x} = \frac{1}{r}\frac{\partial f}{\partial r}\frac{\partial r}{\partial x} - \frac{f}{r^2}\frac{\partial r}{\partial x} = \frac{x}{r^2}\frac{\partial f}{\partial r} - \frac{xf}{r^3}$$

$$\frac{\partial^2 V}{\partial x^2} = \frac{1}{r^2}\frac{\partial f}{\partial r} - \frac{2x}{r^3}\frac{\partial r}{\partial x}\frac{\partial f}{\partial r} + \frac{x}{r^2}\frac{\partial^2 f}{\partial r^2}\frac{\partial r}{\partial x} - \frac{f}{r^3} - \frac{x}{r^3}\frac{\partial f}{\partial r}\frac{\partial r}{\partial x} + \frac{3x}{r^4}\frac{\partial r}{\partial x}f$$

$$= \left(-1 + \frac{3x^2}{r^2}\right)\frac{f(t,r)}{r^3} + \left(1 - \frac{3x^2}{r^2}\right)\frac{1}{r^2}\frac{\partial f(t,r)}{\partial r} + \frac{x^2}{r^3}\frac{\partial^2 f(t,r)}{\partial r^2}$$

so that adding the corresponding terms in y and z and using $x^2 + y^2 + z^2 = r^2$, we find

$$\nabla^2 V = \left(-3 + \frac{3r^2}{r^2}\right)\frac{f}{r^3} + \left(3 - 3\frac{r^2}{r^2}\right)\frac{1}{r^2}\frac{\partial f}{\partial r} + \frac{r^2}{r^3}\frac{\partial^2 f}{\partial r^2}$$

Hence the wave equation yields for $f(t,r)$

$$\frac{1}{r}\frac{\partial^2 f}{\partial r^2} = \frac{1}{rc^2}\frac{\partial^2 f}{\partial t^2}$$

and f must have the form of an ordinary wave, so that we can write for V

$$V = \frac{1}{r}f_1\left(t - \frac{r}{c}\right) + \frac{1}{r}f_2\left(t + \frac{r}{c}\right) \tag{10.3-8}$$

The first term represents a diverging wave moving outward from the origin, and the second represents a converging wave moving inward toward the origin. We shall return to spherical waves of this sort later.

The Retarded Potentials. We have shown that Maxwell's equations have wave-type solutions and that the velocity of propagation is c in free space. We have not shown, however, when these solutions are physically relevant or meaningful, nor how they are related to the charges and currents that must be their sources. Our next step is to construct general expressions for the scalar and vector potentials in the presence of free charges and currents that answer these questions.

Let us substitute the expressions for **E** and **B** in terms of **A** and **V**, namely,

$$\mathbf{E} = -\frac{\partial \mathbf{A}}{\partial t} - \nabla V \qquad \text{eq. 7.9-5}a \quad (10.3-9)$$

$$\mathbf{B} = \nabla \times \mathbf{A} \qquad \text{eq. 7.6-6} \quad (10.3-10)$$

into the general equations for div **E** and **curl B**, eqs. 10.1–1a and 10.1–3b, neglecting polarization and magnetization, or including them in ρ and **J**. We obtain (cf. eq. 7.9–6)

$$\mathbf{\nabla} \cdot \mathbf{E} = -\frac{\partial}{\partial t}(\mathbf{\nabla} \cdot \mathbf{A}) - \mathbf{\nabla} \cdot \mathbf{\nabla} V = \rho/\epsilon_0$$

$$\mathbf{\nabla} \times \mathbf{B} = \mathbf{\nabla} \times (\mathbf{\nabla} \times \mathbf{A}) = \mu_0 \mathbf{J} + \mu_0 \epsilon_0 \left(-\frac{\partial^2 \mathbf{A}}{\partial t^2} - \mathbf{\nabla} \frac{\partial V}{\partial t} \right)$$

Utilizing the relation eq. 7.8–5 = eq. 10.2–22 and the expansion of $\mathbf{\nabla} \times (\mathbf{\nabla} \times \mathbf{A})$ we have

$$-\frac{\partial}{\partial t}\left(-\mu_0 \epsilon_0 \frac{\partial V}{\partial t} \right) - \nabla^2 V = \rho/\epsilon_0$$

$$\mathbf{\nabla}(\mathbf{\nabla} \cdot \mathbf{A}) - \nabla^2 \mathbf{A} + \mu_0 \epsilon_0 \mathbf{\nabla} \frac{\partial V}{\partial t} = \mu_0 \mathbf{J} - \mu_0 \epsilon_0 \frac{\partial^2 \mathbf{A}}{\partial t^2}$$

which finally reduce to

$$\nabla^2 V - \frac{1}{c^2}\frac{\partial^2 V}{\partial t^2} = -\rho/\epsilon_0 \qquad (10.3\text{–}11)$$

$$\nabla^2 \mathbf{A} - \frac{1}{c^2}\frac{\partial^2 \mathbf{A}}{\partial t^2} = -\mu_0 \mathbf{J} \qquad (10.3\text{–}12)$$

The similarity between the equation for V and that for each component of **A** recalls the similarity between the steady-state formulas for V and **A**:

$$V = \frac{1}{4\pi\epsilon_0} \int_{\text{all space}} \frac{\rho \, d\tau}{r} \qquad \text{eq. 1.7–7} \quad (10.3\text{–}13)$$

$$\mathbf{A} = \frac{\mu_0}{4\pi} \int_{\text{all space}} \frac{\mathbf{J} \, d\tau}{r} \qquad \text{eq. 7.6–8a} \quad (10.3\text{–}14)$$

If V and ρ are independent of t, we know from section 1.10 that eq. 10.3–13 satisfies eq. 10.3–11, and similarly we can conclude that if **A** and **J** are constant in time, eq. 10.3–11 satisfies eq. 10.3–12. Our desire now is to find expressions for **A** and V of a similar nature that satisfy eq. 10.3–11 and eq. 10.3–12 when all quantities depend on t. It is useful to note here that, if we think of the integral in eq. 10.3–13 as a sum and consider for a moment just one element $\rho \, d\tau$, we can verify that for points not in $d\tau$, $\nabla^2 V = 0$ because $\nabla^2(1/r) = 0$. The coefficient $\rho \, d\tau/4\pi\epsilon_0$ can be verified as the proper multiplier for $1/r$ by the use of the Gauss flux law in the neighborhood of the charge element—i.e., this coefficient provides a correct boundary condition for the solution.

Now, in the case of time variations, we want a solution of eq. 10.3–11 with $\rho = 0$, and then a coefficient that gives the boundary condition. A solution dependent only on r and t has been found above, namely a converging or diverging wave like eq. 10.3–8. We choose only the diverging wave since we consider the element to act as a source of V but not as a receiver. The boundary condition is satisfied by noting that as $r \to 0$, $f_1(t - r/c) \to f_1(t)$, so that near the charge we can use the static solution, with $f_1(t) = \rho(t)\, d\tau / 4\pi\epsilon_0$. The same treatment can be given to each component of $\mathbf{A}$.

Consequently, if $\rho(t)$ and $\mathbf{J}(t)$ are functions that give the charge and current densities as functions of the time, the scalar and vector potentials are given by

$$V(x, y, z, t) = \frac{1}{4\pi\epsilon_0} \int_{\substack{\text{all space}}} \frac{\rho\left(t - \dfrac{r}{c}\right)}{r}\, d\tau \qquad (10.3\text{–}15)$$

$$\mathbf{A}(x, y, z, t) = \frac{\mu_0}{4\pi} \int_{\substack{\text{all space}}} \frac{\mathbf{J}\left(t - \dfrac{r}{c}\right)}{r}\, d\tau \qquad (10.3\text{–}16)$$

where r is the distance from the volume element $d\tau$ to the point (x, y, z). These quantities are called the retarded potentials and give a general expression for the fields generated by arbitrary charge and current densities. They show that all electromagnetic effects are propagated with the velocity c. A particular motion of charge at a particular time produces potentials and fields at a distance r at time r/c later.[1]

These expressions are of course the generalization of the formulas for V given in Chapter 1, and they have the same limitation as all the material of that chapter—they can only be used if the charge densities and currents are already known. Thus we can use them to find the field radiated by an oscillating dipole, as we will in section 10.5, but we cannot use them when conductors are present which will contain induced currents and charges dependent on the fields. For this latter purpose, we have to use a generalization of the point of view of Chapters 2 and 4, in which the geometrical arrangements of the conductors determine the boundary conditions. An introduction to the boundary-condition approach will be given in sections 10.6 and 10.7.

[1] Expressions can be written for $\mathbf{A}$ and V with $t + r/c$ in place of $t - r/c$, and are called "advanced potentials." Their use appears to violate the law of causality, by making the potentials at a given time and place depend on later events elsewhere. Nevertheless, they are sometimes used in a symmetrical way with the retarded potentials in some theoretical developments.   J. A. Wheeler and R. Feynman, *Revs. Mod. Phys.*, **21**, 425 (1949), have given an interesting discussion and resolution of the paradox involved in this approach.

10.4   The Energy and Momentum Theorems

Electromagnetic radiation is a means of transfer of energy and momentum from one set of charges and currents to another. We can in fact attribute definite amounts of energy and momentum to each elementary volume of space occupied by electromagnetic fields. It is the purpose of this section to demonstrate the theorems upon which these statements depend.

The Energy Theorem. To study energy transfer, we start with the work done by the fields on charges. The rate of doing work, or power, is given in mechanics as $\mathbf{F} \cdot \mathbf{v}$. Since the magnetic force $q(\mathbf{v} \times \mathbf{B})$ is always perpendicular to the velocity, only the electric force $q\mathbf{E}$ is involved in energy transfer. Let us assume that all charges can be described in terms of a continuous volume density ρ. Then power per unit volume will be $P_t = \rho\mathbf{E} \cdot \mathbf{v} = \mathbf{E} \cdot \rho\mathbf{v} = \mathbf{E} \cdot \mathbf{J}$. From the **curl B** equation, we can write

$$P_\tau = \mathbf{E} \cdot \mathbf{J} = \frac{1}{\mu_0} \mathbf{E} \cdot \nabla \times \mathbf{B} - \epsilon_0 \mathbf{E} \cdot \frac{\partial \mathbf{E}}{\partial t} \qquad (10.4\text{–}1)$$

This equation can be simplified if we use the identity obtained by writing $\nabla \cdot (\mathbf{E} \times \mathbf{B})$ so that the actions of the operator on the two vectors are explicitly separated:

$$\nabla \cdot (\mathbf{E} \times \mathbf{B}) = \overline{\nabla \times \mathbf{E} \cdot \mathbf{B}} = -\overline{\nabla \times \mathbf{B} \cdot \mathbf{E}}$$

$$= \mathbf{B} \cdot \nabla \times \mathbf{E} - \mathbf{E} \cdot \nabla \times \mathbf{B} \qquad (10.4\text{–}2)$$

The bars over ∇, $\mathbf{E}$, and $\mathbf{B}$ in the first line indicate that the derivatives in ∇ operate on both vectors. Each form of the triple scalar product is then rewritten to show only one derivative operation for each term. If we use eq. 10.4–2 together with the equation for **curl E**, we can convert eq. 10.4–1 into

$$P_\tau = -\frac{1}{\mu_0} \nabla \cdot (\mathbf{E} \times \mathbf{B}) - \frac{1}{\mu_0} \mathbf{B} \cdot \frac{\partial \mathbf{B}}{\partial t} - \epsilon_0 \mathbf{E} \cdot \frac{\partial \mathbf{E}}{\partial t}$$

$$= -\frac{1}{\mu_0} \nabla \cdot (\mathbf{E} \times \mathbf{B}) - \frac{1}{2}\frac{\partial}{\partial t}\left(\frac{B^2}{\mu_0} + \epsilon_0 E^2\right)$$

The theorem we wish to prove is derived by multiplying this result by $d\tau$ and integrating over an arbitrary closed surface. The integral of the divergence of $\mathbf{E} \times \mathbf{B}$ can then be replaced by a surface integral by use of the divergence theorem, eq. A.2–22. We find for the rate at which work is done on all the charges in an arbitrary volume τ the expression

$$P = \int_\tau P_\tau \, d\tau = -\frac{1}{\mu_0} \int_{\text{surface of } \tau} \mathbf{E} \times \mathbf{B} \cdot d\mathbf{S} - \frac{d}{dt} \int_\tau \left(\frac{B^2}{2\mu_0} + \frac{\epsilon_0 E^2}{2}\right) d\tau$$

$$(10.4\text{–}3)$$

To interpret this result, we consider first a very large volume whose surface lies outside the region in which the fields of interest have any appreciable value. Then the surface integral vanishes, and we see that the rate of doing work is equal to the rate of decrease of a certain volume integral, which can be interpreted as the energy contained in the electromagnetic field:

$$U = \int_{\tau}\left(\frac{B^2}{2\mu_0} + \frac{\epsilon_0}{2} E^2\right) d\tau \tag{10.4--4a}$$

which is often written in symmetrical fashion as

$$U = \int_{\tau}\tfrac{1}{2}(\mathbf{B}\cdot\mathbf{H} + \mathbf{D}\cdot\mathbf{E})\, d\tau \qquad \text{MKS} \quad (10.4\text{--}4b)$$

$$= \int_{\tau}\frac{1}{8\pi}(\mathbf{B}\cdot\mathbf{H} + \mathbf{D}\cdot\mathbf{E})\, d\tau \quad \text{Gaussian} \quad (10.4\text{--}4c)$$

This latter equation remains valid if we do not count polarization charges and magnetization currents in ρ and $\mathbf{J}$ but include them by using the $\mathbf{D}$ and $\mathbf{H}$ vectors. Equations 10.4–4 are seen to be a generalization to the case of arbitrary fields of eqs. 4.7–6 and 7.12–8. We can always get the correct total amount of energy if we assign an amount $\tfrac{1}{2}(\mathbf{B}\cdot\mathbf{H} + \mathbf{D}\cdot\mathbf{E})$ to each unit volume, although there is no way of proving that each unit volume actually contains this energy.

Now if we consider a smaller volume so that the surface integral does not vanish, we can find an interpretation for it as well. We have, in fact, that (using again a symmetrical notation)

$$\int_{S}(\mathbf{E}\times\mathbf{H})\cdot d\mathbf{S} = -P - \frac{dU}{dt} \tag{10.4--5}$$

so that the integral is equal to the rate of gain of energy from the charges, $-P$, plus the rate of decrease of the field energy within the surface. That is, if conservation of energy is to be maintained,[2] the surface integral must represent the rate of outflow of energy through the surface. We can then assign to each unit area of the surface a rate of outflow of energy given by

$$\mathbf{N} = \mathbf{E}\times\mathbf{H} \qquad \text{MKS} \quad (10.4\text{--}5a)$$

$$\mathbf{N} = \frac{c}{4\pi}\mathbf{E}\times\mathbf{H} \qquad \text{Gaussian} \quad (10.4\text{--}5b)$$

[2] The success of the calculations given below in accounting for the flow of energy in several specific cases is evidence that the law of conservation of energy can be maintained for electromagnetic radiation. There exists, of course, an overwhelming amount of such evidence.

where **N** is called the "Poynting vector," happily named after the physicist J. H. Poynting.[3]   The quantity $\int \mathbf{N} \cdot \mathbf{dS}$ for any surface is called the Poynting flux.   Thus we see that the direction rule for plane waves given in the last section also gives the rate of energy flow through a fixed surface.

An important question arises if we consider what happens to energy transferred to moving charges.   They may accelerate, as in the case of ionic beams, and energy goes into mechanical form.   The charges may be moved into positions of higher potential energy, but only non-electrical energy can be involved, since we saw in section 4.6 that the energy stored in a condenser may be calculated as if possessed by each charge $(\frac{1}{2}\Sigma qV)$ *or* as if located in the field $(\frac{1}{2}\int\epsilon_0 E^2 \, d\tau)$, but not of course in both ways at once. The theorem we have established includes electrostatic potential energy in the volume integral of eq. 10.4–4, so that we cannot picture an additional gain of energy by the charges.   Furthermore, we cannot picture currents as transporting energy directly—the energy associated with currents was calculated in section 7.12 in terms of $\int(B^2/\mu_0) \, d\tau$.

Another demonstration that we cannot picture energy as being carried by a current is found if we consider the d-c case of a length L of a long straight cylindrical wire, of resistance R, and of radius r.   If current i flows in it, the PD between its ends will be $V = iR$, and the electric field component parallel to the wire at its outside will be $E_x = V/L = iR/L$. The magnetic field H at the surface of the wire will be $H_\phi = i/2\pi r$.   The Poynting vector **N** will then be directed into the wire, as a little consideration will show, and will have the magnitude

$$N = |\mathbf{E} \times \mathbf{H}| = E_x H_\phi = i^2 R/2\pi r L$$

Since $2\pi r L$ is the area of the outside of the wire, we see that the rate of flow of energy through its sides is

$$\int \mathbf{E} \times \mathbf{H} \cdot \mathbf{dS} = 2\pi r L E_x H_\phi = i^2 R \qquad (10.4\text{–}6)$$

which is the rate at which heat is developed.   That is, all the Joule heat enters the wire through its sides in the form of Poynting flux and none enters through its two ends.   This is actually not surprising when we consider that the current involves a continual jumping of electrons between energy levels, without any significant action of one electron on another. It is the fields that make the charges flow, and from which this energy is derived.

As another example, consider the coaxial cable.   We saw in section 10.2 that the electric field is radial and that H has only a circuital component.

---

[3] Cf. J. H. Poynting, *Collected Scientific Papers*, Cambridge Univ. Press, Cambridge, 1920, Article 10, pp. 175–193; and *Phil. Trans. Roy. Soc.*, **175**, 343 (1884).   We write the formula in terms of **H** so that it is valid both in free space and in ideal materials.

Thus $\mathbf{E} \times \mathbf{H}$ lies parallel to the axis of the cable. Taking as an element of area a coaxial ring of radius r and width dr in a plane perpendicular to the axis, we find the total rate of transfer of energy through the plane perpendicular to the axis to be

$$P = \int \mathbf{N} \cdot d\mathbf{S} = \int_a^b 2\pi r E_r H_\phi \, dr$$

which is easily evaluated by using $E_r = -\partial V/\partial r$ and $2\pi r H_\phi = i$, along with $V = 0$ when $r = b$, and $V = V_c$ when $r = a$:

$$P = \int_a^b \left(-\frac{\partial V}{\partial r}\right) i \, dr = iV_c \qquad (10.4\text{--}7)$$

Thus the expected power transfer along the central wire can be calculated by use of Poynting's vector and can be considered as transferred through the space between the conductors. It is easy to see that the direction of $\mathbf{N}$ corresponds to the direction of progression of the waves, as discussed in section 10.2.

   The Momentum Theorem. Let us now turn to the question of momentum. The force on an object is the rate at which momentum is transferred to that object. The force per unit volume on the charges and currents in a given region is the rate of transfer of momentum per unit volume. We shall see that the total rate of transfer can be interpreted as the rate of decrease of momentum residing in the field. We can find this rate by writing the Lorentz force equation and substituting field expressions for the charge and current densities. We have, in fact,

$$\mathbf{f}_\tau = \rho\mathbf{E} + \rho(\mathbf{v} \times \mathbf{B}) = \rho\mathbf{E} + \mathbf{J} \times \mathbf{B}$$

$$= \epsilon_0\mathbf{E}(\nabla \cdot \mathbf{E}) + \left(\frac{1}{\mu_0}\nabla \times \mathbf{B} - \epsilon_0\frac{\partial\mathbf{E}}{\partial t}\right) \times \mathbf{B}$$

We shall convert this into an expression involving $\partial(\mathbf{E} \times \mathbf{B})/\partial t$ by adding to this equation another involving $-\epsilon_0\mathbf{E} \times \partial\mathbf{B}/\partial t$, namely, the equation derived from $\nabla \times \mathbf{E} = -\partial\mathbf{B}/\partial t$;

$$0 = -\epsilon_0\mathbf{E} \times (\nabla \times \mathbf{E}) - \epsilon_0\mathbf{E} \times \partial\mathbf{B}/\partial t$$

so that we get

$$\mathbf{f}_\tau = \epsilon_0\mathbf{E}(\nabla \cdot \mathbf{E}) - \frac{1}{\mu_0}\mathbf{B} \times (\nabla \times \mathbf{B}) - \epsilon_0\mathbf{E} \times (\nabla \times \mathbf{E}) - \epsilon_0\frac{\partial}{\partial t}(\mathbf{E} \times \mathbf{B})$$

All terms but the last can be converted into forms that on volume integration become surface integrals. Let us convert each triple vector product into the sum of two terms and use bars again to indicate the range of action of the derivatives in ∇.   For the $\mathbf{B}$ term, we have

$$\mathbf{B} \times (\nabla \times \mathbf{B}) = \overline{\nabla(\mathbf{B} \cdot \mathbf{B})} - \overline{(\mathbf{B} \cdot \nabla)\mathbf{B}}$$

$$= \tfrac{1}{2}\overline{\nabla(\mathbf{B} \cdot \mathbf{B})} - \overline{(\mathbf{B} \cdot \nabla)\mathbf{B}} \qquad (10.4\text{--}8)$$

Now, since $\nabla \cdot \mathbf{B} = 0$, we have $(\overline{\nabla \cdot \mathbf{B}})\mathbf{B} = 0$, so that we can add this expression to $(\mathbf{B} \cdot \overline{\nabla})\mathbf{B}$ and obtain $(\overline{\nabla \cdot \mathbf{B}})\mathbf{B}$ in which the derivatives operate on each $\mathbf{B}$ vector.   For the $\mathbf{E}$ term, there already is an $(\overline{\nabla \cdot \mathbf{E}})\mathbf{E}$ term in the equation to combine with an $(\mathbf{E} \cdot \overline{\nabla})\mathbf{E}$ term.   The final result for $\mathbf{f}_\tau$ is

$$\mathbf{f}_\tau = -\epsilon_0 \frac{\partial}{\partial t}(\mathbf{E} \times \mathbf{B}) - \frac{1}{2\mu_0}\nabla B^2 - \frac{\epsilon_0}{2}\nabla E^2$$

$$+ \frac{1}{\mu_0}(\overline{\nabla \cdot \mathbf{B}})\mathbf{B} + \epsilon_0(\overline{\nabla \cdot \mathbf{E}})\mathbf{E} \qquad (10.4\text{--}9)$$

Let us integrate this expression over an arbitrary volume τ to find the rate of transfer of momentum to the charges in τ.   Using the vector theorems A.2–24 and A.2–27 to convert all but the first term on the right into integrals over the surface S of τ, we obtain

$$\int_\tau \mathbf{f}_\tau \, d\tau = -\epsilon_0 \frac{d}{dt}\int_\tau \mathbf{E} \times \mathbf{B} \, d\tau - \tfrac{1}{2}\int_S \left(\frac{1}{\mu_0}B^2 + \epsilon_0 E^2\right) d\mathbf{S}$$

$$+ \int_S \frac{1}{\mu_0}\mathbf{B}(\mathbf{B} \cdot d\mathbf{S}) + \int_S \epsilon_0 \mathbf{E}(\mathbf{E} \cdot d\mathbf{S}) \qquad (10.4\text{--}10)$$

Just as in the energy calculation, we get an interpretation of the volume integral by taking a volume so large that the fields are negligible all over its surface.[4]   We see in view of our remarks on momentum that the electromagnetic field appears to carry momentum in the amount

$$\mathbf{G}_\tau = \epsilon_0(\mathbf{E} \times \mathbf{B}) = \frac{1}{c^2}(\mathbf{E} \times \mathbf{H}) \qquad \text{MKS} \quad (10.4\text{--}11a)$$

$$\mathbf{G}_\tau = \frac{1}{4\pi c}(\mathbf{E} \times \mathbf{H}) \qquad \qquad \text{Gaussian} \quad (10.4\text{--}11b)$$

per unit volume.

  If we then consider the surface integrals in cases in which they do not vanish, we can interpret these integrals as representing forces per unit area

---

[4] In cases in which radiation goes off to "infinity," it is not possible to set the surface integrals equal to zero in either calculation.   However, this mathematical difficulty, which is handled in detail in more advanced texts, in no way modifies our interpretations of the vector $\mathbf{E} \times \mathbf{H}$.

or stresses, exerted on the region within the surface by the fields without. Considerations of this sort lead to the study of the so-called Maxwell stress tensor but are too complicated to consider in this book (see, however, problem 10.8*m*).

Let us close with a remark on the relation between G_r and $\mathbf{N}$. When an electromagnetic wave travels perpendicularly through a given surface in space at the speed c, a volume of radiation equal in magnitude to c passes each square meter each second. The amount of momentum that passes per square meter per second is therefore equal to $(1/c)(\mathbf{E} \times \mathbf{H})$, whereas the transport of energy is $|(\mathbf{E} \times \mathbf{H})|$ per square meter per second. Corresponding to any transported quantity of energy U there is therefore a momentum transport of magnitude U/c. For instance, according to the quantum theory, electromagnetic energy is transported in units of $h\nu$, where ν is the frequency. Then each photon of energy $h\nu$ must carry momentum $h\nu/c = h/\lambda$. This result has been verified by experiments such as the Compton effect in which the energy and momentum transferred to an electron by a single X ray photon can be detected.

Problem 10.4a. Use the Poynting vector to calculate the energy flow from a parallel-plate condenser being discharged through a resistor R, and draw a sketch showing the paths along which energy flows to R.

Problem 10.4b. Using the surface integrals in eq. 10.4–10, find the stress (*a*) in the y-direction on a surface whose normal lies in the z-direction and (*b*) in the y-direction on a surface whose normal lies in the y-direction.

Problem 10.4c. Show that the angular momentum about a given origin $\mathcal{O}$ that is carried by electromagnetic radiation is $\mathbf{r} \times G_r$, by starting with eq. 10.4–9 and calculating the integral of $\mathbf{r} \times \mathbf{f}_r$. *Hints*: it will be necessary to use eqs. A.2–26 and A.2–27, and item 12 in Table A.2B, which in turn can be derived from item 11.

Problem 10.4d. Consider two charges separated by a vector distance $\mathbf{r}$ whose velocities are $\mathbf{v}_1$ and $\mathbf{v}_2$, so oriented that the planes that each makes with $\mathbf{r}$ are mutually perpendicular, and $\mathbf{v}_1$ is perpendicular to $\mathbf{r}$ while $\mathbf{v}_2$ makes an angle of 45° with $\mathbf{r}$. Show that the forces of each on the other fail to obey the law of action and reaction, and show without a detailed calculation how the momentum theorem, eq. 10.4–10, preserves the conservation of momentum in spite of this failure.

10.5   Dipole and Plane-Sheet Radiation

Let us now calculate the fields produced at an arbitrary distance from an element of current. It is clear that an isolated current element is not a meaningful concept, since we must either consider a closed circuit or we must take into account the charges on conductors at the ends of the element. We shall use the latter method of constructing a suitable element. Let us suppose we have two small fixed spherical conductors a distance δl apart, connected with a thin straight wire.   Let q and $-q$ denote the amounts of charge on the two conductors (together they constitute a dipole), and let $i = dq/dt$ be the current between them.   A series of such elements can be added so as to be equivalent to a long antenna with uniform or non-uniform current and charge distributions.

It will be convenient to take a specific frequency and to write charge and current as complex quantities.   Vector quantities that are also complex will be written in bold-face sans-serif type, e.g., **E**.   We write the

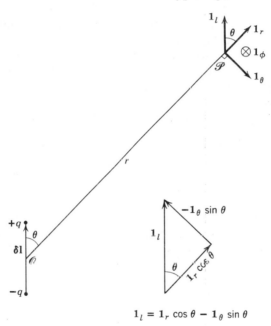

$$1_l = 1_r \cos\theta - 1_\theta \sin\theta$$

Fig. 10.5a.   An oscillating dipole.   The vector 1_ϕ at $\mathscr{P}$ is directed into the page.

charge as $q = q_{max}e^{j\omega t}$ and the current as $i = i_{max}e^{j\omega t} = j\omega q_{max}e^{j\omega t}$.   The dipole moment **p** is given by $\mathbf{p} = q\,\delta l = q_{max}\,\delta l e^{j\omega t} = \mathbf{p}_{max}e^{j\omega t}$.   Figure 10.5a shows such an oscillating dipole with a set of coordinates for use in describing the potentials and fields.

The vector potential at point $\mathscr{P}$ in the figure is readily found by using eq. 10.3–16:

$$\mathbf{A} = \frac{\mu_0 i_{ret}}{4\pi r}\,\delta l = \frac{\mu_0 j\omega q_{max}}{4\pi r}\,e^{j\omega(t-r/c)}\,\delta l \qquad (10.5\text{–}1)$$

The scalar potential is the difference between the retarded potentials of q and $-q$.   By a calculation similar to that of section 3.1, we have

$$\mathbf{V} = -\delta l \cdot \nabla(q_{ret}/4\pi\epsilon_0 r) = -\delta l \cdot \nabla(q_{max}e^{j\omega(t-r/c)}/4\pi\epsilon_0 r)$$

Now, since the potential $q/4\pi\epsilon_0 r$ is a function of r and t but not of θ or ϕ, the only relevant component of ∇ is $\mathbf{1}_r \, \partial/\partial r$. Thus we have $(\boldsymbol{\delta l} \cdot \nabla) = \delta l \cos\theta \, \partial/\partial r$, and

$$V = \frac{-\delta l \, q_{max} \cos\theta}{4\pi\epsilon_0} \frac{\partial}{\partial r}\left[\frac{e^{j\omega(t-r/c)}}{r}\right] = \frac{\delta l \, q_{max} \cos\theta}{4\pi\epsilon_0}\left[\frac{1}{r^2} + \frac{j\omega}{cr}\right] e^{j\omega(t-r/c)}$$

$$(10.5\text{--}2)$$

The reader will find it easy to show that $\nabla \cdot \mathbf{A} + \mu_0\epsilon_0 \, \partial V/\partial t = 0$ in this case if he notes that only $\partial/\partial r$ can give a non-vanishing result in the divergence and that $\boldsymbol{\delta l} \cdot \mathbf{1}_r = \delta l \cos\theta$.

Now let us find the field vectors $\mathbf{E}$ and $\mathbf{B}$. Again using only the $\mathbf{1}_r \, \partial/\partial r$ part of ∇ and noting that $\mathbf{1}_r \times \mathbf{1}_l = -\sin\theta \, \mathbf{1}_\phi$, we have $\nabla \times \mathbf{A} = \mathbf{1}_r \times \mathbf{1}_l \, \partial A/\partial r = -\sin\theta \, \mathbf{1}_\phi \, \partial A/\partial r$, or

$$\mathbf{B} = \frac{\mu_0 j\omega \, \delta l}{4\pi} q_{max} \frac{\partial}{\partial r}\left[\frac{e^{j\omega(t-r/c)}}{r}\right]\mathbf{1}_r \times \mathbf{1}_l$$

$$= \frac{\mu_0 j\omega \, \delta l \, q_{max} \sin\theta}{4\pi}\left[\frac{1}{r^2} + \frac{j\omega}{cr}\right] e^{j\omega(t-r/c)}\mathbf{1}_\phi \qquad (10.5\text{--}3)$$

The first term of this expression is easily seen to be just the magnetic induction calculated by Laplace's rule for steady current elements, eq. 7.4–2. The second arises from the retarded part of the potential and will shortly be seen to involve radiation.

The electric field calculation is more complex. We will have a component parallel to $\boldsymbol{\delta l}$ from $\mathbf{A}$ and θ and r components from $\nabla V = \mathbf{1}_r(\partial V/\partial r) + \mathbf{1}_\theta(\partial V/\partial\theta)(1/r)$:

$$\mathbf{E} = -\frac{\partial \mathbf{A}}{\partial t} - \nabla V = \frac{\mu_0\omega^2 \, q_{max} \, e^{j\omega(t-r/c)}}{4\pi r}\boldsymbol{\delta l}$$

$$-\frac{\delta l \, q_{max} \cos\theta}{4\pi\epsilon_0}\left[-\frac{2}{r^3} - \frac{2j\omega}{cr^2} + \frac{\omega^2}{c^2 r}\right] e^{j\omega(t-r/c)} \, \mathbf{1}_r$$

$$+\frac{\delta l \, q_{max} \sin\theta}{4\pi\epsilon_0 r}\left[\frac{1}{r^2} + \frac{j\omega}{cr}\right] e^{j\omega(t-r/c)} \, \mathbf{1}_\theta$$

We can combine the term in $\boldsymbol{\delta l}$ with the other two if we write $\boldsymbol{\delta l}$ as a sum of vectors along $\mathbf{1}_r$ and $\mathbf{1}_\theta$:

$$\boldsymbol{\delta l} = (\boldsymbol{\delta l} \cdot \mathbf{1}_r)\mathbf{1}_r + (\boldsymbol{\delta l} \cdot \mathbf{1}_\theta)\mathbf{1}_\theta = (\mathbf{1}_r \cos\theta - \mathbf{1}_\theta \sin\theta) \, \delta l$$

as can be seen from Fig. 10.5a. We also need the relation $\mu_0 = 1/c^2\epsilon_0$.
Then **E** becomes

$$\mathbf{E} = \frac{\delta l \, q_{max} \cos \theta}{4\pi\epsilon_0} \left(\frac{2}{r^3} + \frac{2j\omega}{cr^2} \right) e^{j\omega(t-r/c)} \, \mathbf{1}_r$$

$$+ \frac{\delta l \, q_{max} \sin \theta}{4\pi\epsilon_0} \left(\frac{1}{r^3} + \frac{j\omega}{cr^2} - \frac{\omega^2}{c^2r} \right) e^{j\omega(t-r/c)} \, \mathbf{1}_\theta \quad (10.5\text{-}4)$$

It will be noted that the terms involving $1/r^3$ are exactly the static
dipole field expressions, as in eq. 3.1–7. The $1/r$ term is the largest one
at great distances. It is readily seen that this term bears a relation to
the $1/r$ term in **B** exactly like that for plane waves—namely, that $E_\theta/c = B_\phi$.
Furthermore, $E_\theta\mathbf{1}_\theta$ and $B_\phi\mathbf{1}_\phi$ are perpendicular to each other and to $\mathbf{1}_r$
and related so that $\mathbf{E} \times \mathbf{B}$ for these components points outwardly along
$\mathbf{1}_r$. These components comprise the radiation part of the field.

It is interesting to note that the two $\mathbf{1}_r/r$ terms in E_r that come respectively from **A** and V exactly cancel each other, in a similar fashion to the
cancellation of the axial field in the coaxial cable. Curves showing
instantaneous electric lines of force for an oscillating dipole are given in a
number of advanced textbooks.[5]

Let us write the radiation terms of eqs. 10.5–3 and 10.5–4 using the
unit vectors $\mathbf{1}_l$ and $\mathbf{1}_r$:

$$\mathbf{E}_{rad} = \frac{\mu_0\omega^2 q_{max} \, \delta l e^{j\omega(t-r/c)}[(\mathbf{1}_r \times \mathbf{1}_l) \times \mathbf{1}_r]}{4\pi r} \quad (10.5\text{-}5a)$$

$$\mathbf{B}_{rad} = \frac{\mu_0\omega^2 q_{max} \, \delta l e^{j\omega(t-r/c)}(\mathbf{1}_r \times \mathbf{1}_l)}{4\pi cr} \quad (10.5\text{-}5b)$$

where we have used the relations $\sin\theta \, \mathbf{1}_\phi = (\mathbf{1}_l \times \mathbf{1}_r)$ and $\mathbf{1}_\theta = \mathbf{1}_\phi \times \mathbf{1}_r$.

The average Poynting flux for the radiation part of the field is readily
calculated. We cannot use complex notation, since a power calculation
is involved, and so we use the real parts of **E** and **H**. Since the two
quantities are in phase, products of the real parts yield $\cos^2 \omega(t - r/c)$,
a quantity whose time average is $\frac{1}{2}$. We shall assume that q_{max} is a real
number q_{max}. Thus we can write

$$\mathbf{N}_{rad} = \mathbf{E}_{rad} \times \mathbf{H}_{rad} = \left(\frac{\omega^2 q_{max} \, \delta l \sin \theta}{4\pi\epsilon_0} \right)^2 \frac{\cos^2 \omega(t - r/c)}{\mu_0 c^5 r^2} \mathbf{1}_r \quad (10.5\text{-}6)$$

and

$$\mathbf{N}_{rad, \, av} = \frac{\omega^4 q_{max}^2 \, \delta l^2 \sin^2 \theta}{32\pi^2 \mu_0 \epsilon_0^2 c^5 r^2} \mathbf{1}_r \quad (10.5\text{-}7)$$

[5] Eg. W. K. H. Panofsky and M. Phillips, *Classical Electricity and Magnetism*,
Addison-Wesley, Cambridge, Mass., 1955, p. 224.

which yields for the time average of the total energy radiated through a sphere of radius r,

$$P_{av} = \left(\int \mathbf{N} \cdot d\mathbf{S}\right)_{av} = \frac{\omega^4 q_{max}^2 \, \delta l^2}{32\pi^2 \mu_0 \epsilon_0^2 c^5 r^2} \int_0^\pi 2\pi r^2 \sin^3 \theta \, d\theta$$

and since

$$\int_0^\pi \sin^3 \theta \, d\theta = \int_0^\pi (1 - \cos^2 \theta) \sin \theta \, d\theta = \int_{-1}^1 (1 - u^2) \, du = 4/3,$$

$$P_{av} = \frac{\omega^4 q_{max}^2 \, \delta l^2}{12\pi \mu_0 \epsilon_0^2 c^5} = \frac{\mu_0 \omega^4 q_{max}^2 \, \delta l^2}{12\pi c} = \frac{\mu_0 \omega^4 p_{max}^2}{12\pi c} = \frac{\mu_0 \omega^2 i_{max}^2 \, \delta l^2}{12\pi c}$$

$$(10.5\text{--}8)$$

using $\epsilon_0^2 \mu_0^2 = 1/c^4$. We see that the total rate of radiation depends on the fourth power of the frequency for a given amplitude of oscillation of the dipole and as the square of the frequency for a given current amplitude.

The symbol P_{av} represents an average power radiated, so that the coefficient of $\frac{1}{2}i_{max}^2$ represents a resistance. The dipole acts as if it had a resistance, called the "radiation resistance," given by

$$R_{rad} = \mu_0 \omega^2 \, \delta l^2 / 6\pi c = (\delta l/\lambda)^2 (\mu_0 c/6\pi) \qquad (10.5\text{--}9a)$$

$$= (\delta l/\lambda)^2 (2\mu_0 c\pi/3)$$

and since $\mu_0 c = 119.9\pi$ ohms, we have

$$R_{rad} = 79.94\pi^2 (\delta l/\lambda)^2 = 789.0(\delta l/\lambda)^2 \text{ ohms} \qquad (10.5\text{--}9b)$$

We need only to know the ratio of dipole length to wave length to calculate the radiation resistance.

Equation 10.5–6 can be written in another form. It might appear that the equivalent current and dipole variation associated with an oscillating charge of fixed amount q_{max} could be found by substituting $q_{max}v$ for $i \, \delta l$, and taking v to be a simple harmonic expression, calculated as the time derivative of $\delta l \cos \omega t$. Thus we write $q_{max}v$ as $q_{max}\omega \, \delta l \sin \omega t$. Equation 10.5–6 contains $q_{max}\omega^2 \, \delta l \cos \omega t$, which is $q_{max} (dv/dt)$ or $q_{max}a$, where a is the acceleration of the oscillating charge. Thus we can calculate the instantaneous radiation from an oscillating charge in terms of its retarded acceleration:

$$\mathbf{N}_{rad} = \frac{\mu_0 q_{max}^2 a_{ret}^2 \sin^2 \theta}{16\pi^2 c r^2} \mathbf{1}_r \qquad (10.5\text{--}10)$$

with the total instantaneous rate, in all directions:

$$P = \frac{\mu_0 q_{max}^2 a_{ret}^2}{6\pi c} \qquad (10.5\text{--}11)$$

We have only derived these formulas for charges executing SHM, and furthermore, the substitution of $q_{max}v$ for $i\,\delta l$ is not easy to justify rigorously. However, these formulas can be derived by a calculation beyond the scope of this book for any motion of a point charge, as long as its speed is considerably less than c.[6]

The result was of the first importance in the history of atomic physics, for the general result that an accelerated charge must radiate had to be discarded by Niels Bohr in the original form of his famous atomic theory.[7]

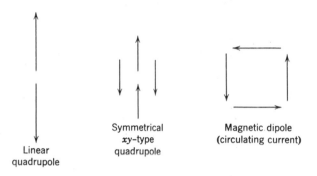

	Symmetrical	Magnetic dipole
Linear	xy-type	(circulating current)
quadrupole	quadrupole	

Fig. 10.5b.   Various quadrupole arrangements.

More complicated forms of radiation than the dipole form just given can be found by the same process used in section 3.3 for multipole static fields. We can consider two equal and opposite radiating dipoles displaced by a vector $\delta l'$ and calculate **A** and **V** by use of the operator $-(\delta l' \cdot \nabla)$, taking care to let the ∇ operate on the r in the retarded sinusoidal factor $e^{j\omega(t-r/c)}$ as well as on the rest of each function. We can then add such quadrupole terms in various ways to represent simple physical cases, as indicated in Fig. 10.5b. The calculations of the resulting radiation are lengthy but involve nothing especially new. The results for the "magnetic dipole" combination indicated in Fig. 10.5b is the expected one that $\mathbf{H}_{rad}$ is given by the same formula as $\mathbf{E}_{rad}$ for the electric dipole case, with ϵ_0 replaced by μ_0 in the denominator, and the magnetic moment $\mu_0 i_{max}S = \mu_0 i_{max}\,\delta l\,\delta l'$ in place of $p_{max} = q_{max}\,\delta l$ in the numerator. It is easy to calculate the rate of radiation for this case. The new $\mathbf{E}_{rad}$ will be $c\mu_0\mathbf{H}_{rad}$ and will thus differ in magnitude from the dipole electric field by a factor $c\mu_0^2(i_{max}\,\delta l\,\delta l'/q_{max}\,\delta l)(\epsilon_0/\mu_0) = \omega\,\delta l'/c = \delta l'/\lambda$, where λ is the reduced wave length of the radiation. Thus we see that

---

[6] This calculation involves finding the so-called Liénard–Wiechert potentials, which give A_{ret} and V_{ret} for a moving point charge. See, e.g., W. K. H. Panofsky and M. Phillips, *op. cit.*, Chapters 18 and 19.

[7] N. Bohr, *Phil. Mag.*, **26**, 1 (1913).

the magnitude of P is reduced by a factor $(\delta l'/\lambda)^2$ which means that for dipoles and current loops that are much smaller in physical dimensions than λ, magnetic dipole radiation is very much weaker than electric dipole radiation.   Electric quadrupole radiation in general will of course be of the same order of intensity as the magnetic dipole variety.   In fact, it is not hard to show that electric 2^n-pole and magnetic 2^{n-1}-pole radiation have P's of the same order of magnitude.   Radiation from atoms or nuclei is called "allowed" if the quantum "jump" corresponds to electric dipole oscillations, "first forbidden" if it corresponds only to electric quadrupole or magnetic dipole, "second forbidden" for electric octupole or magnetic quadrupole, and so forth.

An actual radiating antenna behaves like a dipole only if its length is very small compared to a wave length.   For longer antennas, the analysis is complicated, because the current will not be uniform in the wire.   An antenna wire can in fact have running or standing waves in it, similar to the waves studied in section 10.2.   Such radiating systems must be studied by some analytical or graphical method of summing over elements of the wire's length.

There are numerous methods of getting different patterns of radiated intensity versus direction.   There are two cases that can be readily handled—one in which standing wave patterns are set up on the wires, and the other in which the wires are terminated by the appropriate characteristic impedances so no reflections occur.   The most common example of the first case is the half-wave or doublet antenna—a straight wire $\lambda/2$ in length which is broken in the middle to allow current to enter from the transmitter power circuit.   An example of the second is the so-called rhombic antenna, consisting of four wires in the shape of a rhombus, fed at one corner from the transmitter and terminated properly at the opposite corner.   The reader is referred elsewhere for details of antenna theory.[8]

The last example of radiation we wish to discuss is that of an idealized plane sheet of alternating current.   Suppose that in the x–y plane there is a uniform current in the x-direction (Fig. 10.5c), with a surface current density $\mathbf{J}_S$ given by $\mathbf{J}_S = \mathbf{J}_{S\,max}e^{j\omega t}$; $\mathbf{J}_S$ is so defined that the current in a strip of surface of width Δy is $\mathbf{J}_S\,\Delta y$.   Then at a point $\mathscr{P}$ a height z from the plane, the vector potential will be

$$\mathbf{A} = \frac{\mu_0}{4\pi} \mathbf{J}_{S\,max}\,\mathbf{1}_x \int_{\text{entire plane}} e^{j\omega(t-r/c)}\,dS/r$$

where dS is a unit of area $dx\,dy$ in the plane and r is the distance from dS

[8] An excellent summary is found in G. P. Harnwell, *Principles of Electricity and Electromagnetism*, 2nd ed., McGraw-Hill, New York, 1949, section 16.7.

to $\mathscr{P}$.   Let us use polar coordinates R and ϕ in the plane and choose as elements of area rings of radius R and width dR.   Then $dS = 2\pi R\,dR$. Next, we can change variables and use r in place of R, where $r^2 = R^2 + z^2$. When R goes from 0 to ∞, r goes from z to ∞; furthermore, $2r\,dr = 2R\,dR$. Thus we have

$$\mathbf{A} = \frac{\mu_0 J_{S\,\max}\mathbf{1}_x}{4\pi} \int_z^\infty 2\pi r\,dr\,\frac{e^{j\omega(t-r/c)}}{r} = \frac{\mu_0 J_{S\,\max}\mathbf{1}_x}{2} \int_z^\infty dr\,e^{j\omega(t-r/c)}$$

$$(10.5\text{–}12)$$

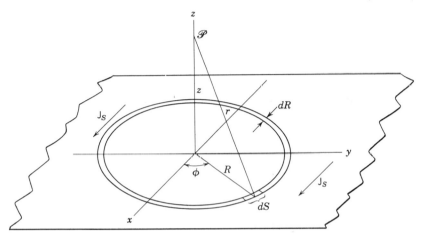

Fig. 10.5c.   A plane radiating sheet.

which gives an undetermined value for the upper limit—we should not be surprised that for an infinite plane the potential involves an uncertain "constant."   We can avoid the difficulty by taking the curl before evaluating the integral.   From plane symmetry and the chosen current direction, we have

$$\mathbf{B} = \operatorname{curl}\mathbf{A} = \frac{\partial A_x}{\partial z}\mathbf{1}_y = \frac{\mu_0 J_{S\,\max}}{2}\mathbf{1}_y\,\frac{\partial}{\partial z}\int_0^\infty R\,dR\,\frac{e^{j\omega(t-r/c)}}{r}$$

As long as we use R as a variable, we can put the derivative inside the integral sign.   Then we have

$$
\begin{aligned}
B_y &= \frac{\mu_0 J_{S\,\max}}{2} \int_0^\infty R\,dR\,\frac{\partial}{\partial z}\left[\frac{e^{j\omega(t-r/c)}}{r}\right] \\
&= \frac{\mu_0 J_{S\,\max}}{2} \int_z^\infty r\,dr\left(\frac{z}{r}\right)\frac{\partial}{\partial r}\left[\frac{e^{j\omega(t-r/c)}}{r}\right] \\
&= \frac{\mu_0 J_{S\,\max}z}{2} \int_z^\infty dr\,\frac{\partial}{\partial r}\left[\frac{e^{j\omega(t-r/c)}}{r}\right] = \frac{\mu_0 J_{S\,\max}z}{2}\left[\frac{e^{j\omega(t-r/c)}}{r}\right]_z^\infty
\end{aligned}
$$

or

$$B_y = -\frac{\mu_0 J_{S\ max}}{2} e^{j\omega(t-z/c)} \tag{10.5-13}$$

Integrating B_y with respect to z, we can find A_x, except for a constant, and thus evaluate the last formula in eq. 10.5-12:

$$A_x = -\frac{j\mu_0 c J_{S\ max}}{2\omega} e^{j\omega(t-z/c)} \tag{10.5-14}$$

from which it is easy to find **E**:

$$\mathbf{E} = E_x \mathbf{1}_x = -\frac{\partial A_x}{\partial t}\mathbf{1}_x = -\tfrac{1}{2}\mu_0 c J_{S\ max}\mathbf{1}_x e^{j\omega(t-z/c)} \tag{10.5-15}$$

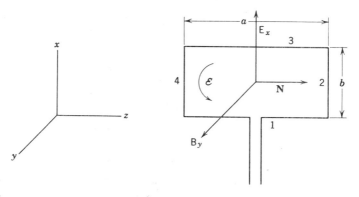

Fig. 10.5d. A loop receiving antenna.

which has the magnitude of $c\mathbf{B}$ and is so oriented that

$$\mathbf{E} \times \mathbf{H} = \tfrac{1}{4}\mu_0 J_{S\ max}{}^2 \mathbf{1}_z e^{2j\omega(t-r/c)}$$

represents radiation along the z direction.

It will be observed that a plane sheet of current will radiate symmetrically on both sides, just as a plane sheet of static charge produces a field on both sides. If a conductor is present, there will be other currents present that affect the field inside the conducting material (see section 10.6).

Let us now consider the reception of electromagnetic radiation. A simple type of receiving antenna is a plane loop. Figure 10.5d shows a rectangular loop arranged to receive energy from a plane wave like that just discussed. The wave is shown as traveling in the z-direction, with electric field along x given by $E_x = E_{x\ max}e^{j\omega(t-z/c)}$ and the magnetic field by $B_y = E_{x \, max} e^{j\omega(t-r/c)}/c$. We can calculate the emf induced in the loop by finding the flux through it, or by using $\mathbf{A}$:

$$\mathcal{E} = -\frac{d\Phi}{dt} = -\frac{d}{dt}\int_s B_y \, dS = -\frac{1}{c}\frac{d}{dt}\int_{z_4}^{z_2} E_{x \, max} e^{j\omega(t-z/c)} b \, dz$$

$$= b\frac{d}{dt}\frac{E_{x \, max}}{j\omega}[e^{j\omega(t-z_2/c)} - e^{j\omega(t-z_4/c)}] \qquad (10.5\text{–}16)$$

$$= bE_{x \, max}[e^{j\omega(t-z_2/c)} - e^{j\omega(t-z_4c)}]$$

where the limits of integration refer to the values of z at sides 4 and 2. We also have

$$\mathcal{E} = -\frac{d}{dt}\int_{boundary} \mathbf{A}\cdot d\mathbf{l} = \int_{boundary} \mathbf{E}\cdot d\mathbf{l} = b[E_x(z_2) - E_x(z_4)]$$

as another way of getting the same result. The electric and magnetic fields in an electromagnetic wave should be considered as two aspects of the same entity, since not only are they each derivable from $\mathbf{A}$ (in the plane-wave case), but either can be used to calculate the emf. (If this connection were not made clear, one might be tempted fallaciously to calculate the emf in both ways and add the results.)

It is interesting to calculate the emf induced in a length $\delta \mathbf{l}_1$ of a receiving antenna by dipole radiation, using the electric field given by eq. 10.5–5a. We have

$$d\mathcal{E} = \mathbf{E}\cdot\delta\mathbf{l}_1 = \mu_0\omega^2 q_{max} e^{j\omega(t-r/c)}[(\mathbf{1}_r \times \delta\mathbf{l}) \times \mathbf{1}_r]\cdot\delta\mathbf{l}_1/4\pi r$$

$$= \frac{\mu_0\omega^2 q_{max}}{4\pi r} e^{j\omega(t-r/c)}(\mathbf{1}_r \times \delta\mathbf{l})\cdot(\mathbf{1}_r \times \delta\mathbf{l}_1) \qquad (10.5\text{–}17)$$

This formula is symmetric in $\delta\mathbf{l}$ and $\delta\mathbf{l}_1$ and shows that the effectiveness of a given receiving antenna with respect to radiation from a given transmitter must be given by the same integrations over eq. 10.5–17 as the effectiveness for transmission when the antenna roles are reversed. That is, various antennas for a given transmitter will operate as receivers in proportion to their abilities to transmit, so that studies of antenna radiation can be taken over for receivers.

Problem 10.5a. Find by the method outlined in the text the fields produced by a sinusoidally oscillating quadrupole composed of two equal and opposite dipoles with $\delta\mathbf{l} = \mathbf{1}_z \, \delta l$ and $\delta\mathbf{l}' = \mathbf{1}_z \, \delta l'$.

Problem 10.5b. Find the radiation field of a rectangular-current magnetic dipole by adding quadrupole fields due to (a) dipoles with $\delta\mathbf{l} = \mathbf{1}_z \, \delta l$ separated by $\delta\mathbf{l}' = \mathbf{1}_y \, \delta l$ and (b) dipoles with $\delta\mathbf{l} = -\mathbf{1}_y \, \delta l$ separated by $\delta\mathbf{l}' = \mathbf{1}_z \, \delta l$. Take the magnetic moment to be $\mathbf{p}_m = \mu_0 i_{max} e^{j\omega t} \delta l^2 \mathbf{1}_x$.

10.6   Application to Physical Optics

We wish in this section to give a brief introduction to the treatment of physical optics by means of electromagnetic-radiation theory. Let us first consider plane waves approaching a plane conductor of very small resistivity in the x–y plane, at normal incidence (in the $+z$-direction). The emf induced by the wave in the conductor will at any instant be the same everywhere and will induce a very large current because of the high conductivity.   This current will then reradiate a field of its own, as we saw in the last section.   Rather than calculate the induced J_S and then the resultant field, we can find the field easily by assuming the ideal case of zero resistivity.   The reradiated field must cancel exactly the oncoming field within the metal, for any finite field would produce an infinite current. This allows us to determine J_S, if we wish, and more important to find the reradiated field on the outside of the metal.   If the original wave is characterized by, say,

$$\left.\begin{aligned} E_x &= f(t - z/c) \\ B_y &= \frac{1}{c} f(t - z/c) \end{aligned}\right\} \text{original wave} \qquad (10.6\text{–}1)$$

then the reradiated wave inside the metal (for $z > 0$) must be

$$\left.\begin{aligned} E_x &= -f(t - z/c) \\ B_y &= -\frac{1}{c} f(t - z/c) \end{aligned}\right\} \begin{aligned} &\text{reradiated wave,} \\ &z > 0 \end{aligned} \qquad (10.6\text{–}2)$$

For $z < 0$, we must have the appropriately symmetrical reradiated wave. $\partial A_x/\partial t$ must be the same at points (x, y, z) and $(x, y, -z)$, but $\partial A_x/\partial z$ must have opposite sign, for it will be seen in the calculation of the last section that the absolute value of z has to be used.   Thus B_y changes its sign as we go through the plane, as indeed it must if $\mathbf{N}$ is to be directed away from the plane on each side.   Thus we have

$$\left.\begin{aligned} E_x &= -f(t + z/c) \\ B_y &= \frac{1}{c} f(t + z/c) \end{aligned}\right\} \begin{aligned} &\text{reradiated wave,} \\ &z < 0 \end{aligned} \qquad (10.6\text{–}3)$$

We have thus a reflected wave and have accounted in detail for the reflection of light at normal incidence by a metallic surface.   Note in particular that the sum of the two waves just outside the surface gives $E_x = 0$ and $B_y = 2f(t)/c$.   The reflected wave reduces the electric field to zero at the surface of the metal as well as in its interior.

Now consider a plane wave heading for the surface at some angle with the normal, given by functions like eq. 10.3–7, namely,

$$F(t - \mathbf{r} \cdot \mathbf{1}_u/c)$$

where $\mathbf{1}_u$ represents a certain unit vector making an angle θ, say, with the normal. This function F might represent the component of $\mathbf{E}$ perpendicular to a plane containing $\mathbf{1}_u$ and the surface normal or a component in this plane or in some intermediate direction. The surface currents will be more complicated than previously, having certain particular phase

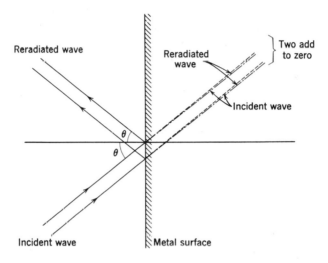

Fig. 10.6a. Proving the law of reflection by symmetry.

variations over the surface (which are actually not hard to calculate). The simplest fact about them is that they will radiate a field inside the metal which exactly cancels the initial wave there and hence by symmetry with respect to the surface plane will radiate a wave on the same side of the normal at the angle θ in the same plane as the incident wave but on the opposite side, thus demonstrating the optical law of reflection (Fig. 10.6a).

Now let us consider radiation incident on an isotropic dielectric medium with, possibly, magnetic properties. We shall assume that ϵ and μ are meaningful constants—in particular that they are evaluated for the frequency or range of frequencies we are considering. At the boundary of the medium (we take a plane again) there will be induced polarization charges and magnetic poles which oscillate at the frequency of the incident radiation and thus will also produce reradiated waves. However, polarization and magnetization will appear throughout the medium, so that the situation is not nearly so simple as for the ideal conductor. In fact, the change of velocity from $c = (\mu_0 \epsilon_0)^{-\frac{1}{2}}$ to $v = (\mu \epsilon)^{-\frac{1}{2}}$ inside the material can be attributed to a continuous reradiation process. Detailed calculations based on this notion lead in fact to theories of dispersion (meaning the variation of v with ω).

Hence we shall use here only the method of boundary conditions. We know that the tangential components of H and E are continuous across the boundary, as are the normal components of B and D. If we have an incident plane wave of effectively infinite extent, we can be sure that the reradiated waves on both sides will be plane waves. Because of different velocities on both sides, we can no longer expect symmetry, and in fact we expect the phase variations in P_n and P_{inn} along the surface as a function of time to radiate waves at different angles in the two media.

Without going into detail concerning the directions of the electric and magnetic vectors, we can assert for instance that the function representing the tangential components of E must satisfy the boundary condition mentioned above. Thus if we represent the incident wave by $F_{in}[t - (\mathbf{r} \cdot \mathbf{1}_u)/c]$, the other waves must involve the same function F_{in} so that the boundary condition will be satisfied at all times. Let us choose $\mathbf{1}_u$ so that it has just x and z components: $\mathbf{1}_u = u_x \mathbf{1}_x + u_z \mathbf{1}_z$, where $u_x^2 + u_z^2 = 1$. Then the incident wave is $F_{in}[t - (xu_x + zu_z)/c]$ and at the boundary ($z = 0$) we will have $F_{in}[t - xu_x/c]$. The reflected wave must vary in the same way over the surface, that is with x, and so for this reason also it must be proportional to F_{in}. The refracted wave which travels at velocity v must also be proportional to F_{in} on the boundary.

From these statements, we can find the form of the $\mathbf{r} \cdot \mathbf{1}_u/v$ terms in the reflected and refracted wave functions. There can be no y dependence for either function. The reflected wave travels at the speed c, and the requirements that the term be xu_x/c when $z = 0$, that the wave travel in the $-z$-direction, and that $u_x^2 + u_z^2 = 1$ lead to the form $(xu_x - zu_z)/c$.

The refracted wave travels at speed v. Calling the new unit vector $\mathbf{u}'$, we have within the material the term $(xu'_x + zu'_z)/v$; the condition at the boundary yields $u'_x/v = u_x/c$, and u'_z can be found if we wish from $u'_z = (1 - u'^2_x)^{\frac{1}{2}}$. Since $\mathbf{1}_u$ and $\mathbf{1}'_u$ are unit vectors, we see from Fig. 10.6b, which shows the x–z plane, that $u_x = \sin \theta$ and $u'_x = \sin \theta'$, leading us directly to Snell's law for refraction:

$$\sin \theta' / \sin \theta = v/c = 1/n \qquad (10.6\text{–}4)$$

where n is c/v, a number greater than unity called the "index of refraction." Note that we do not need the form of $F(t)$ to prove Snell's law, although the frequency enters into the value of v.

In terms of F_{in} given above, we can write expressions for the reflected and refracted waves:

$$F_{refl} = k_1 F_{in}[t - (xu_x - zu_z)/c] \qquad (10.6\text{--}5)$$

$$F_{refr} = k_2 F_{in}[t - (xu'_x + zu'_z)/v] \qquad (10.6\text{--}6)$$

where k_1 and k_2 are constants that determine the phases and amplitudes of the waves. The condition that the tangential components of **E** at the boundary are the same on the two sides leads to the equation

$$k_1 + 1 = k_2 \qquad (10.6\text{--}7)$$

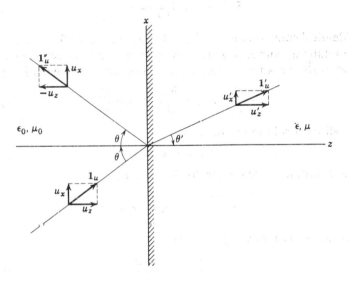

Fig. 10.6b.   Illustrating plane radiation incident on a plane piece of dielectric.

Detailed calculation of the intensities of reflected and refracted waves in their dependence on the angle θ and the directions of **E** and **H** involves writing similar equations for the other components, leading to Fresnel's equations, Brewster's law, the study of polarization of light by reflection, etc. The reader is referred elsewhere for these calculations.[9] Optical-polarization phenomena can be quite well explained by the directional relations of **E**, **B**, and **N**, together with the refractive properties of crystalline substances.

[9] Harnwell, *op. cit.*, section 16.3. Panofsky and Phillips, *op. cit.*, pp. 176–181. R. M. Whitmer, *Electromagnetics*, Prentice-Hall, Englewood Cliffs, 1952, Chapter 12; L. Page and N. I. Adams, Jr., *Principles of Electricity*, 3rd ed. D. Van Nostrand, Princeton, 1958, section 137; B. Rossi, *Optics*, Addison-Wesley, Cambridge, 1957.

The Penetration of Fields Into Conductors. Let us now consider briefly how to treat a conductor with a finite conductivity and also, perhaps, appreciable paramagnetism. We shall follow the treatment of section 10.3. Equation 10.3–1c is the only one of eqs. 10.3–1 that needs modifying. We write in place of it, using Ohm's law:

$$\nabla \times \mathbf{B} = \mu \nabla \times \mathbf{H} = \mu\epsilon_0 \frac{\partial \mathbf{E}}{\partial t} + \mu \mathbf{J} = \mu\epsilon_0 \frac{\partial \mathbf{E}}{\partial t} + \mu\sigma\mathbf{E} \quad (10.6\text{–}8)$$

Then when we calculate **curl curl E** and need $\partial(\text{curl } \mathbf{B})/\partial t$, we use eq. 10.6–8 and obtain in place of eq. 10.3–2

$$\nabla^2\mathbf{E} = \mu\epsilon_0 \frac{\partial^2 \mathbf{E}}{\partial t^2} + \mu\sigma \frac{\partial \mathbf{E}}{\partial t} \quad (10.6\text{–}9)$$

The identical equation can readily be found to hold for **B**. Let us consider plane solutions, with $\mathbf{E} = E_x\mathbf{1}_x$, varying only in the z-direction and in time, and let us see if a wave solution exists. The differential equation becomes

$$\frac{\partial^2 E_x}{\partial z^2} = \mu\epsilon_0 \frac{\partial^2 E_x}{\partial t^2} + \mu\sigma \frac{\partial E_x}{\partial t} \quad (10.6\text{–}10)$$

We shall try a solution of the form

$$E_x = E_m e^{j\omega(t - z/v')} \quad (10.6\text{–}11)$$

On substitution, we find after dividing out E_x

$$-\frac{\omega^2}{v'^2} = -\mu\epsilon_0\omega^2 + j\omega\mu\sigma$$

which can be written using $v = (\mu\epsilon_0)^{-\frac{1}{2}}$

$$\frac{v^2}{v'^2} = 1 - \frac{j\sigma}{\omega\epsilon_0} \quad (10.6\text{–}12)$$

which shows that such a solution exists, but that v' is not a real number. Now, we saw in section 5.8 that the relaxation time of a conductor is ϵ_0/σ (it is ϵ/σ if there is an appreciable molecular polarization in the conductor) and is of the order of 10^{-19} sec for many conductors. Therefore for frequencies of visible light (about 6×10^{14} sec^{-1}) $\sigma/\omega\epsilon_0$ is enormous compared to 1, and we can neglect the latter. Since

$$(-j)^{\frac{1}{2}} = (e^{3\pi j/2})^{\frac{1}{2}} = \pm e^{3\pi j/4} = \pm(j - 1)/2^{\frac{1}{2}}$$

we can write

$$\frac{1}{v'} = \pm\frac{1}{v}\left(\frac{\sigma}{2\omega\epsilon_0}\right)^{\frac{1}{2}}(j - 1) = \pm\left(\frac{\mu\sigma}{2\omega}\right)^{\frac{1}{2}}(j - 1) \quad (10.6\text{–}13)$$

Since $\sigma/\omega\epsilon_0$ is a very large number, we see that the magnitude of v' is very much less than v. Let us choose the negative sign in front so that

v' will have a positive real part. We can then finally write for E_x the expression

$$E_x = E_m e^{-z(\mu\omega\sigma/2)^{\frac{1}{2}}} e^{j\omega[t - z(\mu\sigma/2\omega)]^{\frac{1}{2}}} \tag{10.6-14}$$

The relation between E_x and B_y will be just as in section 10.3 since we can derive it from eq. 10.3-1d which is still valid. Therefore in the conductor we will have

$$B_y = E_x/v' \tag{10.6-15}$$

Now let us consider the boundary conditions for oncoming plane waves normal to a metal surface, using subscripts i, r, and t for the amplitudes of incident, reflected, and transmitted waves, we have

$$E_i + E_r = E_t \tag{10.6-16a}$$

$$H_i + H_r = H_t \tag{10.6-16b}$$

but $H_i = E_i/\mu_0 c$; $H_r = -E_r/\mu_0 c$; and $H_t = E_t/\mu v'$. Thus we get from eq. 10.6-16b

$$E_i - E_r = \frac{\mu_0 c}{\mu v'} E_t \tag{10.6-16c}$$

Adding eqs. 10.6-16a and 10.6-16c we get

$$E_t = \frac{2\mu v'}{\mu_0 c} E_i$$

which shows that E_t is very small compared to E_i, since at high frequencies μ/μ_0 cannot be very large, and v'/c is very small. Thus nearly all the energy is reflected, and the wave inside the metal is small at the boundary. The factor $e^{-z(\mu\omega\sigma/2)^{\frac{1}{2}}}$ in eq. 10.6-14 makes E_x fall off exponentially with increasing depth. The constant δ defined by

$$\delta = (2/\mu\omega\sigma)^{\frac{1}{2}} \tag{10.6-17}$$

is the depth at which the amplitude of E_x has fallen to $1/e$ of its value just inside the boundary and is called the "skin depth." (Cf. discussion of the skin effect in section 7.11.)[10] It gives a measure of the accuracy of our idealized boundary condition which says that the field does not penetrate the conductor at all.

The optical phenomena of diffraction and interference can also be explained by the electromagnetic theory of light, but not in an as elementary a way as can reflection, refraction, and optical polarization. The

[10] Also cf. H. H. Skilling, *Fundamentals of Electric Waves*, 2nd ed., John Wiley, New York, 1948, pp. 125-130 and 130-145, and Harnwell, *op. cit.*, pp. 340-343 and 584-587.

problem has been solved through certain general theorems that relate the field at an arbitrary point $\mathscr{P}$ to certain integrals of the field over an arbitrary surface surrounding $\mathscr{P}$ and that serve to justify Huygens' principle in optics. This principle states that we can treat any wave front as a surface distribution of infinitesimal sources radiating in phase to produce a wave front by constructive interference. It nevertheless is difficult to calculate diffraction patterns rigorously except for certain special cases.[11]

Problem 10.6a. Find the amplitudes of reflected and refracted waves when plane waves are incident at angle θ on a plane piece of dielectric, with the electric vector perpendicular to the plane containing the wave vector and the surface normal.

Problem 10.6b. Solve problem 10.6a, when E lies *in* the plane mentioned.

Problem 10.6c. Write δ in eq. 10.6–17 in terms of the vacuum wave length λ of the incident waves, and find it for (a) copper ($\mu_r = 1$, $\sigma = 5.80 \times 10^7$ mhos/m) and (b) iron ($\mu_r = 600$, $\sigma = 1.00 \times 10^7$ mhos/m) for wave lengths of 100 m, 1 m, 0.1 mm, and 5×10^{-5} cm.

Problem 10.6d. Find the "skin-depth" for sea water, with $\rho = 0.20$ m-ohm, for frequencies of 30 kilocycles and 30 megacycles. How practical is radio communication with submarines?

10.7 Radiation in Pipes and Cavities

Wave guides in the form of rectangular and cylindrical pipes are in common use for high-frequency radiation. In this section we give a brief introduction to their properties.

Let us first see how we can have a plane electromagnetic wave that is restricted in extent by ideal conducting planes. If we consider a wave traveling in the z-direction with E_x and B_y components only, we cannot place conducting planes parallel to E without violating the boundary conditions discussed in the last section. We can, however, introduce planes normal to E, which will then have surface charges induced on them as in the coaxial-line case. Thus we can restrict a plane wave between two planes which must be of infinite extent as shown in Fig. 10.7a, but cannot restrict it between four.

The boundary condition for B needs further study. Inside an ideal resistanceless conductor, currents will always flow so as to cancel completely any external magnetic field. Thus B will be zero in the conductor. Since however the normal component of B is continuous across any boundary, B_n will be zero just outside the metal, and there can only be a tangential component there. The discontinuity in the latter will be

[11] J. A. Stratton, *Electromagnetic Theory*, McGraw-Hill, New York, 1941, pp. 460–470 and 570; P. M. Morse and H. Feshbach, *Methods of Theoretical Physics*, McGraw-Hill, New York, 1953, Vol. I., pp. 847–848.

produced by surface currents, whose amount J_S per unit width of surface can be found from the circuital form of Ampère's law.   A suitable path is shown in Fig. 10.7a.   If its length parallel to B_y in the figure is one unit, and its x-dimension is negligible, we have immediately (cf. problem 7.5h)

$$\mu_0 i = \oint \mathbf{B} \cdot \mathbf{dl} = B_y = \mu_0 J_S \qquad (10.7\text{--}1)$$

Just as in the coaxial-line case, the resulting current will be found to account exactly for the changing charge density on which the electric flux begins and ends.

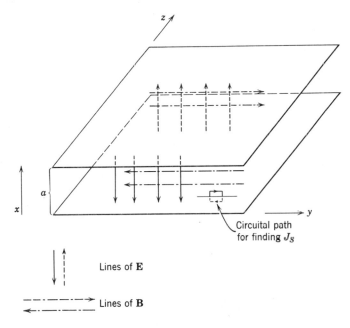

Fig. 10.7a.   A plane wave restricted between two infinite planes.

If we are to have a wave enclosed between four walls in a rectangular pipe, we must have a more complicated field than the plane-wave type. Let us show by an example how one can be constructed.   If, in Fig. 10.7a, E_x varied with y so that it was zero at two places, say $y = 0$ and $y = b$, and remained zero at these y values for all z and all t, then a pair of planes perpendicular to the y-axis could be inserted without violating the boundary condition on **E**.

It would, however, then be necessary to have B_y equal to zero at the same planes.   Since the lines of **B** have no ends, they must turn out of the y-direction.   If the pattern of Fig. 10.7a is not to be modified too drastically, they must bend into the z-direction and in fact surround lines of **E**. Since there will then be components of **B** along the direction of travel of the wave, it would not be amiss to wonder if the speed of these waves is still c, and in fact we will find that it is not.

To put some of these ideas into mathematical form, let us assume that E_x is the product of a sinusoidal traveling wave $\sin(\omega t - z/\lambda)$ and a simple function that vanishes for $y = 0$ and $y = b$; the function $\sin(\pi y/b)$ is a good example to try. (A product is needed, for the vanishing at $y = 0$ and $y = b$ must be independent of values of t and z.) We will expect to find a similar expression for B_y but will not need to assume a form for it in advance. We can write then

$$\left. \begin{aligned} E_x &= C \sin \frac{\pi y}{b} \sin \left(\omega t - \frac{z}{\lambda} \right) \\[2mm] E_y &= 0 \\[2mm] E_z &= 0 \end{aligned} \right\} \qquad (10.7\text{--}2)$$

Note that **E** does not depend on the value of a, the separation of the y–z boundary planes. Substitution in the wave equation $\nabla^2 E_x = c^{-2}\, \partial^2 E_x/\partial t^2$ then gives (dividing out $-E_x$)

$$\frac{\pi^2}{b^2} + \frac{1}{\lambda^2} = \frac{\omega^2}{c^2} \qquad (10.7\text{--}3a)$$

or using $\lambdabar = \lambda/2\pi$ and $\omega = 2\pi f$, and the free-space wave length $\lambda_0 = c/f$,

$$\frac{1}{4b^2} + \frac{1}{\lambda^2} = \frac{f^2}{c^2} = \frac{1}{\lambda_0^2} \qquad (10.7\text{--}3b)$$

Furthermore, writing the velocity of the waves in the pipe (the so-called "phase velocity") as $v = f\lambda = \omega\lambdabar$, we have

$$v^2 = \left[\frac{1}{c^2} - \frac{1}{4b^2 f^2} \right]^{-1} = \frac{4b^2 f^2 c^2}{4b^2 f^2 - c^2} = c^2 + \frac{c^4}{4b^2 f^2 - c^2} \qquad (10.7\text{--}4)$$

which can yield a real velocity only if v^2 is positive or

$$f > \frac{c}{2b} \qquad (10.7\text{--}5)$$

so that a field of the sort we are seeking can only exist for frequencies above a certain lower limit. Since $c = f\lambda_0$, we see that the free-space wave length λ_0 must be less than $2b$. We shall shortly give a geometrical justification for this cutoff.

Let us now find the components of **B**.   We have from curl $\mathbf{E} = -\partial\mathbf{B}/\partial t$,

$$-\frac{\partial B_x}{\partial t} = \frac{\partial E_z}{\partial y} - \frac{\partial E_y}{\partial z} \equiv 0$$

$$-\frac{\partial B_y}{\partial t} = \frac{\partial E_x}{\partial z} = -\frac{C}{\lambda}\sin\frac{\pi y}{b}\cos\left(\omega t - \frac{z}{\lambda}\right)$$

$$-\frac{\partial B_z}{\partial t} = -\frac{\partial E_x}{\partial y} = -\frac{C\pi}{b}\cos\frac{\pi y}{b}\sin\left(\omega t - \frac{z}{\lambda}\right)$$

Fig. 10.7b.   Field lines for a TE$_{0,1}$ mode in a rectangular wave guide, for $t = 0$. (Taken from H. H. Skilling, *Fundamentals of Electric Waves*, 2nd ed., John Wiley, New York, 1948, p. 200, Fig. 74, modified.)

from which on integration and setting of constants equal to zero we find

$$B_x = 0$$

$$B_y = \frac{C}{\lambda\omega}\sin\frac{\pi y}{b}\sin\left(\omega t - \frac{z}{\lambda}\right) \qquad (10.7\text{-}6)$$

$$B_z = -\frac{C\pi}{b\omega}\cos\frac{\pi y}{b}\cos\left(\omega t - \frac{z}{\lambda}\right)$$

Let us see how the magnetic lines of force are curved.   The ratio B_z/B_y will give their slope in the z–y plane.   This ratio is

$$\frac{B_z}{B_y} = -\frac{\pi\lambda}{b}\cot\frac{\pi y}{b}\cot\left(\omega t - \frac{z}{\lambda}\right) \qquad (10.7\text{-}7)$$

For, say, $t = 0$, we have the result that for $z = 0$ and $z = \pi\lambda$, the ratio is infinite, so all lines for these values of z are in the z-direction; for

$z = \pm \pi \lambda/2$, the ratio is zero and the lines are in the y-direction. For intermediate values of z, we can conclude from the factor $\cot(\pi y/b)$ that for $y = 0$ and $y = b$ the lines again are in the z-direction, whereas for $y = b/2$ they are in the y-direction. The result is evidently as shown in Fig. 10.7b.

Now, let us examine the velocity formula 10.7–4 a bit further. It is evident that, besides being dependent on the frequency, v is greater than c. This seems to contradict the well-established principle of relativity, and needs further investigation. We begin by using some elementary trigonometry to rewrite eqs. 10.7–2 and 10.7–6. Using the formulas for $\cos(a \pm b)$, we have

$$\left.\begin{aligned}
E_x &= \frac{C}{2}\left[\cos\left(\omega t - \frac{z}{\lambda} - \frac{\pi y}{b}\right) - \cos\left(\omega t - \frac{z}{\lambda} + \frac{\pi y}{b}\right)\right] \\
E_y &= 0 \\
E_z &= 0
\end{aligned}\right\} \qquad (10.7\text{–}8)$$

$$B_x = 0$$

$$B_y = \frac{C}{2\lambda\omega}\left[\cos\left(\omega t - \frac{z}{\lambda} - \frac{\pi y}{b}\right) - \cos\left(\omega t - \frac{z}{\lambda} + \frac{\pi y}{b}\right)\right]$$

$$B_z = -\frac{C\pi}{2b\omega}\left[\cos\left(\omega t - \frac{z}{\lambda} - \frac{\pi y}{b}\right) + \cos\left(\omega t - \frac{z}{\lambda} + \frac{\pi y}{b}\right)\right] \qquad (10.7\text{–}9)$$

We have resolved our simple wave into two of a more familiar variety, namely sinusoidal waves of the form 10.3–7. Comparing the expression $\omega t - (z/\lambda) \pm (\pi y/b)$ with $\omega(t - \mathbf{r} \cdot \mathbf{1}_u/c)$ we find that the vector corresponding to $\mathbf{1}_u/c$ has components 0, $\mp(\pi/b\omega)$, and $1/\lambda\omega$ and magnitude given by

$$\left[\frac{\pi^2}{b^2\omega^2} + \frac{1}{\lambda^2\omega^2}\right]^{\frac{1}{2}} = \frac{1}{c} \qquad (10.7\text{–}10)$$

by use of eq. 10.7–3a. Hence each of the two component waves travels with the velocity c; the vector $\mathbf{1}_u$ has components

$$u_x = 0; \qquad u_y = \pm\frac{\pi c}{b\omega} = \frac{\lambda_0}{2b}; \qquad u_z = \frac{c}{\lambda\omega} = (1 - u_y{}^2)^{\frac{1}{2}} = \left[1 - \left(\frac{\lambda_0}{2b}\right)^2\right]^{\frac{1}{2}}$$

$$(10.7\text{–}11)$$

Our new waves therefore travel along lines in the y–z plane, making angles α with the z-axis given by

$$\cot\alpha = \frac{u_z}{u_y} = \frac{2b}{\lambda_0}[1 - (\lambda_0/2b)^2]^{\frac{1}{2}} \qquad (10.7\text{–}12)$$

The effective reduced wave length λ_e of these waves is given by

$$\lambda_e = \frac{\omega}{c} = \left[\frac{\pi^2}{b^2} + \frac{1}{\lambda^2}\right]^{\frac{1}{2}} \tag{10.7-13}$$

These waves do not travel straight down the pipe but criss-cross back and forth. At each reflection the waves with the plus and minus signs must exchange places, in accordance with our study of reflection in the previous section. Figure 10.7c illustrates the two waves in their zigzag behavior.

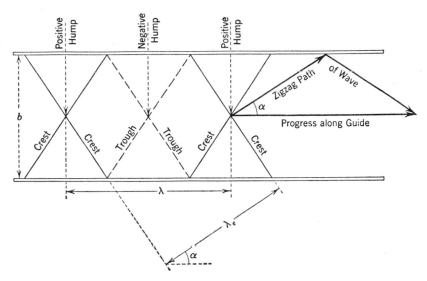

Fig. 10.7c.   The zigzag passage of plane waves down a pipe.
(Taken from Skilling, *op. cit.*, Fig. 75).

The meaning of the cutoff for free-space wave length equal to $2b$ becomes clear from eq. 10.7–12. At this wave length $\cot \alpha = 0$ and the waves reflect back and forth in the y-direction without traveling down the tube at all. The meaning of the phase velocity greater than c for the resultant of the two reflected waves is that the positions where constructive interference occurs travel at this speed (see Fig. 10.7d).

Note that the phase velocity v depends on the frequency. If any actual pulse or finite wave train is introduced into the wave guide, the analysis of section 9.8 shows that it must always contain effectively a series of wave lengths. We wish to show that the velocity of such pulses of energy down the pipe is always less than c. Consider two signals of frequencies f and $f + \Delta f$. They will reflect back and forth at different angles and have different velocities, v and $v + \Delta v$, and wave lengths, λ and $\lambda + \Delta\lambda$.

Fig. 10.7d. The velocity of a wave in a pipe is the velocity of points of constructive interference. (Taken from Skilling, *op. cit.*, Fig. 76.)

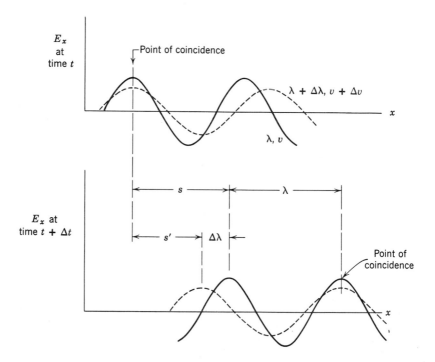

Fig. 10.7e. Two waves whose coincidence point moves forward. The ratio $\Delta v/\Delta \lambda$ is negative in this diagram but is positive for electromagnetic waves in pipes.

Figure 10.7e shows a graph of, say, the resultant E_x plotted along the z-axis, at a time t and at a time $t + \Delta t$. At t, two particular crests coincide, and at $t + \Delta t$, the next two coincide. In this figure, Δv is clearly negative. In time Δt, the solid-line wave travels a distance $s = v \, \Delta t$ and the dashed wave $s' = (v + \Delta v) \, \Delta t$. The difference $s' - s$ is $-\Delta\lambda$, as shown in the figure:

$$s' - s = \Delta v \, \Delta t = -\Delta\lambda$$

so that

$$\Delta t = -\Delta\lambda/\Delta v$$

The "point of coincidence" has traveled a distance $s + \lambda$. Denoting the velocity of this "point" by v_g, we have

$$v_g \, \Delta t = s + \lambda$$

or

$$v_g = \frac{v \, \Delta t + \lambda}{\Delta t} = v - \lambda \frac{\Delta v}{\Delta\lambda}$$

Now, if we consider a group of waves of nearly equal characteristics in which v is a continuous function of λ, the ratio $\Delta v/\Delta\lambda$ can be taken as the derivative $dv/d\lambda$. The "point of coincidence" for the group of waves becomes the place of maximum constructive interference—i.e., the center of the pulse—and the speed v_g becomes the pulse speed, generally called the group velocity. We have then

$$v_g = v - \lambda \frac{dv}{d\lambda} = \lambda f - \lambda \frac{d(\lambda f)}{d\lambda} = -\lambda^2 \frac{df}{d\lambda} = \frac{df}{d(1/\lambda)} = \frac{d\omega}{d(1/\lambda)}$$

$$(10.7\ 13)$$

From eq. 10.7–3 we find

$$v_g = (c/\lambda)\left[\frac{\pi^2}{b^2} + \frac{1}{\lambda^2}\right]^{-\frac{1}{2}} = \frac{c^2}{\omega\lambda} = \frac{c^2}{v} \qquad (10.7\text{–}14)$$

which says that when $v > c$, $v_g < c$, so that all pulses and in fact all communications travel with a velocity less than that of light. The values of λ, ω, and v used in calculating v_g must of course be the average or central values for the pulse. A pulse with a wide range of ω's and v's will consequently have a spread of v_g's and must spread out and become distorted as it travels.

We have described thus far only one arrangement or mode of wave propagation in rectangular pipes. There are many possible modes, which we shall only briefly describe. If E_x varies sinusoidally in y in such a way as to vanish one or more times between the walls, the resulting field will have a pattern like two or more of the kind just described, compressed in the y-direction and placed side by side.   We can also have the electric field only in the y-direction, with one or more "repeats" of our standard pattern.   And we can have any combination of these patterns based on E_x and on E_y.   All such patterns are called "transverse electric" modes and are designated by the symbols $TE_{m,n}$ where m and n tell the number of half-cycles of E_y-pattern there are between the x boundaries and vice versa.   The mode we have described is a $TE_{0,1}$ mode, and is called the dominant mode (in case $b > a$) for it has the lowest cutoff frequency.

We can also have a purely transverse magnetic field.   Since, however, the magnetic lines cannot end, we must start patterns in the x–y plane involving closed loops like those for the magnetic lines in the y–z plane of Fig. 10.7b.   The electric lines will curve around the magnetic lines, as well as beginning and ending on the metal surface.   We can then have, for instance, an array of $m \times n$ such patterns, where m and n are any two integers, giving us the transverse magnetic or $TM_{m,n}$ modes.   Figure 10.7f shows the field patterns for the $TM_{1,1}$ and $TE_{1,1}$ modes.

In cylindrical pipes there can also exist a series of TE and TM modes.   Their mathematical description involves the use of Bessel functions, and we shall not attempt it here.   For details on these modes as well as the rectangular ones, the reader is referred elsewhere.[12]   The mode of propagation in the coaxial line described in section 10.2 can be called a TEM mode (transverse electric and magnetic fields).   TE and TM modes can also exist in coaxial cables but are usually avoided by operating below the cutoff frequency (the TEM mode has no cutoff, as is evident from the derivation in section 10.2).

The introduction of radiation into a wave guide in a particular mode can be affected by using a small "antenna" in the form of a loop or probe or combination of such elements arranged to produce a field of approximately the same pattern as that desired.   Reception can be made with the same sort of elements.   The radiation can also be allowed to leave the open end of the pipe and travel in free space.   However, a simple open end will, like a coaxial cable, reflect a good deal of energy, so that radiating ends should be "matched" to free space with suitable horn shapes.

Bends, corners, and junctions used in wave-guide "plumbing" must be carefully designed to allow the desired mode to pass through and prevent the excitation of others.

We have neglected the effect of finite conductivity of the metal sides of the pipe, but of course there must be attenuation because of this effect. Its calculation is more complicated than that for the coaxial line and will not be carried out here.   For most modes, the attenuation is very high

[12] Skilling, *loc. cit.*, pp. 207–218;   F. E. Terman, *Electronic and Radio Engineering*, McGraw-Hill, New York, 1955, Chapter 5.

near cutoff, decreases to a minimum at some two or three times the cutoff frequency, and then increases roughly with $f^{\frac{1}{2}}$.

If a wave guide is closed at both ends, it becomes a cavity that can have standing wave patterns in it, but only of wave lengths properly related to its dimensions.   For such a cavity, there is therefore only *one* allowable

$TM_{1,1}$ Wave

$TE_{1,1}$ Wave

Sections through c-d   Sections through a-b

———— Electric Field
- - - - Magnetic Field

Fig. 10.7f.   The field patterns for the $TM_{1,1}$ and $TE_{1,1}$ modes. (Taken from Skilling, *op. cit.*, p. 213, Fig. 79.)

frequency for each mode.   Cavity resonators are used in high-frequency oscillating circuits to produce good frequency control; a large cavity can be arranged so as to radiate a small portion of its energy into a wave guide in an appropriate mode, in place of the use of an antenna.

A precisely constructed cavity resonator can be used to furnish a value of *c*, for the wave length of a given mode will be related to the dimensions which can be measured with great precision by optical interferometry, and the frequency can be measured by the use of a frequency divider and scaling circuit.

Problem 10.7a.   Write formulas for the electric and magnetic field components for a TE_{21} wave in a rectangular pipe.

Problem 10.7b.   Write formulas for the electric and magnetic field components for a TM_{11} wave in a rectangular pipe.

Problem 10.7c.   Find the cutoff frequencies for the TE_{01} modes in wave guides whose dimensions are 3 cm × 5 cm and 1 cm × 2 cm.

Problem 10.7d.   Prove that for the TE_{01} mode discussed in the text, we can have div $\mathbf{A} = 0$ and $V = 0$ by proper choice of constants.   Find $\mathbf{A}$ for this example.

Problem 10.7e.   Construct a diagram like Fig. 10.7e for the case that $\Delta v/\Delta \lambda > 0$.

10.8   Special Relativity

There is an intimate relation between the theory of special relativity and ordinary electromagnetic theory, which we shall demonstrate in this section. We shall not present a detailed argument for, nor an interpretation of, Einstein's theory[13] but shall base our argument on the algebra of invariance as given in Appendix A.4.

Let us first remark that the velocity of light $c = (\mu_0 \epsilon_0)^{-\frac{1}{2}}$ is a fundamental constant of our theory.   The basic principle of special relativity that postulates the equivalence of the laws of physics in any two reference frames moving with a constant relative velocity has as a consequence that c must be the same in each frame.   If not, we could distinguish between frames by measuring ϵ_0 or c and thus establish a "favored" one—for instance, that with the smallest value of c.

Einstein showed, by arguments to be found in any elementary account of relativity, that, if c is to be constant, time scales must be relative—i.e., simultaneity is a relative concept.

Furthermore, our laws of physics are basically linear in length and time, at least to a very good approximation.   Hence we can postulate that the position and time coordinates x, y, z, and t of an "event" in one frame must be linear combinations of those for another, x', y', z', and t'.   Constancy of c can be maintained if we require that the speed recorded for the passage of a beam of light from, say, the origin at time $t = 0$ to a point (x, y, z) at time t, will be the same in either frame of reference (allowing the two origins and clocks to coincide at the instant the beam or photon is emitted).

---

[13] An excellent discussion is to be found in W. K. H. Panofsky and M. Phillips *op. cit.*, Chapters 14–17.

Thus we have

$$c = (x^2 + y^2 + z^2)^{\frac{1}{2}}/t = (x'^2 + y'^2 + z'^2)^{\frac{1}{2}}/t'$$

These relations are more symmetric if we square them and write

$$x^2 + y^2 + z^2 - c^2t^2 = 0 \quad \text{and} \quad x'^2 + y'^2 + z'^2 - c^2t'^2 = 0$$

We can find a general condition that these relations hold if we require that the linear transformation we referred to keeps invariant the quantity $x^2 + y^2 + z^2 - c^2t^2$, even if this quantity is not zero. By an argument exactly like that in Appendix A.4, the "interval" $(x_a - y_a)^2 + (y_a - y_b)^2 + (z_a - z_b)^2 - c^2(t_a - t_b^2)$ between any two events will also be invariant, so that, if the events are the emission and the absorption of a photon in vacuo, its speed will be the same in each frame.

We can in fact follow Appendix A.4 exactly in a *formal* way if we use four coordinates $x_1 = x$, $x_2 = y$, $x_3 = z$, and $x_4 = ict$ where we use $i = \sqrt{-1}$ in accordance with convention (outside the field of a-c circuits). We emphasize the word "formal" because the introduction of the imaginary unit is purely for algebraic simplicity—time is still measured by real numbers. The "four-dimensional rotation" that seems to be involved is just a convenient mathematical construct. We merely assume that all sums run from 1 to 4 instead of from 1 to 3 unless explicitly indicated. (A detailed justification of the transfer of the three-dimensional formulas to the four-dimensional case can be found in books treating the algebra of relativity.)

Let us then write a general linear transformation (neglecting trivial shifts of origin and clock zero) as

$$x'_j = \sum_k a_{jk}x_k \qquad j, k = 1, 2, 3, 4 \tag{10.8-1}$$

with the inverse relation

$$x_k = \sum_j x'_j a_{jk} \tag{10.8-2}$$

Our invariance requirement is that

$$\sum_j x'^2_j = \sum_k x_k^2 \tag{10.8-3}$$

which must entail

$$\sum_k a_{jk}a_{lk} = \delta_{jl} \tag{10.8-4a}$$

$$\sum_j a_{jk}a_{jm} = \delta_{km} \tag{10.8-4b}$$

Next let us show that this linear transformation represents in general a translatory motion of one frame with respect to the other. Consider the spatial origin in the x_k frame, where $x_1 = 0, x_2 = 0$, and $x_3 = 0$. Then we have for the coordinates of this point, viewed in the other system,

$$\left.\begin{aligned}
x'_1 &= a_{14}x_4 = ica_{14}t \\
x'_2 &= a_{24}x_4 = ica_{24}t \\
x'_3 &= a_{34}x_4 = ica_{34}t \\
x'_4 &= ict' = a_{44}x_4 = ica_{44}t
\end{aligned}\right\} \tag{10.8-5}$$

Solving the last of these equations for t in terms of t', we have $t = t'/a_{44}$ and find that the primed coordinates (x'_1, x'_2, x'_3) of the unprimed origin increase uniformly with t', indicating a constant velocity which we shall call $\mathbf{u}$. The components of $\mathbf{u}$ are seen to be

$$u_1 = ica_{14}/a_{44}, \qquad u_2 = ica_{24}/a_{44}, \qquad u_3 = ica_{34}/a_{44} \tag{10.8-6}$$

Writing eq. 10.8–4b for $k = m = 4$, we have

$$a_{14}^2 + a_{24}^2 + a_{34}^2 + a_{44}^2 = 1$$

so that, substituting from eq. 10.8–6 we have

$$a_{44}^2\left(-\frac{u_1^2}{c^2} - \frac{u_2^2}{c^2} - \frac{u_3^2}{c^2} + 1\right) = 1$$

or

$$a_{44} = 1/(1 - u^2/c^2)^{\frac{1}{2}} \tag{10.8-7}$$

where we have taken the positive root to avoid the consideration of time reversals.

Now, if the two frames of reference are on an equal footing, the speed of the origin in the primed system, as measured in the unprimed system, must also be u, although of course oppositely directed if measured with respect to similarly oriented x, y, and z axes. This means that the coefficients with reversed subscripts must be the negatives of those listed in eq. 10.8–6. We can finally conclude for six of the a_{jk}'s the following:

$$a_{14} = -a_{41} = \frac{a_{44}u_1}{ic} = \frac{u_1}{ic(1 - u^2/c^2)^{\frac{1}{2}}}$$

$$a_{24} = -a_{42} = \frac{a_{44}u_2}{ic} = \frac{u_2}{ic(1 - u^2/c^2)^{\frac{1}{2}}} \tag{10.8-8}$$

$$a_{34} = -a_{43} = \frac{a_{44}u_3}{ic} = \frac{u_3}{ic(1 - u^2/c^2)^{\frac{1}{2}}}$$

It is inconvenient to solve for the other coefficients, for the general case involves a pure space rotation between the two sets of axes. However, one can calculate the components of the vector $\mathbf{x'} = \sum\limits_{j=1}^{3} x'_j \mathbf{1}'_j$ in the **u** direction. We have for the product of this component of $\mathbf{x'}$ with u,

$$\mathbf{x'} \cdot \mathbf{u} = \sum_{j=1}^{3} x'_j u_j = \sum_{j=1}^{3}\sum_{k=1}^{4} u_j a_{jk} x_k = \sum_{j=1}^{3}\sum_{k=1}^{3} u_j a_{jk} x_k + \sum_{j=1}^{3} u_j a_{j4} x_4. \qquad \text{Using}$$

eq. 10.8–6 for u_j and eq. 10.8–4b, we have

$$\mathbf{x'} \cdot \mathbf{u} = \frac{ic}{a_{44}} \sum_{j=1}^{3}\sum_{k=1}^{3} a_{j4} a_{jk} x_k + \frac{ic}{a_{44}} \sum_{j=1}^{3} a_{j4}{}^2 x_4$$

$$= \frac{ic}{a_{44}} \sum_{k=1}^{3} x_k (-a_{44} a_{4k}) + \frac{ic}{a_{44}} x_4 (1 - a_{44}{}^2)$$

which by eqs. 10.8–7 and 10.8–8 reduces to

$$\mathbf{x'} \cdot \mathbf{u} = \frac{\mathbf{x} \cdot \mathbf{u} + u^2 t}{(1 - u^2/c^2)^{\frac{1}{2}}} \qquad (10.8\text{–}9)$$

Using eq. 10.8–8 on eq. 10.8–1, written for the fourth component $x'_4 = ict'$, we readily find

$$t' = \frac{\mathbf{x} \cdot \mathbf{u}/c^2 + t}{(1 - u^2/c^2)^{\frac{1}{2}}} \qquad (10.8\text{–}10)$$

It is left to the reader to show that the quantity $(\mathbf{x} \cdot \mathbf{u})^2 - u^2 c^2 t^2$ is invariant under the transformation. Since the first term is u^2 times the square of the component of $\mathbf{x}$ in the direction of $\mathbf{u}$, it follows that the sum of the squares of the components of $\mathbf{x}$ normal to $\mathbf{u}$ is itself conserved (problem 10.8a). We can write therefore

$$\mathbf{x'}_\perp = \mathbf{x}_\perp \qquad (10.8\text{–}11)$$

It is easy to show (problem 10.8e) that if $\mathbf{u}$ is parallel to the x_1-direction and no space rotation takes place (i.e., so that $x'_2 = x_2$ and $x'_3 = x_3$) the coefficients a_{jk} become

$j\backslash k$	1	2	3	4
1	γ	0	0	$\gamma u/ic$
2	0	1	0	0
3	0	0	1	0
4	$-\gamma u/ic$	0	0	γ

$$a_{jk} = \qquad\qquad (10.8\text{–}12)$$

where for brevity we have written

$$\gamma = \frac{1}{(1 - u^2/c^2)^{\frac{1}{2}}} \qquad (10.8\text{–}13)$$

When written in an array like this, the group of coefficients is called a matrix.   Note that the first subscript enumerates the rows and the second one the columns.

Equations 10.8–9, 10.8–10, and 10.8–11 which are equivalent to eq. 10.8–1 describe what is generally known as a Lorentz transformation. Any four-component quantity which transforms under a Lorentz transformation in the same way as (x_1, x_2, x_3, x_4) is called a "four-vector." For instance, the space-time interval $(dx_1, dx_2, dx_3, ic\ dt)$ is a four-vector. A theory whose equations are invariant in form under such a transformation is said to be "Lorentz-invariant."[14]

An important example of a four-vector is the so-called "four-velocity." Let us find the transformation law for velocities.   When a particle suffers a displacement **dx** in time dt as seen in the unprimed frame, we write $\mathbf{dx} = \mathbf{v}\ dt$, with $\mathbf{dx'} = \mathbf{v'}\ dt'$ in the primed reference frame.   Then since $(dx_1, dx_2, dx_3, ic\ dt)$ is a four-vector, we can write

$$v'_j\ dt' = \sum_{k=1}^{3} a_{jk}v_k\ dt + a_{j4}ic\ dt \qquad j = 1, 2, 3 \qquad (10.8\text{–}14)$$

$$ic\ dt' = \sum_{k=1}^{3} a_{4k}v_k\ dt + a_{44}ic\ dt$$

The invariant form $dx^2 - c^2\ dt^2$ becomes now $(v^2 - c^2)\ dt^2$ so we have

$$(v'^2 - c^2)\ dt'^2 = (v^2 - c^2)\ dt^2$$

or

$$dt'(1 - v'^2/c^2)^{\frac{1}{2}} = dt(1 - v^2/c^2)^{\frac{1}{2}} \qquad (10.8\text{–}15)$$

for the ratio of the corresponding time elements for the given displacement.   Dividing each of eqs. 10.8–14 by eq. 10.8–15, we find that

$$v'_j/(1 - v'^2/c^2)^{\frac{1}{2}} = \sum_{k=1}^{3} a_{jk}v_k/(1 - v^2/c^2)^{\frac{1}{2}} + a_{j4}ic/(1 - v^2/c^2)^{\frac{1}{2}}$$
$$j = 1, 2, 3 \qquad (10.8\text{–}16)$$
$$ic/(1 - v'^2/c^2)^{\frac{1}{2}} = \sum_{k=1}^{3} a_{4k}v_k/(1 - v^2/c^2)^{\frac{1}{2}} + a_{44}ic/(1 - v^2/c^2)^{\frac{1}{2}}$$

which shows that $v_1/(1 - v^2/c^2)^{\frac{1}{2}}$, $v_2/(1 - v^2/c^2)^{\frac{1}{2}}$, $v_3/(1 - v^2/c^2)^{\frac{1}{2}}$, and $ic/(1 - v^2/c^2)^{\frac{1}{2}}$ form a four-vector.

The product of each of these components with the rest mass m_0 of the particle forms what is called the four-momentum.   The first three components form the ordinary relativistic momentum **p**, and the fourth may

[14] Sometimes called by the technically more accurate term "Lorentz covariant."

be written as iU/c, where U is the total energy, including rest energy. Thus it is seen that conservation of momentum and conservation of energy are linked together in the properties of the four-momentum. We shall not go further into the details of relativistic mechanics.

To demonstrate the Lorentz invariance of Maxwell's equations, we need to express these equations in terms of four-vectors and quantities derived from them. We can get a four-vector from a scalar by the four-component gradient (or four-gradient) operation $(\partial/\partial x_1, \partial/\partial x_2, \partial/\partial x_3, \partial/\partial x_4)$ whose components we can denote by ∂_j; $j = 1, 2, 3, 4$. We can, conversely, get a scalar from the scalar product of two four-vectors or from the four-divergence of a four-vector. That is, if A_1, A_2, A_3, and A_4 are the components of a four-vector, the quantity

$$\sum_j \frac{\partial A_j}{\partial x_j} = \frac{\partial A_1}{\partial x_1} + \frac{\partial A_2}{\partial x_2} + \frac{\partial A_3}{\partial x_3} + \frac{1}{ic}\frac{\partial A_4}{\partial t} \qquad (10.8\text{--}17)$$

will be a scalar and will not change its value under a Lorentz transformation.

We can also have entities called "tensors" that transform like products of vectors. Specifically, a four-tensor of the second rank is a collection of 16 numbers (9 for three-dimensional tensors) which we can denote by a symbol with two subscripts, T_{jk}. Any particular component, such as T_{23}, can be associated with both the x_2- and x_3-direction simultaneously. The stresses considered briefly in eq. 10.4–10 can be written componentwise in terms both of the components of the surface element $\mathbf{dS}$ and of components of the force-element associated with that surface (problem 10.8m). Another example of a three-dimensional tensor is the quadrupole moment, defined by eq. 3.3–5.

Tensors can also be of third rank—i.e., act like products of three vectors—and so forth. The transformation properties of a Lorentz-invariant tensor are given by a sort of duplication of eq. 10.8–1. For second-rank tensors, we have

$$T'_{jk} = \sum_{l,m} a_{jl} a_{km} T_{lm} \qquad (10.8\text{--}18)$$

Note that the "scalar product" of a tensor and a vector, such as $B_m = \sum_l A_l T_{lm}$ is itself a vector. In fact, we can write, using eq. 10.8–2,

$$\sum_m a_{km} B_m = \sum_m a_{km} \sum_l A_l T_{lm} = \sum_m \sum_l a_{km} T_{lm} \sum_j A'_j a_{jl}$$

$$= \sum_j A'_j \sum_m \sum_l a_{km} a_{jl} T_{lm} \qquad (10.8\text{--}19)$$

$$= \sum_j A'_j T'_{jk} = B'_k$$

so that B_m transforms as a four-vector.   A clear distinction must be made between a tensor, which may be written for any particular reference frame, and a transformation matrix, such as a_{jk}, which always refers to *two* frames of reference.

We intend to show that Maxwell's equations can be written as one equation relating two four-vectors and another relating two tensors.   Let us start by noting that electric charge q must be a scalar, since electric charge is conserved for moving systems.   The charge in a small element of volume will thus be the same as seen in different frames of reference. Because of the Lorentz-Fitzgerald contraction (problem 10.8d), $d\tau$ will contract along the direction of motion when observed in a moving frame, but not transversely.   The transformation rule from a rest frame to a moving frame is

$$d\tau = d\tau_0(1 - u^2/c^2)^{\frac{1}{2}} \tag{10.8-20}$$

Hence, ρ must obey the inverse transformation

$$\rho = \rho_0/(1 - u^2/c^2)^{\frac{1}{2}} \tag{10.8-21}$$

Now if we consider a group of charges first at rest and then moving with a velocity $\mathbf{v}$, we can treat $-\mathbf{v}$ as the velocity $\mathbf{u}$ of a reference frame that reduces the motion to a state of rest.   If ρ_0 is the charge density in the rest frame, we can form a four-vector by use of eq. 10.8–21 and the four-vector velocity given in eq. 10.8–16.   In fact, the quantity

$$J_k = [\rho_0 v_1/(1 - v^2/c^2)^{\frac{1}{2}}, \quad \rho_0 v_2/(1 - v^2/c^2)^{\frac{1}{2}}, \quad \rho_0 v_3/(1 - v^2/c^2)^{\frac{1}{2}},$$

$$ic\rho_0/(1 - v^2/c^2)^{\frac{1}{2}}] = (\rho v_1, \rho v_2, \rho v_3, ic\rho) \tag{10.8-22}$$

is a Lorentz-invariant four-vector, called the charge-current density.   The first three components are, of course, the ordinary vector $\mathbf{J} = \rho\mathbf{v}$.

Now let us look at eqs. 10.3–11 and 10.3–12 for V and $\mathbf{A}$.   These equations involved the so-called d'Alembertian operator

$$\square = \nabla^2 - \frac{1}{c^2}\frac{\partial^2}{\partial t^2} = \partial_1^2 + \partial_2^2 + \partial_3^2 + \partial_4^2 \tag{10.8-23}$$

which is a four-scalar.   The right-hand sides of the two equations are proportional to the components of J_k.   This leads us to try forming a four-vector out of $\mathbf{A}$ and V.   The two equations just mentioned can in fact be written as a single one if we define A_j as the four-vector whose components are given by

$$A_j = (A_1, A_2, A_3, iV/c) \tag{10.8-24}$$

Multiplying eq. 10.3–11 by $ic\epsilon_0\mu_0 = i/c$, and combining it with eq. 10.3–12, we can write

$$\Box\, A_j = \sum_k \partial^2 A_j/\partial x_k{}^2 = -\mu_0 J_j, \qquad j = 1, 2, 3, 4 \qquad (10.8\text{–}25)$$

If A_j as defined is indeed a four-vector, this equation will have the same form in any reference system, for each side will transform in the same way.

To show that A_j is a four-vector, let us assume that the retarded solution of eq. 10.8–25 is *uniquely* given by eqs. 10.3–15 and 10.3–16, a proposition that requires a lengthy demonstration in a mathematical sense, but which is physically evident from the relation between the retarded solutions just referred to and the original steady-state formulas for V and $\mathbf{A}$.   With this in mind, let us multiply both sides of eq. 10.8–25 by a_{kj} and sum over j. We have then

$$\Box \sum_j a_{kj} A_j = -\mu_0 \sum_j a_{kj} J_j = -\mu_0 J'_k$$

But in the new system we must have the same equations for the potentials, so that we have

$$\Box\, A'_k = -\mu_0 J'_k$$

The scalar $\Box$ being the same in both systems, we see that, if there is only one solution of the last equation, we must have

$$A'_k = \sum_j a_{kj} A_j$$

so that A_j is indeed a four-vector.

Equation 7.8–5 for div $\mathbf{A}$ takes on a simple form in terms of A_j.   It is in fact just the vanishing of the four-divergence since $\mu_0\epsilon_0 \partial V/\partial t = \partial(iV/c)/\partial(ict)$:

$$\sum_j \partial_j A_j = \frac{\partial A_1}{\partial x_1} + \frac{\partial A_2}{\partial x_2} + \frac{\partial A_3}{\partial x_3} + \frac{\partial A_y}{\partial x_y} = 0 \qquad (10.8\text{–}26)$$

which equation represents the vanishing of a Lorentz-invariant scalar.

Now let us write the components of $\mathbf{E}$ and $\mathbf{B}$ in terms of A_j.   We have

$$\left.\begin{aligned}
E_x = E_1 &= -\partial A_x/\partial t - \partial V/\partial x = -ic(\partial_4 A_1 - \partial_1 A_4)\\
E_y = E_2 &= -\partial A_y/\partial t - \partial V/\partial y = -ic(\partial_4 A_2 - \partial_2 A_4)\\
E_z = E_3 &= -\partial A_z/\partial t - \partial V/\partial z = -ic(\partial_4 A_3 - \partial_3 A_4)
\end{aligned}\right\} \quad (10.8\text{–}27)$$

$$\left.\begin{aligned}
B_x = B_1 &= \partial A_z/\partial y - \partial A_y/\partial z = \partial_2 A_3 - \partial_3 A_2\\
B_y = B_2 &= \partial A_x/\partial z - \partial A_z/\partial x = \partial_3 A_1 - \partial_1 A_3\\
B_z = B_3 &= \partial A_y/\partial x - \partial A_x/\partial y = \partial_1 A_2 - \partial_2 A_1
\end{aligned}\right\} \quad (10.8\text{–}28)$$

This form for the field components demonstrates in a remarkable form the connection between **B** and **E**. We can write all six components in terms of a single tensor f_{jk}:

$$f_{jk} = \partial_j A_k - \partial_k A_j \tag{10.8-29}$$

This tensor has the property of being anti-symmetric, i.e.,

$$f_{jk} = -f_{kj}; \quad j, k = 1, 2, 3, 4 \tag{10.8-30}$$

with vanishing values for equal subscripts

$$f_{jj} = 0 \tag{10.8-31}$$

Then we can write

$$E_j = -icf_{4j} = icf_{j4}; \quad j = 1, 2, 3 \tag{10.8-32}$$

$$B_1 = f_{23} = -f_{32}; \quad B_2 = f_{31} = -f_{13}; \quad B_3 = f_{12} = -f_{21} \tag{10.8-33}$$

We can express these results most simply by writing the components of f_{jk} in a square array:

$$f_{jk} = \begin{pmatrix} f_{11} & f_{12} & f_{13} & f_{14} \\ f_{21} & f_{22} & f_{23} & f_{24} \\ f_{31} & f_{32} & f_{33} & f_{34} \\ f_{41} & f_{42} & f_{43} & f_{44} \end{pmatrix} = \begin{pmatrix} 0 & B_z & -B_y & -iE_x/c \\ -B_z & 0 & B_x & -iE_y/c \\ B_y & -B_x & 0 & -iE_z/c \\ iE_x/c & iE_y/c & iE_z/c & 0 \end{pmatrix} \tag{10.8-34}$$

This tensor is called the "electromagnetic-field tensor." It will transform as the product of two four-vectors, since it is formed from the two pairs of four-vectors, $\partial_j A_k$ and $\partial_k A_j$. We should reiterate the fact that the presence of the imaginary unit is a formality. The field tensor is a perfectly real physical entity; with a different and more complicated mathematical formalism,[15] it can be written entirely in terms of real numbers.

We are finally ready to consider Maxwell's equations in free space. The equation div $\mathbf{E} = \rho/\epsilon_0$ can be written

$$\frac{\partial E_x}{\partial x} + \frac{\partial E_y}{\partial y} + \frac{\partial E_z}{\partial z} = ic\, \partial f_{14}/\partial x_1 + ic\, \partial f_{24}/\partial x_2 + ic\, \partial f_{34}/\partial x_3 \tag{10.8-35}$$

$$= \rho/\epsilon_0 = \mu_0 c^2 \rho$$

The expression on the left appears to be the fourth component of the vector formed from the tensor f_{jk} and the vector ∂_j. Since $ic\rho$ is the

[15] Panofsky and Phillips, *op. cit.*, Chapter 17.

fourth component of the charge-current vector, let us seek the other three components in the Maxwell equation containing **J**.   Componentwise this equation 10.1–3 reads

$$
\left.
\begin{aligned}
\frac{\partial B_z}{\partial y} - \frac{\partial B_y}{\partial z} - \mu_0 \epsilon_0 \frac{\partial E_x}{\partial t} &= -\frac{\partial f_{21}}{\partial x_2} - \frac{\partial f_{31}}{\partial x_3} - \frac{\partial f_{41}}{\partial x_4} = \mu_0 J_1 \\[4pt]
\frac{\partial B_x}{\partial z} - \frac{\partial B_z}{\partial x} - \mu_0 \epsilon_0 \frac{\partial E_y}{\partial t} &= -\frac{\partial f_{32}}{\partial x_3} - \frac{\partial f_{12}}{\partial x_1} - \frac{\partial f_{42}}{\partial x_4} = \mu_0 J_2 \\[4pt]
\frac{\partial B_y}{\partial x} - \frac{\partial B_x}{\partial y} - \mu_0 \epsilon_0 \frac{\partial E_z}{\partial t} &= -\frac{\partial f_{13}}{\partial x_1} - \frac{\partial f_{23}}{\partial x_2} - \frac{\partial f_{43}}{\partial x_4} = \mu_0 J_3
\end{aligned}
\right\}
\tag{10.8-36}
$$

To each of these equations, the appropriate term involving the vanishing components $f_{11}, f_{22},$ or f_{33} can be added to give a four-dimensional divergence.   We can then write the single equation

$$
\sum_{j-1}^{4} \frac{\partial f_{jk}}{\partial x_j} = -\mu_0 J_k; \qquad k = 1, 2, 3, 4
\tag{10.8-37}
$$

which is the clearly Lorentz-invariant expression of the equations div **E** = ρ/ϵ_0 and **curl B** = $\mu_0 \mathbf{J} + \mu_0 \, \partial \mathbf{D}/\partial t$.

The other two Maxwell equations combine to form a tensor of the third rank.   For div **B** = 0 we obtain

$$
\frac{\partial B_x}{\partial x} + \frac{\partial B_y}{\partial y} + \frac{\partial B_z}{\partial z} = \frac{\partial f_{23}}{\partial x_1} + \frac{\partial f_{31}}{\partial x_2} + \frac{\partial f_{12}}{\partial x_3} = 0
\tag{10.8-38}
$$

and for the three components of **curl E** + $\partial \mathbf{B}/\partial t = 0$ we get

$$
\begin{aligned}
\frac{\partial E_z}{\partial y} - \frac{\partial E_y}{\partial z} + \frac{\partial B_x}{\partial t} &= ic\frac{\partial f_{34}}{\partial x_2} + ic\frac{\partial f_{42}}{\partial x_3} + ic\frac{\partial f_{23}}{\partial x_4} = 0 \\[4pt]
\frac{\partial E_x}{\partial z} - \frac{\partial E_z}{\partial x} + \frac{\partial B_y}{\partial t} &= ic\frac{\partial f_{14}}{\partial x_3} + ic\frac{\partial f_{43}}{\partial x_1} + ic\frac{\partial f_{31}}{\partial x_4} = 0 \\[4pt]
\frac{\partial E_y}{\partial x} - \frac{\partial E_x}{\partial y} + \frac{\partial B_z}{\partial t} &= ic\frac{\partial f_{24}}{\partial x_1} + ic\frac{\partial f_{41}}{\partial x_2} + ic\frac{\partial f_{12}}{\partial x_4} = 0
\end{aligned}
\tag{10.8-37}
$$

We can summarize all four of these equations by writing, with the understanding that j, k, and l are all different,

$$
\frac{\partial f_{jk}}{\partial x_l} + \frac{\partial f_{kl}}{\partial x_j} + \frac{\partial f_{lj}}{\partial x_k} = 0
\tag{10.8-40}
$$

There are only four possible sets of the three subscripts that are all unequal (each set leaves out one of the integers 1, 2, 3, or 4).   If jkl are taken successively as 231, 342, 143, 241, we get the equations above. A change in the order of any of these sets will either give the same equation with the terms rearranged or the negative of the same equation.

Let us now show that the expression in eq. 10.8–40 represents indeed a tensor of the third rank. The expression $\partial f_{jk}/\partial x_l$ where j, k, and l may now be *any* indices will transform as a tensor of the third rank (cf. problem 10.8f). Its components will vanish whenever j and k are equal and will change sign when j and k (being unequal) are interchanged. The sum of three such tensors with indices interchanged as in eq. 10.8–40 is also a tensor. This sum will vanish when any two of the subscripts are equal, for the term that contains these two subscripts in the numerator will be zero by itself and the other two terms will be equal and opposite.

Therefore we can remove the restriction on the subscripts in eq. 10.8–40, since the added possibilities are all zero. Consequently we have written the div **E** and **curl B** equations together as the vanishing of a Lorentz-invariant tensor of the third rank.

We can finally conclude that Maxwell's equations will retain their form when the transformation from one frame of reference to another moving with constant velocity with respect to the first is carried out by the Lorentz rule, eq. 10.8–1. The way in which the components of **E** and **B** change may be found by applying the transformation matrix in the form of eq. 10.8–12 to the electromagnetic field tensor, eq. 10.8–34. It is left to the reader (problem 10.8g) to show that, using subscripts $\parallel$ and $\perp$ for the fields parallel and perpendicular to the relative velocity **u**,

$$\left.\begin{aligned} \mathbf{E}'_{\parallel} &= \mathbf{E}_{\parallel} \\ \mathbf{B}'_{\parallel} &= \mathbf{B}_{\parallel} \end{aligned}\right\} \tag{10.8–41}$$

$$\left.\begin{aligned} \mathbf{E}'_{\perp} &= \gamma[\mathbf{E}_{\perp} - (\mathbf{u} \times \mathbf{B}_{\perp})] \\ \mathbf{B}'_{\perp} &= \gamma[\mathbf{B}_{\perp} + (\mathbf{u} \times \mathbf{E}_{\perp})/c^2] \end{aligned}\right\} \tag{10.8–42}$$

When $u \ll c$, γ is very close to unity, and these formulas are seen to agree with the Galilean relativity results of section 7.9. It should be noted that these formulas relate the field quantities observed in the two frames of reference at the same point of space and instant of time, which of course are measured by different coordinates in the two systems.

A Direct Calculation for a Uniformly Moving Point Charge. Another way of seeing the connection between electromagnetic theory and relativity is to calculate the fields surrounding a uniformly moving point charge, without using a transformation from one frame of reference to another. We saw in section 7.9 that a succession of induced electric and magnetic fields is expected in addition to those derived from Coulomb's and Ampère's laws, but we were not at that time in a position to calculate them completely.   Part of the reason was that, although we showed that changing currents modified $\mathbf{E}$ by the term $-\partial \mathbf{A}/\partial t$ and also by some change in V, we did not calculate the latter change.   Its existence was made clear by the modification of the Poisson equation in the extra term $-c^{-2}\,\partial^2 V/\partial t^2$ added to $\nabla^2 V$.   The condition that governs this extra term is that div $\mathbf{E} = \rho/\epsilon_0$ is to be preserved.

For a point charge moving with a constant velocity (in, let us say, the positive x-direction) the calculation is relatively simple.   We must first assume that any radiation that may have occurred while the particle was getting accelerated has passed beyond the region in which we wish to calculate $\mathbf{E}$ and $\mathbf{B}$ before the time at which the calculation is to be made. Then we can expect a steady state of affairs that propagates itself with the velocity $\mathbf{v}$.   We can describe this state of affairs as a wave traveling in the x-direction.   Any function of x, y, z, and t must then be of the form $F(x - vt, y, z)$.

We can say that, after an interval dt, the field at a point (x, y, z) is replaced by the field that before the interval was found at $(x - v\,dt, y, z)$. That is, the derivative $\partial/\partial t$ of any field quantity can be replaced by the operator $-v\partial/\partial x$.   Thus we can write for empty space

$$\nabla^2 V - \frac{1}{c^2}\frac{\partial^2 V}{\partial t^2} = \frac{\partial^2 V}{\partial x^2} + \frac{\partial^2 V}{\partial y^2} + \frac{\partial^2 V}{\partial z^2} - \frac{v^2}{c^2}\frac{\partial^2 V}{\partial x^2} = 0 \qquad (10.8\text{--}43)$$

If we make the algebraic substitution of a new variable x' defined by

$$x' = (x - vt)/(1 - v^2/c^2)^{\frac{1}{2}} \qquad (10.8\text{--}44)$$

we can write the ordinary Laplace equation for V as a function $V(x', y, z)$:

$$\frac{\partial^2 V}{\partial x'^2} + \frac{\partial^2 V}{\partial y^2} + \frac{\partial^2 V}{\partial z^2} = 0 \qquad (10.8\text{--}45)$$

Since $\mathbf{A}$ satisfies the same wave equation as V, we can reduce it in the same way to get

$$\frac{\partial^2 \mathbf{A}}{\partial x'^2} + \frac{\partial^2 \mathbf{A}}{\partial y^2} + \frac{\partial^2 \mathbf{A}}{\partial z^2} = 0 \qquad (10.8\text{--}46)$$

The solution of these equations that corresponds to a point charge q must be one that has the property of giving an electric flux q/ϵ_0 out through any surface surrounding the point where $x = vt$ or $x' = 0$, $y = 0$, and $z = 0$.   We know that simple solutions of eqs. 10.8–45 and 10.8–46 are

$$V = \frac{k}{(x'^2 + y^2 + z^2)^{\frac{1}{2}}}\,; \qquad \mathbf{A} = \frac{\mathbf{C}}{(x'^2 + y^2 + z^2)^{\frac{1}{2}}} \qquad (10.8\text{--}47)$$

Let us see if this solution has the above-mentioned flux property, given a suitable value for the constant scalar k and the constant vector $\mathbf{C}$.

The constant $\mathbf{C}$ can be related to k by the condition on div $\mathbf{A}$. Let us assume that $\mathbf{C}$ is a vector parallel to $\mathbf{v}$, $\mathbf{C} = C\mathbf{1}_x$, as has been the case heretofore for the vector potential. Then we have, writing $x'^2 + y^2 + z^2 = r'^2$,

$$0 = \nabla \cdot \mathbf{A} + \frac{1}{c^2} \frac{\partial V}{\partial t} = \frac{\partial A_x}{\partial x} - \frac{v}{c^2} \frac{\partial V}{\partial x} = -\frac{C}{r'^2} \frac{\partial r'}{\partial x} + \frac{vk}{c^2 r'^2} \frac{\partial r'}{\partial x}$$

so that

$$C = vk/c^2 \tag{10.8–48}$$

We shall now calculate the electric flux through a sphere of radius r surrounding the charge and moving with it. The equation of such a sphere will be

$$r^2 = (x - vt)^2 + y^2 + z^2 \tag{10.8–49}$$

so that, with $\gamma = (1 - v^2/c^2)^{-\frac{1}{2}}$

$$r'^2 = \gamma^2(x - vt)^2 + y^2 + z^2 = (\gamma^2 - 1)(x - vt)^2 + r^2$$

and if we introduce the polar angle θ given by

$$x - vt = r \cos \theta \tag{10.8–50}$$

we have

$$r' = r[(\gamma^2 - 1)\cos^2 \theta + 1]^{\frac{1}{2}}$$

Now to calculate the flux we will need the radial component of $\mathbf{E}$:

$$E_r = -\frac{\partial A_r}{\partial t} - \frac{\partial V}{\partial r} = -\frac{\partial A_x}{\partial t} \cos \theta - \frac{\partial V}{\partial r} = v \frac{\partial A_x}{\partial x} \cos \theta - \frac{\partial V}{\partial r}$$

$$= \frac{-(v^2 k/c^2) \cos \theta \,(x - vt)}{(1 - v^2/c^2)[\gamma^2(x - vt)^2 + y^2 + z^2]^{\frac{3}{2}}} + \frac{k}{r^2[(\gamma^2 - 1)\cos^2 \theta + 1]^{\frac{3}{2}}}$$

$$= \frac{-(v^2 k/c^2)\cos^2 \theta + k(1 - v^2/c^2)[(\gamma^2 - 1)\cos^2 \theta + 1]}{(1 - v^2/c^2) r^2[(\gamma^2 - 1)\cos^2 \theta + 1]^{\frac{3}{2}}}$$

which reduces to

$$E_r = k/r^2[(\gamma^2 - 1)\cos^2 \theta + 1]^{\frac{3}{2}} \tag{10.8–51}$$

The flux is then

$$\frac{q}{\epsilon_0} = \Phi_E = \int_0^{\pi} E_r(2\pi r^2 \sin \theta)\, d\theta = 2\pi k \int_0^{\pi} \frac{\sin \theta \, d\theta}{[(\gamma^2 - 1)\cos^2 \theta + 1]^{\frac{3}{2}}}$$

$$= -2\pi k \cos \theta \,[(\gamma^2 - 1)\cos^2 \theta + 1]^{-\frac{1}{2}} \Big|_0^{\pi}$$

$$= 4\pi k/\gamma = 4\pi k(1 - v^2/c^2)^{\frac{1}{2}}$$

We conclude that eq. 10.8–7 gives the correct values for V and $\mathbf{A}$ for a charge moving with an arbitrary velocity $\mathbf{v}$, if only we have

$$k = \frac{q}{4\pi\epsilon_0(1 - v^2/c^2)^{\frac{1}{2}}} \; ; \qquad C = \frac{q\mathbf{v}}{4\pi c^2\epsilon_0(1 - v^2/c^2)^{\frac{1}{2}}} \qquad (10.8\text{--}52)$$

Let us now find $\mathbf{E}$ and $\mathbf{B}$. It is easy to show that $\mathbf{E}$ is in the radial direction (problem 10.8i). In accordance with eq. 10.8–51, we have then

$$\mathbf{E} = \frac{q\mathbf{1}_r}{4\pi\epsilon_0 r^2(1 - v^2/c^2)^{\frac{1}{2}}[(\gamma^2 - 1)\cos^2\theta + 1]^{\frac{3}{2}}}$$

$$= \frac{q\mathbf{1}_r(1 - v^2/c^2)}{4\pi\epsilon_0 r^2[1 - (v^2/c^2)\sin^2\theta]^{\frac{3}{2}}} \qquad (10.8\text{--}53)$$

The magnetic field $\mathbf{B}$ can only have a hoop or ϕ component. It is easiest to calculate it with cylindrical coordinates, with $y^2 + z^2 = R^2 = r^2\sin^2\theta$:

$$\mathbf{B} = \nabla \times \mathbf{A} = -\mathbf{1}_\phi \frac{\partial A_x}{\partial R} = \frac{q v \mathbf{1}_\phi R}{4\pi\epsilon_0 c^2(1 - v^2/c^2)^{\frac{1}{2}}[R^2 + x'^2]^{\frac{3}{2}}}$$

$$= \frac{\mu_0 q v \mathbf{1}_\phi(1 - v^2/c^2)\sin\theta}{r^2[1 - (v^2/c^2)\sin^2\theta]^{\frac{3}{2}}} = (\mathbf{v} \times \mathbf{E})/c^2 \qquad (10.8\text{--}54)$$

These results are exactly the same as those obtained by the transformation, eq. 10.8–41 and eq. 10.8–42, on the field of a stationary charge, along with a Lorentz transformation on the coordinates (problem 10.8j). The latter transformation appears here merely as a convenience in making the wave equation easy to solve. We can also describe the resulting electric field, eq. 10.8–53, as a foreshortened field. When $\theta = 0$, the value of $r = x$ at which $\mathbf{E}$ has a particular value E_0 is reduced by $(1 - v^2/c^2)^{\frac{1}{2}}$ over its value for the charge at rest. We can thus describe the Lorentz-Fitzgerald contraction as being an expression of the foreshortening of the electric field of a moving charge. It is not surprising, therefore, that a macroscopic piece of material composed of electric charges will also foreshorten. It was the contribution of Einstein that this contraction is general and not just a property of the electric fields of charged particles.

Problem 10.8a. Prove that $(\mathbf{x} \cdot \mathbf{u})^2 - u^2 c^2 t^2$ is invariant under the transformation eq. 10.8–1, and hence demonstrate eq. 10.8–11.

Problem 10.8b. Let $\mathbf{u}$ and $\mathbf{v}$ both be along the x-axis. Using the last of eqs. 10.8–14 together with eq. 10.8–8 to get $dt'/dt = a_{44}(1 + uv/c^2)$, deduce the relativistic law for the addition of parallel velocities.

Problem 10.8c. Find the law of addition of velocities as in the previous problem, when $\mathbf{u}$ and $\mathbf{v}$ have arbitrary directions.

Problem 10.8d.   By considering that a length measurement of an object in a frame of reference in which the object is at rest does not require simultaneous observation of both ends but that measurement in another frame does require simultaneity ($\Delta t' = 0$), show that a moving object always appears shortened along the direction of motion by a factor $(1 - v^2/c^2)^{\frac{1}{2}}$ (Lorentz-Fitzgerald contraction).   Show also that no transverse change of length occurs.

Problem 10.8e.   Find all the coefficients of a Lorentz transformation for the case in which the origin of the unprimed system moves with speed u along the positive x-axis as seen in the primed system.   Also write down the inverse transformation by inspection.   The spatial orientation is the same for the two systems.

Problem 10.8f.   Prove explicitly that $f_{jk} = \partial_j A_k - \partial_k A_j$ transforms like a tensor of the second rank and that $\partial f_{jk}/\partial x_l$ transforms like a tensor of the third rank.

Problem 10.8g.   Prove eqs. 10.8–41 and 10.8–42 for the transformation of **E** and **B**.

Problem 10.8h.   Using cylindrical coordinates, show that any component of **C** in eq. 10.8–47 normal to $\mathbf{1}_x$ must be zero if div $\mathbf{A} + \mu_0\epsilon_0 \, \partial V/\partial t = 0$.

Problem 10.8i.   Prove that E_θ and E_ϕ are zero for the field of a moving point charge, using spherical coordinates with the x-axis as pole.

Problem 10.8j.   Derive the fields of a moving charge from those of a stationary one by use of eqs. 10.8–41 and 10.8–42.

Problem 10.8k.   Find the effect on **E**, at points for which $\theta = 90°$, of the motion of a point charge.   What happens to **E** at such points as $v \to c$?

Problem 10.8l.   Write the equations for a Lorentz transformation of the four-vectors J_k and A_k, in terms of **J**, ρ, **A**, and V.

Problem 10.8m.   Consider a particular surface element **dS** for the integrals of eq. 10.4–10, and write the three components of force associated with each of the components of **dS**, in the form of a tensor.

Appendix

A.1   Notes on Calculus

Taylor's theorem for functions of one variable says that, if we are given the value of a function $g(x)$ and its derivatives for $x = x_0$, we can find $g(x)$ for a neighboring value of x, from a suitable number of terms of the series

$$g(x) = g(x_0) + (x - x_0)g'(x_0) + \frac{1}{2!}(x - x_0)^2 g''(x_0)$$

$$+ \frac{1}{3!}(x - x_0)^3 g'''(x_0) + \cdots \tag{A.1-1}$$

The textbooks that prove this theorem give formulas for the upper limit of the error made by stopping with any particular number of terms.

If we wish similarly to evaluate $f(x, y)$ at points (x, y) in the neighborhood of a point (x_0, y_0), we can write Taylor's theorem in two variables (the generalization to more variables is obvious)

$$f(x, y) = f(x_0, y_0) + (x - x_0)\left(\frac{\partial f}{\partial x}\right)_{\substack{x=x_0 \\ y=y_0}} + (y - y_0)\left(\frac{\partial f}{\partial y}\right)_{\substack{x=x_0 \\ y=y_0}}$$

$$+ \tfrac{1}{2}\left[(x - x_0)^2 \left(\frac{\partial^2 f}{\partial x^2}\right)_{\substack{x=x_0 \\ y=y_0}} + 2(x - x_0)(y - y_0)\left(\frac{\partial^2 f}{\partial x\,\partial y}\right)_{\substack{x=x_0 \\ y=y_0}}\right.$$

$$\left. + (y - y_0)^2 \left(\frac{\partial^2 f}{\partial y^2}\right)_{\substack{x=x_0 \\ y=y_0}}\right] + \cdots \tag{A.1-2}$$

This formula can be derived from eq. A.1-1 if we set

$$G(\theta) = f[x_0 + \theta(x - x_0), y_0 + \theta(y - y_0)] \tag{A.1-3}$$

so that $G(0) = f(x_0, y_0)$ and $G(1) = f(x, y)$. Then writing a Taylor's series for $G(\theta)$ with $\theta_0 = 0$, we have

$$(\theta - \theta_0)G'(\theta_0) = \theta G'(0) = (x - x_0)\left(\frac{\partial f}{\partial x}\right)_{\substack{x=x_0 \\ y=y_0}} + (y - y_0)\left(\frac{\partial f}{\partial y}\right)_{\substack{x=x_0 \\ y=y_0}}$$

and so on for the higher terms.   The rule that

$$\partial^2 f/\partial x\,\partial y = \partial^2 f/\partial y\,\partial x$$

etc., is required for this calculation.

545

The increment of a function $g(x)$ of one variable is written $\Delta g(x)$ and is related to the increment Δx of x by

$$\Delta g(x) = g(x + \Delta x) - g(x)$$

By eq. A.1–1, we can write

$$\Delta g(x) = \Delta x g'(x) + \tfrac{1}{2} \Delta x^2 g''(x) + \cdots \tag{A.1-4}$$

The differential dg of a function $g(x)$ is defined as the principal part of the increment, or the first term in eq. A.1–4; the differential dx of an independent variable x is defined to be equal to its increment Δx. Thus we write

$$dg = g'(x)\, dx \tag{A.1-5}$$

For a function of several variables, say $f(x, y, z)$, we can write from the three-variable form of eq. A.1–2

$$\Delta f(x, y, z) = f(x + \Delta x, y + \Delta y, z + \Delta z) - f(x, y, z)$$

$$= \Delta x \frac{\partial f}{\partial x} + \Delta y \frac{\partial f}{\partial y} + \Delta z \frac{\partial f}{\partial z} + \tfrac{1}{2}\left[(\Delta x)^2 \frac{\partial^2 f}{\partial x^2} \right.$$

$$+ 2\Delta x\, \Delta y \frac{\partial^2 f}{\partial x\, \partial y} + (\Delta y)^2 \frac{\partial^2 f}{\partial y^2} + 2\Delta y\, \Delta z \frac{\partial^2 f}{\partial y\, \partial z} + (\Delta z)_2 \frac{\partial^2 f}{\partial z^2}$$

$$\left. + 2\Delta x\, \Delta z \frac{\partial^2 f}{\partial x\, \partial z} \right] + \cdots \tag{A.1-6}$$

and for the differential of $f(x, y, z)$ we write again the principal part of the increment

$$df = \frac{\partial f}{\partial x}\, dx + \frac{\partial f}{\partial y}\, dy + \frac{\partial f}{\partial z}\, dz \tag{A.1-7}$$

If x, y, and z are all functions of another variable u, then from eq. A.1–7 (more strictly from eq. A.1–6) we can show that

$$\frac{\partial f}{\partial u} = \frac{\partial f}{\partial x}\frac{\partial x}{\partial u} + \frac{\partial f}{\partial y}\frac{\partial y}{\partial u} + \frac{\partial f}{\partial z}\frac{\partial z}{\partial u} \tag{A.1-8}$$

An ordinary integral (so-called Riemann integral) of a function $g(x)$ of one variable between limits a and b is defined as the limit of a sum found by dividing the interval ab into small parts Δx_i, all of which approach zero in the limit. We write

$$\int_a^b g(x)\, dx = \lim_{n \to \infty} \sum_{i=1}^n g(x_i)\, \Delta x_i \tag{A.1-9}$$

where x_i is a value of x within the range Δx_i. Then it is proved in calculus that the integral may be evaluated by finding a function $G(x)$ whose derivative is $g(x)$, $G'(x) = g(x)$.

An integral of a function $f(x, y)$ of two variables, taken over an area S, is defined as the limit of a single sum formed by dividing S into infinitesimal elements ΔS_i and evaluating $f(x, y)$ at an arbitrary point in each ΔS_i. We write

$$\int_S f(x, y)\, dS = \lim_{n \to \infty} \sum_{i=1}^{n} f(x_i, y_i)\, \Delta S_i \qquad \text{(A.1-10)}$$

using a single integral sign to indicate the single sum.

Then it is proved in advanced calculus books that the integral may be evaluated as an iterated integral, for instance over x and y:

$$\int_S f(x, y)\, dS = \int_{x_1}^{x_2} dx \int_{y_1}^{y_2} dy\, f(x, y) \qquad \text{(A.1-11)}$$

where in this order of integration (the y integration is to be evaluated first) y_2 and y_1 are generally functions of x. The possibility of using either order of integration sometimes leads to useful transformations of complicated expressions. The following transformation is fairly common and should be illustrated by the reader with a suitable sketch of the region S:

$$\int_a^b dx \int_a^x dy\, f(x, y) = \int_a^b dy \int_y^b dx\, f(x, y) \qquad \text{(A.1-12)}$$

The generalization to multiple integrals in three or more variables is straightforward. It can be seen from the definition that integrals representing physical quantities can readily be defined in a physical meaningful way without reference to axes or coordinates that may be required for their evaluation. One of the principal exercises required in the application of integral calculus to physics is the choosing of suitable variables and the writing of the various physical quantities in terms of them, in order to evaluate the integrals.

The law of the mean for integrals states that, if the integrand is continuous and the range of integration finite, the value of an integral can always be set equal to the product of the interval (length, area, or volume) integrated over, times the value of the integrand taken at some (generally unknown) point in the interval. That is, for a surface integral we have

$$\int_S f(x, y)\, dS = f(x', y')S \qquad \text{(A.1-13)}$$

where S is the area integrated over and (x', y') is that point within S which makes the equality hold.

Problem A.1a.   Show that the nth term of eq. A.1-2 can be written

$$\frac{1}{n!}\left[(x - x_0)\frac{\partial}{\partial x} + (y - y_0)\frac{\partial}{\partial y}\right]^n f(x, y)$$

where the derivatives in the expanded nth power act on $f(x, y)$ but not on $(x - x_0)$ or $(y - y_0)$ and x and y are replaced by x_0 and y_0 in $f(x, y)$ after the derivatives are calculated.

Problem A.1b.   Illustrate the order change in eq. A.1–12 by a suitable sketch of the region of integration in the x–y plane.

A.2   Vectors

Introduction.   The ordinary symbols of physics, such as m (mass), t (time), p (pressure) etc. are *algebraic* quantities which can take on any real values, positive or negative.   We can call them *scalars* because their values can be represented on a one-dimensional scale.   An *arithmetic* quantity is one which takes on only positive values, such as kinetic energy or the radius in polar coordinates.

There are, however, many physical entities which are measurable in a more complex way, namely in terms of arithmetic quantity (magnitude) and direction, and are called vectors.   Displacement, velocity, acceleration, and force are the basic vectors of mechanics, and others can be derived from them (e.g., torque as a vector).   We also represent plane surfaces, or infinitesimal surfaces of any shape, as vectors, whose magnitudes are the areas and whose directions are along the normals (see below). We represent vectors by bold-faced letters, as $\mathbf{r}$, $\mathbf{F}$, $\mathbf{v}$, $\mathbf{E}$, $\mathbf{S}$, etc., with the understanding that each vector symbol represents both the magnitude and direction of the physical entity.   Light-face type is used for the magnitude of the quantity; (the magnitude may also be denoted by vertical bars: $F = |\mathbf{F}|$).   The direction may be specified by a suitable angle or set of angles, but we shall not need a general symbol for direction (the use of components will obviate this need).

Two vectors are equal if their magnitudes are equal and they lie in the same direction.   Vectors can be combined by addition and subtraction and by two kinds of multiplication.   Before giving the rules for vector combination, let us write down for comparison the combining rules of algebra.   Algebraic quantities, denoted by a, b, c, etc., can be added and multiplied; the result of these operations or any combination of them is another algebraic quantity.   There are five rules or laws for combination from which (along with some definitions) all of algebra can be constructed:

$a + b = b + a$	The commutative law of addition
$a + (b + c) = (a + b) + c$	The associative law of addition
$ab = ba$	The commutative law of multiplication
$a(bc) = (ab)c$	The associative law of multiplication
$a(b + c) = ab + ac$	The distributive law

Vector Addition; Components and Coordinate Systems.   Vectors can be added graphically or by analytic procedures derived from graphical addition by geometry and trigonometry.   We represent a vector graphically as an arrow with the appropriate direction whose length on a suitable scale represents the magnitude.

Figure A.2*a* represents the summation **A** + **B** = **C** and also of course the subtraction **B** = **C** − **A**.   If **A** = **C**, **B** is a vector of zero length and unspecified direction called a "null vector."   If **A** = **B**, **C** = **A** + **A** = 2**A**,

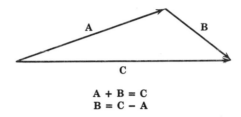

$$A + B = C$$
$$B = C - A$$

Fig. A.2*a*.   Addition and subtraction of vectors.

a vector collinear with **A** of twice the length.   We can extend this process of doubling a vector so that a vector can be multiplied by any scalar whether dimensionless or not—e.g., the acceleration **a** can be multiplied by the scalar *m* to give the force **F** = *m***a**, a vector in the same direction as **a** but measured in different physical units.   Vector addition obeys the same commutative and associative laws as ordinary addition, as is evident from geometry.

Any vector can be represented as the sum of three at right angles (or any number at more or less arbitrary angles).   There are three systems of coordinates to which we make reference and which specify convenient directions into which we can resolve vectors.   The Cartesian system uses three perpendicular axes labeled *x*, *y*, and *z*.   For reasons to appear shortly, we always use a right-handed system, in which, if the fingers of the right hand are pointed from the positive *x*-axis to the positive *y*-axis through the 90° angle separating them, the thumb will be found to point on the side of the *x*–*y* plane that contains the positive *z*-axis.

Cylindrical coordinates are those in which one Cartesian axis, usually the *z*-axis, is retained, and points are located in planes perpendicular to this axis by polar coordinates *r* and *ϕ*.   In spherical coordinates a point is located by its distance *r* from the origin, by the angle *θ* between a chosen polar axis and the radius vector (line from origin to the point), and by the angle *ϕ* between the plane containing the polar axis and the radius vector and an arbitrary fixed plane through the polar axis.

Vectors are conveniently resolved in any of these systems by the use of unit vectors, which are vectors of unit (dimensionless) length, directed at any given point along the three perpendicular directions that correspond to infinitesimal motions of the point when each variable respectively is allowed to increase.   The variable that is allowed to change is used as a subscript on a bold-face figure **1** that represents the vector.   Figures A.2*b*, *c*, and *d* represent the three coordinate systems with their associated unit vectors.

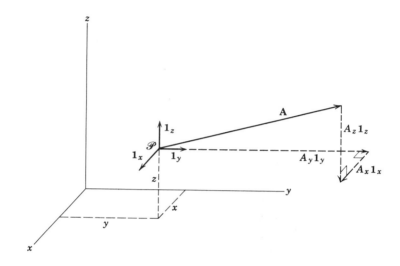

Fig. A.2*b*.   Cartesian coordinates.

A vector **A** can thus be represented as the sum of three vectors, each of which is a scalar (called a component) multiplied by a unit vector.   For the three systems, we have

$$\left.\begin{array}{l} \mathbf{A} = A_x\mathbf{1}_x + A_y\mathbf{1}_y + A_z\mathbf{1}_z \quad \text{Cartesian} \\ \mathbf{A} = A_r\mathbf{1}_r + A_\phi\mathbf{1}_\phi + A_z\mathbf{1}_z \quad \text{Cylindrical} \\ \mathbf{A} = A_r\mathbf{1}_r + A_\theta\mathbf{1}_\theta + A_\phi\mathbf{1}_\phi \quad \text{Spherical} \end{array}\right\} \qquad \text{(A.2-1)}$$

By the theorem of Pythagoras, the magnitude A of **A** is equal to the square root of the sum of the squares of the three components in any system,

$$A = |\mathbf{A}| = (A_x{}^2 + A_y{}^2 + A_z{}^2)^{\frac{1}{2}}$$

with a similar formula for the other coordinate systems.   It is easy to see by suitable constructions in the figures that the cosine of the angle between **A** and any of the unit vectors is given by the ratio of the component of A

Fig. A.2c.   Cylindrical coordinates.

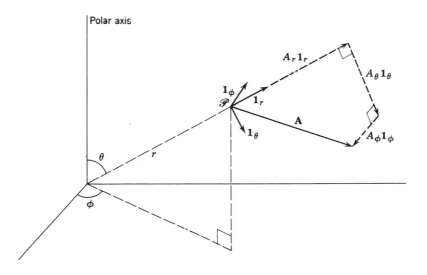

Fig. A.2d.   Spherical coordinates.

in that direction to the magnitude of A itself.   The cosines for the Cartesian case are called the direction cosines, A_x/A, A_y/A, and A_z/A.   It is evident that the sum of the squares of the direction cosines is unity.

The equality of two vectors implies agreement in direction and magnitude, which in turn requires the equality of the corresponding components in any coordinate system.

The radius vector $\mathbf{r}$ or $\mathbf{R}$, representing a displacement from the origin to a given point $\mathscr{P}$, is one of the simplest vectors.   In Cartesian coordinates it is

$$\mathbf{r} = x\mathbf{1}_x + y\mathbf{1}_y + z\mathbf{1}_z \tag{A.2--2a}$$

In cylindrical coordinates, where r has a different significance, we write

$$\mathbf{R} = r\mathbf{1}_r + z\mathbf{1}_z \tag{A.2--2b}$$

and in spherical coordinates it is simply

$$\mathbf{r} = r\mathbf{1}_r \tag{A.2--2c}$$

A unit vector in the direction of a vector A is clearly

$$\mathbf{1}_A = \frac{\mathbf{A}}{A} = \frac{A_x}{A}\mathbf{1}_x + \frac{A_y}{A}\mathbf{1}_y + \frac{A_z}{A}\mathbf{1}_z \tag{A.2--3}$$

The spherical coordinate unit vector $\mathbf{1}_r$ thus is given from eq. A.2--2a by

$$\mathbf{1}_r = \frac{\mathbf{r}}{r} = \frac{x}{r}\mathbf{1}_x + \frac{y}{r}\mathbf{1}_y + \frac{z}{r}\mathbf{1}_z \tag{A.2--4}$$

in Cartesian coordinates.   Any unit vector is thus equal to the sum of the products of each direction cosine with the corresponding Cartesian unit vector.

The Scalar Product.   Two vectors may be "multiplied" together to give a scalar or a vector.   The former type of product is called a scalar product and is defined as the product of the magnitudes of the two vectors and the cosine of the angle between them.   We write the scalar product with a bold-face multiplication dot between the vectors, e.g., $\mathbf{A} \cdot \mathbf{B}$; the product is sometimes called the "dot product" and is generally read "A dot B."   We have thus, if θ is the angle between $\mathbf{A}$ and $\mathbf{B}$,

$$\mathbf{A} \cdot \mathbf{B} = AB \cos \theta \tag{A.2--5}$$

Since $B \cos \theta$ is the projection of $\mathbf{B}$ on $\mathbf{A}$, and vice versa, we can describe the scalar product as the ordinary product of the length of one vector and the projection of the other upon it.   The scalar product obviously obeys the commutative law.   Furthermore, any scalar factor can be factored out:

$$(m\mathbf{A}) \cdot \mathbf{B} = m(\mathbf{A} \cdot \mathbf{B}) = \mathbf{A} \cdot (m\mathbf{B}) \tag{A.2--6}$$

The scalar product of any vector with itself is the square of its magnitude, since in this case $\cos \theta = 1$:

$$\mathbf{A} \cdot \mathbf{A} = A^2 \tag{A.2-7}$$

The scalar products of the unit vectors of any of the coordinate systems are either unity or zero:

$$\mathbf{1}_x \cdot \mathbf{1}_x = \mathbf{1}_y \cdot \mathbf{1}_y = \mathbf{1}_z \cdot \mathbf{1}_z = 1 \tag{A.2-8}$$

$$\mathbf{1}_x \cdot \mathbf{1}_y = \mathbf{1}_y \cdot \mathbf{1}_x = \mathbf{1}_y \cdot \mathbf{1}_z = \mathbf{1}_z \cdot \mathbf{1}_y = \mathbf{1}_z \cdot \mathbf{1}_x = \mathbf{1}_x \cdot \mathbf{1}_z = 0$$

with corresponding results for the other two systems.

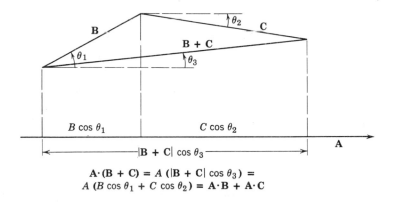

$$\mathbf{A} \cdot (\mathbf{B} + \mathbf{C}) = A \, (|\mathbf{B} + \mathbf{C}| \cos \theta_3) =$$
$$A \, (B \cos \theta_1 + C \cos \theta_2) = \mathbf{A} \cdot \mathbf{B} + \mathbf{A} \cdot \mathbf{C}$$

Fig. A.2e.   The projection of the sum is the sum of the projections.

The scalar product of a vector $\mathbf{A}$ with a unit vector $\mathbf{1}_l$ in any direction is the component of $\mathbf{A}$ in the direction of l:

$$\mathbf{A} \cdot \mathbf{1}_l = A_l \tag{A.2-9}$$

By a theorem of geometry concerning projections, it is easy to see that the scalar product obeys the distributive law (see Fig. A.2e):

$$\mathbf{A} \cdot (\mathbf{B} + \mathbf{C}) = \mathbf{A} \cdot \mathbf{B} + \mathbf{A} \cdot \mathbf{C} \tag{A.2-10}$$

A consequence of eq. A.2–10 is that we can calculate $\mathbf{A} \cdot \mathbf{B}$ in terms of components by use of eqs. A.2–1 and A.2–8:

$$\begin{aligned}
\mathbf{A} \cdot \mathbf{B} &= (A_x \mathbf{1}_x + A_y \mathbf{1}_y + A_z \mathbf{1}_z) \cdot (B_x \mathbf{1}_x + B_y \mathbf{1}_y + B_z \mathbf{1}_z) \\
&= A_x B_x + A_y B_y + A_z B_z && \text{Cartesian} \\
&= A_r B_r + A_\phi B_\phi + A_z B_z && \text{Cylindrical} \\
&= A_r B_r + A_\theta B_\theta + A_\phi B_\phi && \text{Spherical}
\end{aligned} \tag{A.2-11}$$

Derivatives and Integrals. From the definitions of the difference of two vectors and of multiplication and hence division by a scalar, it is easy to derive the concept of the derivative of a vector with respect to a scalar variable. The derivative $d\mathbf{A}/dt$ is thus defined as the limit of $(\mathbf{A}_2 - \mathbf{A}_1)/(t_2 - t_1)$ when $t_2 \to t_1$.

Similarly, the concept of the integral can be extended to vectors. The integral $\int_l \mathbf{F} \cdot d\mathbf{l}$ represents the work done on an object by a force $\mathbf{F}$ when the object moves along a path l and is defined by

$$\int_l \mathbf{F} \cdot d\mathbf{l} = \lim_{n \to \infty} \sum_{i=1}^{n} \mathbf{F}_i \cdot \mathbf{\Delta l}_i \qquad (A.2\text{--}12)$$

$$= \lim_{n \to \infty} \sum_{i=1}^{n} F_i \, \Delta l_i \cos \theta_i$$

in accordance with the usual definition of an integral.

A surface integral of the scalar product of a variable vector and a differential of area is called a flux. The flux of $\mathbf{A}$ through a surface $\mathbf{S}$ is written

$$\int_S \mathbf{A} \cdot d\mathbf{S} = \lim_{n \to \infty} \sum_{i=1}^{n} \mathbf{A}_i \cdot \mathbf{\Delta S}_i = \lim_{n \to \infty} \sum_{i=1}^{n} A_i \, \Delta S_i \cos \theta_i \quad (A.2\text{--}13)$$

The integrands in the last two expressions are scalars. An example of an integral over vector elements is the one involved in the vector potential, eq. 7.6–7:

$$\oint_l \frac{d\mathbf{l}}{r} = \lim_{n \to \infty} \sum_{i=1}^{n} \frac{\mathbf{\Delta l}_i}{r_i}$$

$$= \lim_{n \to \infty} \sum_{i=1}^{n} \left[\mathbf{1}_x \frac{\Delta x_i}{r_i} + \mathbf{1}_y \frac{\Delta y_i}{r_i} + \mathbf{1}_z \frac{\Delta z_i}{r_i} \right] \quad (A.2\text{--}14)$$

The Gradient. Other types of derivative operations can be obtained by use of the vector operator ∇ ("del" or "nabla")[1] which we write in Cartesian coordinates as

$$\nabla = \mathbf{1}_x \frac{\partial}{\partial x} + \mathbf{1}_y \frac{\partial}{\partial y} + \mathbf{1}_z \frac{\partial}{\partial z} \qquad (A.2\text{--}15a)$$

---

[1] The name "del" is derived from "delta"; nabla comes from a Hebrew word for a triangular-shaped harp or psaltery. "Del" is simpler to use, but "nabla" is coming to be preferred because it avoids confusion.

To allow ∇ to operate on a scalar function $f(x, y, z)$ means to calculate

$$\nabla f = 1_x \frac{\partial f}{\partial x} + 1_y \frac{\partial f}{\partial y} + 1_z \frac{\partial f}{\partial z} \qquad \text{(A.2–15b)}$$

This vector is called the gradient of f, written sometimes as **grad** f instead of ∇f.

To derive the properties of the gradient, consider an arbitrary straight line in space, and let l be the distance measured along it from some reference point. Then when the distance increases by dl, the corresponding variations dx, dy, and dz in the coordinates are equal to the products of dl with the respective direction cosines. Hence we can write these cosines as

$$\frac{\partial x}{\partial l}, \frac{\partial y}{\partial l}, \frac{\partial z}{\partial l}; \qquad \text{direction cosines of line } l \qquad \text{(A.2–16)}$$

where the partial derivative notation is used to imply that variation along this line only is being considered. The unit vector along the line is therefore

$$1_l = 1_x \frac{\partial x}{\partial l} + 1_y \frac{\partial y}{\partial l} + 1_z \frac{\partial z}{\partial l} \qquad \text{(A.2–17)}$$

and the scalar product with ∇f is

$$\nabla f \cdot 1_l = \frac{\partial f}{\partial x} \frac{\partial x}{\partial l} + \frac{\partial f}{\partial y} \frac{\partial y}{\partial l} + \frac{\partial f}{\partial z} \frac{\partial z}{\partial l} \qquad \text{(A.2–18)}$$

which is according to calculus the rate of change of f with l.

The component of the gradient of a function, taken in a given direction, is thus the rate of change of the function in that direction. The greatest component of a vector is that taken parallel to itself, and so we can say that the gradient of a particular scalar function is the vector that represents the direction and magnitude of the greatest space rate of increase of that scalar function.

The expressions for ∇f as given in Table A.2A at the end of this section should be easily derivable by the reader (problem A.2a).

Finally, the differential of f corresponding to a vector displacement $dl = 1_x dx + 1_y dy + 1_z dz$ is clearly

$$df = \nabla f \cdot dl = \frac{\partial f}{\partial x} dx + \frac{\partial f}{\partial y} dy + \frac{\partial f}{\partial z} dz \qquad \text{(A.2–19)}$$

From this formula we can write the difference between the values of $f(x, y, z)$ at two different points as a line integral over the gradient:

$$f(x_2, y_2, z_2) - f(x_1, y_1, z_1) = \int_1^2 df = \int_1^2 \nabla f \cdot dl \qquad \text{(A.2–20)}$$

where the scalar-product integral is to be taken from point 1 to point 2 over any path connecting the two (provided f is properly defined, etc., along this path).

The Divergence and the Divergence Theorem.   The scalar product of ∇ and a vector $\mathbf{A}$ yields another type of derivative quantity called the divergence, written div $\mathbf{A}$ or $\nabla \cdot \mathbf{A}$:

$$\text{div } \mathbf{A} = \nabla \cdot \mathbf{A} = \frac{\partial A_x}{\partial x} + \frac{\partial A_y}{\partial y} + \frac{\partial A_z}{\partial z} \qquad \text{(A.2–21)}$$

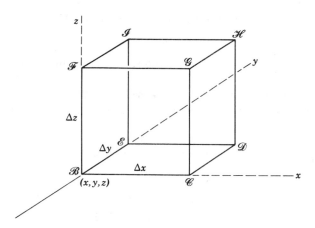

Fig. A.2f.   An element of volume for calculating flux.

It is understood that A_x, A_y, and A_z are each in general functions of x, y, and z, a fact which we can denote by writing them $A_x(x, y, z)$, $A_y(x, y, z)$, and $A_z(x, y, z)$.

We shall now prove that div $\mathbf{A}$ represents the outward flux of $\mathbf{A}$ per unit volume, leaving any infinitesimal volume surrounding the point at which div $\mathbf{A}$ is evaluated. Consider a rectangular box, as shown in Fig. A.2f with sides Δx, Δy, and Δz and one point $\mathscr{B}$ whose coordinates are (x, y, z). The flux of $\mathbf{A}$ out from this box is conveniently calculated by taking the faces in opposite pairs. For faces $\mathscr{CDHG}$ and $\mathscr{BEIF}$, the flux is given by the product of the area $\Delta y \, \Delta z$ and $\bar{A}_x$, the average value of A_x over the respective face. For $\mathscr{CDHG}$, the positive value of $\bar{A}_x$ is needed, and for $\mathscr{BEIF}$, the negative of $\bar{A}_x$. The net flux is thus $\Delta y \, \Delta z$ times the difference of $\bar{A}_x$ on the two faces.

Although A_x will vary over the two faces in question, if the box is small enough the difference between the two averages will be very closely equal to the difference between the values of A_x at $\mathscr{C}$ and at $\mathscr{B}$. This difference is $A_x(x + \Delta x, y, z) - A_x(x, y, z)$, which is an increment of A_x with respect to a small change in x only. Using the calculus expression for the differential, eq. A.1–7, we can write this difference as $(\partial A_x/\partial x)\, \Delta x$ and the net flux out of the two faces normal to the x-axis as $(\partial A_x/\partial x)\, \Delta x\, \Delta y\, \Delta z$, where the derivative is evaluated at (x, y, z). This result is only approximate, because of the difference between the differential and the increment and because the value of A_x at the corner of a face is not generally equal to the average over the face.

The approximate value for the flux out through all the faces is seen to be

$$\left(\frac{\partial A_x}{\partial x} + \frac{\partial A_y}{\partial y} + \frac{\partial A_z}{\partial z}\right) \Delta x\, \Delta y\, \Delta z$$

if points $\mathscr{B}$ and $\mathscr{E}$ are used for the difference of two values of A_y, and points $\mathscr{B}$ and $\mathscr{F}$ for A_z.

The flux out per unit volume is equal to this result divided by $\Delta \tau = \Delta x\, \Delta y\, \Delta z$. If, after dividing, we allow Δx, Δy, and Δz to approach zero, the inaccuracies referred to all disappear, and we see that $\nabla \cdot \mathbf{A}$ represents exactly the flux out per unit volume.[2]

If in place of the vector $\mathbf{A}$ we use a hydrodynamic velocity $\mathbf{v}$, we have a quantity div $\mathbf{v}$ that represents the outflowing fluid per unit volume, thus accounting for the name "divergence" and that of its negative, the "convergence." Such an outflow must (except for a creation of matter) be accompanied by a time rate of decrease in the density of that fluid. The application of this concept to the flow of charge is taken up in section 5.8.

Let us now apply the theorem we have just proved to the calculation of the flux out of an arbitrary volume of any size.

If we divide the arbitrary volume into infinitesimal, rectangular volume elements $d\tau = dx\, dy\, dz$ and add the net flux out of each element, we obtain an integral which represents the net flux out of the surface bounding the volume, since every pair of adjacent faces of two volume elements will have equal and opposite fluxes that cancel. The effect of "left-over" pieces of irregular shape just inside the boundary will disappear in the limit.

Thus the flux out through the surface becomes the volume integral

$$\int_\tau \nabla \cdot \mathbf{A}\, d\tau$$

But the same flux can be found by the surface integral

$$\int_S \mathbf{A} \cdot d\mathbf{S}$$

---

[2] For a calculation that shows more explicitly how the errors disappear in the limit, see E. R. Peck, *Electricity and Magnetism*, McGraw-Hill, New York, 1953, pp. 38–40, or any advanced calculus text.

in which S is the bounding surface of the volume τ. Hence the two integrals must be equal, and we arrive at a purely mathematical relation between the divergence of any vector $\mathbf{A}$ and the values of its normal component on the surface:

$$\int_S \mathbf{A} \cdot d\mathbf{S} = \int_\tau \nabla \cdot \mathbf{A} \, d\tau \qquad (A.2\text{-}22a)$$

or, without using vector notation,

$$\int_S A_n \, dS = \int_\tau \left(\frac{\partial A_x}{\partial x} + \frac{\partial A_y}{\partial y} + \frac{\partial A_z}{\partial z} \right) d\tau \qquad (A.2\text{-}22b)$$

This theorem is known as Green's theorem, or sometimes as Gauss' theorem, and is proved by direct integration in books on advanced calculus. We shall call it the divergence theorem.

We can define the divergence in general by a limiting process, taking an infinitesimal volume $\Delta\tau$ and its surface ΔS,

$$\nabla \cdot \mathbf{A} = \text{div } \mathbf{A} = \lim_{\Delta\tau \to 0} \frac{1}{\Delta\tau} \int_{\Delta S} \mathbf{A} \cdot d\mathbf{S} \qquad (A.2\text{-}23)$$

The expressions of div $\mathbf{A}$ in cylindrical and spherical coördinates can be found by similar processes to that used for Cartesian coordinates if care is taken to note that, in calculating the difference between the fluxes through two opposite faces, the variation in the product of the relevant component of $\mathbf{A}$ and the area must be considered. For instance, the face in a cylindrical coordinate box whose vector lies along $\mathbf{1}_r$ has an area $r \, d\phi \, dz$. We will end up with an expression involving $(1/r) \, \partial \, (rA_r)/\partial r$ for this term. It is left to the reader (problem A.2b) to derive these expressions in detail.

There are several theorems of a similar nature to the divergence theorem that can in fact be derived from it. Four of them are the following, each relating an integral over a volume τ and one over the bounding surface S of τ:

$$\int_S u \, d\mathbf{S} = \int_\tau \nabla u \, d\tau \qquad (A.2\text{-}24)$$

$$\int_S \mathbf{r}(\mathbf{M} \cdot d\mathbf{S}) = \int_\tau [\mathbf{r}(\nabla \cdot \mathbf{M}) + \mathbf{M}] \, d\tau \qquad (A.2\text{-}25)$$

$$\int_S d\mathbf{S} \times \mathbf{A} = \int_\tau \nabla \times \mathbf{A} \, d\tau \qquad (A.2\text{-}26)$$

$$\int_S \mathbf{A}(\mathbf{M} \cdot d\mathbf{S}) = \int_\tau \overline{(\nabla \cdot \mathbf{M})\mathbf{A}} \, d\tau \qquad (A.2\text{-}27)$$

The proofs of these involve simple vector identities discussed later in this appendix and are left as exercises for the reader (suitable hints are given in problems A.2e, A.2f, A.2g, and A.2h). In these formulas, u is a variable scalar, **M** and **A** are variable vectors, and **r** is the displacement vector from an arbitrary origin. The bar over the integrand in eq. A.2–27 signifies that ∇ operates derivativewise on both **M** and **A**.

The various quantities we have introduced up to now either have been defined in a way independent of the coordinate system or, as in the case

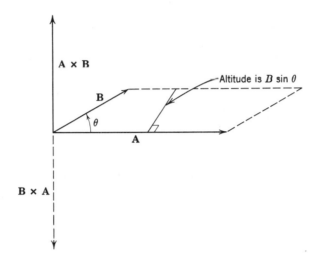

Fig. A.2g. Illustrating the vector product.

of the gradient, are easily seen to be independent of the coordinates. It is less evident in the case of the divergence; the various physical applications serve intuitively to make it clear that, if $\nabla \cdot \mathbf{A}$ were calculated with a differently oriented set of axes, the same value would result. A formal proof is given in Appendix A.4.

The Vector Product. The other type of vector multiplication is called the vector product. The vector product (or "cross product") of two vectors **A** and **B** is written $\mathbf{A} \times \mathbf{B}$, read "*A* cross *B*." It is a vector whose magnitude is $AB \sin \theta$, where θ is the angle between **A** and **B**, and whose direction is normal to the plane of **A** and **B**, related to **A** and **B** as z is to x and y in a right-handed system (stated shortly: rotate **A** toward **B** with the fingers of the right hand, and the thumb will point along $\mathbf{A} \times \mathbf{B}$). As shown in Fig. A.2g, $\mathbf{A} \times \mathbf{B}$ has the magnitude of the area of the parallelogram constructed on **A** and **B** and may in fact be taken to represent that area. The product $\mathbf{B} \times \mathbf{A}$, from its definition, is oppositely directed to **A ✕ B**, and so the vector product does not obey the commutative law; we have instead

$$\mathbf{A} \times \mathbf{B} = -\mathbf{B} \times \mathbf{A} \qquad (A.2\text{--}28a)$$

It is clear that, if m is a scalar,

$$(m\mathbf{A}) \times \mathbf{B} = \mathbf{A} \times (m\mathbf{B}) = m(\mathbf{A} \times \mathbf{B}) \qquad (A.2\text{--}28b)$$

If **A** and **B** are parallel, $\mathbf{A} \times \mathbf{B} = 0$; a special case of this is

$$\mathbf{A} \times \mathbf{A} = 0 \qquad (A.2\text{--}28c)$$

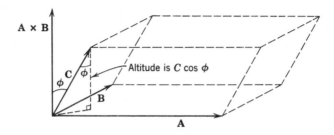

Fig. A.2h.   Illustrating the triple scalar product.

From the unit coordinate vectors $\mathbf{1}_x$, $\mathbf{1}_y$, $\mathbf{1}_z$ we get immediately the results

$$\begin{aligned}
\mathbf{1}_x \times \mathbf{1}_x &= \mathbf{1}_y \times \mathbf{1}_y = \mathbf{1}_z \times \mathbf{1}_z = 0 \\
\mathbf{1}_x \times \mathbf{1}_y &= -\mathbf{1}_y \times \mathbf{1}_x = \mathbf{1}_z \\
\mathbf{1}_y \times \mathbf{1}_z &= -\mathbf{1}_z \times \mathbf{1}_y = \mathbf{1}_x \\
\mathbf{1}_z \times \mathbf{1}_x &= -\mathbf{1}_x \times \mathbf{1}_z = \mathbf{1}_y
\end{aligned} \qquad (A.2\text{--}29)$$

The right-handed nature of the coordinate system becomes evident in the locations of the minus signs in these equations.   Exactly similar relations can be written for the unit vectors of cylindrical and spherical coordinate systems.

Before we prove the distributive law for the vector product, it is convenient to consider the triple scalar product, which is the scalar product of one vector with the vector product of two others.   In Fig. A.2h we show a parallelepiped constructed on three vectors **A**, **B**, and **C**.   The component of **C** in the direction of $\mathbf{A} \times \mathbf{B}$, namely $C \cos \phi$, is the altitude of the three-dimensional figure, so that $(\mathbf{A} \times \mathbf{B}) \cdot \mathbf{C} = \mathbf{C} \cdot (\mathbf{A} \times \mathbf{B})$ is equal to its volume τ (area of base times altitude).   The expression $(\mathbf{B} \times \mathbf{A}) \cdot \mathbf{C}$ represents the negative of the volume in the figure shown.

Since any two of the three vectors can be used to form a base of the figure, there are three vector products we can use, two ways of writing the scalar product, and both positive and negative results for each way. Thus the volume τ can be written in twelve ways as a triple scalar product:

$$\tau = (\mathbf{A} \times \mathbf{B}) \cdot \mathbf{C} = \mathbf{C} \cdot (\mathbf{A} \times \mathbf{B}) = -(\mathbf{B} \times \mathbf{A}) \cdot \mathbf{C} = -\mathbf{C} \cdot (\mathbf{B} \times \mathbf{A})$$
$$= (\mathbf{B} \times \mathbf{C}) \cdot \mathbf{A} = \mathbf{A} \cdot (\mathbf{B} \times \mathbf{C}) = -(\mathbf{C} \times \mathbf{B}) \cdot \mathbf{A} = -\mathbf{A} \cdot (\mathbf{C} \times \mathbf{B})$$
$$= (\mathbf{C} \times \mathbf{A}) \cdot \mathbf{B} = \mathbf{B} \cdot (\mathbf{C} \times \mathbf{A}) = -(\mathbf{A} \times \mathbf{C}) \cdot \mathbf{B} = -\mathbf{B} \cdot (\mathbf{A} \times \mathbf{C})$$

$$(A.2\text{--}30)$$

The parentheses are not needed in these expressions, since $(\mathbf{A} \cdot \mathbf{B}) \times \mathbf{C}$ is meaningless, but are sometimes useful for clarity. It will be noted that equal expressions are always obtained by interchanging the dot and the cross. This operation, together with the commutation for the dot product and the "anti-commutation" relation for the cross product, will serve to transform any given triple scalar product into any other desired form.

Since $\mathbf{A} \times \mathbf{A} = 0$, it follows that, if any two of the members of a triple scalar product are equal, the triple product vanishes. The volume of Fig. A.2h is then zero.

Now let us prove the distributive law for vector products. We wish to show that

$$\mathbf{A} \times (\mathbf{B} + \mathbf{C}) = \mathbf{A} \times \mathbf{B} + \mathbf{A} \times \mathbf{C} \qquad (A.2\text{--}31)$$

This relation will hold if it is true for each component of the two sides of the equation—that is, if it is true for the scalar product of each side with each of the unit vectors in any coordinate system. Thus it will be adequate to prove the relation derived by taking the dot product of eq. A.2–31 with an arbitrary vector $\mathbf{D}$ (the scalar product is distributive). We wish to prove that

$$\mathbf{D} \cdot \mathbf{A} \times (\mathbf{B} + \mathbf{C}) = \mathbf{D} \cdot \mathbf{A} \times \mathbf{B} + \mathbf{D} \cdot \mathbf{A} \times \mathbf{C} \qquad (A.2\text{--}32)$$

But by eq. A.2–30, we have

$$\mathbf{D} \cdot \mathbf{A} \times \mathbf{B} + \mathbf{D} \cdot \mathbf{A} \times \mathbf{C} = (\mathbf{D} \times \mathbf{A}) \cdot \mathbf{B} + (\mathbf{D} \times \mathbf{A}) \cdot \mathbf{C}$$
$$= (\mathbf{D} \times \mathbf{A}) \cdot (\mathbf{B} + \mathbf{C})$$

and the latter, again by eq. A.2–30, is equal to $\mathbf{D} \cdot \mathbf{A} \times (\mathbf{B} + \mathbf{C})$. Letting $\mathbf{D}$ represent in succession $\mathbf{1}_x$, $\mathbf{1}_y$, and $\mathbf{1}_z$, we see that eq. A.2–32 is proved.

A consequence of this proof is that the sum of the vectors representing two areas with a common side is equal to the vector of the area produced by the common side and the vector sum of the other two sides as shown in Fig. A.2i. The vectors $\mathbf{A} \times \mathbf{B}$ and $\mathbf{A} \times \mathbf{C}$ represent the areas $\mathcal{MN2P}$ and $\mathcal{NOR2}$ respectively. Their sum is equal to the vector representing the area $\mathcal{MORP}$. This result is a proof that the area vectors can be added in the ordinary way, corresponding to the result that one would obtain by projecting the areas on the three coordinate planes. (If this property were proved first from geometrical considerations, eq. A.2–32 will follow immediately.)

With the distributive law and eqs. A.2–29 we can write the vector product in terms of Cartesian components

$$\mathbf{A} \times \mathbf{B} = (A_x \mathbf{1}_x + A_y \mathbf{1}_y + A_z \mathbf{1}_z) \times (B_x \mathbf{1}_x + B_y \mathbf{1}_y + B_z \mathbf{1}_z) \qquad (\text{A.2–33})$$
$$= (A_y B_z - A_z B_y)\mathbf{1}_x + (A_z B_x - A_x B_z)\mathbf{1}_y + (A_x B_y - A_y B_x)\mathbf{1}_z$$

which can be written in a symmetric way in determinant form (see Appendix A.5):

$$\mathbf{A} \times \mathbf{B} = \begin{vmatrix} \mathbf{1}_x & \mathbf{1}_y & \mathbf{1}_z \\ A_x & A_y & A_z \\ B_x & B_y & B_z \end{vmatrix} \qquad (\text{A.2–34})$$

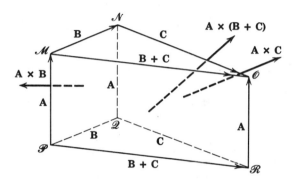

Fig. A.2i. The addition of area vectors.

A similar determinant can be written for the other two coordinate systems, provided the unit vectors are written in such an order that they form a right-handed system.

This determinant form is convenient for writing the triple scalar product, for the scalar product of one vector with another can be found by replacing the unit vectors in the Cartesian expression of the former by the corresponding components of the latter. Thus we can write

$$\mathbf{A} \cdot \mathbf{B} \times \mathbf{C} = \begin{vmatrix} A_x & A_y & A_z \\ B_x & B_y & B_z \\ C_x & C_y & C_z \end{vmatrix} \qquad (\text{A.2–35})$$

and the various forms of $\mathbf{A} \cdot \mathbf{B} \times \mathbf{C}$ can be found from the rules for determinants (section A.5).

As an example of a vector product different from most of the examples in the text, consider the torque produced by a force $\mathbf{F}$ acting on an object at a point $\mathcal{O}'$ whose displacement is $\mathbf{r}$ from a point $\mathcal{O}$ on an axis about

which the torque is desired.   The direction of the axis we shall denote
by 1_l (Fig. A.2j).   Let us first consider the torque produced by $\mathbf{r}'$ and $\mathbf{F}'$
in the plane $\mathscr{P}$ normal to 1_l.   As shown in the figure, the moment arm
for $\mathbf{F}'$ is $r' \sin \theta$, and the torque is $F'r' \sin \theta = |\mathbf{r}' \times \mathbf{F}'|$ which we can
write $\mathbf{r}' \times \mathbf{F}' \cdot 1_l$ since $\mathbf{r}' \times \mathbf{F}'$ is in the direction of 1_l.

Now, for $\mathbf{F}$ which is not in $\mathscr{P}$, we need consider only the component of
$\mathbf{F}$ in $\mathscr{P}$, which we can obtain as a vector $\mathbf{F}'$ by subtracting from $\mathbf{F}$ the
vector $1_l(1_l \cdot \mathbf{F})$ which is parallel to 1_l and of length equal to the component

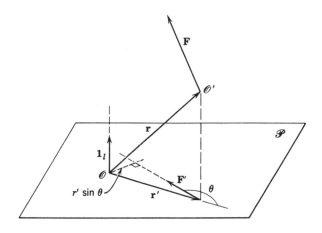

Fig. A.2j. Illustrating a torque as a vector.

of $\mathbf{F}$ in that direction.   We can find the projection $\mathbf{r}'$ of $\mathbf{r}$ on $\mathscr{P}$ in the same
way.   Thus

$$\mathbf{F}' = \mathbf{F} - 1_l(1_l \cdot \mathbf{F})$$

$$\mathbf{r}' = \mathbf{r} - 1_l(1_l \cdot \mathbf{r})$$

Now we can find the torque as

$$\mathscr{L} = \mathbf{r}' \times \mathbf{F}' \cdot 1_l = \mathbf{r} \times \mathbf{F} \cdot 1_l \qquad \text{(A.2–36)}$$

by use of the distributive law and the vanishing of the triple scalar product
with two equal vectors.   Since eq. A.2–36 holds for any 1_l, we are justified
in writing a torque as a vector:

$$\mathscr{L} = \mathbf{r} \times \mathbf{F} \qquad \text{(A.2–37)}$$

whose component in any direction gives the torque about an axis through
the origin of $\mathbf{r}$ in that direction.

The Curl and Stokes' Theorem.   The curl of a vector $\mathbf{A}$ is defined in terms of the operator ∇ as $\nabla \times \mathbf{A}$.   By reference to eqs. A.2–33 and A.2–34, we see that it may be written in the forms

$$\mathbf{curl}\ \mathbf{A} = \nabla \times \mathbf{A} = \left(\frac{\partial A_z}{\partial y} - \frac{\partial A_y}{\partial z}\right)\mathbf{1}_x + \left(\frac{\partial A_x}{\partial z} - \frac{\partial A_z}{\partial x}\right)\mathbf{1}_y$$

$$+ \left(\frac{\partial A_y}{\partial x} - \frac{\partial A_x}{\partial y}\right)\mathbf{1}_z \quad \text{(A.2–38}a\text{)}$$

$$= \begin{vmatrix} \mathbf{1}_x & \mathbf{1}_y & \mathbf{1}_z \\ \dfrac{\partial}{\partial x} & \dfrac{\partial}{\partial y} & \dfrac{\partial}{\partial z} \\ A_x & A_y & A_z \end{vmatrix} \quad\quad\quad \text{(A.2–38}b\text{)}$$

Fig. A.2k.   An element of area for calculating circulation.

where the determinant form must be understood as a symbolic abbreviation for the other form.

We shall now prove that the component of **curl A** in any direction represents the circulation per unit area of the vector **A**, taken around a small area of any shape in a plane normal to the given direction.   Let us choose first a rectangular area parallel to the x–y plane, whose sides are Δx and Δy and one of whose corners is at the point (x, y, z), as in Fig. A.2k. Next we must choose a positive direction for the calculation of the circulation $\oint \mathbf{A} \cdot \mathbf{dl}$.   We use the right-hand rule, whereby the fingers are directed around the periphery in the positive direction while the thumb points along the normal to the area selected as positive.   In the figure, the choice of the z-direction as positive for the normal to the area leads to the order of circulation $\mathscr{BCDE}$.

Along paths $\mathscr{BC}$ and $\mathscr{DE}$, the component A_x is required in the integral. Since $\mathbf{dl}$ is $\mathbf{1}_x\,dx$ on $\mathscr{BC}$ and is $-\mathbf{1}_x\,dx$ on $\mathscr{DE}$, the difference between the averages of A_x on the two segments will enter the calculation when the contributions of $\mathscr{BC}$ and $\mathscr{DE}$ are added.   Exactly as in the divergence calculation, we can approximate this difference by evaluating A_x at $\mathscr{B}$ and at $\mathscr{E}$ instead of averaging along the paths.   The difference between A_x at $\mathscr{E}$ and that at $\mathscr{B}$ can be written as a differential.

The part of $\oint \mathbf{A} \cdot \mathbf{dl}$ arising from the two paths parallel to the x-axis is then

$$\bar{A}_{x\mathscr{BC}}\,\Delta x - \bar{A}_{x\mathscr{DE}}\,\Delta x \simeq (A_{x\mathscr{B}} - A_{x\mathscr{E}})\,\Delta x$$

$$= -(A_{x\mathscr{E}} - A_{x\mathscr{B}})\,\Delta x \simeq -\left(\frac{\partial A_x}{\partial y}\,\Delta y\right)\Delta x$$

where the derivative is evaluated at (x, y, z).

Similarly, the contribution from sides $\mathscr{CD}$ and $\mathscr{EB}$ involves A_y.   We have

$$\bar{A}_{y\mathscr{CD}}\,\Delta y - \bar{A}_{y\mathscr{EB}}\,\Delta y \simeq (A_{y\mathscr{C}} - A_{y\mathscr{B}})\,\Delta y \simeq \left(\frac{\partial A_y}{\partial x}\,\Delta x\right)\Delta y$$

so the total circulation is, approximately,

$$\oint \mathbf{A} \cdot \mathbf{dl} \simeq \left(\frac{\partial A_y}{\partial x} - \frac{\partial A_x}{\partial y}\right)\Delta x\,\Delta y = (\text{curl } \mathbf{A})_z\,\Delta x\,\Delta y$$

and the z component of the curl as given in eq. A.2–38a is seen to be, accurately, the circulation per unit area around a rectangle of sides $\Delta x\,\Delta y$, in the limit when the sides go to zero.

This proof is immediately extendable to the other two components. The method of proving formally that these three components form a vector is indicated in section A.4.   Let us now consider an arbitrary area of any size lying in the x–y plane and calculate the circulation around it.   We first divide it into small rectangular areas of sides Δx and Δy, as shown in Fig. A.2l.   Then the sum of the circulations around all the small rectangles, plus that around the left-over pieces at the edges, will add up to the circulation around the periphery l, since each interior segment is included once in each direction with a resultant cancellation.

Since the circulation about the ith area is $(\text{curl } \mathbf{A})_{zi}\,\Delta x_i\,\Delta y_i$, approximately, the sum is also a sum of the type used in a surface integral.   We have

$$\oint_l \mathbf{A} \cdot \mathbf{dl} \simeq \sum_i \oint_i \mathbf{A} \cdot \mathbf{dl} \simeq \sum_i (\text{curl } \mathbf{A})_{zi}\,\Delta x_i\,\Delta y_i$$

and in the limit in which all the Δx_i and Δy_i go to zero, we have

$$\oint \mathbf{A} \cdot d\mathbf{l} = \int_S (\operatorname{curl} \mathbf{A})_z \, dS$$

This is a statement of Stokes' theorem, applied to one component of the curl. From this result, we can say that around any small area ΔS, the circulation is a scalar product $\operatorname{curl} \mathbf{A} \cdot \Delta \mathbf{S}$. Furthermore, we can treat Fig. A.2l as showing a general area that need not be a plane. The rectangles can become small areas of any shape and orientation. In place of the one-component equation just given, we can write the general form of Stokes' theorem

$$\oint \mathbf{A} \cdot d\mathbf{l} = \int_S (\nabla \times \mathbf{A}) \cdot d\mathbf{S} = \int_S \operatorname{curl} \mathbf{A} \cdot d\mathbf{S} \qquad (\text{A.2--39})$$

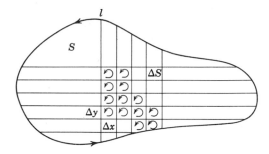

Fig. A.2l.   A method of proving Stokes' theorem.

where the surface integral is over any surface whose boundary is a given closed path l.

We can now write a general definition for any component of **curl A**, by applying Stokes' theorem to any small area $\Delta \mathbf{S}$ whose normal is along the unit vector $\mathbf{1}_n$:

$$(\operatorname{curl} \mathbf{A})_n = \nabla \times \mathbf{A} \cdot \mathbf{1}_n = \lim_{\Delta S \to 0} \frac{1}{\Delta S} \oint_{\substack{\text{boundary} \\ \text{of } \Delta S}} \mathbf{A} \cdot d\mathbf{l} \qquad (\text{A.2--40})$$

where again the right-hand rule is used to relate the direction of circulation to $\mathbf{1}_n$. A convenient and graphic synonym for the curl of a vector is "circulation density."

The rule of eq. A.2–40 can be used to find expressions for the curl in cylindrical and spherical coordinates, using a differential method similar to that used for Cartesian coordinates. Care must be taken that when two opposite sides of an elementary area are unequal—e.g., $r \, d\theta$ and $(r + dr) \, d\theta$—this difference is considered when differentials are written. We must, for instance, write $d(rE_\theta)$ in place of $r \, d(E_\theta)$.

The results are listed in Table A.2A and are left to the reader for verification.

The hydrodynamic significance of the curl is useful for illustrating its meaning.   Consider **curl v** where **v** is the vector representing the velocity of the fluid at any point.   We wish to show that $\frac{1}{2}$ **curl v** represents the angular velocity of a small portion of the fluid.   Consider two short lines of length δx and δy in the x- and y-direction connecting particles in the fluid at a certain point (Fig. A.2m).   Each line will tend to rotate in a

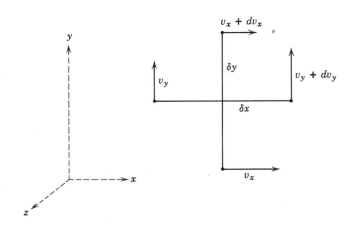

Fig. A.2m.   Illustrating the calculation of mean angular velocity in a fluid.

plane parallel to the x–y plane if the components of velocity perpendicular to it are different at each end.   The angular velocity of δx, for example, is given by dv_y, the relative y velocity of the forward end with respect to the rear end, divided by δx, namely, $[(\partial v_y/\partial x)\,\delta x]/\delta x = \partial v_y/\partial x$.   Similarly, the angular velocity of δy is $-\partial v_x/\partial y$ (the negative sign is evident from the figure; positive is taken as rotation from x toward y).   Thus the average angular velocity for the two lines is

$$\omega_z = \tfrac{1}{2}(\partial v_y/\partial x - \partial v_x/\partial y) = \tfrac{1}{2}(\text{curl } \mathbf{v})_z$$

It is not hard to prove that we get the same result if we consider a variable line of length δl at an arbitrary angle θ with the x-axis, and average over θ (problem A.2n).   The generalization to the other components of angular velocity is straightforward.   Because of this connection with angular velocity, the curl is sometimes called the "rotation;" the symbol **rot A** is used in place of **curl A** in European textbooks.

There are four theorems readily derivable from Stokes' theorem, corresponding to those derived from the divergence theorem:

$$\oint u\,\mathbf{dl} = \int_S \mathbf{dS} \times \nabla u \tag{A.2–41}$$

$$\int_S \mathbf{r}(\nabla \times \mathbf{A} \cdot \mathbf{dS}) - \oint \mathbf{r}(\mathbf{A} \cdot \mathbf{dl}) = \int_S \mathbf{dS} \times \mathbf{A} \tag{A.2–42}$$

$$\oint \mathbf{dl} \times \mathbf{A} = \int_S \nabla(\mathbf{A} \cdot \mathbf{dS}) - \int_S \mathbf{dS}(\nabla \cdot \mathbf{A}) \tag{A.2–43}$$

$$\oint \mathbf{A}(\mathbf{M} \cdot \mathbf{dl}) = \int_S \mathbf{dS} \times \overline{(\nabla \cdot \mathbf{M})\mathbf{A}} \tag{A.2–44}$$

Proofs are called for and hints given in problems A.2*o*, A.2*p*, A.2*q*, and A.2*s*.

Triple Vector Product.　Another vector quantity of some importance is the triple vector product, $(\mathbf{A} \times \mathbf{B}) \times \mathbf{C}$.　The parentheses are needed for this product, for $\mathbf{A} \times (\mathbf{B} \times \mathbf{C})$ is for instance quite a different quantity. The product $(\mathbf{A} \times \mathbf{B}) \times \mathbf{C}$ is a vector perpendicular to $\mathbf{C}$ and to $\mathbf{A} \times \mathbf{B}$; since the latter is normal to the plane of $\mathbf{A}$ and $\mathbf{B}$, the triple product $(\mathbf{A} \times \mathbf{B}) \times \mathbf{C}$ lies in the plane of $\mathbf{A}$ and $\mathbf{B}$.　On the other hand $\mathbf{A} \times (\mathbf{B} \times \mathbf{C})$ lies in the plane of $\mathbf{B}$ and $\mathbf{C}$.

We are thus led to expect that:

$$(\mathbf{A} \times \mathbf{B}) \times \mathbf{C} = m\mathbf{A} + n\mathbf{B}$$

where m and n are scalars.　If we take the scalar product of each term with $\mathbf{C}$, the quantity on the left will vanish and we will have

$$m(\mathbf{A} \cdot \mathbf{C}) + n(\mathbf{B} \cdot \mathbf{C}) = 0$$

Letting $n/(\mathbf{A} \cdot \mathbf{C}) = -m/(\mathbf{B} \cdot \mathbf{C}) = k$, where k is another scalar, we have

$$(\mathbf{A} \times \mathbf{B}) \times \mathbf{C} = k[\mathbf{B}(\mathbf{A} \cdot \mathbf{C}) - \mathbf{A}(\mathbf{B} \cdot \mathbf{C})]$$

Since the magnitudes of the vectors appear equally in all terms, k must be independent of them.　It is not hard to show by expansion in terms of Cartesian coordinates that $k = 1$.　Thus we have

$$(\mathbf{A} \times \mathbf{B}) \times \mathbf{C} = -\mathbf{C} \times (\mathbf{A} \times \mathbf{B}) = \mathbf{C} \times (\mathbf{B} \times \mathbf{A}) = \mathbf{B}(\mathbf{A} \cdot \mathbf{C}) - \mathbf{A}(\mathbf{B} \cdot \mathbf{C}) \tag{A.2–45}$$

A useful mnemonic rule for these relations is that the first term in the expansion of the triple scalar product contains as a factor the vector that lies in the middle of the product, multiplied by the scalar product of the other two and that the second term is the product of the other vector inside the original parenthesis, again multiplied by the scalar product of the remaining two vectors.

Vector Identities.   There are a number of vector identities involving ∇ that are of importance.   Let us first consider expressions involving one application of the operator ∇ and two scalar or vector variables.   We shall denote arbitrary scalars by u and v and vectors by $\mathbf{A}$ and $\mathbf{B}$.   The various possible combinations are:

1. $\nabla(uv)$	7. $v\nabla u$	13. $\mathbf{A} \cdot \nabla \times \mathbf{B}$	19. $\overline{(\nabla u) \cdot \mathbf{A}}$
2. $\overline{\nabla(\mathbf{A} \cdot \mathbf{B})}$	8. $\mathbf{A} \cdot \nabla u$	14. $\mathbf{A} \times (\nabla \times \mathbf{B})$	20. $\overline{(\nabla u) \times \mathbf{A}}$
3. $\overline{\nabla(\mathbf{A} \cdot \mathbf{B})}$	9. $\mathbf{A} \times \nabla u$	15. $(\mathbf{A} \cdot \nabla)\mathbf{B}$	21. $\overline{(\nabla \cdot \mathbf{A})\mathbf{B}}$
4. $\nabla \cdot (\mathbf{A} \times \mathbf{B})$	10. $u(\nabla \cdot \mathbf{B})$	16. $\overline{\nabla \cdot (\mathbf{B} \times \mathbf{A})}$	22. $\overline{(\nabla \times \mathbf{A}) \cdot \mathbf{B}}$
5. $\overline{\nabla \times (\mathbf{A} \times \mathbf{B})}$	11. $\mathbf{A}(\nabla \cdot \mathbf{B})$	17. $(\mathbf{A} \times \nabla) \cdot \mathbf{B}$	23. $\overline{(\nabla \times \mathbf{A}) \times \mathbf{B}}$
6. $\overline{\nabla \times (\mathbf{A} \times \mathbf{B})}$	12. $u(\nabla \times \mathbf{B})$	18. $(\mathbf{A} \times \nabla) \times \mathbf{B}$	

Many of these can be reduced to simpler forms by combining the vector rules established above with the rule for differentiation of products.[3] We have to keep in mind that the vector and derivative characters of ∇ are essentially independent.   When it is not clear upon which vectors written after ∇ the derivatives operate, a superior bar as in certain items above can be used to show "how far" the ∇ operates—e.g., we can write $\overline{\nabla \times (\mathbf{A} \times \mathbf{B})} = \overline{\nabla \times (\mathbf{A} \times \mathbf{B})} - \overline{\nabla \times (\mathbf{B} \times \mathbf{A})}$, where the order of the vectors in the last term has been interchanged to put the vector acted on adjacent to ∇.   As an example we have $\overline{(\nabla u)} \cdot \mathbf{A} = (\partial/\partial x)(uA_x) + (\partial/\partial y)(uA_y) + (\partial/\partial z)(uA_z)$, but $\overline{(\nabla u)} \cdot \mathbf{A} = A_x(\partial u/\partial x) + A_y(\partial u/\partial y) + A_z(\partial u/\partial z)$.

Of the expressions listed above, several cannot be reduced to simpler terms.   The third one can be written as a fairly complicated expression involving terms like items 14 and 15 in the list, if we first write $\overline{\nabla(\mathbf{A} \cdot \mathbf{B})} = \overline{\nabla(\mathbf{A} \cdot \mathbf{B})} + \overline{\nabla(\mathbf{B} \cdot \mathbf{A})}$ and then compare with expansions of $\mathbf{A} \times (\nabla \times \mathbf{B})$ and $\mathbf{B} \times (\nabla \times \mathbf{A})$.   An example of item 15 is found in eq. 3.2–3.   Some of the resulting identities are listed in Table A.2B.

Another set of identities is that with two applications of ∇ on one scalar or vector.   The various possible combinations are $\nabla \cdot \nabla\varphi$, $(\nabla \cdot \nabla)\mathbf{A}$, $\nabla \times (\nabla\varphi)$, $\nabla(\nabla \cdot \mathbf{A})$, $\nabla \cdot \nabla \times \mathbf{A}$, $\nabla \times (\nabla \times \mathbf{A})$, and $(\nabla \times \nabla) \times \mathbf{A}$, where φ is an arbitrary scalar function and $\mathbf{A}$ an arbitrary vector function.   Of these, the third, fifth, and last are zero because the symmetry considerations which lead to the vanishing of $\mathbf{A} \times \mathbf{A}$ and $\mathbf{B} \cdot \mathbf{B} \times \mathbf{A}$ apply also to the

---

[3] The simpler forms can also be established by writing in terms of Cartesian components.

expressions with ∇. The fourth operation is not generally reducible to a simpler form, and the result of the sixth one is given in Table A.2*B*.

The first two operations are by far the most important. The operation $\nabla \cdot \nabla$ is often written ∇^2, and sometimes Δ, and is called the Laplacian operator. Its form in Cartesian coordinates is simple (cf. section 1.10):

$$\nabla^2 u = \frac{\partial^2 u}{\partial x^2} + \frac{\partial^2 u}{\partial y^2} + \frac{\partial^2 u}{\partial z^2} \tag{A.2–45}$$

For the other coordinate systems, $\nabla^2 u$ can be found by combining the expression for $\nabla \cdot \mathbf{A}$ and that for $\mathbf{A} = \nabla u$. The results are given in Table A.2*A* and can be derived by inspection.

Table A.2A

Expressions with ∇ in Cylindrical and Spherical Coordinates

u is an arbitrary scalar function of coordinates,
$\mathbf{A}$ is an arbitrary vector function of coordinates.

Cylindrical Coordinates

$$\nabla u = \frac{\partial u}{\partial r} \mathbf{1}_r + \frac{1}{r}\frac{\partial u}{\partial \phi} \mathbf{1}_\phi + \frac{\partial u}{\partial z} \mathbf{1}_z$$

$$\nabla \cdot \mathbf{A} = \frac{1}{r}\frac{\partial(rA_r)}{\partial r} + \frac{1}{r}\frac{\partial A_\phi}{\partial \phi} + \frac{\partial A_z}{\partial z}$$

$$\nabla \times \mathbf{A} = \left(\frac{1}{r}\frac{\partial A_z}{\partial \phi} - \frac{\partial A_\phi}{\partial z}\right)\mathbf{1}_r$$
$$+ \left(\frac{\partial A_r}{\partial z} - \frac{\partial A_z}{\partial r}\right)\mathbf{1}_\phi$$
$$+ \frac{1}{r}\left(\frac{\partial(rA_\phi)}{\partial r} - \frac{\partial A_r}{\partial \phi}\right)\mathbf{1}_z$$

$$\nabla^2 u = \frac{1}{r}\frac{\partial}{\partial r}\left(r\frac{\partial u}{\partial r}\right)$$
$$+ \frac{1}{r^2}\frac{\partial^2 u}{\partial \phi^2} + \frac{\partial^2 u}{\partial z^2}$$

Spherical Coordinates

$$\nabla u = \frac{\partial u}{\partial r} \mathbf{1}_r + \frac{1}{r}\frac{\partial u}{\partial \theta} \mathbf{1}_\theta + \frac{1}{r \sin \theta}\frac{\partial u}{\partial \phi} \mathbf{1}_\phi$$

$$\nabla \cdot \mathbf{A} = \frac{1}{r^2}\frac{\partial(r^2 A_r)}{\partial r} + \frac{1}{r \sin \theta}\frac{\partial(\sin \theta\, A_\theta)}{\partial \theta}$$
$$+ \frac{1}{r \sin \theta}\frac{\partial A_\phi}{\partial \phi}$$

$$\nabla \times \mathbf{A} = \frac{1}{r \sin \theta}\left(\frac{\partial(\sin \theta\, A_\phi)}{\partial \theta} - \frac{\partial A_\theta}{\partial \phi}\right)\mathbf{1}_r$$
$$+ \left(\frac{1}{r \sin \theta}\frac{\partial A_r}{\partial \phi} - \frac{1}{r}\frac{\partial(rA_\phi)}{\partial r}\right)\mathbf{1}_\theta$$
$$+ \frac{1}{r}\left(\frac{\partial(rA_\theta)}{\partial r} - \frac{\partial A_r}{\partial \theta}\right)\mathbf{1}_\phi$$

$$\nabla^2 u = \frac{1}{r^2}\frac{\partial}{\partial r}\left(r^2\frac{\partial u}{\partial r}\right) + \frac{1}{r^2 \sin \theta}$$
$$\times \frac{\partial}{\partial \theta}\left(\sin \theta\frac{\partial u}{\partial \theta}\right) + \frac{1}{r^2 \sin^2 \theta}\frac{\partial^2 u}{\partial \phi^2}$$

Table A.2B

Some Vector Identities

1. $\mathbf{A} \times (\mathbf{B} \times \mathbf{C}) = (\mathbf{C} \times \mathbf{B}) \times \mathbf{A} = \mathbf{B}(\mathbf{A} \cdot \mathbf{C}) - \mathbf{C}(\mathbf{A} \cdot \mathbf{B})$

2. $\nabla(u\,v) = u\nabla v + v\nabla u$

3. $\nabla(\mathbf{A} \cdot \mathbf{B}) = \mathbf{A} \times (\nabla \times \mathbf{B}) + (\mathbf{A} \cdot \nabla)\mathbf{B} + \mathbf{B} \times (\nabla \times \mathbf{A}) + (\mathbf{B} \cdot \nabla)\mathbf{A}$

4. $\nabla \cdot u\mathbf{A} = u\nabla \cdot \mathbf{A} + \mathbf{A} \cdot \nabla u$

5. $\nabla \cdot (\mathbf{A} \times \mathbf{B}) = \mathbf{B} \cdot \nabla \times \mathbf{A} - \mathbf{A} \cdot \nabla \times \mathbf{B}$

6. $\nabla \times (u\mathbf{A}) = u\nabla \times \mathbf{A} - \mathbf{A} \times \nabla u$

7. $\nabla \times (\mathbf{A} \times \mathbf{B}) = (\mathbf{B} \cdot \nabla)\mathbf{A} + \mathbf{A}(\nabla \cdot \mathbf{B}) - (\mathbf{A} \cdot \nabla)\mathbf{B} - \mathbf{B}(\nabla \cdot \mathbf{A})$

8. $\overline{(\nabla \cdot \mathbf{A})\mathbf{B}} = (\mathbf{A} \cdot \nabla)\mathbf{B} + \mathbf{B}(\nabla \cdot \mathbf{A})$

9. $(\mathbf{M} \cdot \overline{\nabla})(\mathbf{A} \times \mathbf{B}) = \mathbf{A} \times (\mathbf{M} \cdot \nabla)\mathbf{B} - \mathbf{B} \times (\mathbf{M} \cdot \nabla)\mathbf{A}$

10. $\nabla \times (\nabla \times \mathbf{A}) = \nabla (\nabla \cdot \mathbf{A}) - (\nabla \cdot \nabla)\mathbf{A}$

11. $(\mathbf{A} \cdot \nabla)\mathbf{r} = \mathbf{A} \ (\mathbf{r} = \mathbf{1}_x x + \mathbf{1}_y y + \mathbf{1}_z z)$

12. $\mathbf{r} \times \overline{(\nabla \cdot \mathbf{A})\mathbf{B}} = \overline{(\nabla \cdot \mathbf{A})(\mathbf{r} \times \mathbf{B})} - \mathbf{A} \times \mathbf{B}$

Problem A.2a.   Derive expressions for the gradient in cylindrical and spherical coordinates.

Problem A.2b.   Derive expressions for the divergence in cylindrical and spherical coordinates, and for $\nabla^2 u$.

Problem A.2c.   Prove that the vector sum of the areas of a closed figure is zero.

Problem A.2d.   Derive expressions for the curl in cylindrical and spherical coordinates.

Problem A.2e.   Apply the divergence theorem A.2–22 to the vector $u\mathbf{C}$, where u is a given variable scalar and $\mathbf{C}$ is an arbitrary constant vector, and prove eq. A.2–24. (*Hint*: See method of proving eq. A.2–31.)

Problem A.2f.   Apply the divergence theorem in succession to the vectors $x\mathbf{M}$, $y\mathbf{M}$ and $z\mathbf{M}$, and prove eq. A.2–25.

Problem A.2g.   Apply the divergence theorem to the vector $\mathbf{A} \times \mathbf{C}$ where $\mathbf{A}$ is a given variable vector and $\mathbf{C}$ is an arbitrary constant vector, and prove eq. A.2–26.

Problem A.2h.   Apply the divergence theorem to the vector $\mathbf{M}(\mathbf{A} \cdot \mathbf{C})$ where $\mathbf{M}$ and $\mathbf{A}$ are given variable vectors and $\mathbf{C}$ is an arbitrary constant vector, and prove eq. A.2–27.

Problem A.2i.   Write and simplify the consequence of applying the divergence theorem to the vector $u\nabla v - v\nabla u$ where u and v are arbitrary scalar functions.

Problem A.2j.   Write and simplify the result of applying the divergence theorem to a vector $\mathbf{A} \times \mathbf{B}$, where $\mathbf{A}$ and $\mathbf{B}$ are both variable.

Problem A.2k.   Write an expression for $\overline{(\nabla \times \mathbf{A})} \times \mathbf{B}$ involving terms in each of which ∇ operates on one vector only.

Problem A.2l.   Simplify $(\mathbf{A} \times \nabla) \times \mathbf{B}$ and $\mathbf{A} \times (\nabla \times \mathbf{B})$.

Problem A.2m.   Find all the ways of writing $\mathbf{A} \cdot (\nabla \times \mathbf{B})$.

Problem A.2n.   Prove that the average angular velocity in a fluid for lines at arbitrary angles with the x-axis lying in the x–y plane, is $\frac{1}{2}(\mathbf{curl\ v})_z$.

Problem A.2o.   Prove eq. A.2–41 using Stokes' theorem on the vector $u\mathbf{C}$ where $\mathbf{C}$ is an arbitrary constant vector.

Problem A.2p.   Prove eq. A.2–42 using Stokes' theorem on the vectors $x\mathbf{A}$, $y\mathbf{A}$, and $z\mathbf{A}$.

Problem A.2q.   Prove eq. A.2–43 using Stokes' theorem on the vector $\mathbf{A} \times \mathbf{C}$, where $\mathbf{C}$ is an arbitrary constant vector.

Problem A.2r. Prove that for any vector **A** we have
$$(\mathbf{A} \cdot \nabla)\mathbf{r} = \mathbf{A}$$
if **r** is the displacement vector from the origin.

Problem A.2s. Prove eq. A.2–44 using Stokes' theorem on the vectors MA_x, MA_y, and MA_z.

A.3   Notes on Differential Equations

An ordinary differential equation of the first order for a function $g(x)$ is a relation connecting dg/dx with g and x. We may always imagine it to be solved for dg/dx:

$$dg/dx = F_1(g, x) \tag{A.3–1}$$

A solution of this equation is a function $g(x)$ which may be plotted as a curve in a plane. We can imagine finding this curve directly, but approximately, from eq. A.3–1 by starting at any value of x, say $x = 0$, choosing g at will for this x, and with the value of dg/dx thus determined finding the differential of g for some chosen increment in x (see eq. A.1–5). With the new values of g and x we can repeat the process. We can get different curves by choosing different values of g at $x = 0$. Since in general every solution will have a value $g(0)$ for $x = 0$, we get all solutions this way. Any function $g(x, a)$ that satisfies eq. A.3–1 and contains an adjustable constant a that allows $g(0, a)$ to take on any chosen value is called a general solution, since by the above argument all particular solutions may be obtained from it.

A second-order differential equation for $g(x)$ is one that contains d^2g/dx^2 as well as (in general) dg/dx, g, and x. We may imagine it solved for d^2g/dx^2, and write

$$d^2g/dx^2 = F_2(dg/dx, g, x) \tag{A.3–2}$$

We now need, in order to find an approximate solution, to assume both a value for g and a value for dg/dx for $x = 0$ or any arbitrary starting point. Once started, we can find the increment in dg/dx and the increment in g, for a chosen Δx, and get to a new point from which to start again. The general solution of eq. A.3–2 will thus be a function $g(x, a, b)$ with two adjustable constants for determining g and dg/dx at $x = 0$. It is easy to see that an nth-order differential equation will have n adjustable constants in its general solution.[4]

A partial differential equation of the first order in two variables, for instance for a function $f(x, y)$, is a relation connecting the derivatives $\partial f/\partial x$ and $\partial f/\partial y$ with the values of the function f and the two independent

---

[4] This type of argument can be developed into a set of rigorous existence theorems, in which case it is called the "Cauchy-Lipschitz Method."

variables x and y. If we solve for one of the derivatives, say $\partial f/\partial x$, we can write

$$\partial f/\partial x = F_3(f, \partial f/\partial y, x, y) \tag{A.3-3}$$

An argument like that given for eq. A.3-1 can be constructed here if we temporarily think of y as a kind of auxiliary parameter. Then we have to specify f and x at the starting point of an approximate calculation for all the values of y of interest, and also of course $\partial f/\partial y$. Then for a slightly larger x, we can use the value of $\partial f/\partial x$ from eq. A.3-3 to find the new f for all y. The new value of $\partial f/\partial y$ can then be found by differentiation, and we can proceed another step. As a practical procedure the process is even less accurate than the one for ordinary equations, but it serves to demonstrate that we can specify an arbitrary function $f(0, y)$ for a specific value of x. It is easy to see that the starting "point" could be an arbitrary line in the x–y plane, and f can be arbitrarily specified all along this line. The general solution thus is expected to contain one arbitrary, adjustable function.

A second-order partial differential equation will have a general solution that involves two arbitrary functions. Such an equation can be written, for a function $f(x, y)$

$$\partial^2 f/\partial x^2 = F_4(f, \partial f/\partial x, \partial f/\partial y, \partial^2 f/\partial y^2, \partial^2 f/\partial x\,\partial y, x, y) \tag{A.3-4}$$

The specification of f and $\partial f/\partial x$ as functions of y for $x = 0$ will allow the calculation of $\partial f/\partial y$, $\partial^2 f/\partial y^2$ and $\partial^2 f/\partial x\,\partial y$ for all y, and so again we can start to calculate $f(x, y)$ by a stepwise approximation method.

These remarks are intended to make the above-mentioned properties of differential equations geometrically evident but are not intended as proofs or as exhaustive of special cases that might be exceptions. Details are to be found in books on differential equations.

There are two more properties of differential equations we shall state here, the details of solutions being given where needed in the text. A linear differential equation is one in which the function and its derivatives appear to the first or zero powers in every term. If only first-power terms appear, the equation is also homogeneous. The homogeneous equation obtained on omitting the zero-power term from an inhomogeneous equation is called the "reduced equation."

The first property we wish to state is that any linear combination of two solutions of a homogeneous equation is also a solution of the equation. For instance, if

$$A\,\frac{\partial^2 f}{\partial x\,\partial y} + Bx^2\,\frac{\partial f}{\partial x} + Cxyf = 0 \tag{A.3-5}$$

and $f_1(x, y)$ and $f_2(x, y)$ are separately solutions, we have

$$A \; \partial^2[af_1(x, y) + bf_2(x, y)]/\partial x \; \partial y + Bx^2 \; \partial[af_1(x, y) + bf_2(x, y)]/\partial x$$

$$+ Cxy[af_1(x, y) + bf_2(x, y)]$$

$$= a[A \; \partial^2 f_1(x, y)/\partial x \; \partial y + Bx^2 \; \partial f_1(x, y)/\partial x + Cxyf_1(x, y)]$$

$$+ b[A \; \partial^2 f_2(x, y)/\partial x \; \partial y + Bx^2 \; \partial f_2(x, y)/\partial x + Cxyf_2(x, y)] \quad \text{(A.3–6)}$$

$$= a \cdot 0 + b \cdot 0 = 0$$

The second property is that the general solution of an inhomogeneous linear equation can be written as the sum of the general solution of the reduced equation and any particular solution of the complete inhomogeneous equation. For instance, if the equation reads

$$A(x) \frac{d^2g}{dx^2} + B(x) \frac{dg}{dx} + C(x)g = R(x) \quad \text{(A.3–7)}$$

and if $g_1(x, a, b)$ and $g_2(x)$ satisfy respectively

$$A(x) \frac{d^2 g_1(x, a, b)}{dx^2} + B(x) \frac{dg_1(x, a, b)}{dx} + C(x)g_1(x, a, b) = 0 \quad \text{(A,3–8a)}$$

where a and b are adjustable constants, and

$$A(x) \; d^2 g_2(x)/dx^2 + B(x)dg_2(x)/dx + C(x)g_2(x) = R(x) \quad \text{(A.3–8b)}$$

it is easy to see by adding the last two equations that a solution of eq. A.3–7 with two adjustable constants is

$$g(x, a, b) = g_1(x, a, b) + g_2(x) \quad \text{(A.3–9)}$$

A.4   Vector Invariance

The vector relations developed in Appendix A.2 were derived in a largely geometric fashion that makes evident their independence of particular coordinate systems. In this section, we wish to prove this invariance in a formal algebraic fashion for Cartesian coordinates, not only to complete the discussion in section A.2 but to provide a basis for the discussion of relativity in section 10.8. The extension of this discussion to curvilinear coordinates would take us beyond the scope of this book.

The invariance we wish to consider is the independence of the various vector relations with respect to translations, rotations, and reflections of the coordinate axes. Translations—shifts of the origin without rotation—produce an almost trivial effect, and we shall not treat them. Reflections will be treated briefly after we have discussed rotations.

A rotation can be defined by starting with a set of orthogonal axes and unit vectors $\mathbf{1}_x$, $\mathbf{1}_y$, $\mathbf{1}_z$, and then relating a new set $\mathbf{1}'_x$, $\mathbf{1}'_y$, and $\mathbf{1}'_z$ to the old set. To shorten our writing and make the formulas easier to remember, let us rename the coordinates, using x_1, x_2, and x_3 in place of x, y, and z, and $\mathbf{1}_1$, $\mathbf{1}_2$, and $\mathbf{1}_3$ in place of $\mathbf{1}_x$, $\mathbf{1}_y$, and $\mathbf{1}_z$. Then we can use letter subscripts, as $i, j, k \cdots$, to indicate sums over the three coordinates. Each sum we indicate will run from 1 to 3, so we do not need to write the limits explicitly.

Now we can write a relation between the new unit vectors and the old, in the compact form

$$\mathbf{1}'_i = \sum_k a_{ik} \mathbf{1}_k \qquad (A.4\text{-}1)$$

where the nine numbers a_{ik}—i.e., a_{11}, a_{12}, etc.—are the components of the three new unit vectors along the three original axes. Any other letters can of course be used for the i and k here; eq. A.4-1 clearly represents three separate equations. In accordance with eq. A.2-3, these constants are the direction cosines between the respective unit vectors to which their subscripts refer. Since a_{ik} is the cosine of the angle between $\mathbf{1}'_i$ and $\mathbf{1}_k$, we can write $\mathbf{1}_k$ as a sum over the $\mathbf{1}'_i$, with the same coefficients

$$\mathbf{1}_k = \sum_i \mathbf{1}'_i a_{ik} \qquad (A.4\text{-}2)$$

(for mnemonic purposes we write the factors in such an order that the index summed over appears in two adjacent places).

The same coefficients allow us to relate the components of any vector $\mathbf{A}$ in the new system to those in the old system. Denoting the components in the old system with subscripts, and those in the new system with both subscripts and primes, we have

$$A'_i = \mathbf{A} \cdot \mathbf{1}'_i = \mathbf{A} \cdot \sum_k a_{ik} \mathbf{1}_k = \sum_k a_{ik} A_k \qquad (A.4\text{-}3)$$

In particular, if $\mathbf{A} = \mathbf{r}$, the displacement vector from the origin, we have a relation between the new coordinates and the old

$$x'_i = \sum_k a_{ik} x_k \qquad (A.4\text{-}4)$$

and using eq. A.4-2

$$x_k = \sum_i x'_i a_{ik} \qquad (A.4\text{-}5)$$

The components of the gradient of any scalar f can now be determined with respect to the new axes:

$$\frac{\partial f}{\partial x'_i} = \sum_k \frac{\partial f}{\partial x_k} \frac{\partial x_k}{\partial x'_i} = \sum_k a_{ik} \frac{\partial f}{\partial x_k} \qquad (A.4\text{-}6)$$

where the derivatives $\partial x_k / \partial x'_i$ are determined from eq. A.4–5. Thus we see that the components of the gradient transform in exactly the same way as the components of the vector **r**. We can in fact use this transformation property as *defining* a vector.

Let us now use the facts that each set of unit vectors have unit length and are mutually perpendicular, to get relations among the coefficients. These facts can be succinctly written as

$$\mathbf{1}_k \cdot \mathbf{1}_l = \delta_{kj} \tag{A.4-7a}$$

$$\mathbf{1}'_i \cdot \mathbf{1}'_j = \delta_{ij} \tag{A.4-7b}$$

where the symbol δ_{kj} called the "Kronecker delta" stands for 1 when the two subscripts are equal and for 0 when they are not:

$$\delta_{kj} = \begin{cases} 1 & \text{if } k = j \\ 0 & \text{if } k \neq j \end{cases} \tag{A.4-8}$$

Using eqs. A.4–7b and A.4–1 we have (taking care not to use the same subscript letter in more than one summation)

$$\delta_{ij} = \mathbf{1}'_i \cdot \mathbf{1}'_j = \left(\sum_k a_{ik} \mathbf{1}_k \right) \cdot \left(\sum_l a_{jl} \mathbf{1}_l \right)$$

$$= \sum_k \sum_l a_{ik} a_{jl} \delta_{kl} = \sum_k a_{ik} a_{jk}$$

where the last reduction arises because in summing over l, only the term for $l = k$ gives a non-vanishing contribution. Using eq. A.4–2 we get a relation involving a sum over the first subscripts, and so together we have

$$\sum_k a_{ik} a_{jk} = \delta_{ij} \tag{A.4-9a}$$

$$\sum_j a_{jk} a_{jl} = \delta_{kl} \tag{A.4-9b}$$

The scalar product of two vectors can now be shown to be invariant (have the same value) when expressed in the two systems in terms of components. We have

$$\mathbf{A} \cdot \mathbf{B} = \sum_k A_k B_k = \sum_k \left(\sum_i A'_i a_{ik} \right) \left(\sum_j B'_j a_{jk} \right)$$

$$= \sum_i \sum_j A'_i B'_j \delta_{ij} = \sum_i A'_i B'_i \tag{A.4-10}$$

In particular, the length of a vector $(\mathbf{A} \cdot \mathbf{A})^{\frac{1}{2}}$ remains the same.

The constancy of length of a radius vector **r** can in fact be used to *define* a rotation.   If we require that the x'_i are linear functions of the x_k, with the same origin, we are led to write eqs. A.4–4 and then to require that

$$\sum_i x'^2_i = \sum_i \left(\sum_k a_{ik}x_k\right)\left(\sum_l a_{il}x_l\right)$$

$$= \sum_k \sum_l x_k x_l \sum_i a_{ik}a_{il} \qquad\qquad \text{(A.4–11)}$$

$$= \sum_k x_k^2$$

which can only hold for all points (x_1, x_2, x_3) if eq. A.4–9b holds for the sum over i.   From this we conclude that the vectors formed by eqs. A.4–1 are indeed orthogonal unit vectors and the a_{ik} are direction cosines. It can be shown then that the distance between any two points is invariant (problem A.4a) and thus triangles and angles are preserved, which must be true for a rotation of coordinates.

It is easy to prove that $\nabla \cdot \mathbf{A}$ is invariant for any vector **A**:

$$\sum_k \frac{\partial A_k}{\partial x_k} = \sum_k \sum_i \frac{\partial A_k}{\partial x'_i}\frac{\partial x'_i}{\partial x_k} = \sum_k \sum_i \sum_j \frac{\partial}{\partial x'_i}(A'_j a_{jk})\frac{\partial x'_i}{\partial x_k}$$

$$= \sum_k \sum_i \sum_j \frac{\partial A'_j}{\partial x'_i} a_{jk}a_{ik} = \sum_i \sum_j \frac{\partial A'_j}{\partial x'_i}\delta_{ij}$$

$$= \sum_i \frac{\partial A'_i}{\partial x'_i} \qquad\qquad\qquad\qquad \text{(A.4–12)}$$

The vector nature of the cross product is a little more complicated to show.   Let us introduce another symbol that shortens the writing much as does the Kronecker delta, namely the epsilon symbol, ε_{ijk}, which is zero if any two or three of the subscripts are equal and is ± 1 when they are all different.   The plus sign belongs to values i, j, k that are cyclic permutations of 1, 2, 3 and the minus sign to cyclic permutations of 3, 2, 1. That is

$$\left.\begin{array}{l} \varepsilon_{ijk} = 0 \qquad \text{unless } i \neq j \neq k \\[6pt] \varepsilon_{123} = \varepsilon_{231} = \varepsilon_{312} = 1 \\[6pt] \varepsilon_{321} = \varepsilon_{132} = \varepsilon_{213} = -1 \end{array}\right\} \qquad \text{(A.4–13)}$$

Then we can write the vector product of **A** and **B** in a short form:

$$\mathbf{A} \times \mathbf{B} = \mathbf{1}_1(A_2 B_3 - A_3 B_2) + \mathbf{1}_2(A_3 B_1 - A_1 B_3) + \mathbf{1}_3(A_1 B_2 - A_2 B_1)$$

$$= \sum_i \sum_j \sum_k \mathbf{1}_i A_j B_k \varepsilon_{ijk} \qquad\qquad \text{(A.4–14)}$$

The property of the unit vectors of being mutually perpendicular and forming a right-handed system can be written

$$\mathbf{1}_j \times \mathbf{1}_k = \sum_i \mathbf{1}_i \varepsilon_{ijk} \qquad (A.4\text{--}15)$$

(If j and k are equal, all terms on the right vanish. If they are unequal, only one term on the right is not zero, and it has the proper sign.) This property can be proven in a formal way from eq. A.4–7a, but we shall leave this as an exercise for the reader (problem A.4b).

Now we can write eq. A.4–15 for the new system of vectors and use eq. A.4–1. We get

$$\sum_m \sum_n a_{jm} a_{kn}(\mathbf{1}_m \times \mathbf{1}_n) = \sum_i \mathbf{1}'_i \varepsilon_{ijk}$$

$$= \sum_p \sum_m \sum_n a_{jm} a_{kn} \mathbf{1}_p \varepsilon_{pmn} = \sum_i \sum_p a_{ip} \mathbf{1}_p \varepsilon_{ijk}$$

and comparing the coefficients of $\mathbf{1}_p$ on each side, we have

$$\sum_m \sum_n a_{jm} a_{kn} \varepsilon_{pmn} = \sum_i a_{ip} \varepsilon_{ijk} \qquad (A.4\text{--}16a)$$

as a new set of relations among the a_{ik}'s. These relations constitute a form of solution of the set of equations A.4–9a for the a_{ik} with a particular first subscript, in terms of the coefficients with the other two first subscripts. (See problem A.4c.) It must be assumed that the new set of vectors is a right-handed system like the old set—i.e., the rotation does not also involve a reflection (see below).

A similar set can be obtained by interchanging the original and new sets of unit vectors. We get

$$\sum_j \sum_k a_{jm} a_{kn} \varepsilon_{ijk} = \sum_p a_{ip} \varepsilon_{pmn} \qquad (A.4\text{--}16b)$$

Now we can use eqs. A.4–16 to show that the expression $\mathbf{A} \times \mathbf{B}$ transforms as a vector. We have, using eqs. A.4–14, A.4–16b, and A.4–9b,

$$\sum_i \sum_j \sum_k \mathbf{1}'_i A'_j B'_k \varepsilon_{ijk} = \sum_i \sum_j \sum_k \sum_l \sum_m \sum_n a_{il} \mathbf{1}_l a_{jm} A_m a_{kn} B_n \varepsilon_{ijk}$$

$$= \sum_i \sum_l \sum_m \sum_n \sum_p a_{il} \mathbf{1}_l A_m B_n a_{ip} \varepsilon_{pmn}$$

$$= \sum_l \sum_m \sum_n \sum_p \mathbf{1}_l A_m B_n \varepsilon_{pmn} \delta_{lp} \qquad (A.4\text{--}17)$$

$$= \sum_l \sum_m \sum_n \mathbf{1}_l A_m B_n \varepsilon_{lmn}$$

which shows that the vector product as defined by eq. A.4–14 yields the same vector in either system of coordinates.

The calculations above on ∇f and $\nabla \cdot \mathbf{A}$ show that for these quantities the components of $\nabla = \sum_i \mathbf{1}_i (\partial / \partial x_i)$ transform just like the components of a vector.   Hence it follows that $\nabla \times \mathbf{A}$ transforms like a vector;   the demonstration is algebraically just like eq. A.4–17, and we shall not write it out explicitly.   The same argument can be used for the vector operations $(\mathbf{A} \cdot \nabla)$ and $(\mathbf{A} \times \nabla)$ and of course for all the more complicated vector combinations given in section A.2.

Let us now consider reflections.   A simple example would be reflection in the y–z plane, in which we change x to $-x$ and $\mathbf{1}_x$ to $-\mathbf{1}_x$ but leave y, z, $\mathbf{1}_y$, and $\mathbf{1}_z$ unchanged.   A reflection in any plane can be reduced to a reflection in the y–z plane by use of a rotation, so our example will cover all such reflections.

When we change x to $-x$, we change the sign of the x-component of any vector such as $\mathbf{F}$ or $\mathbf{v}$, whose definition does not involve the right-hand rule.   If in the original system we have $\mathbf{F} = \mathbf{1}_x F_x + \mathbf{1}_y F_y + \mathbf{1}_z F_z$, in the new system we have $\mathbf{F} = \mathbf{1}'_x F'_x + \mathbf{1}'_y F'_y + \mathbf{1}'_z F'_z = (-\mathbf{1}_x)(-F_x) + \mathbf{1}_y F_y + \mathbf{1}_z F_z$.   The vector is the same as before.   Similarly, the scalar product $\mathbf{A} \cdot \mathbf{B}$ is unchanged, and furthermore, since if $x' = -x$, $\partial/\partial x' = -\partial/\partial x$, ∇f and $\nabla \cdot \mathbf{A}$ are unchanged.

The situation is different for the vector product.   The x-component of $\mathbf{A} \times \mathbf{B}$ remains unchanged, and the y and z components each change sign. In the expression eq. A.4–14 for $\mathbf{A} \times \mathbf{B}$, every term has either $\mathbf{1}_x$, A_x, or B_x in it and so every term changes sign, which is of course a result of a right-hand rule turning into a left-hand rule in a mirror image.

We call a vector which does not change sign on reflection, while one component does, a "polar vector" or a "true vector," and a vector which does change, while the corresponding component does not, an "axial vector "or a "pseudovector."   An example of a pseudovector is the area vector associated with a parallelogram constructed on two vectors $\mathbf{A}$ and $\mathbf{B}$.   If we did not associate a vector with the area, we might describe its (component) sign as follows.   Suppose the plane of $\mathbf{A}$ and $\mathbf{B}$ to be the y–z plane.   We can call the area positive if a rotation of $\mathbf{A}$ toward $\mathbf{B}$ through the smaller angle between them is in the same sense of rotation as that obtaining in rotating $\mathbf{1}_y$ toward $\mathbf{1}_z$.   A reflection of the x-axis will not change this sign.   If the area were located in the x–y or the z–x plane, the sign defined by the appropriate rotation would change, and the situation would still be like that of the vector product (see problem A.4f).

Similarly, a vector defined as the curl of a polar vector is an axial vector and has the same properties as the area vector.   The circulation density in the y–z plane can be given a sign in the same way as for the area vector.

It will be noted that the magnetic induction $\mathbf{B}$ is defined in section 7.2 in a way that makes clear its pseudovector character.   This is also evident in the derivation of $\mathbf{B}$ from the curl of the vector potential $\mathbf{A}$, which by *its* definition is clearly a true or polar vector.   The vector product $\mathbf{v} \times \mathbf{B}$ on the other hand is a true vector since $\mathbf{B}$ is a pseudovector (cf. problem A.4*e*).

It will also be noted that, if $\mathbf{A}$, $\mathbf{B}$, and $\mathbf{C}$ all represent true vectors, the triple scalar product $\mathbf{A} \cdot (\mathbf{B} \times \mathbf{C})$ is not a true scalar, for it will change signs with a reflection.   Such a product is called a "pseudoscalar."

If two reflections are considered, say in both the x and y axes, we get a right-handed system back, and there are no sign changes in pseudovectors and pseudoscalars.   Three reflections, however, have the same effect as one.   The reflection of x to $-x$, y to $-y$ and z to $-z$ is called a "reflection through the origin."   Since atomic and nuclear forces seem generally to be symmetric with respect to such reflections, the invariance or non-invariance of the physical quantities entering into theories of these systems is of considerable interest and importance.   Invariant quantities are said to have even parity, and those that change sign are said to have odd parity.   "Parity conservation" refers to the idea that physical forces do not display the arbitrary right- or left-handedness of axial vectors and that therefore any right- or left-handed character of a physical system must arise because of some initial state into which it was put.   Symmetric physical forces cannot then change the parity initially acquired.   The discovery of a physical effect related to the direction of an axial vector (e.g., the magnetic moment vector for certain radioactive nuclei) was a dramatic denial of this assertion.[5]   However, the discovery seems to be related to non-electromagnetic forces and hence is beyond the scope of our book.

Problem A.4a.   Show that from the requirement that the distance $(x_1^2 + x_2^2 + x_3^2)^{\frac{1}{2}}$ of a point from the origin be invariant under a rotation one can deduce that the distance between any two points (x_1, x_2, x_3) and (X_1, X_2, X_3) is also invariant.

Problem A.4b.   Three vectors $\mathbf{A}$, $\mathbf{B}$ and $\mathbf{C}$ satisfy the equations $\mathbf{A} \cdot \mathbf{A} = \mathbf{B} \cdot \mathbf{B} = \mathbf{C} \cdot \mathbf{C} = 1$ and $\mathbf{A} \cdot \mathbf{B} = \mathbf{B} \cdot \mathbf{C} = \mathbf{C} \cdot \mathbf{A} = 0$.   Consider equivalent expressions for $\mathbf{A} \times (\mathbf{B} \times \mathbf{C})$, $(\mathbf{B} \times \mathbf{C}) \cdot (\mathbf{B} \times \mathbf{C})$ and $[\mathbf{A} \times (\mathbf{B} \times \mathbf{C})] \cdot [\mathbf{A} \times (\mathbf{B} \times \mathbf{C})]$, and show that $\mathbf{A} \cdot (\mathbf{B} \times \mathbf{C}) = \pm 1$.   By considering expansions of $[\mathbf{A} \mp (\mathbf{B} \times \mathbf{C})] \cdot [\mathbf{A} \mp (\mathbf{B} \times \mathbf{C})]$, show that $\mathbf{A} = \pm \mathbf{B} \times \mathbf{C}$, $\mathbf{B} = \pm \mathbf{C} \times \mathbf{A}$, and $\mathbf{C} = \pm \mathbf{A} \times \mathbf{B}$. Show that the choice of signs determines whether the system of vectors is right handed or left handed.

Problem A.4c.   Show that, if $p = 1$, $j = 2$, $k = 3$, eq. A.4–16a becomes $a_{11} = a_{22}a_{33} - a_{23}a_{32}$, and find similar equations for $a_{12}, a_{13}, \cdots a_{33}$.

Problem A.4d.   Write eq. A.4–9a for (i, j) respectively equal to $(1, 1)$, $(1, 2)$, and $(1, 3)$.   Solve the second two equations for a_{11} and a_{12}, obtaining the ratios

[5] L. S. Rodberg and V. F. Weisskopf, "Fall of Parity," *Science*, **125**, 627–33 (1957); C. S. Wu, E. Ambler, R. W. Hayward, D. D. Hoppes, R. P. Hudson, *Phys. Rev.*, **105**, 1413–1415 (1957).

$a_{11} : a_{12} : a_{13}$.   Use the first equation to get values of a_{11}, a_{12}, and a_{13} and verify eq. A.4–16a.   Show that a choice of signs enters that can be settled by consideration of right- and left-handedness.

Problem A.4e.   Show that the vector product of a polar vector and an axial vector is itself a polar vector.   Which of Maxwell's equations involve on each side (a) a true vector, (b) a pseudovector, (c) a true scalar, (d) a pseudoscalar?

Problem A.4f.   Show what happens to the y- and z-components of $\mathbf{A} \times \mathbf{B}$ when $\mathbf{A}$ and $\mathbf{B}$ are polar vectors and a reflection is made in the y–z plane.

A.5   Complex numbers

The complex-number system in algebra is based on the quantity $\sqrt{-1}$, which we shall call j in accordance with engineering usage, except in section 10.8 (the mathematician's symbol i conflicts with our symbol for current).   This quantity j is not definable in terms of any ordinary "real" number and so is called "imaginary."   Its relation to real numbers is simply that $j^2 = -1$, which of course implies that $j^{-1} = -j$.   We combine j with real numbers (represented here by x and y) to form complex numbers, which obey the rules of ordinary algebra (see Appendix A.2), and which we denote by symbols like z, $\mathscr{E}$, i, etc.[6]   We then write for a general complex number

$$z = x + jy \qquad\qquad (A.5\text{–}1)$$

and add or subtract numbers by the rules

$$z_1 + z_2 = (x_1 + jy_1) + (x_2 + jy_2) = x_1 + x_2 + j(y_1 + y_2)$$
$$\qquad\qquad (A.5\text{–}2)$$
$$z_1 - z_2 = (x_1 + jy_1) - (x_2 + jy_2) = x_1 - x_2 + j(y_1 - y_2)$$

The numbers x, x_1, and x_2 are called the *real parts* of their respective numbers, and the numbers y, y_1, and y_2 are called the *imaginary parts*. Either part may of course be positive or negative.   The real and imaginary parts do not combine directly with each other.   They act like the x and y components of a vector in a plane; the addition of two complex numbers involves the addition of the separate components.   Therefore we can represent the numbers as vectors, or if we please, as points at the heads of the vectors.   Figure A.5a shows the addition of two complex numbers in graphical form.

The length of a vector $z = x + jy$, which we can call its magnitude (amplitude or rms value for electrical quantities) is obviously given by $(x^2 + y^2)^{\frac{1}{2}}$, which we can write as $|z|$ or as plain z in ordinary type.

---

[6] A special type face ("sans serif" in this book) is used in electrical theory, although it is not necessary in mathematical analysis to distinguish the complex and ordinary numbers that refer to the same physical quantities.

We can multiply complex numbers in the ordinary algebraic way, replacing j^2 where it appears by -1. Thus we have

$$z_1 z_2 = (x_1 + jy_1)(x_2 + jy_2) = x_1 x_2 - y_1 y_2 + j(x_1 y_2 + x_2 y_1) \qquad (A.5\text{-}3)$$

This expression shows that the product of two complex numbers is another one but does not immediately show any geometrical relation of the product to the factors. There is, indeed, a simple relationship which it is easiest to derive by first representing complex numbers in terms of their magnitudes and the angles they make with the axis of reals.

In Fig. A.5b, we have shown the magnitude z and angle φ of a complex number z. Evidently we can write

$$z = z(\cos \varphi + j \sin \varphi) \qquad (A.5\text{-}4)$$

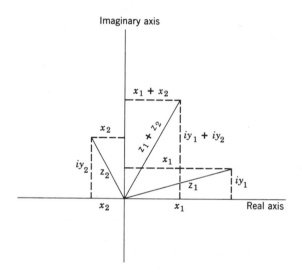

Fig. A.5a.   The addition of two complex numbers.

Now we should like to show that $\cos \varphi + j \sin \varphi$ can be written as $e^{j\varphi}$. One property of $e^{j\varphi}$ that we need here is that

$$e^{j\varphi_1} \cdot e^{j\varphi_2} = e^{j(\varphi_1 + \varphi_2)}$$

in accordance with the usual law of exponents, and we can show readily that $\cos \varphi + j \sin \varphi$ has this property. In fact, using the trigonometrical addition rules,

$$(\cos \varphi_1 + j \sin \varphi_1)(\cos \varphi_2 + j \sin \varphi_2)$$
$$= \cos \varphi_1 \cos \varphi_2 - \sin \varphi_1 \sin \varphi_2 + j(\sin \varphi_1 \cos \varphi_2 + \cos \varphi_1 \sin \varphi_2)$$
$$= \cos (\varphi_1 + \varphi_2) + j \sin (\varphi_1 + \varphi_2) \qquad (A.5\text{-}5)$$

so that we are entitled to use the shorthand formula

$$\cos \varphi + j \sin \varphi = e^{j\varphi} \qquad \text{(A.5-6)}$$

or

$$z = ze^{j\varphi} \qquad \text{(A.5-7)}$$

It is left to the reader in problems A.5a and b to show that $e^{j\varphi}$ as thus defined possesses the other properties of the exponential function ($de^{j\varphi}/d\varphi = je^{j\varphi}$; $e^{j \cdot 0} = 1$; and the proper series expansion).

Now we can give a simple interpretation of the product of two complex numbers, for we have

$$z_1 z_2 = z_1 e^{j\varphi_1} z_2 e^{j\varphi_2} = z_1 z_2 e^{j(\varphi_1 + \varphi_2)} \qquad \text{(A.5-8)}$$

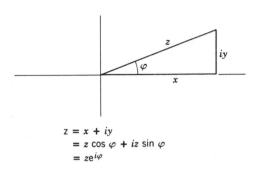

$$z = x + iy$$
$$= z \cos \varphi + iz \sin \varphi$$
$$= ze^{i\varphi}$$

Fig. A.5b.   Three ways to represent a complex number.

so that the product of two given complex numbers is seen to be another complex number whose magnitude is the product of the two given magnitudes and whose angle is the sum of the two given angles. This result can also be obtained directly from eq. A.5–3, with some algebra (problem A.5c).

One special type of multiplication should be pointed out. Suppose that $z_1 = x + jy$ and $z_2 = x - jy$. We call z_2 the complex conjugate of z_1, and write it $\bar{z}_1$. Then if the angle of z_1 is $\varphi = \tan^{-1}(y/x)$, the angle of $\bar{z}_1$ is $-\varphi = \tan^{-1}(-y/x)$; the magnitudes are each equal to $(x^2 + y^2)^{\frac{1}{2}}$. By eq. A.5–8 we then have, dropping subscripts,

$$z\bar{z} = z^2 e^{j(\varphi - \varphi)} = z^2 = x^2 + y^2 \qquad \text{(A.5-9)}$$

which result also comes immediately from eq. A.5–3. We can use eq. A.5–9 to find z by purely algebraic means, and we also can use it for division, as we now show. Consider the quotient

$$\frac{z_1}{z_2} = \frac{x_1 + jy_1}{x_2 + jy_2} = \frac{z_1 e^{j\varphi_1}}{z_2 e^{j\varphi_2}}$$

From the last expression we have clearly the result $(z_1/z_2)e^{j(\varphi_1-\varphi_2)}$ which is the inverse of eq. A.5–8. However, if the real and imaginary parts are given, we would like to be able to reduce the middle ratio directly to an expression without j in the denominator. The way to do this is to multiply numerator and denominator by $\bar{z}_2 = x_2 - jy_2$:

$$\frac{z_1}{z_2} = \frac{(x_1 + jy_1)(x_2 - jy_2)}{x_2{}^2 + y_2{}^2} = \frac{x_1 x_2 + y_1 y_2}{x_2{}^2 + y_2{}^2} + \frac{j(y_1 x_2 - x_1 y_2)}{(x_2{}^2 + y_2{}^2)} \qquad \text{(A.5–10)}$$

which has the desired form.[7]

A word might be said about approximations. Sometimes one of the parts of a complex number is considerably bigger than the other. Then one can neglect the smaller part. What is the extent of the error? Suppose that in the number $z = x + jy$, $y = mx$ where m is a number, say 10 or larger. Then we have $z = jy + (y/m) \simeq jy$; in magnitude and angle,

$$z = y\left(1 + \frac{1}{m^2}\right)^{\frac{1}{2}} e^{j\tan^{-1}m} = y\left(1 + \frac{1}{m^2}\right)^{\frac{1}{2}} e^{j[\pi/2 - \tan^{-1}(1/m)]}$$

since the tangent of the complement of an angle is the reciprocal of the tangent of the angle. For a small angle, the angle in radians equals the tangent, so that

$$\tan^{-1}(1/m) \simeq (1/m) \text{ radians} \approx 57/m \text{ degrees}$$

The radical $(1 + 1/m^2)^{\frac{1}{2}}$ is approximately $1 + 1/2m^2$. Hence $z = jy(1 + 1/2m^2)$ $e^{-(57/m)j}$; the error made in the magnitude of z by neglecting x is very small ($\frac{1}{2}\%$ or less if $m > 10$) and that in the angle is a matter of less than 6°. Similar calculations with the same results can be made for $x = my$.

We conclude this appendix with the formulas for the sine and cosine in terms of exponentials, which are readily derivable from eq. A.5–6, and the corresponding relations for the hyperbolic functions, used in the text in section 9.6 and in the problems of section 5.6:

$$\cos \varphi = (e^{j\varphi} + e^{-j\varphi})/2 \qquad \text{(A.5–11}a)$$

$$\sin \varphi = (e^{j\varphi} - e^{-j\varphi})/2j \qquad \text{(A.5–11}b)$$

$$\tan \varphi = (e^{j\varphi} - e^{-j\varphi})/(e^{j\varphi} + e^{-j\varphi}) \qquad \text{(A.5–11}c)$$

$$\cosh x = (e^x + e^{-x})/2 \qquad \text{(A.5–12}a)$$

$$\sinh x = (e^x - e^{-x})/2 \qquad \text{(A.5–12}b)$$

$$\tanh x = (e^x - e^{-x})/(e^x + e^{-x}) \qquad \text{(A.5–12}c)$$

Problem A.5a. Show that if $e^{j\varphi}$ is defined by eq. A.5–6, it satisfies $de^{j\varphi}/d\varphi = je^{j\varphi}$, $\int e^{j\varphi}\, d\varphi = e^{j\varphi}/j = -je^{j\varphi}$, and $e^{j \cdot 0} = 1$.

---

[7] By analogy to the process of rationalizing the denominator of a fraction involving quadratic surds, like $4/(3 + 2\sqrt{5})$, one is tempted to call this process "realizing the denominator!"

Problem A.5b. Show by use of the MacLaurin series expansions for sin φ, cos φ, and e^u where $u = j\varphi$ that eq. A.5–6 is correct.

Problem A.5c. Show from eq. 9.5–3 and the addition theorem for tan $(\varphi_1 + \varphi_2)$ that $|z_1 z_2| = |z_1| \cdot |z_2|$ and that the angle of $z_1 z_2$ is the sum of the angles of z_1 and z_2.

Problem A.5d. Show that $e^{j\pi/2} = j$; $e^{j\pi} = e^{-j\pi} = -1$ and that $e^{2j\pi n} = 1$ when n is any integer, positive, negative, or zero.

A.6   Notes on Determinants[8]

A determinant is a number formed from a square array of n^2 numbers. This number is formed as a sum of $n!$ distinct products, each one of which has n factors.   Each factor is drawn from a different row in the square array and also from a different column.   The sign attached to each term of n factors may be found by a number of equivalent rules, one of which is this:

Arrange the factors in the order of the rows to which they belong (counting down), and then inspect their arrangement with respect to the columns.   If an even number of interchanges of adjacent factors will put them in order of the columns from which they come (counting from the left), the sign is positive; if odd, it is negative.

As a consequence, if any two columns or any two rows of a determinant are interchanged, the sign of the determinant will be changed.   If two rows or columns are identical or proportional, the determinant will be zero.

If a constant factor is introduced (or removed) from all the elements of one row or column, the determinant is multiplied (or divided) by that factor.

A determinant is unchanged in value if any fixed multiple of the terms of one row (or column) is added to the respective terms of another row (or column), while leaving unaltered the rest of the determinant including the row (or column) first mentioned.   This rule can often be used to transform a determinant into another with all the terms of one column or row save one equal to zero.

A determinant can be evaluated by the cofactor rule: Choose any row or column, and successively multiply each term by the positive or negative value of the determinant formed by striking out of the array the row and column that intersect at that term.   The sign to be attached to the reduced determinant in each case is determined by the evenness ($+$) or oddness ($-$) of the sum of the row number and column number of the term, counting from the upper left-hand corner.   This rule combined with the previous one can make a fairly easy reduction of a fourth- or fifth-order determinant ($n = 4$ or 5) to one of a lower order.

[8] Proofs of the statements made here, and many more details, are to be found in most textbooks on college algebra or theory of equations.

A second order determinant is easily evaluated:

$$\begin{vmatrix} a_{11} & a_{12} \\ a_{21} & a_{22} \end{vmatrix} = a_{11}a_{22} - a_{21}a_{12} \qquad \text{(A.6–1)}$$

A third-order determinant can be evaluated by a simple rule that associates the positive terms with groups of factors two or three of which lie parallel to the main diagonal (down from the left) and the negative terms with the other diagonal. The solid curves in the array below connect the factors of the positive terms and the dashed lines the negative.

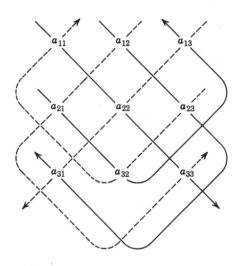

$$= a_{11}a_{22}a_{33} + a_{12}a_{23}a_{31} + a_{21}a_{32}a_{13}$$
$$- a_{13}a_{22}a_{31} - a_{12}a_{21}a_{33} - a_{23}a_{32}a_{11} \qquad \text{(A.6–2)}$$

There is no similar simple rule for fourth- and higher-order determinants.

The rule for solving simultaneous linear equations with determinants is given in the text (section 5.4), for the case of three unknowns, but the generalization to the case of more unknowns is immediate.

A.7   Electrical Units

Table A.7A lists the units in which each important electrical quantity is measured, in both the MKS and Gaussian systems. Equivalences are given between different units for the same quantity. In some cases, more than one equivalent set of dimensions for a unit is given; different forms

Table A.7A

Physical Concept	MKS Unit	Defining Equation MKS	Defining Equation Gaussian	Gaussian Unit	Equivalence
1. Mass, length, time	kilogram, meter, second			gram, centimeter, second	1 kg = 10^3 gm 1 m = 10^2 cm
2. Force	newton = kilogram-meter/second²	$F = ma$		dyne = gram-centimeter/second²	1 newton = 10^5 dyne
3. Work, energy	joule = newton-meter	$W = \int \mathbf{F} \cdot \mathbf{ds}$		erg = dyne-centimeter	1 joule = 10^7 erg
4. Power	watt = joule/second	$P = dW/dt$		erg/second	1 watt = 10^7 erg/sec
5. Charge	coulomb = ampere-second	$q = \int i\, dt$	$F = qq'/r^2$	statcoulomb; [statcoulomb] = $[\text{dyne}]^{\frac{1}{2}}$ [centimeter]	1 coulomb = $(c/10)$ statcoulomb $\simeq 3 \times 10^9$ statcoulomb
6. Current	ampere; [ampere] = $[\text{newton}]^{\frac{1}{2}}/\mu_0^{\frac{1}{2}}$	$F = \mu_0 ii'L/4\pi r$	$i = dq/dt$	statampere = statcoulomb/second = $(1/c)$ abampere	1 amp = (1/10) abamp = $(c/10)$ statamp $\simeq 3 \times 10^9$ statamp
7. Volume charge density	coulomb/meter³	$\rho = \lim \Delta q/\Delta\tau$		statcoulomb/centimeter³	1 coulomb/m³ = $(10^{-7}c)$ statcoulomb/cm³ $\simeq 3 \times 10^3$ statcoulomb/cm³
8. Surface charge density	coulomb/meter²	$\sigma = \lim \Delta q/\Delta S$		statcoulomb/centimeter²	1 coulomb/m² = $(10^{-5}c)$ statcoulomb/cm² $\simeq 3 \times 10^5$ statcoulomb/cm²

Table A.7A (*continued*)

Physical Concept	MKS Unit	Defining Equation MKS	Gaussian	Gaussian Unit	Equivalence
9. Linear charge density	coulomb/meter	$\lambda = \lim \Delta q / \Delta l$		statcoulomb/centimeter	1 coulomb/m = $(10^{-3}c)$ statcoulomb/cm $\simeq 3 \times 10^{7}$ statcoulomb/cm
10. Current density	ampere/meter^2	$J = \lim \Delta i / \Delta S$		statampere/centimeter^2	1 amp/m^2 = $(c/10^5)$ statamp/cm^2 $\simeq 3 \times 10^{5}$ statamp/cm^2
11. Surface current density	ampere/meter	$J_s = \lim \Delta i / \Delta l$		statampere/centimeter	1 amp/m = $(c/10^3)$ statamp/cm $\simeq 3 \times 10^{7}$ statamp/cm
12. Electric field intensity	newton/coulomb = volt/meter	$\mathbf{E} = \lim \Delta \mathbf{F} / \Delta q$		dyne/statcoulomb = statvolt/centimeter	1 newton/coulomb = $(10^6/c)$ dynes/statcoulomb $\simeq (10^{-4}/3)$ dynes/statcoulomb
13. Electric field flux	newton meter^2/coulomb	$\Phi_E = \int \mathbf{E} \cdot \mathbf{dS}$		dyne-centimeter^2/statcoulomb; $[\Phi_E]$ = [statcoulomb]	1 newton-m^2/coulomb = $(10^{10}/c)$ dyne-cm^2/statcoulomb $\simeq (1/3)$ dyne-cm^2/statcoulomb
14. Potential, emf, Peltier heat	volt = joule/coulomb	$\mathscr{E}, V = W/q = \int \mathbf{E} \cdot \mathbf{dl}$		statvolt = erg/statcoulomb	1 v = $(10^8/c)$ statv $\simeq (1/300)$ statv

588

No.	Quantity	MKS unit	Defining equation	Gaussian (cgs) unit	Conversion
15.	Capacitance	farad = coulomb/volt; [farad] = ϵ_0[meter]	$C = Q/V$	statfarad = statcoulomb/statvolt; [statfarad] = [centimeter]	1 farad $\equiv (10^{-9}/c^2)$ statfarad $\simeq 9 \times 10^{11}$ statfarad
16.	Electric dipole moment	meter-coulomb	$\mathbf{p} = q\,\delta\mathbf{l}$	centimeter-statcoulomb	1 m-coulomb $= (10c)$ cm-statcoulomb $\simeq 3 \times 10^{11}$ cm-statcoulomb
17.	Electric quadrupole moment	meter²-coulomb	$Q = q\,\delta l\,\delta l'$ or $Q_{xx} = \int \rho x^2\, d\tau$, etc.	centimeter²-statcoulomb	1 m²-coulomb $= (10^3 c)$ cm²-statcoulomb $\simeq 3 \times 10^{13}$ cm²-statcoulomb
18.	Electric polarization	coulomb/meter²	$\mathbf{P} = \lim \Delta\mathbf{p}/\Delta\tau$	statcoulomb/centimeter²	1 coulomb/m² $= (10^{-5}c)$ statcoulomb/cm² $\simeq 3 \times 10^5$ statcoulomb/cm²
19.	Permittivity ϵ_0, ϵ	coulomb²/newton-meter² = farad/meter	$\epsilon_0 = qq'/4\pi r^2 F = 10^7/4\pi(c^2) \simeq 10^{-9}/36\pi$	not used in Gaussian system	*1 coulomb²/newton-m² $= (4\pi c^2/10^{11})$ statcoulomb²/dyne-cm² $\simeq 36\pi \times 10^9$ statcoulomb²/dyne-cm² of κ
20.	Relative permittivity or dielectric constant; electric susceptibility	dimensionless ratio	$\kappa = D/(\epsilon_0 E) = \epsilon/\epsilon_0$ $\chi = \kappa - 1$ $\kappa = D/E$ $\chi = \dfrac{(\kappa - 1)}{4\pi}$	dimensionless ratio (statcoulomb²/dyne-cm)	κ same in both systems; *1 unit of χ (MKS) = $(1/4\pi)$ unit of χ (Gaussian)
21.	Displacement	coulomb/meter²	$\mathbf{D} = \epsilon_0\mathbf{E} + \mathbf{P}$ $\mathbf{D} = \mathbf{E} + 4\pi\mathbf{P}$	dyne/statcoulomb	*1 coulomb/m² $= (4\pi \times 10^{-5}c)$dyne/statcoulomb $\simeq 12\pi \times 10^5$ dyne/statcoulomb of $\mathbf{D}$

589

Table A.7A (*continued*)

Physical Concept	MKS Unit	Defining Equation MKS / Gaussian	Gaussian Unit	Equivalence
22. Displacement flux	coulomb	$\Phi_D = \int \mathbf{D} \cdot \mathbf{dS}$	dyne-centimeter²/statcoulomb; $[\Phi_D] = $[statcoulomb]	*1 coulomb = $(4\pi c/10)$ dyne-cm²/statcoulomb $\simeq 12\pi \times 10^9$ dyne-cm²/statcoulomb of Φ_D
23. Resistance	ohm = volt/ampere [ohm] = [second/meter]/ϵ_0 = μ_0[meter/second]	$R = V/i$	statohm = statvolt/statampere; [statohm] = [second/centimeter]	1 ohm = $(10^9/c^2)$ statohm $\simeq (10^{-11}/9)$ statohm
24. Conductance	mho = ampere/volt	$G = i/V$	statmho = statampere/statvolt	1 statmho = $(c^2/10^9)$ statmho $\simeq 9 \times 10^{11}$ statmho
25. Resistivity	meter-ohm	$\rho = E/J$	statohm-centimeter	1 m-ohm = 100 ohm-cm = $(10^{11}/c^2)$ statohm-cm $\simeq (10^{-9}/9)$ statohm-cm
26. Conductivity	mho/meter	$\sigma = J/E$	statmho/centimeter	1 mho/m = $(c^2/10^{11})$ statmhos/cm $\simeq 9 \times 10^9$ statmhos/cm

No.	Quantity	MKS units	Formula	Gaussian units	Conversion
27.	Magnetic induction (**B**)	weber/meter² = tesla = newton/ampere-meter	$F = q(\mathbf{v} \times \mathbf{B})$ $F = (q/c)(\mathbf{v} \times \mathbf{B})$	gauss = (c) dyne/stat-ampere-centimeter (= oersted); [gauss] = μ_0[oersted] = $\mu_0^{\frac{1}{2}}$[dyne$^{\frac{1}{2}}$/cm]	1 weber/m² = 10^4 gauss
28.	Magnetic flux	weber = tesla-meter² = volt-second = joule/ampere = ampere-henry; [weber] = $\mu_0^{\frac{1}{2}}$[newton$^{\frac{1}{2}}$-meter]	$\Phi = \int \mathbf{B} \cdot d\mathbf{S}$	maxwell = gauss-centimeter² = (c) erg/stat-ampere (= oersted-centimeter²)	1 weber = 10^8 maxwells
29.	Permeability μ_0, μ	weber/meter-ampere = henry/meter = newton/ampere²	$\mu_0 = 4\pi \times 10^{-7}$ henry/m	$\mu_0 = 1$ gauss/oersted = $cB/i\nabla\Omega$ gauss/oersted (=1)	*1 henry/m = $(10^7/4\pi)$ gauss/oersted of μ
30.	Relative permeability; magnetic susceptibility	dimensionless ratio	$\mu_r = \mu/\mu_0$ $\chi_m = \mu_r - 1$ $\mu_r = \mu$ $\chi_m = \dfrac{\mu - 1}{4\pi}$	dimensionless ratio	μ_r same in both systems; *1 unit of χ_m (MKS) = $(1/4\pi)$ unit of χ_m (Gaussian)
31.	Inductance	henry = weber/ampere; [henry] = μ_0[meter]	$\begin{cases} L = \Phi/i & L = \Phi/ic \\ \mathscr{E} = -L\, di/dt & L = \Phi/ic \end{cases}$	statvolt-second/statampere = erg/statampere²	1 weber/amp = $(10^9/c^2)$ statv-sec/statamp $\simeq$ $(10^{-11}/9)$ statv-sec/statamp
32a. 32b.	Vector potential Circulation of **B**	weber/meter	$\begin{cases} \mathbf{A} = (\mu_0 i/4\pi)\displaystyle\int \dfrac{d\mathbf{l}}{r} \\ \text{circul. of } \mathbf{B} = \oint \mathbf{B} \cdot d\mathbf{l} \end{cases}$ $\mathbf{A} = (i/c)\displaystyle\int \dfrac{d\mathbf{l}}{r}$	gauss-centimeter (= gilbert)	1 weber/m = 10^6 gauss-cm

591

Table A.7A (*continued*)

	Physical Concept	MKS Unit	Defining Equation MKS / Gaussian	Gaussian Unit	Equivalence
33.	Magnetic moment	$\begin{cases}\text{ampere-meter}^2 \\ \text{weber-meter}\end{cases}$	$\mathbf{m} = i\mathbf{S}$ $\mathbf{m} = (i/c)\mathbf{S}$ $\mathbf{p}_m = \mu_0 i\mathbf{S}$	gauss-centimeter^3 = erg/oersted (= erg/ gauss)	*1 amp-m^2 = $4\pi \times 10^{-7}$ weber-m = 10^3 gauss-cm^3 of $\mathbf{m}$
34.	Magnetization	$\begin{cases}\text{ampere/meter} \\ \text{weber/meter}^2\end{cases}$	$\mathbf{M} = \lim \Delta\mathbf{m}/\Delta\tau$ $\mathbf{P}_m = \mu_0\mathbf{M} = \lim \Delta\mathbf{p}_m/\Delta\tau$	gauss (= oersted)	*1 amp/m = $4\pi \times 10^{-7}$ weber/m^2 = 10^{-3} gauss (= 10^{-3} oersted) of $\mathbf{M}$
35.	Magnetic intensity ($\mathbf{H}$)	ampere/meter	$\mathbf{H} = \mathbf{B}/\mu_0 - \mathbf{M}$ $\mathbf{H} = \mathbf{B} - 4\pi\mathbf{M}$ $= i\nabla\Omega/c$	oersted (= gauss) = $(1/c)$ statampere/ centimeter; [oersted] = [dyne$^{\frac{1}{2}}$/centimeter]	*1 amp/m = $4\pi \times 10^{-3}$ oersted of $\mathbf{H}$
36.	Magnetic scalar potential and mmf	ampere (ampere-turn)	$V_m = \int \mathbf{H} \cdot d\mathbf{l}$ $\mathscr{H} = \oint \mathbf{H} \cdot d\mathbf{l}$	oersted-centimeter = gilbert (= gauss-centimeter)	*1 amp-turn = $(4\pi/10)$ gilberts of $\mathscr{H}$
37.	Surface pole density	weber/meter^2	$\sigma_m = \mu_0 M_n = P_{mn}$ $\sigma_m = M_n$	gauss = emu/centimeter^2 (= oersted)	1 weber/m^2 = $(10^4/4\pi)$ emu/cm^2
38.	Volume pole density	weber/meter^3	$\rho_m = -\nabla \cdot \mathbf{P}$	gauss/centimeter = emu/cm^3 (= oersted/ centimeter)	1 weber/m^3 = $(10^2/4\pi)$ emu/cm^2

592

39. Pole strength	weber	$q_m = \int \sigma_m \, dS$	gauss-centimeter² (= oersted-centimeter²)	*1 weber = $(10^8/4\pi)$ emu of q_m
40. Reluctance	ampere/weber (ampere-turn/weber)	$\mathcal{R} = \mathcal{H}/\Phi$	gilbert/maxwell	*1 amp/weber = $(4\pi/10^9)$ gilbert/maxwell of $\mathcal{R}$
41. Hall coefficient	volt-meter³/ampere-weber = meter³/coulomb	$R_H = E/JB$	statvolt-centimeter/statampere-gauss = centimeter³/(c) statcoulomb	1 v-m³/amp-weber = $(10^7/c^2)$ statv-cm/statamp-gauss $\simeq (10^{-13}/9)$ statv-cm/statamp-gauss
42. Entropy transport per electron (S^*)	joule/degree	$S^* = J_Q e/JT$	erg/degree	1 joule/°C = 10^7 ergs/°C $\simeq 0.239$ cal/°C
43. Thermopower, Thomson heat, entropy transport per unit charge	volt/degree Centigrade = joule/coulomb-degree Centigrade	$d\mathscr{E}/dT = S^*/e$ $\sigma_{Th} = (T/e)\, dS^*/dT$	statvolt/degree Centigrade	1 v/°C = $(10^8/c)$ statv/°C $\simeq (1/300)$ statv/°C

593

are more convenient for checking equations in differing circumstances. A consistent set of dimensions without fractional exponents requires the use of four "basic" quantities, such as length, mass, time, and current. For this reason, both systems are sometimes called "four-dimensional."

This table is also useful for determining how the magnitude of any electrical quantity would change if any of the fundamental units of mass, length, and time were to be modified in the future. From the point of view of such possible changes, each system may be called "three-dimensional."

Relations between units that are written as equations may be treated as such—i.e., direct substitutions can be made for any quantity by its equal in the units attached to any physical quantity. For instance,

$$2.0 \times 10^{-2}\, \text{mho/m} = 2.0 \times 10^{-2}\, \text{amp/m-v}$$

$$= 2.0 \times 10^{-2}\, \text{coulombs}^2/\text{newton-m}^2\text{-sec}$$

$$= 2.0 \times 10^{-2} \times 9 \times 10^{18}\, \text{statcoulombs}^2/10^9\, \text{dyne cm}^2\, \text{sec}$$

$$= 18 \times 10^7\, \text{statcoulombs}^2/\text{dyne cm}^2\, \text{sec, etc.}$$

Relations between quantities in brackets give correct dimensional relationships but have no meaning when used as numerical equalities. They can of course be used to check the dimensional correctness of equations. For this purpose, μ_0 may be treated as a dimensional quantity, although its definition as having the exact MKS value $4\pi \times 10^{-7}$ or exact Gaussian value unity would not be affected by any future change in the adopted units for mass, length, and time. Similar considerations hold for the quantity $\epsilon_0 = 1/4\pi$ in the Gaussian system.

Numerical relations that are starred involve quantities defined differently in the two systems and cannot in general be modified by substitution of equivalent units.

The electrostatic system of units (esu) is based on the statcoulomb; the electromagnetic system (emu) on the abampere, which is the unit of current for which the force in dynes between two parallel wires is $2i_1 i_2 L/r$. The ratio of the abampere and the statampere is c in centimeters/second. From the table it is seen that 1 abamp is 10 amps.

The Gaussian system uses esu for electrical quantities and emu for magnetic quantities. This system seems likely to be used for some time to come in atomic and nuclear physics, and so it is used as a secondary system throughout the book. Although no distinction is made in the main part of the text between the gauss and the oersted, the distinction is maintained in the table for purposes of comparison. Parentheses are used to indicate the equivalences we have adopted.

The quantity c when written in parentheses represents the velocity of light in cm/sec.   The approximate numbers 3 and 9 following the $\simeq$ signs represent actually the numbers 2.99793 and $(2.99793)^2$.   The quantity c written in curly brackets $\{\}$ represents the velocity of light in meters/second.

Relations between quantities measured in the two systems can be easily read from the table in a "reciprocal" sort of way.   For instance, if E_G and E_M represent the electric field intensity in the Gaussian and MKS systems, we have $E_G = (10^{-4}/3)E_M$, since if E_M is 1 newton/coulomb, E_G is $(10^{-4}/3)$ dynes/statcoulomb, as given in item 12 of the table.

Problem A.7a.   Write dimensions for all the MKS quantities in Table A.7A in terms of length L, mass M, time T, and μ_0.

Problem A.7b.   Force is more frequently used in electromagnetism than is mass.   Take μ_0 as dimensionless and write FLT-dimensional formulas for all the MKS quantities in the table.

Problem A.7c.   Write FLT formulas for all the Gaussian formulas in the table, taking both $\epsilon_0 = 1/4\pi$ and μ_0 as dimensionless.

A.8   Physical constants[9]

1. Charge on the electron	$e = (1.60209 \pm 0.00003) \times 10^{-19}$ coulomb
	$= (4.80294 \pm 0.00008) \times 10^{-10}$ statcoulomb (esu)
2. Mass of the electron	$m_0 = (9.1086 \pm 0.0003) \times 10^{-31}$ kg
3. Mass of the proton	$M_p = (1.67245 \pm 0.00005) \times 10^{-27}$ kg
4. e/m for the electron	$e/m_0 = (1.75888 \pm 0.00003) \times 10^{11}$ coulombs/kg
	$= (5.27299 \pm 0.00008) \times 10^{17}$ statcoulombs/g
5. Velocity of light	$c = (2.997928 \pm 0.000004) \times 10^8$ m/sec
6. Avogadro's Number[10]	$N_0 = (6.0230 \pm 0.0002) \times 10^{26}$ per kilogram molecule
	$= (6.0230 \pm 0.0002) \times 10^{23}$ per gram molecule
7. Faraday constant[10]	$\mathscr{F} = 96493 \pm 2$ coulombs per chemical equivalent
8. Planck's constant	$h = (6.6254 \pm 0.0002) \times 10^{-34}$ joule-sec
9. Boltzmann's constant	$k = (1.38049 \pm 0.00005) \times 10^{-23}$ joule/deg
	$= (8.6168 \pm 0.0004) \times 10^{-5}$ ev/deg
10. Bohr magneton	$m_B = (0.92733 \pm 0.00002) \times 10^{-23}$ amp-m^2
	$= (0.92733 \pm 0.00002) \times 10^{-20}$ amp/gauss
11. Electron magnetic moment	$m_e = (0.92840 \pm 0.00002) \times 10^{-23}$ amp-m^2
12. Proton magnetic moment	$m_p = (1.41048 \pm 0.00003) \times 10^{-26}$ amp-m^2
13. Permittivity of free space	$\epsilon_0 = (8.85417 \pm 0.00003) \times 10^{-12}$ farad/m
	$= 1/4\pi$ (Gaussian system)
14. Permeability of free space	$\mu_0 = 4\pi \times 10^{-7}$ (MKS system)
15. 1 electron volt (ev)	1 ev $= 1.60209 \times 10^{-19}$ joule $= 1.60209 \times 10^{-12}$ erg

[9] From J. A. Bearden and J. S. Thomsen, "A Survey of Atomic Constants," *Il Nuovo Cimento, Supplemento*, Vol. V, series X, pp. 267–360 (1957).   Slightly different values are given by E. R. Cohen, K. M. Crowe, and J. W. M. DuMond, *Fundamental Constants of Physics*, Interscience, New York, 1957.

[10] Avogadro's number and the Faraday constant are given here on the chemical scale, for which the mean isotopic constitution of oxygen is taken as having atomic weight 16.0000.   On the physical scale, on which O^{16} has weight 16.0000, the significant digits are 6.0247 and 96520, respectively.

A.9   Lists of Symbols and Abbreviations.

Reference is given for the first use of each symbol or abbreviation, or of each particular meaning of a symbol.   Page numbers in italics indicate that the symbol is used in that sense only on those pages.   Numbers marked with p refer to problems.

Subscripts are given only when their presence modifies the meaning of the symbol to which they are attached.

Omitted are script letters used for points in space or on circuits, italic letters used for objects (as K for key), arbitrary function symbols, $f(p)$, $F(x)$, $g(x, a, b)$, $\Phi(\phi)$, etc., summation indices $(i, j, k, \cdots)$, and other letters used only as subscripts.

Roman Alphabet Symbols

$\mathbf{A}, A_k$	arbitrary vector 32, 535
A	expansion coefficient *164–70*
$\mathbf{A}, A$	vector potential 285
$\mathbf{A}, \mathsf{A}$	complex vector potential 505
a	radius 11
a	constant 43, *194, 474–5*
a_n	expansion coefficient *169, 299,* 460
$\mathbf{a}, a$	acceleration 252
a_{jk}	coefficients for rotation or Lorentz transformation 531, 575
B	expansion coefficient *164–70*
$\mathbf{B}, B$	magnetic induction 253, 254
B_r	residual induction 363
B	susceptance 430
$\mathbf{B}, \mathsf{B}$	complex magnetic induction vector 506
b	constant 11, *233, 474–5*
b_n	expansion coefficient *169–70*
b	radius of wire *276*
b	damping constant 395
C	capacitance 85
C	expansion coefficient *164–70*
C_l	capacitance per unit length 480
C	amplitude of wave in pipe *522–4*
$\mathbf{C}, C$	constant in vector potential equation *541–3*
c_{ij}	coefficients of capacitance and induction 172
c	constant *246,* 398
c	velocity of light 256

$\mathbf{J}_S$	vector surface current density *348*
J_S	complex magnitude of surface current density 510
j	integer *207–8*, 327
j	$(-1)^{\frac{1}{2}}$ *401, 581*
K	constant *98, 355*
K	constant for waves on cables and lines 489
k	Boltzmann constant 56
k	scale factor *94p*
k	constant *158–62, 168, 355p, 541–3, 568*
k	function of resistances *210*
k	integer 327
k	quantum number *382p*
k	torque constant 395
k	force constant 425
k	coefficient of coupling 440
k_1, k_2	relative amplitudes *517*
$\mathscr{L}, \mathscr{L}$	torque 101
L	self-inductance 318
L_l	inductance per unit length 481
L	length *501*
l	length, distance 8
l	function of resistances *210*
M	molecular weight 246
M	mutual inductance 299
M_S	surface density of electromagnetic moment 338
$\mathbf{M}, M$	magnetization 341
M_p	proton mass 421
m	particle mass 43
m	scalar constant *85, 552, 584*
m	integer *207–8, 462, 528*
m	mass deposited *246*
$\mathbf{m}, m$	electromagnetic moment 335
m_0	electron mass 374
m_B	Bohr magneton 374
m_p	proton magnetic moment 421
N	integer 7
N	density of molecules *109–10*
N_n	Bessel function 168
N_0	density of acceptors and donors 231
N_A	density of acceptors 231
N_D	density of donors 231

N_0	Avogadro's number 246
N	number of turns 277
$\mathbf{N}, N$	Poynting vector 500
n	arbitrary multiple 37p, 568
n	integer *81*, 146, 172, *269–70*, 327, 402, 462, *528*
n	degree of harmonic 163, 168
n	charge carrier density 183
n	bridge ratio 218
n_l	number of turns per unit length 278
n	number of turns 353
n	atom density 372
n	turns ratio 443
n	index of refraction *516*
$\mathbf{P}$	electric polarization 108
P_S	electric dipole moment per unit area 123
$P_n(\cos\theta)$	Legendre polynomial 165
P	power 187
P_S	power per unit area 187
P_τ	power per unit volume 187
P_{mS}	surface density of magnetic dipole moment 338
$\mathbf{P}_m, P_m$	magnetic polarization 341
$\mathbf{p}, p$	electric dipole moment 97
p_{lk}	coefficients of potential 173
p	function of resistances *210*
$\mathbf{P}_m, p_m$	magnetic dipole moment 336
p	variable used in Laplace transform method 473
$\mathbf{P}, P$	complex dipole vector 505
Q	charge 8
Q_{xx}, Q_{xy}, etc.	components of quadrupole tensor 106
Q_{Th}	heat *240*
Q	figure of merit 417
q	charge 2
q	function of resistances *210*
q_m	magnetic pole strength 336
q_l	charge per unit length 482
q	complex charge 505
R	radial distance 8
R	resistance 185
R_H	Hall coefficient *266*
$\mathscr{R}$	reluctance 384
R_l	resistance per unit length 481

r	distance 2
r	resistance 191
S	surface 6
S^*	entropy transport per electron 235
S	entropy *238*
S_i	current sensitivity 396
S_V	voltage sensitivity 397
S_Q	Coulomb sensitivity 406
S_Φ	flux-linkage sensitivity 407
$\mathbf{s}, s$	distance or displacement 271
T	absolute temperature 140
T_0	undamped period 397
T	period 410
T_{jk}	tensor component 535
t_m	mean free time 57
t	thickness of disk electret *123–4*
t	time 182
t_c	characteristic time of pulse 470
U	energy 55
U_F	energy of Fermi level 55
u	ionic mobility 247
u_1, u_2, u_3	components of unit vector $\mathbf{1}_u$ 495
u	integration variable *508*
$\mathbf{u}, u$	velocity vector 532
V	potential 29
V_m	magnetic scalar potential 283
V	complex scalar potential 506
$\mathbf{v}, v$	velocity 8, 14
W	work 29
W_∞	hysteresis loss at saturation *367*
w	width *265*
X	reactance 415
x	coordinate 6
x_a	attenuation factor 216p
x	fractional deviation from balance *219*
x	relative displacement of sliding contact *222p*
$\mathbf{x}, x$	space vector 531
$Y(\theta, \varphi)$	surface spherical harmonic 163
Y	admittance 429
y	coordinate 6
Z	impedance 415
Z	complex impedance 429

z	coordinate 6
z	valence 243, 246
z	arbitrary complex number 581

Greek Alphabet Symbols

α (alpha)	deviation of Coulomb exponent 84
α	molecular polarizability 137
α	temperature coefficient of resistance 187
α_{db}	attenuation, 217p
α	transfer coefficient *246*
α	ratio $2Ra/(R^2 + a^2)$ *291*
α	attenuation constant 398, 451, 489
α	angle 524
β (beta)	constant in exponent 398
β	transformer phase angle *444*
β	reciprocal wave length 489
Γ (gamma)	image transfer constant 451
γ (gamma)	magnetic interaction factor 376
γ	relative damping 398
γ	transformer phase angle *444*
γ	propagation constant for cables and lines 489
γ	value of $(1 - u^2/c^2)^{-\frac{1}{2}}$ 533
δ (delta)	logarithmic decrement 402
δ	relative frequency deviation 423
δ	skin depth 519
δ_{ij}	Kronecker symbol 531, 576
ϵ_0 (epsilon)	permittivity of free space 2
ϵ	permittivity 128
ε_{ijk}	epsilon symbol 577
η (eta)	dimensionless variable, range 0 to 1 *172*
θ (theta)	angle 8
θ	Curie temperature 376
κ (kappa)	dielectric constant 128
κ_Q	coefficient of heat conductivity 238
λ (lambda)	linear charge density 8
λ	depth in semiconductor *44p*
λ	constant in exponent 398
$\lambdabar$ (lambda-bar)	reduced wave length $(\lambda/2\pi)$ 486
$\bar{\mu}$ (mu-bar)	electrochemical potential of the electron 57
μ_0 (mu)	permeability of free space 270
μ	permeability 357

μ_r	relative permeability	357
ν (nu)	frequency	*504*
ξ (xi)	general displacement coordinate	177
Π (pi)	Peltier heat	239
ρ (rho)	volume charge density	7
ρ	resistivity	183
ρ_m	volume pole density	341
σ (sigma)	surface charge density	6
σ	conductivity	183
σ_{Th}	Thomson coefficient	240
σ_m	surface density of pole strength	338
τ (tau)	volume	7
τ	transference number	*247–48*
τ	torque constant for coil	395
Φ_E (phi)	electric flux	13
Φ_v	volume flow	14
Φ_D	flux of displacement	115
Φ	magnetic flux	262
Φ_l	magnetic flux per unit length	487
ϕ (phi)	angle	11
ϕ	work function	70
φ	phase angle	410
χ (chi)	chi potential	72
χ	electric susceptibility	128
χ_m	magnetic susceptibility	357
Ω (omega)	solid angle	15
ω (omega)	angular velocity	*258*
ω	angular frequency	397
$\hat{\omega}$	angular velocity of galvanometer	403

Abbreviations

Å	Ångstrom unit	37
abamp	abampere	587
amp	ampere	182
BW	bandwidth	419
cm	centimeter	1
emf	electromotive force	191
emu	electromagnetic unit	256
esu	electrostatic unit	4
ev	electron volt	30
exp	exponential function of	405

gm	gram 2
kg	kilogram 2
kva	kilovolt-amperes 427
L-section	circuit elements arranged as letter L 433
ln	natural logarithm 35
m	meter 2
ma	milliampere 182
mv	millivolt 30
mmf	magnetomotive force 353
μa	microampere 182
μf	microfarad 86
$\mu\mu$f	micromicrofarad 86
μv	microvolt 30
n-type	negative-carrier semiconductor 60
PD	potential difference 30
p-type	positive-carrier semiconductor 60
π-section	circuit elements arranged as letter π 217
rms	root mean square 426
sec	second 2
statamp	statampere 270
statv	statvolt 30
SUN	Commission on Symbols, Units, and Nomenclature 336
T-section	circuit elements arranged as letter T 216
$\text{TE}_{m,n}$; $\text{TM}_{m,n}$, TEM	modes in wave guides 528
v	volt 30
va	volt-ampere 427
var	volt-ampere-reactive 427

Operational and Other Symbols

1	unit vector 2
Σ	summation sign 4
Δ	increment of 7
$\mathbf{A} \cdot \mathbf{B}$	scalar product 13, 552
∇	del or nabla 20, 554
$\text{div } \mathbf{A} = \nabla \cdot \mathbf{A}$	divergence of $\mathbf{A}$ 20, 556
δ	small but not infinitesimal increment 30
$\text{curl } \mathbf{A} = \nabla \times \mathbf{A}$	curl of $\mathbf{A}$ 38, 564
$\mathbf{A} \times \mathbf{B}$	vector product 38, 559
$\text{grad } V = \nabla V$	gradient of V 40, 555
Σ_i	sum over index 108

Index

In this index certain page numbers are followed by ff, n, and p: ff following a page number means that page to the end of the section in which it lies; n refers to a footnote or figure reference on the page; p refers to one or more problems on the page; the + sign may be read "and."